Numbers and Arithmetic

A BLAISDELL BOOK IN
PURE AND APPLIED MATHEMATICS

CONSULTING EDITOR

Seymour Schuster,
University of Minnesota

Numbers and Arithmetic

JOHN N. FUJII
MERRITT COLLEGE
OAKLAND, CALIFORNIA

BLAISDELL PUBLISHING COMPANY
A Division of Ginn and Company
NEW YORK · TORONTO · LONDON

FOR
Joanne, Laura, Nancy,
and Patricia Ann

Preface

THE PURPOSE of this text is to furnish a basic classroom book on arithmetic. It has been developed for a pre-algebra review course and as such should be well suited for use in many one-semester or one-quarter and two-quarter courses designed to cover the fundamental number concepts and operations of arithmetic. It is assumed that the reader will have had some previous instruction, however weak, in arithmetic. The text proceeds from specific to general patterns of computations and ideas. Observations and questions are used freely to motivate the topics. Sufficient practice material is included to insure the development of adequate skill for most computations. The book is arranged into two parts:

Part A: Natural Numbers and the Integers.
Part B: Rational Numbers and Measurement.

A vocabulary list and comprehensive check-test follow at the end of each part.

There are five chapters in each part with three sections to each chapter. Each section is divided into short units. Examples and illustrations are used extensively. Reader involvement is often elicited by questions in the text; practice sets and exercises are included with answers. Section exercises, also with answers, are included at the end of each section; and there are fill-in review summaries at the end of each chapter, two sets of chapter exercises and a short problem set, which should challenge the reader to do his best, complete each chapter. Answers to the chapter exercises are included at the end of the text. Chapter 10 reaches quite high and is intended for the more sophisticated reader.

Further features of this text are that there is an early consideration of negative integers and the use of negative signs in operations. A chapter on statements, word problems, and equations anticipates beginning algebra. Vocabulary is introduced implicitly and naturally as necessary while numerous examples and illustrations help to establish the ideas and computations. The text is an integrated development of both structural concepts and practical computational skills in numbers and arithmetic. A supplement to the text offering a brief commentary on points of emphasis and difficulties, references and sources for related material, and further problem material for tests with answers is available.

I wish to acknowledge the many sources of ideas and development in both content and style used in this text. Not the least were the critical reviewers of earlier drafts of the manuscript. In particular, Professor Seymour Schuster, who read the entire manuscript, deserves my special gratitude for helping to overcome the many shortcomings in the manuscript. Any vagueness or errors, however, I must confess are my own. I hope that the text reflects much of what was sound and meaningful in traditional arithmetic while catching some of the spirit and trends of the contemporary "revolution in mathematics." In the final analysis, the material reflects my experiences and views in teaching basic mathematics at Merritt College in Oakland, California.

Finally, my daughters are responsible for pushing the manuscript to its conclusion.

JOHN N. FUJII

Contents

Part B. Rational Numbers and Measurement

NATURAL NUMBERS AND THE INTEGERS

CHAPTER 1

Numbers and Numerals

1.1 Names

1.1.1   One of the special advantages which humans have as a result of their language ability is that they give names to things and ideas. Look at Figures 1, 2, and 3. Could you describe the ideas illustrated without using

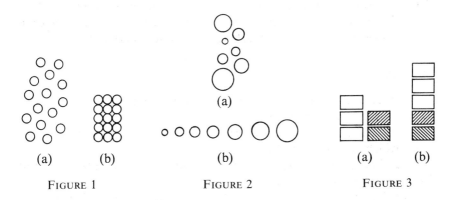

(a)   (b)   (b)   (a)   (b)

FIGURE 1   FIGURE 2   FIGURE 3

common names for the ideas? Would anyone understand you if you made up names of your own?

Imagine how difficult it would be if we forgot how to write and speak! We write and talk about things and ideas by using names for them. Names are invented and created, then agreed upon. When a new object or idea is observed a name is given to the object or idea. In order to properly use and not abuse names, we must be careful to observe and use the names meaningfully and as intended.

We might describe Figure 1 as follows: "There are two collections of circles; each collection has the same number of circles, fifteen. One collection is scattered, the other is neatly arranged and easy to count."

Figure 2 could be described by: "There are two collections of circles of different sizes. The circles in Figure 2(b) are neatly arranged in order of size, from smallest to largest going from left to right."

A description of Figure 3 might be the following: "In Figure 3(a) we have two small collections, one has two objects the other three. In Figure 3(b) the two small collections have been 'put together' to form one collection."

Notice that we have used pictures and words, the only means available, to suggest some ideas. It is the idea, what you "see" behind the pictures and words, that is of importance. However, since we will need special words and symbols to represent ideas, you should pay special attention to these special words and symbols as they are introduced. These will be noted and the words will be **boldfaced** as they first occur. When the usage is clear we do not normally distinguish between the name and the thing or idea being named. For example, between the idea of two in "two collections" and the word "two" with three letters.

We begin our proper study with an idea which is common to all three figures above, the idea of a collection or group of things or objects. This idea of a collection is called a **set**. The things or objects in the set are called **elements** and are said to **belong** to or be **members** of the set.

Examples.

(a) The set of circles in Figure 1(a). Each circle in the figure is an element that belongs to the set.

(b) The set of words on this page. Each word on this page is an element which is a member of the set.

(c) The set of letters in the English alphabet. The letters "a" and "z" are members of the set.

(d) The set of days in a week. Monday is an element of the set.

(e) The set of elephants on the moon. There are probably no elements in this set.

(f) The set of points on a line. There are probably more points on a line than we can count.

The idea of number probably arose from noticing a common property between certain sets. As different sets were observed, names were needed to describe different numbers.

In Figure 4(a) the common number property of the three sets is four, named by the symbol "4." The sets in Figure 4(b) have the common

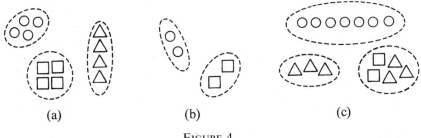

(a)   (b)   (c)

FIGURE 4

number property two, named by the symbol "2." In Figure 4(c) we have sets whose number properties are named by "3," "5," and "7." It will be convenient to be able to distinguish between the idea of number and the name of the number. The symbols used to name a number are called **numerals**. That is, "3" and "5" are numerals naming the numbers 3 and 5.

Unlike the primitive savage and contrary to historical evolution we learn the names of numbers long before we have a clear idea of what the names are used for. Examination of the ordinary word names of numbers, however, shows two distinct uses for numbers. Consider the number 2: two, twice, second, pair. Note that the idea of "two" and "pair" is distinct from the idea of "second" and "twice." In two sentences we might write:

There are *two* apples on the table.
I will take the *second* apple from the table.

In the first sentence, "two" is used to describe the size or total number of apples on the table. When we use a number in this way, we say that we are using a **cardinal** concept of number. In the second sentence, "second" is used to describe an order or position of an apple being taken from the table. When we use a number in this way, we say that we are using an **ordinal** concept of number.

TABLE 1

Cardinal number names	Ordinal number names
One	First
Two	Second
Three	Third
Four	Fourth
Five	Fifth
Six	Sixth
Seven	Seventh
Eight	Eighth

When we **match** the set of chairs at a dinner table with the set of persons to be seated, we are using the cardinal number idea. When we guess the number of beans in a jar at a county fair, we are guessing the cardinal number of the set of beans. Ordinary counting, on the other hand, uses the ordinal number idea. When tennis players are ranked in a tennis tournament, the ordinal concept of number is used. Figure 1 suggests an observation concerning the cardinal number property (cardinality) of a set while Figure 2 suggests an ordering property (ordinality) of the set. Figures 4(a) and 4(b) suggest sets of objects with common cardinal number properties while Figure 4(c) suggests an ordering of the sets with respect to the cardinality of the sets.

To illustrate further, the set of circles in Figure 5 has a cardinal size

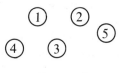

FIGURE 5

which we describe as a "fiveness." The circles in Figure 6, however, have been arranged to suggest an ordinal position or succession of the circles.

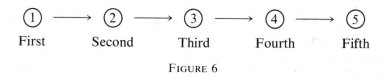

FIGURE 6

1.1.2   Our first idea of number probably comes with observing the distinction between one and many. Let us examine this cardinal concept as a first step in building an understanding of numbers.

Questions.

1. In the two sets in Figure 7, are there the same number of elements?

2. In the two sets in Figure 8, which set has the smaller (that is, fewer) number of elements?

FIGURE 7   FIGURE 8

3. What is the cardinal number property of each of the sets in Figure 9?

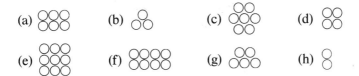

FIGURE 9

Answers.

   1. No.
   2. The set of circles.
   3. (a) 6   (b) 3   (c) 7   (d) 4   (e) 9   (f) 8   (g) 5   (h) 2.

In answering the above questions, the chances are that we will have counted each set separately. Unlike the primitive savage who could not count and who merely matched sets, our thinking has been complicated by a learned language process.

In the third question above we asked for the cardinal number property of each of the sets. Rather than naming the cardinal sizes, we might have rearranged the collections as shown in Figure 10.

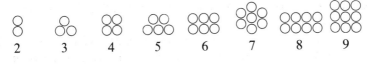

FIGURE 10

Notice that we could have obtained the set with cardinal size 8 from the set with cardinal size 9 by "throwing away an element" and re-arranging the set. The set with cardinal size 7 could be obtained by throwing another element out and rearranging the set. When a set is formed from another set by selecting elements from the given set, the new set is called a **subset** of the given set.

Examples.

(a)

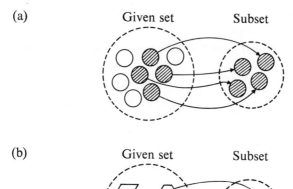

Given set   Subset

(b)

Given set   Subset

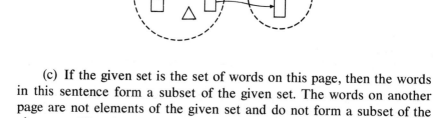

(c) If the given set is the set of words on this page, then the words in this sentence form a subset of the given set. The words on another page are not elements of the given set and do not form a subset of the given set. The given set is, however, a subset of all the words in this book.

(d) If the given set is the set of words on this page, then the set of words on this page is a subset of the given set. That is, any set is a subset of itself. We should also note that the set with no elements is a subset of the given set. That is, a set with no elements is a subset of every set. Such a set is said to be **empty** and is often called the **null** set.

Consider a set with a single element, its cardinality is one, 1. Sets can be ordered and rearranged as shown in Table 2 along with their cardinal and ordinal number properties and numerals.

TABLE 2

First	○ 1	One
Second	○○ 1 + 1 = 2	Two
Third	○○○ 1 + 1 + 1 = 2 + 1 = 3	Three
Fourth	○○○○ 1 + 1 + 1 + 1 = 3 + 1 = 4	Four
Fifth	○○○○○ 1 + 1 + 1 + 1 + 1 = 4 + 1 = 5	Five
and so on	and so on	. . .

Table 2 suggests that there are many ways of naming the number property of sets. Here we are interested in the numerals "1," "2," "3," "4," "5," and so on. In using these numerals, notice that we will be shifting from the "concrete" idea of five objects to the abstract idea of a fiveness. With appropriate numerals we will be able to answer questions of "How many?" by **matching** elements one by one to the numerals. To compare two sets, we can match the elements of each set with the numerals and then compare the last numerals matched.

Examples.

(a) Determining the cardinal number of a set:

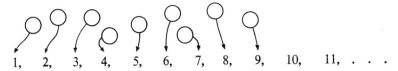

1,   2,   3,   4,   5,   6,   7,   8,   9,   10,   11, . . .

From our matching, we could conclude that the cardinal number of the set is 9.

(b) Comparing the cardinal sizes of two sets:

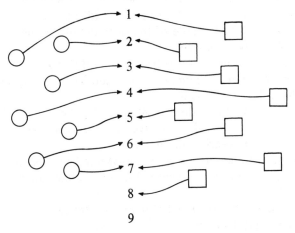

From the last numerals matched, we could conclude that there are 7 circles and 8 squares so that there is one more square than circles (or one less circle than squares).

We are no longer comparing sets directly, we are counting the separate sets using a process of matching with a set of numerals. The resulting numerals are then compared. The standard set of counting numerals naming the cardinal and ordinal number properties names a set of ideas called the **natural numbers**. The natural numbers are often called the **counting numbers**. The natural numbers are the simplest set of numbers used. In our familiar numerals, the natural numbers are:

1, 2, 3, 4, 5, 6, 7, 8, 9, 10, 11, 12, . . .

Exercises

1. Things and ideas are referred to by _____.
2. Briefly describe Figure 11.

FIGURE 11

3. The idea of a collection of things is called a _____. The things in the collection are called _____ and are said to _____ or be _____ of the collection.

4. Give a specific example of a set with cardinal number property
   (a) five   (b) nine   (c) twelve   (d) thirty.

5. Give a specific example of the ordering of the elements of a set with cardinal number property
   (a) five   (b) nine   (c) twelve   (d) thirty.

6. Insert the words "numeral" or "number" appropriately in the blanks in the following sentences:

The _____ 3 and 2 are ideas symbolized by the _____ "3" and "2." When we observe the cardinal or ordinal _____ property in a situation, we use a _____ to describe and name it.

7. Write a sentence using the cardinal number concept of the number five. Write another sentence using the ordinal number concept of the number five.

8. Determine whether the following statements refer to a cardinal or ordinal concept of number.
   (a) The numbers of the pages of this book.
   (b) The number of words on this page.
   (c) The number of months in a year.
   (d) The number referring to this year.

9. Do as in Exercise 8 with:
   (a) The number referring to the address of your house.
   (b) The number of dollars a person earns in one year.

(c) The number of this exercise.

(d) The number of students taking an examination.

10. Name the cardinal size of each of the following sets. Now arrange the sets into ordinal positions according to their cardinality with the smallest first.

11. Do as in Exercise 10 with:

12. Given the set shown in Figure 12, form the set of subsets obtained by "throwing out" two elements from each successive remaining subset.

FIGURE 12   FIGURE 13

13. Do as in Exercise 12 with Figure 13.

14. Compare the sizes of the sets illustrated in Figures 12 and 13 by matching each set with the counting numerals.

15. Do as in Exercise 14 with the sets shown in Figure 14.

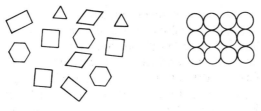

FIGURE 14

16. If we combined the sets shown in Figures 12 and 13 to form a single set, what would be the cardinal number of the new set?

17. In Figures 12 and 13, if we match elements of one set with the other and "throw out" all the matched elements, then what would be the cardinal number of the set of remaining unmatched elements?

18. In counting a set, must a particular element be counted first? Can we count a set in different ways?

19. Once we begin counting a set, what mistakes must be avoided to make sure that we obtain a "correct" counting of the set?

20. The standard counting set of numbers is called the set of _____ _____.

Answers.

1. Name.

2. There are five sets with cardinal number sizes: 3, 4, 5, 6, and 7. The set with cardinal size 3 can be obtained as a subset of the set with cardinal size 4. The sets are arranged in two rows and show that every other set has an odd number of elements.

3. set; elements, belong to, members.

4. (a) A basketball team; the set of fingers on one hand.

(b) A baseball team; the set consisting of the numerals "1," "2," "3," "4," "5," "6," "7," "8," and "9."

(c) A carton with a dozen eggs; the set of arms and legs on three people.

(d) A pack and one-half of cigarettes; the set consisting of six basketball teams together.

5. (a) The set of fingers on one hand: thumb, forefinger, middle finger, ring finger, and the little finger (in that order).

(b) The set of numerals as ordered in Answer 4(b).

(c) A set of a dozen eggs might be ordered by weight, lightest to heaviest (or by volume, smallest to largest).

(d) A pack and one-half of cigarettes might be ordered as they are smoked.

6. numbers, numerals; number, numeral.

7. A bowling team usually consists of a set of five players. The team member bowling fifth is called the anchor man.

8. (a) ordinal   (b) cardinal   (c) cardinal   (d) ordinal.

9. (a) ordinal   (b) cardinal   (c) ordinal   (d) cardinal.

10. (a) 6; (b) 4; (c) 12; (d) 5.   (b) 4; (d) 5; (a) 6; (c) 12.

11. (a) 1; (b) 8; (c) 6; (d) 10.   (a) 1; (c) 6; (b) 8; (d) 10.

12.

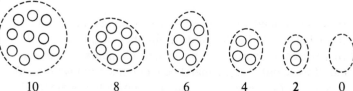

| 10 | 8 | 6 | 4 | 2 | 0 |

13.

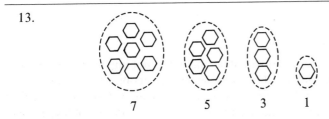

14. The set of circles has cardinal number property ten, 10. The set of hexagons has cardinal number property seven, 7.

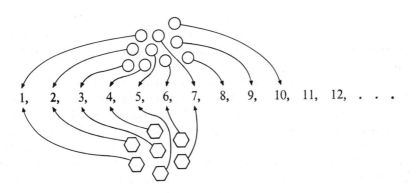

15.

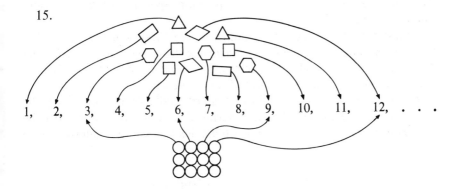

16. Seventeen, 17.
17. The remaining set would consist of three circles; 3.
18. No; yes.
19. We must avoid counting the same object twice or more or missing any object. We must also avoid skipping numerals or using the same numeral twice or more.
20. Natural numbers.

1.2 History

1.2.1   As we have seen, it would be difficult, if not impossible, to point to ideas without special words and symbols. As people first began to talk and write they invented and created number names. One of the earliest systems of numerals was devised by the Egyptians about 5,000 years ago. The Egyptian numerals were carved on wood or stone to record commercial and government transactions. For example, the number 12 was indicated by "∩ | |." The number 1,232 by " ⚡ ⁹ ⁹ ∩∩∩ | |." Of course "∩ | |" names the same number as 12. We might ask, "Why have the numerals changed?" As we proceed, keep in mind our use of numerals for both recording and computing results of numerical situations.

The Babylonians, who came about 1,000 years after the Egyptians, did their record keeping on clay tablets with a piece of wood called a *stylus*. The wedge shape of the stylus probably determined the shape of their numerals. The numeral for one appeared like a wedge, Ⅴ; the numeral for ten like ◄. The number 12 was ◄ⅤⅤ. For large numbers the Babylonians used the idea of a relative place position as we do in our decimal system. The quantity sixty was used as we use ten. A small space was left between groups of marks to indicate the different sizes. However, the Babylonians did not have a "position spacer" mark equivalent to our symbol "0."

Among the oldest systems of numerals are those which were used in the Orient. The oriental system originated from the use of sticks laid flat on a surface for calculating. It is interesting to observe the changes that have taken place in the form of the numerals.

We are told that our modern western civilization grew from the "Golden Age of Greece." It was during this period of history that the foundations not only of modern mathematics but also of modern science

TABLE 3.   Oriental Numerals.

Original symbols:	I	II	T	—	⊥
Modern symbols:	一	二	六	十	六十
Our symbols:	1	2	6	10	60

and philosophy were established. It was the age in which not only the question of "how?" but also the modern question of "why?" was asked. It was from this period that man began to ask about fundamental principles, about unifying concepts, about man's place in the universe according to a rational scheme. It was during this period, about the fourth century B.C., that the philosophers Socrates, Plato, and Aristotle lived. The famous mathematicians Euclid, Archimedes, and Apollonios emerged from this period of Greek rationalism.

The Greeks had several ways of writing numerals. In one method they simply used the initial letters of the words for numerals; later on they generally used the letters of their alphabet. The Greek system was based on counting by tens but they did not have a numeral for zero nor did they use the place position idea as we do in writing numerals.

TABLE 4.   Greek Numerals.

α	β	γ	δ	ϵ	ζ	η	θ	ι	κ
1	2	3	4	5	6	7	8	9	10

1.2.2   A system of numerals which is still in use today was developed by the Romans. Historians believe that these symbols arose from pictures of the fingers (Figure 15).

Through the years gradual changes took place in the form of the symbols used until we arrived at the familiar Roman numerals as used today. The quantity fifty was represented in a variety of ways, but "L" was most commonly used. The symbols "C" and "M" probably arose from the Roman words *centum* and *millie* for 100 and 1,000 respectively. The symbol "D" is also in common usage for the quantity 500.

Notice in Table 5 that two methods were used to denote the numbers 4 and 19. Since it was easier to think "five less one" than "four," it seemed natural to write IV rather than IIII. The idea of "twenty less one"

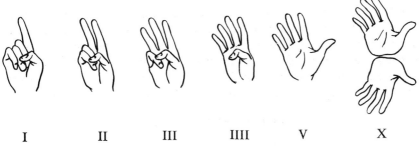

| I | II | III | IIII | V | X |

FIGURE 15

TABLE 5

Our Numerals	Roman Numerals
2	II
4	IV or IIII
7	VII
19	XIX or IXX
1962	MDCDLXII

could be written IXX and the idea of "ten and ten less one" could be written XIX while "nineteen" was written XVIIII. The idea of "fifteen and five less one" could be written XVIV. In general, however, numerals for smaller numbers followed the symbols for larger values.

Seven distinct symbols or marks are used in writing Roman numerals. These are shown in Table 6.

Examples.

26	XXVI	34	XXXIV
49	XLIX	67	LXVII
106	CVI	260	CCLX
435	CDXXXV	524	DXXIV
789	DCCLXXXIX	957	CMLVII
1056	MLVI	1402	MCDII
1699	MDCXCIX	3949	MMMCMXLIX

Roman numerals were commonly used in bookkeeping and for other records until the eighteenth century. Although easy to add and subtract with, Roman numerals are cumbersome to write with and difficult to multiply and divide with. Much of the calculation was performed on the *abacus,* a counting device which is still widely used in the Orient.

1.2.3 The numerals which we commonly use today are often called Arabic or Hindu-Arabic numerals. As a matter of fact, these numerals were probably never used by the Arabs or Hindus. The original form of the numerals appeared in a book written in India about twelve hundred years ago. The book was translated into Arabic and, falling into some merchant's hands, was carried to Europe where it was in turn translated

TABLE 6.   Roman Numerals.

I	V	X	L	C	D	M
1	5	10	50	100	500	1,000

TABLE 7

Hindu (900 A.D.)	୬	୪	୨	8	୪	୬	୭	୬	୧	୦
Arabic	I	ᴎ	ᴃ	ε	0	ᒣ	V	Λ	۹	॰
European (1000 A.D.)	I	ᘮ	ᘓ	ᒪ	ᒨ	ᒧ	ʃ	8	ᘐ	0
European (1400 A.D.)	I	ᘐ	ᘓ	ᔭ	ᘎ	6	ᘐ	8	9	ᘏ
Modern (1960 A.D.)	1	2	3	4	5	6	7	8	9	0

into Latin. Since this was long before the development of mass printing, the material was known only in individual manuscript form.

When multiple printing developed and books appeared, the form of numerals tended to a standard of design. Although the superiority of Hindu-Arabic numerals was recognized, the system was not immediately accepted in Europe. Indeed, it was not until the nineteenth century that they were in general use.

Ten distinct symbols are used in the Hindu-Arabic system. These symbols, illustrated in Table 7, are called **digits** after the finger form of counting. Using these ten digits and a systematic method of enumeration, we can write the names of all the counting numbers.

Two principles are vitally important in making this numeral system useful:

1. We must write neatly and legibly so that we can read our writing.

2. We must pay careful attention to spacing, for the Hindu-Arabic system employs the principle of place position in writing numerals.

The various place positions of a digit in a numeral have been given proper names as shown in Table 8. A numeral is read from the left to the

TABLE 8

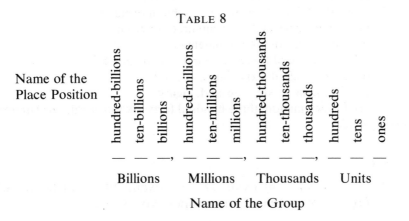

Name of the Place Position	hundred-billions	ten-billions	billions	hundred-millions	ten-millions	millions	hundred-thousands	ten-thousands	thousands	hundreds	tens	ones
	—	—	—,	—	—	—,	—	—	—,	—	—	—
Name of the Group		Billions			Millions			Thousands			Units	

right by groups. For example, "123,987,654,321" is read "one hundred twenty-three billion, nine hundred eighty-seven million, six hundred fifty-four thousand, three hundred twenty-one." Notice that we do not mention units, but simply understand it as the last group read. "300,040" is read "three hundred thousand, forty." "1,372" is read "one thousand, three hundred seventy-two." The numeral "2,760,203" is read "two million, seven hundred sixty thousand, two hundred three." The word "and" is not used in reading whole number numerals. The numeral for "two hundred two million, fifty-one thousand, one hundred twenty-two" is written "202,051,122." The numeral for "one million, two hundred sixty-five thousand, four" is written "1,265,004." "Ten billion, sixty million, three hundred thousand, two" is written "10,060,300,002." The place positions of larger and smaller sized groups have also been given names.

Practice 1.

1. Write the Roman and Hindu-Arabic numerals for:
   (a) Forty-four.
   (b) Seventy-two.
   (c) One hundred ninety-three.
   (d) Six hundred seven.
   (e) One thousand, one hundred sixty-six.
   (f) Three thousand, six hundred seventy-four.
2. Write the following in Roman numerals:
   (a) 9   (b) 56   (c) 149   (d) 606   (e) 1,435   (f) 3,650.
3. Write the following in Hindu-Arabic numerals:
   (a) XIV   (b) XVI   (c) CLX   (d) XCVII   (e) LDI   (f) MDCLXVI.
4. Write out in words how the following numerals should be read:
   (a) 1,347   (b) 10,403   (c) 105,630   (d) 150,063
   (e) 42,309,801   (f) 672,503,498,306.
5. Write the following in Hindu-Arabic numerals:
   (a) Eleven thousand, four hundred nineteen.
   (b) Fifty-three thousand, nineteen.
   (c) One hundred three thousand, one hundred.
   (d) Five hundred sixty thousand, eight.
   (e) One million, six thousand, eighty.
   (f) Fifteen million, three hundred forty-six thousand, one hundred twenty-three.

Answers.

1. (a) XLIV; 44   (b) LXXII; 72   (c) CXCIII; 193   (d) DCVII; 607
   (e) MCLXVI; 1,166   (f) MMMDCLXXIV; 3,674.

2. (a) IX   (b) LVI   (c) CIL   (d) DCVI   (e) MCDXXXV
   (f) MMMDCL.
3. (a) 14   (b) 16   (c) 160   (d) 97   (e) 451   (f) 1,666.
4. (a) One thousand, three hundred forty-seven.
   (b) Ten thousand, four hundred three.
   (c) One hundred five thousand, six hundred thirty.
   (d) One hundred fifty thousand, sixty-three.
   (e) Forty-two million, three hundred nine thousand, eight hundred
one.
   (f) Six hundred seventy-two billion, five hundred three million,
four hundred ninety-eight thousand, three hundred six.
5. (a) 11,419   (b) 53,019   (c) 103,100   (d) 560,008
   (e) 1,006,080   (f) 15,346,123.

1.2.4   In writing numerals we have already noted the place position idea.
The size of the group (collection or set) used in developing the place position is called the **base** of the system of writing. Our common decimal
system uses the base ten. The use of ten for a base is probably due to the
use of fingers in counting. The name *decimal* comes from the medieval
Latin word *decem* for ten.

Each place position in a simple numeral has ten times the value (size)
of the place position to its right. For example, in 111 the left-hand digit 1
stands for ten times the middle digit 1. The middle digit 1 stands for ten
times the right-hand digit 1. Of course, we could think of the left-hand
digit 1 as standing for one hundred times the right-hand digit 1. The
numeral can be pictured by a succession of sets as shown in Figure 16.

In writing 3204, each digit tells us something concerning the number
being referred to. Each digit is in a particular place position. Each place
position stands for a given sized group; from right to left in 3204, we call
the place positions the ones, the tens, the hundreds, and the thousands.
The digit in a given place position tells us the number of groups of the

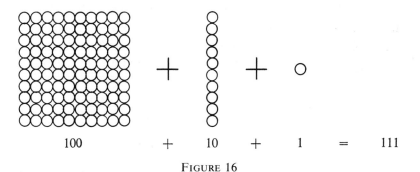

100   +   10   +   1   =   111

FIGURE 16

given place position size that are being named. When the digit 0 appears, it tells us that there are no groups of that given size for the number being referred to. In 3204 we have 3 groups of 1000, 2 groups of 100, 0 (or no) groups of 10, and the "4" tells us that there are 4 groups of 1. That is, we think "3 thousands, 2 hundreds, no tens, 4 ones."

In 2020 the left-hand digit 2 tells us that there are 2 thousands, the right-hand digit 2 tells us that there are 2 tens. The left-hand 0 tells us that there are no hundreds while the right-hand 0 tells us there are no ones. The numeral "3" tells us that we have 3 ones while the numeral "30" tells us that we have 3 tens and no ones. Writing "300" is quite different from writing "3," since 300 tells us that we have 3 hundreds rather than 3 ones as in "3." Of course, 30 ones would give us the same idea as 3 tens and 30 tens would result in 3 hundreds; 3 hundreds would be the same as 300 ones.

In developing the simple counting numerals we might have begun as suggested in Figure 17.

FIGURE 17

The first nine objects in a collection (or set) could be ordered and given names as shown. We might give the tenth object a proper name as the Romans did, but then there is a limit to the names one could invent or remember. If in writing, we could distinguish sets of fixed sizes, that is, with fixed cardinality, then we could repeat our counting in terms of both ones and the fixed cardinal sizes. For example, we might count 1, 2, 3, then introduce groups of fours:

1, 2, 3, 1 four, 1 four and 1, 1 four and 2, 1 four and 3,
2 fours, 2 fours and 1, 2 fours and 2, 2 fours and 3,
3 fours, 3 fours and 1, 3 fours and 2, 3 fours and 3,
1 group of four-fours, 1 four-fours and 1, and so on.

Of course the above form of writing is cumbersome, tedious, and groups of four might be unnatural to our experience. To overcome the difficulties in writing we might introduce a symbol for four, say "4," and a place holding symbol, say "0." Thus, we might write:

1, 2, 3, 1(4), 1(4)1, 1(4)2, 1(4)3, 2(4), 2(4)1, 2(4)2, 2(4)3,
3(4), 3(4)1, 3(4)2, 3(4)3, 1(4)(4), 1(4)(4)1, . . .

Or by "understanding" that we are writing in terms of groups of four:

1, 2, 3, 10, 11, 12, 13, 20, 21, 22, 23, 30, 31, 32, 33, 100, 101, . . .

Notice that the place holding symbol "0" in 10 tells us that we have 1 four and no ones as contrasted to 1 which tells us that we have just 1 one. The numeral 101 above tells us that we have 1 four-fours no fours and 1 one.

In the decimal system we use the more natural cardinal number ten as a fixed size. This is accomplished by using the place holding symbol "0." We thus indicate one collection of ten as 10. In this way, in special situations, we can use different fixed cardinal sizes in counting. Observe also that the fixed cardinal sizes depend on the number of counting symbols used in writing. For example, in using groups of four we also used four symbols in writing the numerals. In the Hindu-Arabic numerals, these symbols are the ten **digits**: 1, 2, 3, 4, 5, 6, 7, 8, 9, 0 forming a system with base ten.

The place position idea for writing numerals quite likely arose from the use of counting boards with columns of beads. The number of beads in a column suggests the base of the counting system used on the board. A base three counting board would have three beads in each column. A base five board would have five beads in each column. A base three writing system would have two counting symbols and a place holder symbol. A base five writing system would have four counting symbols and a place holder symbol.

Examples.

(a) Counting, base three (using Hindu-Arabic symbols):

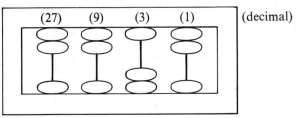

1, 2, 1 three 0 ones, 1 1, 1 2, 2 0, 2 1, 2 2

Writing, base three:

  1, 2, 10, 11, 12, 20, 21, 22, 100, 101, 102, 110
  1, 2, 3, 4, 5, 6, 7, 8,   9, 10 (decimal)

(b) Base three counting board:

![base three counting board with columns labeled (27) (9) (3) (1) and (decimal)]

$$1(27) + 1(9) + 2(3) + 1(1) = 1121 \text{ base three.}$$

The base three numeral $1121 = 27 + 9 + 6 + 1 = 43$ in the decimal (base ten) form.

(c) Base five counting and counting board:

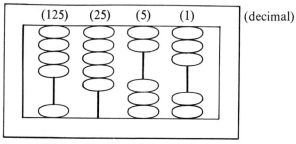

| (125) | (25) | (5) | (1) | (decimal) |

$$1(125) + 0(25) + 3(5) + 2(1) = 1032 \text{ base five.}$$

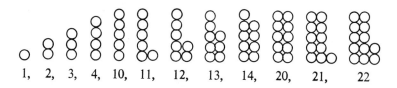

1, 2, 3, 4, 10, 11, 12, 13, 14, 20, 21, 22

The base five numeral $1032 = 142$ in decimal form (base ten).

In our base ten decimal system each column of beads of a counting board would have ten beads. The columns of beads are named (in our examples) from the right the ones column, the tens column, the hundreds column, and so on. Each bead in the tens column stands for one group of ten beads in the ones column. A bead in the hundreds column stands for ten beads in the tens column or one hundred beads in the ones column. A bead in any column stands for ten beads in the column to its right and it takes ten beads to represent one bead in the column to its left.

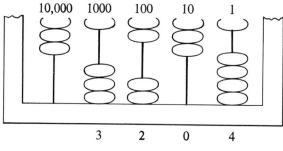

10,000   1000   100   10   1

3   2   0   4

FIGURE 18

The number 3204 can be represented on a decimal counting board as shown in Figure 18. We could **expand** the numeral and write it as:

3204 = 3 thousands + 2 hundreds + 0 tens + 4 ones.
3204 = 3(1000)   +   2(100)   +   0(10) + 4(1).
3204 =   3000   +   200   +   00   + 4.

Examples.

(a) 231 = 2 hundreds + 3 tens + 1 ones
      = 2(100) + 3(10) + 1(1)
      = 200 + 30 + 1.

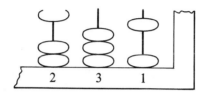

(b) 4,100 = 4 thousands + 1 hundreds + 0 tens + 0 ones
        = 4(1000) + 1(100) + 0(10) + 0(1)
        = 4000 + 100 + 00 + 0.

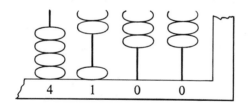

(c) 2,120 = 2 thousands + 1 hundreds + 2 tens + 0 ones
        = 2(1000) + 1(100) + 2(10) + 0(1)
        = 2000 + 100 + 20 + 0.

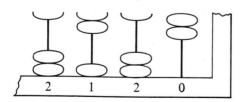

(d) $20,372 = 2$ ten thousands $+ 0$ thousands $+ 3$ hundreds $+ 7$ tens
$+ 2$ ones
$= 2(10,000) + 0(1,000) + 3(100) + 7(10) + 2(1)$
$= 20,000 + 0,000 + 300 + 70 + 2.$

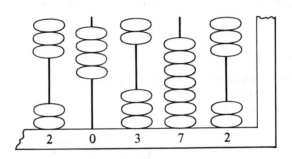

When we expand numerals and write them in terms of place positions, it "brings out" the place positions and emphasizes the proper role of digits in writing a numeral. For example, when we write $3204 = 3000 + 200 + 00 + 4$ it separates the digits and reveals something of the structure of the number referred to.

Practice 2.

1. How many digits are there in each of the following?
   (a) 101   (b) 2,300   (c) 10   (d) 5   (e) 69
   (f) 31,000   (g) 420   (h) 0   (i) 7,010   (j) 465.

2. How many place positions do each of the following have?
   (a) 790   (b) 40   (c) 2   (d) 500   (e) 1,009
   (f) 3,848   (g) 50,320   (h) 0   (i) 36   (j) 36,000.

3. Using the necessary Hindu-Arabic symbols (as in the examples), write the first thirty counting numerals in a base three system; a base five system.

4. Write the following base three numerals in our decimal system:
   (a) 220   (b) 1,201   (c) 1,000.

5. Write the following base five numerals in our decimal system:
   (a) 21   (b) 2,123   (c) 1,300.

6. Write the following decimal numerals in the base three and the base five systems:
   (a) 20   (b) 35   (c) 74.

7. Write the following decimal numerals in expanded form:
   (a) 362   (b) 508   (c) 1,031   (d) 21,900   (e) 2,100,103.

8. Write the following expanded numerals in ordinary decimal form:
(a) $6000 + 300 + 00 + 4$.   (b) $1(1000) + 0(100) + 7(10) + 0(1)$.
(c) $100,000 + 00,000 + 0,000 + 100 + 00 + 8$.
(d) $5(1,000,000) + 3(100,000) + 1(10,000) + 0(1,000) + 5(100) + 0(10) + 9(1)$.

Answers.

1. (a) 3 (b) 4 (c) 2 (d) 1 (e) 2 (f) 5 (g) 3 (h) 1 (i) 4 (j) 3.
2. (a) 3 (b) 2 (c) 1 (d) 3 (e) 4 (f) 4 (g) 5 (h) 1 (i) 2 (j) 5.
3. Base three: 1, 2, 10, 11, 12, 20, 21, 22, 100, 101, 102, 110, 111, 112, 120, 121, 122, 200, 201, 202, 210, 211, 212, 220, 221, 222, 1000, 1001, 1002, 1010.
Base five: 1, 2, 3, 4, 10, 11, 12, 13, 14, 20, 21, 22, 23, 24, 30, 31, 32, 33, 34, 40, 41, 42, 43, 44, 100, 101, 102, 103, 104, 110.
4. (a) 24   (b) 46   (c) 27.
5. (a) 11   (b) 288   (c) 200.
6. Base three: (a) 202   (b) 1022   (c) 2202.
Base five: (a) 40   (b) 120   (c) 244.
7. (a) $3(100) + 6(10) + 2(1)$ or $300 + 60 + 2$.
(b) $5(100) + 0(10) + 8(1)$ or $500 + 00 + 8$.
(c) $1(1000) + 0(100) + 3(10) + 1(1)$ or $1000 + 000 + 30 + 1$.
(d) $20,000 + 1,000 + 900 + 00 + 0$.
(e) $2,000,000 + 100,000 + 00,000 + 0,000 + 100 + 00 + 3$.
8. (a) 6,304   (b) 1,070   (c) 100,108   (d) 5,310,509.

Exercises

1. Name the civilization that used each of the following forms of numerals:
(a) $I\alpha$ (b) $\prec V$ (c) 11   (d) $\cap I$ (e) $\dagger -$ (f) XI.
2. Two important uses of numerals are for _____ and _____ results of numerical situations.
3. The "Golden Age of Greece" was notable not only for the question of _____ but also the modern question of _____.
4. The seven distinct symbols or marks used in writing Roman numerals are _____ for 1, _____ for 5, _____ for 10, _____ for 50, _____ for 100, _____ for 500, and _____ for 1,000.
5. In Roman numerals the numeral for 94 can be written in at least six ways. Write the Roman numeral for 94 in at least four ways.

6. Write the Roman and Hindu-Arabic numerals for:
   (a) Four hundred fifty-four.
   (b) Six hundred forty-five.
   (c) One thousand, nine hundred seventy-six.
7. Write the following in Roman numerals:
   (a) 26   (b) 62   (c) 109   (d) 901   (e) 1,456   (f) 2,542.
8. Write the following in Hindu-Arabic numerals:
   (a) LIX   (b) XCII   (c) CDLXII   (d) MMCMVII   (e) MCDXLIV.
9. The ten distinct symbols used in writing Hindu-Arabic numerals are called _____ after the finger form of counting. The modern symbols used are _____, _____, _____, _____, _____, _____, _____, _____, _____, and _____.
10. In using numerals, two principles are vitally important. These are:
   (a) _____   (b) _____.
11. The symbol "4" can be described by at least three words depending on how we intend to use the symbol. When used as the name of a number we call it a _____. When used to name the idea, we call the idea a _____. When considered as a symbol used in writing Hindu-Arabic numerals, we call 4 a _____.
12. 7540 tells us that we have _____ thousands, 5 _____, 4 tens, _____.
13. Write the four digit Hindu-Arabic numeral with two in the thousands place, no hundreds, four tens, and three ones.
14. Write out in words how the following numerals should be read:
   (a) 12,045   (b) 152,405   (c) 702,027   (d) 14,000,362,010.
15. Write the following in Hindu-Arabic numerals:
   (a) Fifteen thousand, five hundred nineteen.
   (b) Forty-seven thousand, ninety.
   (c) Three hundred twenty-eight thousand, six hundred.
   (d) Seventy-five million, fifty thousand, seven.
   (e) Ninety-nine billion, ninety million, nine hundred thousand, nine hundred ninety-nine.
16. In writing numerals, the size of the group used in developing the place positions is called the _____ of the system. In the decimal system, the base is _____. Each place position has _____ times the value of the place position to its _____.
17. In 2,101 the left-hand digit 1 stands for _____ times the right-hand digit 1. The digit 2 represents 2 _____ or _____ hundreds.
18. In 2,100 the "0's" position the digits 2 and 1 to tell us that we have 21 _____. In 2,010 the "0's" tell us that the digit 1 stands for 1 _____ and the digit 2 for 2 _____.
19. The decimal numeral 58 would be written as _____ in a base

three system and as _____ in a base five system (using the necessary Hindu-Arabic symbols).

20. In terms of our decimal numerals, what would be the successive cardinal sizes of the first three place positions from right to left in a base eight system? Using the necessary Hindu-Arabic symbols, write the following decimal numerals in a base eight system:

    (a) 20   (b) 35   (c) 74.

21. When we write $4000 + 100 + 00 + 1$ or $4(1000) + 1(100) + 0(10) + 1(1)$ we call it an _____ numeral. In ordinary decimal form this would be written _____.

22. Write the numerals indicated by the base ten counting board representations of Figure 19 in ordinary decimal form and in expanded numeral form.

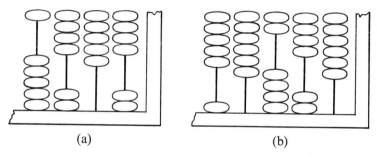

(a)   (b)

FIGURE 19

23. Write the following decimal numerals in expanded form:

    (a) 520   (b) 3,572   (c) 401,340   (d) 1,060,307.

24. Write the following expanded numerals in ordinary decimal form:

    (a) $2(1000) + 9(100) + 3(10) + 7(1)$.

    (b) $12(100) + 6(10) + 0(1)$.

    (c) $70,000 + 7,000 + 000 + 50 + 4$.

    (d) $120,000 + 7,000 + 1,200 + 70 + 1$.

    (e) $9(10,000) + 5(1,000) + 16(100) + 6(10) + 18(1)$.

Answers.

    1. (a) Greek   (b) Babylonian   (c) Modern (Hindu-Arabic)
    (d) Egyptian   (e) Oriental   (f) Roman.

    2. recording, calculating (or computing).

    3. "How?" "Why?"

    4. I, V, X, L, C, D, M.

5. XCIV, XCIIII, LXXXXIV, LXXXXIIII, LXLIV, LXLIIII.
6. Roman: (a) CDLIV   (b) DCXLV   (c) MCMLXXVI.
   Hindu-Arabic: (a) 454   (b) 645   (c) 1,976.
7. (a) XXVI   (b) LXII   (c) CIX   (d) CMI   (e) MCDLVI
   (f) MMDXLII.
8. (a) 59   (b) 92   (c) 462   (d) 2,907   (e) 1,444.
9. digits; 1, 2, 3, 4, 5, 6, 7, 8, 9, 0.
10. (a) neatness and legibility   (b) attention to proper spacing.
11. numeral; number; digit.
12. 7; hundreds; 0 (or no) ones.
13. 2,043.
14. (a) Twelve thousand, forty-five.
    (b) One hundred fifty-two thousand, four hundred five.
    (c) Seven hundred two thousand, twenty-seven.
    (d) Fourteen billion, three hundred sixty-two thousand, ten.
15. (a) 15,519   (b) 47,090   (c) 328,600   (d) 75,050,007
    (e) 99,090,900,999.
16. base; ten (or 10); 10; right. (Note: $\frac{1}{10}$; left would be correct also.)
17. 100; thousands; 20.
18. hundreds; ten; thousands.
19. 2011 in base three; 213 in base five.
20. ones, eights, sixty-fours; (a) 24   (b) 43   (c) 112.
21. expanded; 4,101.
22. (a) $5,202 = 5000 + 200 + 00 + 2$
    (b) $10,420 = 10,000 + 0,000 + 400 + 20 + 0.$
23. (a) $520 = 500 + 20 + 0$ (b) $3,572 = 3000 + 500 + 70 + 2.$
    (c) $401,340 = 400,000 + 00,000 + 1,000 + 300 + 40 + 0.$
    (d) $1,060,307 = 1,000,000 + 000,000 + 60,000 + 0,000 + 300 + 00 + 7.$
24. (a) 2,937   (b) 1,260 (notice that $12(100) = 1(1000) + 2(100)$)
    (c) 77,054   (d) 128,271 (notice that $7,000 + 1,200 = 8,000 + 200$)
    (e) 96,678 (notice that $16(100) = 1(1000) + 6(100)$ and $18(1) = 1(10) + 8(1)$).

1.3 The Natural Numbers

1.3.1 When a new object or idea is observed a name is given to the object or idea. In asking the question of "How many?" and in comparing sets we have introduced the set of **natural numbers**. In the preceding section we discussed some of the history and development of the names (numerals) used in writing about the natural numbers. In this section we will examine a few of the properties which we expect of these natural numbers.

Remember, the natural numbers are ideas. What do we expect of these numbers? We might imagine that since the Greeks asked the question "Why?" and searched for unifying concepts, that questions concerning the natural numbers would have been answered long ago. As a matter of fact, possibly due to the difficulties with inadequate numerals, not much was known concerning the properties of numbers until the nineteenth century. The importance of the natural numbers was described in the words of Leopold Kronecker (1823-1891): "God created the natural numbers; everything else is man's handiwork."

An Italian mathematician, G. Peano (1858-1932), is credited with the first precise description of the natural numbers and their properties in 1889. If we think of numbers as "mathematical objects," we can illustrate and describe the natural numbers as suggested in Figure 20.

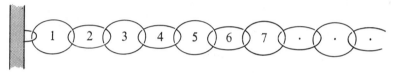

FIGURE 20

Where do we begin? At the beginning, of course! There is a number which we call one and write as "1." As the Greek philosopher, Aristotle, observed, one is the measure of number, the beginning of numbers. One is the unit out of which the other numbers are built.

One has a **successor**, two. And, two has a successor, three; three a successor, four; four a successor, five; and so on. Each natural number has a successor, for we can add another one to it. Thus, the natural numbers continue without end. As another Greek, Archimedes, observed, there is always a natural number that succeeds any natural number.

Each natural number except one has exactly one **predecessor**, and one has no predecessor. Our conception of the natural numbers can be likened to a chain, which has exactly one link following and another link preceding every link except for the beginning link of the chain. We often speak of **consecutive** natural numbers meaning successive natural numbers without skipping successors. For example, 7, 8, 9, 10 are consecutive numbers while 5, 7, 9, 11 are not.

The natural numbers do not "loop" or "split." Given a set with the natural number one and the successor to each natural number, we can guarantee that the collection includes all the natural numbers.

From the above four simple observations concerning our conception of the natural numbers we can develop all the remaining necessary properties of the natural numbers.

The Greeks made a distinction between the "practical" applications of numbers in daily life, which they called *logistica*, and the study of the properties of numbers, which they called *arithmetica*. In our contemporary civilization much of what was once "practical" is now "mechanical" and done by machines. History and experience have shown amply that the by-products of apparently useless investigations often pay high rewards. Thus, let us take a brief excursion into some observations concerning the properties of the natural numbers.

Our first observation is to note that the natural numbers divide themselves into two groups, the **odd** and the **even** numbers. If a set of objects can be divided into two sets such that each set has the same cardinal

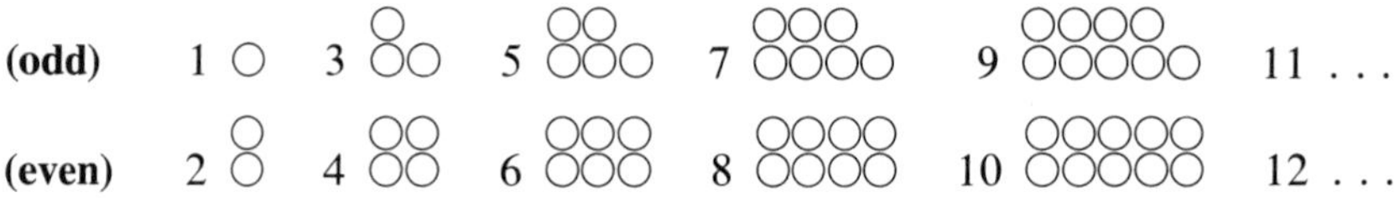

FIGURE 21

number property, then we say that the cardinality of the original set is **even**. Otherwise, we say that it is **odd**. (See Figure 21.)

Both the odd and even numbers have a beginning number and continue without end. If we choose an odd (or even) number, we can obtain consecutive odd (or even) numbers from the natural succession of numbers by choosing every other natural number. If we are given two consecutive natural numbers, one of them must be odd and the other even. Notice that an even set can be arranged into two rows so that the rows have the same number of elements. If a set has an odd number of elements, when the set is arranged into two rows, one row must have one more element than the other. If two even sets are "put together" the resulting set will be even. (For convenience we refer to even and odd

8 + 6 = 14   5 + 7 = 12   6 + 5 = 11
Even and even is even. Odd and odd is even. Even and odd is odd.
(a)   (b)   (c)

FIGURE 22

sets meaning their cardinal properties.) If two odd sets are "put together" the resulting set will be even! If an even and an odd set are "put together" the resulting set will be odd (Figure 22).

Noticing how even sets can be arranged in rows, let us extend the idea of rows with the same number of elements to three rows, four rows, and so on.

Three rows with the same number of elements:

3 ⦿ 6 ⦿⦿ 9 ⦿⦿⦿ 12 ⦿⦿⦿⦿ 15 ⦿⦿⦿⦿⦿ 18 . . .

Four rows with the same number of elements:

4 ⦿ 8 ⦿⦿ 12 ⦿⦿⦿ 16 ⦿⦿⦿⦿ 20 ⦿⦿⦿⦿⦿ 24 . . .

Observing the natural numbers associated with the succession of sets, we can write:

By threes: 3, 6, 9, 12, 15, 18, 21, 24, 27, 30, 33, . . .
By fours: 4, 8, 12, 16, 20, 24, 28, 32, 36, 40, 44, . . .

These subsets of the natural numbers are called the **multiples** of three and four, respectively. The set of even numbers is also called the set

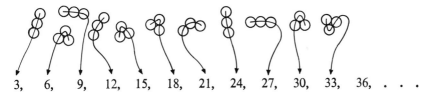

3,   6,   9,   12,   15,   18,   21,   24,   27,   30,   33,   36,   . . .

FIGURE 23. Counting by threes.

of multiples of two. Using a convenient set of multiples, we can count by twos, threes, fours, fives, and so on. See, for example, Figure 23.

1.3.2   Looking again at the arrangement of the sets, notice that if we count the columns in a given succession of sets of multiples, we have 1, 2, 3, 4, 5, . . . columns. The set of four threes are like the set of three fours, five threes are like three fives, six threes are like three sixes, and so on. A set of 30 elements could be arranged in any of the ways shown in Figure 24.

From our representation of a set with cardinal property 30, we could conclude that it has four distinct "shapes." These could be described as indicated in Figure 24(a), (b), (c), and (d). A set with cardinal number property 12 might be described by twelve ones, six twos, four threes, or by three fours, two sixes, or one twelve.

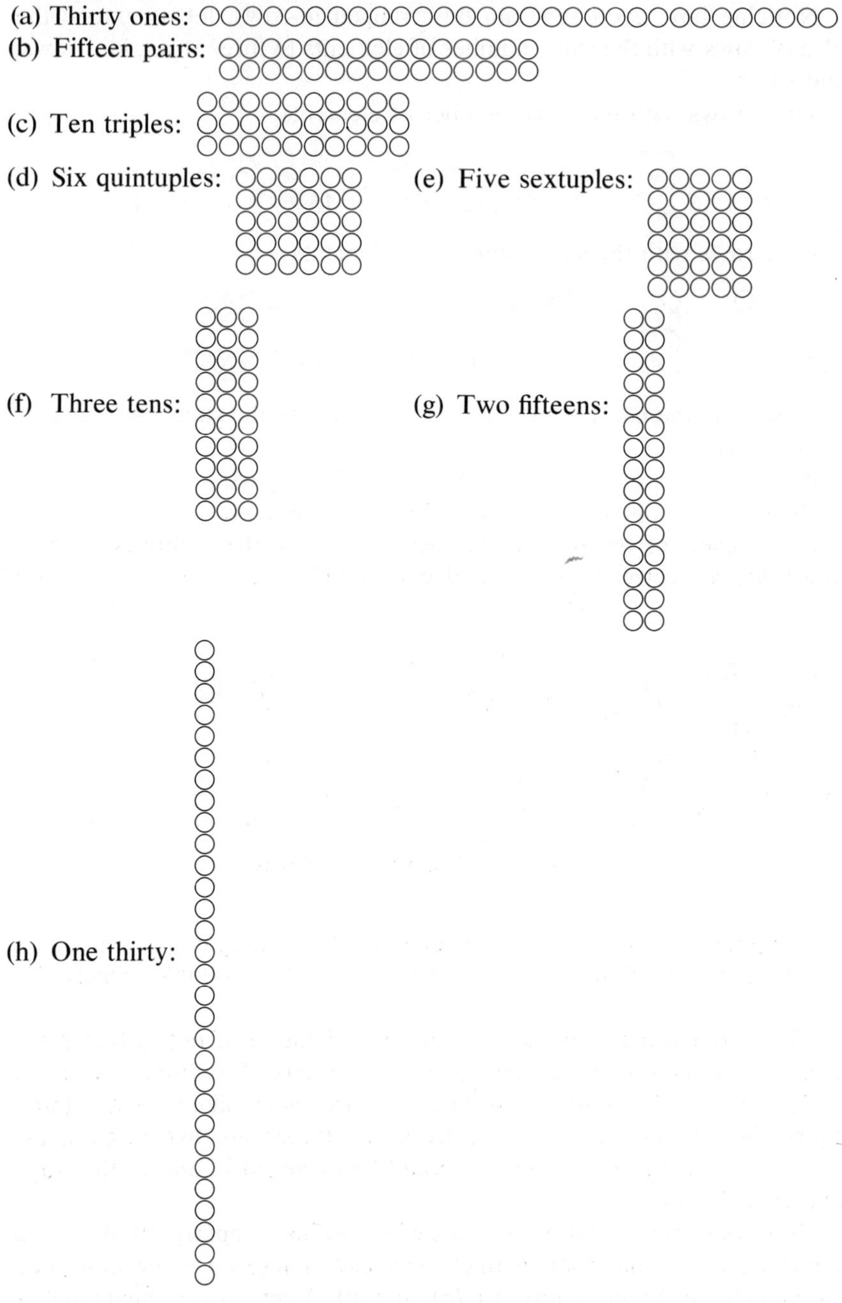

(a) Thirty ones: OOOOOOOOOOOOOOOOOOOOOOOOOOOOOO

(b) Fifteen pairs: OOOOOOOOOOOOOOOO
OOOOOOOOOOOOOOOO

(c) Ten triples: OOOOOOOOOO
OOOOOOOOOO
OOOOOOOOOO

(d) Six quintuples: OOOOOO
OOOOOO
OOOOOO
OOOOOO
OOOOOO

(e) Five sextuples: OOOOO
OOOOO
OOOOO
OOOOO
OOOOO
OOOOO

(f) Three tens:

(g) Two fifteens:

(h) One thirty:

FIGURE 24

Continuing with our examination of the "shapes" of individual sets with a fixed cardinal property, study the following examples for their individual properties.

Examples.

(a) Four: ⚬⚬/⚬⚬   (b) Five: ⚬⚬⚬⚬⚬

(c) Six: ⚬⚬⚬/⚬⚬⚬   (d) Seven: ⚬⚬⚬⚬⚬⚬⚬

(e) Eight: ⚬⚬⚬⚬/⚬⚬⚬⚬   (f) Nine: ⚬⚬⚬/⚬⚬⚬/⚬⚬⚬

(g) Ten: ⚬⚬⚬⚬⚬/⚬⚬⚬⚬⚬   (h) Eleven: ⚬⚬⚬⚬⚬⚬⚬⚬⚬⚬⚬

What are the possible distinct "shapes" of each of the sets? To what set of multiples do each of the cardinal numbers belong? To what set of multiples do the cardinal numbers of the even sets belong? Can we distinguish different kinds of "shapes" of sets?

Each of the sets can be represented as its cardinal number multiple of one and as one of its cardinal number. All of the even sets can be represented as multiples of two as shown. (Notice that we are identifying the cardinal number property of a set with the arrangement and "shape" of the set.) The set with six elements can be represented as two threes, the set with eight elements as two fours, "ten" as two fives, and so on.

Observe that the set with four elements is represented as a "square." The set with nine elements as a "square." What is the cardinality of the next larger set which can be represented as a "square"? (Answer: 16.) Could we rapidly determine the "square" sets (and numbers)?

The sets with six, eight, and ten elements might be described as "rectangular" sets with "rectangular" cardinal number properties. What about the sets with five, seven, and eleven elements? These sets are neither "square" nor "rectangular," they can only be represented as their cardinal number multiple of one and as one of their cardinal number. The cardinal numbers of these latter sets form a very useful and important set of numbers among the natural numbers. They are called the **prime numbers**. All other natural numbers in comparison are then called **composite** numbers. The first few prime numbers are:

$$2, 3, 5, 7, 11, 13, 17, 19, 23, 29, 31, 37, 41, \ldots$$

As we consider an individual set or cardinal number, notice how our attention is inevitably drawn to a whole class of sets or set of natural numbers having a common property. For example, the sets of even and odd numbers, multiples of numbers, "square" numbers, "rectangular" numbers, and prime numbers. As we proceed, we will find that it is very helpful to have a "feeling" for and understanding of the "shapes" and sets of natural numbers having a common property.

1.3.3 Due to its importance in our particular study and also in mathematics in general, let us examine the set of **prime numbers** somewhat further. Although both Aristotle and Euclid were aware of the distinction between the prime numbers and the composite numbers, a famous French mathematician, Pierre de Fermat (1601–1665), is usually given credit for many important developments in this field of study. It is interesting to note that Fermat's life was apparently singularly quiet and uneventful as a civil servant, that mathematics was his recreation and favorite amusement.

In essence, Fermat described the prime numbers as any natural number other than 1 which is **only** a multiple of 1 and itself. For example, those numbers listed as the first few primes above: 257, 641, and 65,537. Clearly, 2 is the only even prime number since all other even numbers are multiples of 2; for example, 4, 6, 8. Notice that the prime numbers, unlike multiples, are not "evenly spaced" among the natural numbers. However, they continue endlessly. (This was shown by Euclid.) A simple way to find the prime numbers, although tedious, is called the *sieve of Eratosthenes*. We begin by listing the natural numbers following 1 in order. 2 is listed separately as a prime number. Now we cross out from our list of natural numbers all the multiples of 2: 4, 6, 8, and so on. The first number that is not crossed out from our list is 3; place this

	2	3	4	5	6	7	8	9	10
11	~~12~~	13	~~14~~	~~15~~	~~16~~	17	~~18~~	19	~~20~~
~~21~~	~~22~~	23	~~24~~	~~25~~	~~26~~	~~27~~	~~28~~	29	~~30~~
31	~~32~~	~~33~~	~~34~~	~~35~~	~~36~~	37	~~38~~	~~39~~	~~40~~
41	~~42~~	43	~~44~~	~~45~~	~~46~~	47	~~48~~	~~49~~	~~50~~
~~51~~	~~52~~	53	~~54~~	~~55~~	~~56~~	~~57~~	~~58~~	59	~~60~~
61	~~62~~	~~63~~	~~64~~	~~65~~	~~66~~	67	~~68~~	~~69~~	~~70~~
71	~~72~~	73	~~74~~	~~75~~	~~76~~	~~77~~	~~78~~	79	~~80~~
~~81~~	~~82~~	83	~~84~~	~~85~~	~~86~~	~~87~~	~~88~~	89	~~90~~
~~91~~	~~92~~	~~93~~	~~94~~	~~95~~	~~96~~	97	~~98~~	~~99~~	~~100~~

FIGURE 25

with 2 on the list of prime numbers. Now we cross out all the multiples of 3 from our list of natural numbers: 9, 15, 21, and so on. Notice that 6, 12, 18 have already been crossed out as multiples of 2. The first number now that is not crossed out on our list of natural numbers is 5; place this with our other two prime numbers. Cross out all the multiples of 5 from our list of natural numbers. This process can be continued indefinitely with the natural numbers. Figure 25 illustrates a "sieve" of the first 100 natural numbers.

In examining the "shapes" of individual sets, we have only considered arranging them into "squares," "rectangles," or single rows. Of course, we might have arranged them in a variety of other ways. Consider any set with a cardinal number property which is not a prime. Can we arrange such a set into "squares" or "rectangles" such that the number of rows and number of columns are all prime numbers? The answer to this question is yes. For example, a set with four elements can be arranged into a "square" with 2 rows and 2 columns, a set with six elements into a "rectangle" with 2 rows and 3 columns (or 3 rows and 2 columns).

Examples.

(a) Eight: OO OO / OO OO
Eight can be represented as two, two-by-two squares.
$$8 = 2 \times (2 \times 2).$$

(b) Twelve: OO OO / OO OO / OO OO
Twelve can be represented as two, two-by-three rectangles.
$$12 = 2 \times (2 \times 3).$$

(c) Twenty-four: OO OO / OO OO / OO OO / OO OO / OO OO / OO OO
Twenty-four can be represented as a two-by-three rectangle consisting of two-by-two squares.
$$24 = (2 \times 3) \times (2 \times 2).$$

(d) Forty-five:
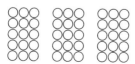

Forty-five can be represented as three, three-by-five rectangles. It could also be represented as five, three-by-three squares.

$$45 = 3 \times (3 \times 5) \quad \text{or} \quad 45 = 5 \times (3 \times 3).$$

(e) Fifty-five: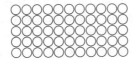

Fifty-five can be represented as one, five-by-eleven or eleven-by-five rectangle.

$$55 = 5 \times 11 \quad \text{or} \quad 55 = 11 \times 5.$$

It can be shown that all the natural numbers other than 1 which are not prime numbers can be represented in the above way. That is, expressed in terms of multiples of the prime numbers alone. Possibly for this important reason, the natural numbers which are not prime numbers are called **composite** numbers.

Many other classes of sets forming various "shapes" might be studied to lead us to interesting subsets of the natural numbers. However, we will conclude this section with the following examples as illustrated in Figures 26, 27, and 28.

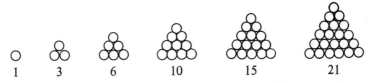

FIGURE 26. Triangular "shapes" and numbers.

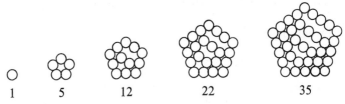

FIGURE 27. Pentagonal "shapes" and numbers.

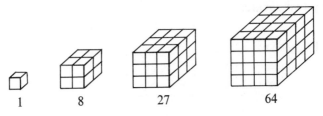

FIGURE 28. Cubic "shapes" and numbers.

Exercises

1. In counting a set we use the set of ideas called the _____ _____.
Describe the four basic properties of these counting numbers.
2. Which of the following statements are true?
   (a) There is no first natural number.
   (b) There is no last natural number.
   (c) Four is the predecessor of three.
   (d) Three is the predecessor of four.
   (e) Four is the successor of three.
   (f) Three is the successor of four.
   (g) Three and four are consecutive natural numbers.
   (h) Three and five are consecutive natural numbers.
3. Rearrange the following sets so that counting them will be easy
(see Figure 29).
4. The set of natural numbers obtained by starting with the first natural number and selecting every other natural number is called the set of
_____ numbers. The remaining set of natural numbers are called the set
of _____ numbers.
5. Show, using set diagrams, that exactly one of any three consecutive natural numbers must be a multiple of three.
6. The natural numbers can be represented by "square," "rectangular," or "prime" number "shapes." List in order the first five "square"
numbers; the first five "rectangular" numbers.
7. What digits are missing in the one's place position in the numerals
naming the multiples of four?
8. Do the multiples of six form a subset of the multiples of three?
Explain.

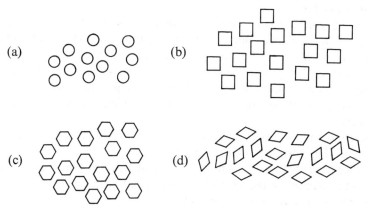

FIGURE 29

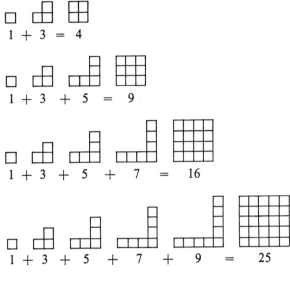

$$1 + 3 = 4$$

$$1 + 3 + 5 = 9$$

$$1 + 3 + 5 + 7 = 16$$

$$1 + 3 + 5 + 7 + 9 = 25$$

FIGURE 30

9. Form a list of the first ten numerals used in counting by sevens beginning with 7; by elevens beginning with 11.

10. Do as in Exercise 9 with
   (a) sixes beginning with 6   (b) eights beginning with 8
   (c) fives beginning with 7   (d) sevens beginning with 5.

11. Use set diagrams to illustrate the distinct "rectangular" shapes possible with (a) 18   (b) 32.

12. The ancient Greeks observed an interesting relation between the odd numbers and "squares." Study Figure 30 and see if you can describe this relationship.

13. Can you find two "square" numbers which when "put together" will result in a "square" number? Can you find a second pair of "square" numbers which when "put together" will result in a "square" number?

14. Use set "diagrams" to show that any two consecutive "triangular" numbers can be "put together" to form a "square" number.

15. Make a list of the prime numbers among the first 100 natural numbers.

16. Find the first two prime numbers such that when they are "put together" they form a "square" number.

17. Represent 36 as "squares" or "rectangles" so that the number of rows and columns in the representation are all primes.

18. Do as in Exercise 17 with 42.

19. Find the seventh "triangular" number (Figure 26).
20. Find the fifth "cubic" number (Figure 28).

Answers.

1. natural numbers; (a) A first element, 1   (b) Each element has a successor   (c) Each element except one has a predecessor   (d) They are ordered so that they do not "loop" or "split."

2. (a) false   (b) true   (c) false   (d) true   (e) true
   (f) false   (g) true   (h) false.

3. (a)
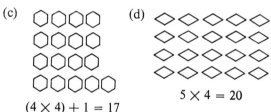

4 X 3 = 12

(b)

6 X 3 = 18

(c)

(4 X 4) + 1 = 17

(d)

5 X 4 = 20

Other arrangements are possible.

4. odd; even.

5.  or   or

6. Squares: 1, 4, 9, 16, 25; Rectangular: 6, 8, 10, 12, 14, 15.

7. 1, 3, 5, 7, 9.

8. Yes, the even multiples of three.

9. By sevens: 7, 14, 21, 28, 35, 42, 49, 56, 63, 70.
   By elevens: 11, 22, 33, 44, 55, 66, 77, 88, 99, 110.

10. (a) 6, 12, 18, 24, 30, 36, 42, 48, 54, 60.
    (b) 8, 16, 24, 32, 40, 48, 56, 64, 72, 80.
    (c) 7, 12, 17, 22, 27, 32, 37, 42, 47, 52, 57.
    (d) 5, 12, 19, 26, 33, 40, 47, 54, 61, 68, 75.

11. (a)

(b)

12. When we "put together" the consecutive odd numbers beginning with the first odd number, we always obtain a "square."

13. $(3 \times 3) + (4 \times 4) = 9 + 16 = 25 = (5 \times 5)$; $36 + 64 = 100$.

14.

15. See the *sieve of Eratosthenes,* Figure 25.

16. 2 and 7. (A second pair is 5 and 11.)

17. $36 = (2 \times 2) \times (3 \times 3)$.

18. $42 = 2 \times (7 \times 3)$.

19. 28 (the next is 36).

20. 125 (the next is 216).

Review Summary

Our consideration of **Numbers** and **Numerals** began with the observation that we give names to things and ideas. We first noted the idea of a collection or group of things or objects. To this idea we gave the name "_____." *set*
We then called the things or objects in the set _____ and *elements*
said that elements belonged to or were _____ of the set. *members*

In studying sets, names were needed to describe the number property of a set. The names of numbers are called _____. The common number property of the set *numerals*
in Figure 31 is named by the _____ "7." If the elements *numeral*
of the set are ordered as shown in Figure 32, they sug-

FIGURE 31   FIGURE 32

gest the ordinal number concept, whereas in Figure 31 the _____ concept is that of a cardinal number. Ordinary word names of numbers reveal these two distinct uses for numbers. The word "four" suggests the _____ number concept while "fourth" suggests the _____ concept of number.

number

cardinal
ordinal

In asking ourselves questions concerning the number property of individual sets and comparing sets, we noted that new sets could be obtained from a given set by a selection process. When a new set is obtained in this way, we say that it is a _____ of the given set. Since all the elements can be selected from a given set to form a new set, any set is a subset of itself. If we conceive of forming a new set by selecting no elements from any given set, such a set would be said to be _____ or be called the _____ set.

subset

empty
null
(or *empty*)

Once standard names for numbers have been developed, we determine the cardinal size or ordinal position of a set by a matching process with the standard names. The set of ideas named by the standard set of counting numerals is called the set of _____ _____.

natural
numbers

Number names were among the earliest words used. An early system of numerals which were carved on wood or stone to record commercial and government transactions was devised by the Egyptians. About 1,000 years later the Babylonians devised a system using a piece of wood called a stylus. The system used the idea of a relative place position as we do in our decimal system. A system of numerals which historians believe arose from pictures of the fingers is still in use today. This is the Roman system which uses the seven distinct symbols: _____ for 1, _____ for 5, _____ for 10, _____ for 50, _____ for 100, _____ for 500, and _____ for 1,000. The numerals which we commonly use today, however, are called _____ _____ numerals. When multiple printing developed, the form of the numerals tended to a uniform standard of design. The ten distinct symbols used are: 1, 2, 3, _____, _____, _____, _____, _____, _____, _____. These symbols are called _____ after the finger form of counting.

I, V, X, L,
C, D, M

Hindu-Arabic

4, 5, 6, 7, 8, 9
0, digits

In using Hindu-Arabic numerals we must be careful to write neatly and legibly. Because of the principle of

_____ _____ employed in writing numerals we must be careful of spacing and alignment of digits. The various positions of _____ in a numeral have been given proper names. In 7,042 the digit 7 is in the _____ place while the digit 0 tells us that there are no _____. The numeral 7,042 is read "_____ _____ _____ _____."

place
position
digits
thousands
hundreds
seven thou-
sand forty-two

In writing numerals in our common _____ system, we use the base ten. Each place position of a digit in a numeral has _____ times the value of the place position of the digit to its right. The _____ in a given place position tells us the number of groups of the given place position size that are being named by the _____. Thus, we can expand 7,042 and write it as:

decimal

ten
digit

numeral

$$7{,}042 = 7 \text{ thousands} + 0 \underline{} + 4 \underline{} + 2 \text{ ones}$$
$$= 7(1000) + 0(100) + 4(10) + 2(1)$$
$$= 7000 \quad + \quad 000 \quad + \quad 40 \quad + \quad 2.$$

hundreds,
tens

Numerals may be written in many bases. The base ten numeral 351 expanded in base six would be written
$$351 = \underline{}(216) + \underline{}(36) + \underline{}(6) + \underline{}(1)$$
or, briefly, 351 base ten is the same as _____ base six. If 2203 is in base seven, we could expand it to

1, 3, 4, 3
1343

$$2(343) + 2(\underline{}) + 0(\underline{}) + 3(\underline{})$$

49, 7, 1

and then rewrite it in base ten as _____ since

787

$$787 = 7(100) + 8(10) + 7(1)$$
$$= 2(343) + 2(49) + 0(7) + 3(1).$$

Returning to the proper consideration of the set of natural numbers, the four observations described by G. Peano to establish the properties of the natural numbers can be summed up briefly by: (1) There is a number which we call one and write as "1." (2) Each natural number has a _____. (3) Each natural number except one has a _____. (4) The natural numbers do not "loop" or "split."

successor
predecessor

In examining the natural numbers, we noted that they could be separated into two subsets such that elements of one subset were not elements of the other. A few of the elements of two such subsets are: 1, 3, 5, 7, . . . and 2, 4, 6, 8, . . . These sets are called the _____ and the

odd

_____ natural numbers, respectively. Consecutive   *even*
odd or even numbers can easily be obtained by selecting
every other natural number. If we are given two _____   *consecutive*
natural numbers, one of them must be odd and the other
even.

If we select subsets of the natural numbers by considering sets with elements which can be arranged in
rows with the same number of elements in each row,
then sets of elements with a fixed number of rows are
called the _____ of the fixed number of rows. The first   *multiples*
four elements in the multiples of four are: 4, _____,   *8*
_____, _____. In listing the multiples of a natural   *12, 16*
number we observed that multiples can also be used for
counting. Counting by fives, we would begin 5, _____,   *10*
_____, _____, _____, . . .   *15, 20, 25*

Of course, elements in one set of multiples may also
be elements in another set of multiples. We can think of
12 as being twelve ones, _____ twos, four _____,   *six, threes*
three _____, two sixes, or one twelve. Continuing with   *fours*
our observations, we described "rectangular" sets
such as a set with the cardinal number property 6, and
"square" sets such as a set with cardinality 4. An especially important set of natural numbers were obtained
when we considered sets which could not be arranged into
"rectangles" or "squares." The number property of these
latter sets are called _____ numbers or simply primes.   *prime*
All other natural numbers in comparison are then called
_____. The first few prime numbers are   *composites*

2, 3, 5, 7, 11, _____, _____, _____, _____, . . .   *13, 17, 19, 23*

The French mathematician Fermat described a prime
number as any natural number other than __ which is   *1*
_____ a multiple of 1 and itself. The importance of the   *only*
prime numbers is the fact that all the _____ numbers   *composite*
can be expressed in terms of the _____. For example,   *primes*
the natural number 30 is a composite which can be
expressed in terms of the prime numbers _____, _____,   *2, 3*
and _____: $30 = 2 \times (3 \times 5)$.   *5*

Noting how our attention is inevitably drawn to whole
classes of sets of natural numbers, we concluded with a
few examples of "triangular," "pentagonal," and "cubic"
sets of natural numbers.

Chapter Exercises (1)

Group 1.

1. Describe and discuss the set shown in Figure 33.
2. Give two examples of sets with cardinal number property
   (a) seven   (b) eleven.
3. Order the elements of the set shown in Figure 33 in two ways.

FIGURE 33

4. Determine whether the following statements refer to a cardinal or ordinal concept of number.
   (a) The serial number of a raffle ticket.
   (b) The number of people who attended a party.
   (c) The number of rooms in a building.
   (d) The numbering of the rooms in a building.
5. Describe the error which has been made in counting each of the sets in Figure 34.

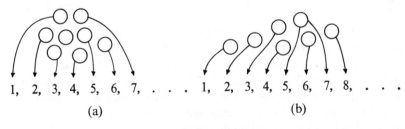

FIGURE 34

6. Match the names in the lettered column with the numbered column so that they refer to the appropriate numerals:
   (a) Roman
   (b) Modern (Hindu-Arabic)
   (c) Egyptian
   (d) Oriental

   1. ＜＜＜Ɣ
   2. ︷ 乙 𝑛
   3. LXI
   4. 201

(e) Greek   5. $\Upsilon =$

(f) Babylonian   6. $? \cap | |$

7. Write the Roman and Hindu-Arabic numerals for:
   (a) Four hundred ninety-two.
   (b) Seven hundred seventy.
   (c) Two thousand, nine hundred fourteen.
   (d) Four thousand, one hundred two.
8. Write the following in Roman numerals:
   (a) 16   (b) 199   (c) 1,666   (d) 2,729.
9. Write the following in Hindu-Arabic numerals:
   (a) XXVII   (b) DXLII   (c) CMXIV   (d) MMDXXI.
10. Write out in words how the following should be read:
    (a) 17,309   (b) 350,268   (c) 10,306,100.
11. Write the following in Hindu-Arabic numerals:
    (a) Nineteen hundred sixty-four.
    (b) Seven million, six thousand, three hundred four.
    (c) Eleven million, one hundred twenty-four thousand, eighty-one.
12. In 1,202,100 the left-hand digit 1 indicates 1 _____ while the right-hand digit 1 indicates 1 _____. The left-hand digit 2 indicates a quantity _____ times larger than the right-hand digit 2.
13. Write the five digit Hindu-Arabic numeral with seven in the ten thousands place, no thousands, no hundreds, two tens, and no ones.
14. How many digits are there in each of the following?
    (a) 3010   (b) 310   (c) 31000   (d) 100300.
15. In Exercise 14, what is the place position name of the digit 3 in each of the numerals?
16. In Exercise 14, how many times the right-hand nonzero digit place position is the place position of the left-hand nonzero digit?
17. A base seven writing system would require _____ distinct counting symbols and a place holding symbol. Using the necessary Hindu-Arabic symbols, the first sixteen counting numerals in a base seven system would be _____, _____, _____, and so on.
18. Write the following decimal numerals in a base seven system:
    (a) 4   (b) 7   (c) 10   (d) 13   (e) 14   (f) 15   (g) 51.
19. Write the following base seven numerals in our decimal system:
    (a) 6   (b) 10   (c) 13   (d) 14   (e) 21   (f) 110   (g) 202.
20. Write the following decimal numerals in expanded form:
    (a) 306   (b) 5,201   (c) 348,725.
21. Write the following expanded numerals in ordinary decimal form:
    (a) $1(1000) + 0(100) + 0(10) + 2(1)$.
    (b) $700,000 + 40,000 + 0,000 + 400 + 00 + 7$.
    (c) $4(1,000,000) + 1(100,000) + 3(10,000) + 9(1,000) + 3(100) + 1(10) + 0(1)$.

22. Which of the following statements are true?
    (a) Every natural number has a predecessor.
    (b) Every natural number has a successor.
    (c) Every even number has an odd successor.
    (d) No odd number has an even predecessor.
23. Write the first ten numerals used in counting by threes beginning with 5; do the same by eights beginning with 4.
24. Use set "diagrams" to illustrate the distinct "rectangular" shapes possible with (a) 16   (b) 105.
25. List the first five prime numbers following 100.
26. Represent 105 as "squares" or "rectangles" so that the number of rows and columns in the representation are all prime numbers.

Group II.

1. Describe and discuss the set shown in Figure 35.
2. Give two examples of sets with cardinal number property
    (a) six   (b) fifteen.
3. Order the elements of the set shown in Figure 35 in two ways.

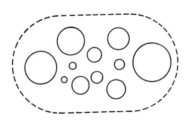

FIGURE 35

4. Determine whether the following statements refer to a cardinal or ordinal concept of number:
    (a) The speed of an automobile.
    (b) The number of exercises in this set of exercises.
    (c) The number of people in California.
    (d) The number indicating the ranking of a person in a class.
5. Describe the error which has been made in counting each of the sets in Figure 36.
6. Write the Hindu-Arabic numeral for each of the following:

    (a) ୮ ⹀   (b) ⋖ ⋖Ⅴ   (c) שׁ 𝚗   (d) CMIX   (e) ⸮∩∣∣
(f) LDI.

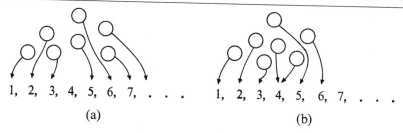

FIGURE 36

7. Write the Roman and Hindu-Arabic numerals for:
   (a) Nine hundred fourteen.
   (b) Twelve hundred thirty-six.
   (c) One thousand, four hundred ninety-nine.
   (d) Two thousand, eight hundred fifty-seven.
8. Write the following in Roman numerals:
   (a) 96   (b) 519   (c) 1,164   (d) 2,671.
9. Write the following in Hindu-Arabic numerals:
   (a) LIV   (b) CDXLII   (c) MCMXIX   (d) MMCIV.
10. Write out in words how the following should be read:
    (a) 23,048   (b) 780,215   (c) 17,681,200.
11. Write the following in Hindu-Arabic numerals:
    (a) Eighteen hundred seventy-two.
    (b) Two million, thirty-six thousand, one hundred twenty-seven.
    (c) Twenty million, four hundred thousand, seven hundred eighty.
12. In 10,045,140 the left-hand digit 1 indicates 1 _____ while the right-hand digit 1 indicates 1 _____. The left-hand digit 4 indicates a quantity _____ times larger than the right-hand digit 4.
13. Write the eight digit Hindu-Arabic numeral with twos in the ten million, ten thousands, and ten hundreds places and zeroes in all the other place positions.
14. How many digits are there in each of the following?
    (a) 205   (b) 50020   (c) 52   (d) 5,002,000.
15. In Exercise 14, what is the place position name of the digit 2 in each of the numerals?
16. In Exercise 14, how many times the right-hand nonzero digit place position is the place position of the left-hand nonzero digit?
17. In terms of our decimal numerals, what would be the successive cardinal sizes of the first three place positions from right to left in a base twelve numeral system?
18. If we use the ten decimal digits and the symbols X and L to write in a base twelve system, then how would we write the decimal numerals 12, 28, 47, 60, and 145 in a base twelve system?

19. Write the following base twelve numerals in our decimal form:
    (a) 12   (b) 28   (c) 4X   (d) LO   (e) 1XL (See Exercise 18).
20. Write the following decimal numerals in expanded form:
    (a) 630   (b) 71,009   (c) 100,371.
21. Write the following expanded numerals in ordinary decimal form:
    (a) $2(10,000) + 8(1,000) + 5(100) + 9(10) + 4(1)$.
    (b) $100,000 + 00,000 + 5,000 + 500 + 00 + 0$.
    (c) $3(1,000,000) + 1(100,000) + 3(10,000) + 2(1,000) + 2(100) + 9(10) + 1(1)$.
22. Which of the following statements are true?
    (a) There are no even prime numbers.
    (b) A composite number is not a prime number.
    (c) There are no odd numbers between nine and eleven.
    (d) There are no natural numbers between nine and eleven.
23. Write the first ten numerals used in counting by fives beginning with 3; do the same by sixes beginning with 2.
24. Use set "diagrams" to illustrate the distinct "rectangular" shapes possible with (a) 36   (b) 70.
25. List the first ten odd composite numbers.
26. Represent 70 as "squares" or "rectangles" so that the number of rows and columns in the representation are all prime numbers.

Problem Set (1)

1. A certain school had a total of 57 students in three classes: a mathematics class with 23 students, a history class with 29 students, and an English class with 19 students. Four students were taking both mathematics and history, five both English and history but not mathematics. Two students were enrolled in all three classes. Find the number of students who were taking
    (a) mathematics and history but not English,
    (b) mathematics and English,
    (c) mathematics or English but not history,
    (d) at least two of the three classes.
2. A thirteenth century mathematician, Leonardo of Pisa (about 1170–1250), posed the following question leading to a very interesting ordered subset of the natural numbers: How many pairs of rabbits can be produced from a single pair, if it is supposed that every month each pair begets a new pair, which from the second month on become productive?
    Ordered subsets such as these are called Fibonacci sequences. By considering the number of new pairs of rabbits each month, find the first twelve numbers of the above sequence.

3. Since the time of the Greeks the study of natural numbers in terms of the sets of multiples to which they belong has been of interest to mathematicians. If we exclude the number of the set of multiples of itself, any natural number can be classified in terms of the sum of the numbers which represent the sets of multiples to which the natural number belongs. For example, 4 belongs to the multiples of 1 and 2 (excepting 4) so that the sum of the numbers which represent the sets of multiples is 3, which is less than 4; the number 6 can be associated with the sum of 1, 2, and 3, which is 6; the number 12 can be associated with 1, 2, 3, 4, and 6 whose sum is 16, which is greater than 12. A natural number such as 6 is called *perfect* since it is exactly the sum of the numbers representing the sets of multiples to which it belongs except itself. Can you find any other perfect numbers? There are only two more such numbers less than 500.

4. Can you show that every prime number greater than 3 is one more or one less than a multiple of 6? What are the smallest composite numbers one more than and one less than a multiple of 6?

CHAPTER 2

Addition and Subtraction

2.1 Addition

2.1.1   A natural activity with sets is to "put together" two or more sets. When we represent this we call it **addition**. This is the first operation one learns to perform. Addition is a "shortcut" for finding the cardinal size of a set formed by "putting together" two other sets, that is, for successively counting two sets.

Examples.

(a)

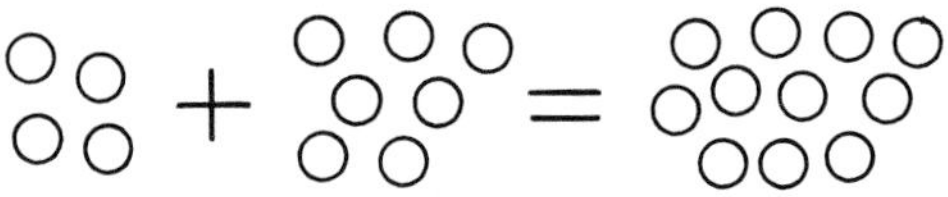

$$\begin{array}{ccccc} 4 & + & 7 & = & 11 \end{array}$$

FIGURE 37

(b)

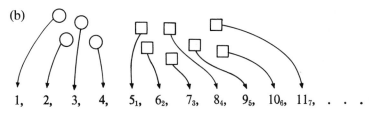

$$1, \quad 2, \quad 3, \quad 4, \quad 5_1, \quad 6_2, \quad 7_3, \quad 8_4, \quad 9_5, \quad 10_6, \quad 11_7, \quad \cdot \ \cdot \ \cdot$$

FIGURE 38

In using Roman numerals, we note that addition is quite simple since we need only count symbols of each kind to determine how to change them to the next higher units. The use of an abacus or counting device also simplifies the need for knowing number combinations.

Examples.

(a) MCXXVIII
     CDLXVII
     ‾‾‾‾‾‾‾‾‾
     MCDCLXXXVVIIIII

     MDXCV

(b)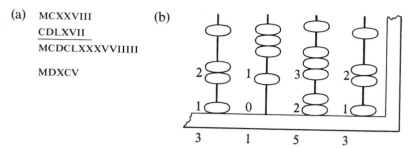

Although the basic process of addition has apparently never changed, the introduction of Hindu-Arabic numerals led to the development of more sophisticated forms for representing addition. The numbers being added together were given names and a symbol was created to indicate the process itself. Thus, when numbers are added together they are called **addends** and the result of the addition is then called the **sum**. The process of addition is denoted by the symbol "+," called a **plus** sign.

$$4 \quad + \quad 7 \quad = \quad 11$$

addend   plus sign **addend   sum**

As with any activity, in order to progress and develop the usefulness of the activity, certain basic manipulations and actions must be made "automatic." Thus we begin with the simplest additions, which are often referred to as the **basic addition facts**. The basic addition facts as shown in Table 9 should be completely memorized so that the results of basic additions are automatic responses. In using the table, the addends appear on the left and top margins. The sum is found in the body of the table at the crossing of the row and column of the addends.

TABLE 9.   **Basic Addition Facts.**

+	1	2	3	4	5	6	7	8	9
1	2	3	4	5	6	7	8	9	10
2	3	4	5	6	7	8	9	10	11
3	4	5	6	7	8	9	10	11	12
4	5	6	7	8	9	10	11	12	13
5	6	7	8	9	10	11	12	13	14
6	7	8	9	10	11	12	13	14	15
7	8	9	10	11	12	13	14	15	16
8	9	10	11	12	13	14	15	16	17
9	10	11	12	13	14	15	16	17	18

Examples.

	Addend in left margin		Addend in top margin		Sum in intersection
(a)	9	+	6	=	15
(b)	3	+	5	=	8
(c)	6	+	9	=	15
(d)	7	+	8	=	15
(e)	4	+	3	=	7

Of course, learning the basic addition facts by rote is not mastery of addition. Mastery is a mental attitude; it requires concentration, motivation, and purpose. **Practice** is, of course, essential to mastery. As in learning any activity, think of bowling or golf, practice of fundamentals is a necessary chore. In practicing, use a "rhythm" or "tempo" which is steady rather than hurried or jerky. Note the facts on which you hesitate, repeat and review these sums to yourself. A good system is to have someone dictate sums while you give oral responses. Another system is to use "flash cards" which can be made or bought in many stores. A few minutes of practice each day should soon enable one to run through simple sums at a fairly steady and rapid pace.

In studying the basic addition facts you have probably already noted that the order of addition is immaterial. That is, $4 + 7 = 7 + 4$ and $3 + 6 = 6 + 3$. This property of addition is clearly evident in the table of basic addition facts; notice that the diagonal entries from lower-left to upper-right are the same. In adding larger numbers, we can take advantage of this property of addition by observing that $35 + 7 = 7 + 35$ and we need only consider one of the two arrangements in addition. A further economy in our study can be attained by noting that $27 + 5, 37 + 5, 25 + 7, 35 + 7, 17 + 5, 55 + 7$ all require the same basic addition fact, mainly that $5 + 7 = 12$. The sums $16 + 9, 29 + 6, 9 + 96$ are all related to the basic addition fact $6 + 9 = 15$. The sums $33 + 4, 24 + 3, 4 + 73, 3 + 14$ might all be said to belong to the $3 + 4 = 7$ family of addition facts.

Finally, observe that the basic addition facts can be divided into two types; those in which the basic addition results in a single-digit sum such as $3 + 4, 2 + 3, 7 + 1$, and so on, and those which result in a two-digit sum such as $5 + 7, 6 + 9, 8 + 3$, and so forth. These are sometimes called the "easy" and "hard" addition facts. A practice set of each type of sum follows. Do the sums mentally and rapidly without paper or pencil. Practice until the answers come without any hesitation.

Practice until you can do one hundred "easy" or "hard" sums mentally within two minutes!

Practice 1.   Easy Sums ("+" has been omitted as understood).

	(a)	(b)	(c)	(d)	(e)	(f)	(g)	(h)	(i)	(j)
1.	27	72	3	61	6	84	30	1	75	14
	2	6	25	5	20	5	7	78	3	3
2.	36	1	2	53	71	45	87	4	35	81
	3	35	22	4	6	2	2	21	3	8
3.	20	4	91	32	57	24	6	9	53	27
	4	80	1	7	1	3	93	70	5	2
4.	16	55	13	90	6	44	17	11	8	76
	3	4	3	3	52	4	1	8	81	1
5.	5	22	52	14	2	27	81	64	9	45
	54	4	1	4	11	2	7	2	20	3

6.	3+16	30+9	7+20	30+2	53+3	26+3	5+80	33+2	4+84	45+3
7.	22+7	63+6	3+43	16+1	82+5	3+21	50+5	42+4	5+72	3+84
8.	4+64	7+40	1+24	90+9	3+63	6+32	1+63	4+72	31+2	66+1
9.	20+1	50+8	52+2	35+4	11+2	7+61	9+20	13+6	84+5	43+4
10.	6+32	54+3	26+3	17+2	88+1	91+6	5+33	13+2	73+5	66+2

Practice 2.   Hard Sums.

	(a)	(b)	(c)	(d)	(e)	(f)	(g)	(h)	(i)	(j)
1.	14	66	72	8	36	29	54	38	5	75
	7	5	9	27	8	7	9	5	86	7
2.	59	4	37	82	9	16	12	56	24	49
	5	46	8	9	75	8	9	4	8	2
3.	1	58	7	76	45	26	59	39	18	5
	19	7	76	5	8	9	4	1	8	49
4.	88	32	66	4	23	9	55	7	38	72
	3	8	9	19	9	87	5	68	9	8
5.	87	78	15	69	28	4	7	39	48	54
	3	2	8	9	8	36	63	8	3	7

6.	28+9	7+17	9+75	45+8	39+4	19+7	7+35	64+8	37+9	8+56
7.	18+7	58+9	39+8	56+9	24+7	8+46	49+9	7+49	28+4	85+9
8.	4+16	35+8	59+7	33+7	6+59	36+6	63+8	7+65	8+43	37+6
9.	15+7	73+9	1+59	6+18	26+7	21+9	56+7	9+74	17+4	23+9
10.	77+7	56+5	36+6	83+7	46+9	9+28	8+44	88+7	68+8	9+33

Answers to Easy Sums.

	(a)	(b)	(c)	(d)	(e)	(f)	(g)	(h)	(i)	(j)
1.	29	78	28	66	26	89	37	79	78	17
2.	39	36	24	57	77	47	89	25	38	89
3.	24	84	92	39	58	27	99	79	58	29
4.	19	59	16	93	58	48	18	19	89	77
5.	59	26	53	18	13	29	88	66	29	48
6.	19	39	27	32	56	29	85	35	88	48
7.	29	69	46	17	87	24	55	46	77	87
8.	68	47	25	99	66	38	64	76	33	67
9.	21	58	54	39	13	68	29	19	89	47
10.	38	57	29	19	89	97	38	15	78	68

Answers to Hard Sums.

	(a)	(b)	(c)	(d)	(e)	(f)	(g)	(h)	(i)	(j)
1.	21	71	81	35	44	36	63	43	91	82
2.	64	50	45	91	84	24	21	60	32	51
3.	20	65	83	81	53	35	63	40	26	54
4.	91	40	75	23	32	96	60	75	47	80
5.	90	80	23	78	36	40	70	47	51	61
6.	37	24	84	53	43	26	42	72	46	64
7.	25	67	47	65	31	54	58	56	32	94
8.	20	43	66	40	65	42	71	72	51	43
9.	22	82	60	24	33	30	63	83	21	32
10.	84	61	42	90	55	37	52	95	76	42

2.1.2   In practicing sums observe that we can think of a number written in expanded form and can add groups of fixed sizes separately. For example, 68 and 17 might be added by thinking of $68 = 60 + 8$, $17 = 10 + 7$ so that we have $6 + 1 = 7$ tens and $8 + 7 = 15$ ones. Thus, $68 + 17 = 7$ tens + 15 ones $= 70 + 15 = 85$.

The above suggests that in rapid mental addition, we might add convenient portions of one addend to the other: $68 + 17 = 68 + 10 + 7 = 78 + 2 + 5 = 80 + 5 = 85$. Notice that grouping by tens is a useful device. In more difficult sums these processes of successive addition enable us to mentally add two or more addends quickly and accurately.

Examples.

  (a) 28   Think: 28 + 50 = 78, 78 + 7 = 70 + 15 = 85 answer.
       +57

  (b) 63   Think: 60 + 50 = 110, 3 + 9 = 12, 110 + 12 = 122 answer.
       +59

Practice 3. Do the following sums mentally:

	(a)	(b)	(c)	(d)	(e)	(f)	(g)	(h)	(i)	(j)
1.	43	32	74	15	42	64	23	16	52	81
	25	27	12	54	36	14	54	73	25	17
2.	56	38	69	27	64	23	77	32	19	61
	17	49	28	55	27	58	16	49	71	29
3.	77	49	87	22	36	79	47	83	57	26
	34	76	95	79	67	41	55	39	67	97
4.	12	45	27	46	14	18	66	72	36	65
	78	27	55	49	57	39	15	18	29	27
5.	65	26	46	97	42	34	51	43	28	93
	79	86	64	39	58	87	99	69	87	38

  6. 11+21 31+68 82+17 15+64 33+22 13+71 12+66 53+36 24+53 17+72
  7. 47+24 65+28 18+23 47+37 26+57 14+49 36+19 71+19 25+59 76+18
  8. 65+43 18+91 72+47 28+80 83+75 92+64 37+72 24+91 55+73 67+71
  9. 36+29 15+37 74+17 47+26 53+39 62+28 47+34 18+27 66+29 25+38
10. 57+75 88+33 42+79 83+37 69+75 42+58 96+77 35+68 48+98 32+69

Answers.

	(a)	(b)	(c)	(d)	(e)	(f)	(g)	(h)	(i)	(j)
1.	68	59	86	69	78	78	77	89	77	98
2.	73	87	97	82	91	81	93	81	90	90
3.	111	125	182	101	103	120	102	122	124	123

4.	90	72	82	95	71	57	81	90	65	92
5.	144	112	110	136	100	121	150	112	115	131
6.	32	99	99	79	55	84	78	89	77	89
7.	71	93	41	84	83	63	55	90	84	94
8.	108	109	119	108	158	156	109	115	128	138
9.	65	52	91	73	92	90	81	45	95	63
10.	132	121	121	120	144	100	173	103	146	101

2.1.3   Another form of addition with which we should be familiar is called column addition. By column addition we mean the addition of three or more addends together. This can be done by repeated addition of two addends at a time. We can "carry" each sum as an addend in the succeeding addition. The addends can also be rearranged to obtain easy sums which in turn can be added together.

Examples.

(a)   5   Think: $5 + 7 = 12$, $12 + 4 = 16$, $16 + 3 = 19$ answer.
    7
    4   Or alternatively: $7 + 3 = 10$, $5 + 4 = 9$, $10 + 9 = 19$ answer.
  +3

(b) $7 + 5 + 9 + 3 + 5 = ?$
Think: $(7 + 3) + (5 + 5) + 9 = 10 + 10 + 9 = 29$ answer.

(c)   15   Separate the tens and ones columns: 1 5
   36   3 6
   83   Or do successively: $15 + 36 = 51$,   8 3
  +27 $83 + 27 = 110$, $51 + 110 = 161$.   2 7
                                    21 ones
                               14 tens
                             1 6 1 answer.

(d) $13 + 86 + 11 + 34 = ?$
Think: $99 + 1 = 100$, $100 + 44 = 144$ answer.

(e)   36   Or: 3 6
   57_____93   5 7
   84   8 4
   23   107   2 3
   51    $200 + 127 = 327$ answer.   5 1
  +76   7 6
                                 27 ones
                             30 tens
                           3 2 7 answer.

Practice 4.   Do the following sums mentally:

	(a)	(b)	(c)	(d)	(e)	(f)
1.	8	5	9	2	7	6
	7	6	8	9	5	2
	4	9	3	7	8	3
	7	3	6	7	6	9
2.	3	9	4	2	5	6
	8	7	5	3	8	7
	1	7	9	6	5	3
	6	4	3	7	7	1
	2	7	5	9	2	1
	4	8	6	5	3	5
	3	9	2	7	6	4
	2	7	5	9	8	1
3.	23	63	36	18	42	27
	56	46	28	32	17	29
	21	53	47	82	28	94
	15	80	37	63	33	25

4.   (a) $4 + 7 + 2 + 6 + 5 + 8$ (b) $8 + 1 + 4 + 3 + 9 + 6$
     (c) $5 + 8 + 3 + 6 + 3 + 9$ (d) $2 + 7 + 4 + 3 + 7 + 8$
     (e) $1 + 3 + 9 + 8 + 9 + 7$ (f) $5 + 7 + 8 + 4 + 3 + 7$.

Answers.

	(a)	(b)	(c)	(d)	(e)	(f)
1.	26	23	26	25	26	20
2.	29	58	39	48	44	28
3.	115	242	148	195	120	175
4.	32	31	34	31	37	34

2.1.4   Once we can do simple sums without hesitation, we are ready to consider the general problem of more difficult additions. For example, to add 653, 387, and 576 we might write

$$653 = 600 + 50 + 3$$
$$387 = 300 + 80 + 7$$
$$+576 = 500 + 70 + 6$$
$$1400 + 200 + 16 = 1616$$

or more briefly

```
 653
 387
+576
1400
 200
  16
1616
```

In using the place position of the digits, note the importance of proper spacing and alignment of the partial additions. A sound knowledge of the basic addition facts and simple sums is also important to rapid, useful, and accurate additions. In practicing it is advisable to adopt a pattern and procedure and stick to it as long as it results in correct and speedy results.

Examples.

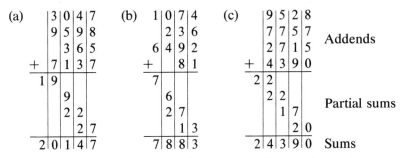

Notice that by careful alignment of the partial sums, we can dispense with place-holding zeroes. In practicing, it is also important to reflect on the processes being used so that adaptability and flexibility is attained. In long additions, answers should be checked for "sense." As a further check, add the addends in a different order independently and compare the two sums obtained.

Practice 5.   Strive for both speed and accuracy in the following:

1.

(a)	(b)	(c)	(d)	(e)	(f)	(g)	(h)
63	47	385	721	596	1062	3748	16,240
18	32	407	189	375	430	1835	3,072
65	65		43	807	508	427	27,815
						6001	5,957

2.

(a)	(b)	(c)	(d)	(e)	(f)	(g)	(h)
52	756	508	974	2638	7070	4728	25,362
30	245	37	630	804	5814	3698	61,045
79	304	146	585	4067	207	7263	7,699
		71	382	2235	1840	5496	65,307

3.

(a)	(b)	(c)	(d)	(e)	(f)	(g)	(h)
47	105	942	8059	6093	4594	10,570	84,306
70	92	717	7546	908	6228	38,679	71,523
86	386	879	358	1527	1077	27,975	97,554
29	420	409	5575	91	3249	72,976	8,225
				362	9170	48,270	47,180
				4750	6453		10,051

4. 81	67	405	192	9679	9054	74,382	14,653
57	19	930	485	41	7905	109	32,974
39	42	64	273	7385	4251	36,754	17,328
75	77	179	849	6	9410	22	35,465
23	30	7	409	672	6355	8,791	90,333
55	89	56	572	8063	2817	64,857	48,901
	45				4738	74	25,694
	16				9876	3,905	13,007

5. 27	726	1082	7369	54,860	27,072	4,386,572
72	491	271	6673	7,951	36,907	3,794
49	508	7695	2325	72,385	44,784	685,475
53	284	4328	591	675	91,273	7,050,581
18	360	600	5777	40,056	62,047	277,007
67	489	9897	2940	38,227	33,985	5,386,995
30			482		95,422	27,475,602
29			8564		88,749	2,587,296

Answers.

	(a)	(b)	(c)	(d)	(e)	(f)	(g)	(h)
1.	81	144	792	953	1778	2000	12,011	53,084
2.	161	1305	762	2571	9744	14,931	21,185	159,413
3.	232	1003	2947	21,538	13,731	30,771	198,470	318,839
4.	330	385	1641	2780	25,846	54,406	188,894	278,355
5.	345	2858	23,873	34,721	214,154	480,239	47,853,322	

Exercises

1. A shortcut for finding the cardinal size of a set formed by combining two other sets is called _____. When numbers are added together, they are called _____ and the result of the addition operation is then called the _____.

2. In studying the basic addition facts, notice that a diagonal from the upper left to the lower right in Table 9 crosses either all even or all odd numerals. Explain why this is so.

3. If in Table 9 we start at an entry marked 7 and move 3 rows down and 4 columns to the right, then what will the entry be?

4. Imagine the columns and rows of Table 9 to be continued to larger values. If we start in row 36 and move to the column headed 79, then what will the entry be?

5. If Table 9 were continued to larger values, would the column headed 186 have the same entries as the row beginning with 186? If so, explain.

6. The examples $5 + 8 = 8 + 5$ and $14 + 36 = 36 + 14$ illustrate the fact that the _____ of addition is _____.

7. The sums $12 + 8$, $48 + 2$, $72 + 8$ are all related to the basic addition fact _____.

8. Repeat the Easy Sums (Practice 1) and Hard Sums (Practice 2) mentally. Practice until you can do both sets mentally within five minutes.

9. Use an expanded form of 481 and 375 to show how they can be added by the place positions of their digits.

10. Use grouping by tens to find the sum of 7, 6, 1, 4, 7, 9, and 3.

11. Find the sums:

(a)	(b)	(c)	(d)	(e)	(f)
54	37	20	69	41	83
79	60	53	81	99	35
46	80	16	27	64	12
56	38	41	70	82	39
27	43	85	13	26	11
67	81	36	27	93	70

12. Find the sums:
(a) $43 + 51 + 30 + 62$ (b) $81 + 36 + 29 + 70$
(c) $136 + 208 + 140 + 379$ (d) $521 + 970 + 604 + 398$.

13. Find the sums:

(a) 3,010 +5,094	(b) 7,900 + 102	(c) 104 71 305 + 80	(d) 20 202 70 + 46	(e) 507 513 30 +560

14. Find the sums:
(a) $300 + 20 + 7 + 800$ (b) $5,060 + 340 + 1,702 + 58$
(c) $4,010 + 3,910 + 6,470 + 7,920 + 5,301 + 500$.

15. Find the sums:

(a)	(b)	(c)	(d)	(e)
3286	1042	689	7462	3805
753	8075	11	5579	1539
6769	93	76	3828	9217
+ 32	+ 961	+2399	+8741	+4228

16. Find the sums:

(a)	(b)	(c)	(d)	(e)
1001	477	367	2194	3608
202	3802	5	4737	8997
34	957	2138	5518	2143
659	8728	16	6623	5276
27	93	9734	4379	1867
+5305	+7136	+ 562	+3015	+3735

17. Find the sums:
    (a) $437 + 1984 + 925 + 3998$ (b) $1431 + 762 + 3685 + 4972$
    (c) $8673 + 27 + 6081 + 7160$ (d) $2169 + 3817 + 190 + 9101$.
18. Find the sums:
    (a) $5041 + 6930 + 158 + 402 + 7563 + 1983$.
    (b) $8273 + 1490 + 3804 + 14 + 3609 + 285$.
    (c) $4382 + 7894 + 6305 + 4918 + 2407 + 9637$.
    (d) $2641 + 6207 + 5770 + 2819 + 4594 + 4506$.
19. Find the sum of the addends:
    (a) 306; 51; 698; 420; 38; 927   (b) 27; 840; 17; 472; 761; 66
    (c) 7,877; 8,009; 5,304; 2,318   (d) 1,384; 659; 40,320; 397.
20. Find the sum of: 72,010,936; 9,065,327; 10,438,052; 1,570,983; 306,482,879; 2,082,375,658; 32,408,750; 6,009,428.

Answers.

1. addition; addends, sum.
2. Moving down one row and moving to the right one column each increases the entry by one. If we start with an even (or odd) number, we will then obtain another even (or odd) number as the next entry on the diagonal.
3. 14.
4. 115.
5. Yes, since the order of addition is immaterial.
6. order, immaterial.
7. $2 + 8 = 10$.
8. Practice.
9. $481 = 400 + 80 + 1$
   $\underline{+375 = 300 + 70 + 5}$
   $700 + 150 + 6 = 856$ answer.
10. $7 + 6 + 1 + 4 + 7 + 9 + 3 = (7 + 3) + (6 + 4) + (1 + 9) + 7$
   $= 10 + 10 + 10 + 7$
   $= 37$ answer.

11. (a) 329   (b) 339   (c) 251   (d) 287   (e) 405   (f) 250.
12. (a) 186   (b) 216   (c) 863   (d) 2493.
13. (a) 8,104   (b) 8,002   (c) 560   (d) 338   (e) 1610.
14. (a) 1127   (b) 7,160   (c) 28,111.
15. (a) 10,840   (b) 10,171   (c) 3,175   (d) 25,610   (e) 18,789.
16. (a) 7,228   (b) 21,193   (c) 12,822   (d) 26,466   (e) 25,626.
17. (a) 7,344   (b) 10,850   (c) 21,941   (d) 15,277.
18. (a) 22,077   (b) 17,475   (c) 35,543   (d) 26,537.
19. (a) 2440   (b) 2183   (c) 23,508   (d) 42,760.
20. 2,520,362,013.

2.2 Subtraction

2.2.1 In practicing sums such as $9 + 5 = ?$, we might practice the related question $9 + ? = 14$. That is, rather than looking for the sum of two addends, we might look for an addend which when added to a given addend will result in a given sum. For example, to check the sum $13 + 42 = ?$ we might ask the question $13 + ? = 55$. To check the sum $37 + 12 = ?$ we can ask $37 + ? = 49$ or $12 + ? = 49$ (Figure 39). These latter questions lead to a new operation.

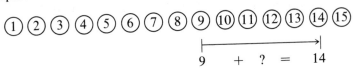

$$9 \quad + \quad ? \quad = \quad 14$$

FIGURE 39

Examples.

(a) $13 + ? = 20$ has the answer 7 since $13 + 7 = 20$.
(b) $9 + ? = 18$ has the answer 9 since $9 + 9 = 18$.
(c) $13 + ? = 55$ has the answer 42 since $13 + 42 = 55$.
(d) $37 + ? = 49$ has the answer 12 since $37 + 12 = 49$.

For convenience we consider this as an operation different from addition and call it **subtraction**. That is, **subtraction** is a "shortcut" for finding the addend necessary to add to a given addend to result in a given sum. Notice that we can also interpret subtraction as a counting of predecessors.

We write $7 - 4 = ?$ meaning $7 = 4 + ?$. The symbol "−" is called a **minus sign**. Informally, we can describe subtraction as a "taking away" operation. The following vocabulary is useful in discussing subtraction:

$$7 \quad - \quad 4 \quad = \quad 3$$

minuend   minus sign   **subtrahend   difference**

We say that we subtract the **subtrahend** from the **minuend** to obtain the **difference**. The difference is the number such that when added to the subtrahend the sum will equal the minuend. Just as with addition we begin with the simplest differences. These should be practiced until they become automatic responses.

TABLE 10. Subtraction Facts.

Subtrahend:	1	2	3	4	5	6	7	8	9	10
Minuend: 1	0									
2	1	0								
3	2	1	0							
4	3	2	1	0						
5	4	3	2	1	0					
6	5	4	3	2	1	0				
7	6	5	4	3	2	1	0			
8	7	6	5	4	3	2	1	0		
9	8	7	6	5	4	3	2	1	0	
10	9	8	7	6	5	4	3	2	1	0

To find $7 - 4$ we locate the minuend 7 along the left margin and the subtrahend 4 along the top margin. The difference is then located at the crossing of the row and column for 7 and 4. Thus, $7 - 4 = 3$. In examining Table 10 we should immediately note two items. First, the diagonal of zeroes from upper left to lower right on the table. What is the significance of these entries? Selecting one of them, we might write $7 - 7 = 0$. But $7 - 7 = 0$ means $7 = 7 + 0$. Can we interpret our writing? Yes.

If we have a set with cardinal number property 7, then recalling that we can think of a set with no elements, that is, the empty or null set, we can say that the empty set has cardinal number property 0 and adding it to the original set we see that the cardinal number property of the resulting set will be unchanged. That is, $7 + 0 = 7$. Alternatively, if we begin with a set with 7 elements and select all the elements for a subset, then the cardinal number property of the set "left over" would be 0 since it must be empty. That is, $7 - 7 = 0$.

Historically, although the symbol for zero was known quite early, perhaps even in 200 B.C., the use of zero as a number did not occur until the Hindus introduced their set of symbols. In fact, in mathematics, the Hindus are mainly known for their system of numerals, the introduction of zero, and the rules for operating with zero. It is interesting to note that in India the contemplation of an absolute void or nothingness characterizes the native philosophy.

Although we have used the **digit** 0 as a **place holder**, this is the first (explicit) use of 0 as a **number**. Thus, we write $7 - 7 = 0$ and $7 = 7 + 0$ and note that 0 is a number which when added to any natural number leaves the number unchanged. Alternatively, it is the number which results when any natural number is subtracted from itself. We do not consider zero, 0, as a natural or counting number, but as a distinctly new number in its own right.

Our second observation consists of noticing the "blank" spaces in Table 10. If we concern ourselves with the counting of "things" and "objects" in the physical sense, then, as noted by the Greeks, numbers for the blank spaces of Table 10 would be "absurd." How can we "take away" from a set of elements more elements than it has? It was not until the Hindu mathematicians Brahmagupta (about 628) and Bhāskara (1114 to about 1185) discussed such quantities that we have a development in this area. We will discuss these quantities, called **negative numbers**, in the next section. However, for our purposes we will temporarily avoid these quantities and concern ourselves with subtractions which result in natural numbers or zero.

In practicing simple subtractions, the auxiliary subtraction Table 11 will be found useful. The auxiliary table tells us that 7 from 11 is 4, 3 from 16 is 13, 9 from 17 is 8, and the difference between 15 and 7 is 8. As in addition certain subtraction facts seem to cause difficulty. Do practice set 1 mentally until you can give the differences without hesitation.

2.2.2 In subtraction, observe that the order of subtraction is important. For example, $7 - 4 = 3$ but $4 - 7$ has no answer (as yet). Another relation-

TABLE 11. **Auxiliary Subtraction Facts.**

Subtrahend:	1	2	3	4	5	6	7	8	9	10
Minuend: 11	10	9	8	7	6	5	4	3	2	1
12	11	10	9	8	7	6	5	4	3	2
13	12	11	10	9	8	7	6	5	4	3
14	13	12	11	10	9	8	7	6	5	4
15	14	13	12	11	10	9	8	7	6	5
16	15	14	13	12	11	10	9	8	7	6
17	16	15	14	13	12	11	10	9	8	7
18	17	16	15	14	13	12	11	10	9	8
19	18	17	16	15	14	13	12	11	10	9
20	19	18	17	16	15	14	13	12	11	10

ship which can be observed is that given a subtraction fact, we can immediately obtain a related second fact. From $7 - 4 = 3$ we can observe that
$7 - 3 = 4$. From $19 - 6 = 13$ we have $19 - 13 = 6$. If the subtrahend and
difference are interchanged we obtain a new subtraction fact.

Practice 1.   Do the following subtractions mentally:

	(a)	(b)	(c)	(d)	(e)	(f)
1.	$8 - 5$	$5 - 2$	$6 - 1$	$9 - 4$	$7 - 3$	$4 - 4$
2.	$9 - 2$	$3 - 1$	$8 - 7$	$6 - 6$	$9 - 7$	$2 - 1$
3.	$14 - 3$	$16 - 6$	$19 - 3$	$12 - 1$	$15 - 4$	$17 - 5$
4.	$11 - 7$	$14 - 5$	$16 - 8$	$15 - 7$	$13 - 6$	$12 - 7$
5.	7 -5	6 -4	5 -2	9 -6	8 -3	7 -7
6.	17 -7	12 -1	15 -4	13 -2	11 -1	18 -5
7.	20 -6	19 -10	11 -9	17 -8	12 -5	15 -7
8.	13 -4	16 -9	14 -7	10 -6	19 -9	11 -3

Answers.

	(a)	(b)	(c)	(d)	(e)	(f)
1.	3	3	5	5	4	0
2.	7	2	1	0	2	1
3.	11	10	16	11	11	12
4.	4	9	8	8	7	5
5.	2	2	3	3	5	0
6.	10	11	11	11	10	13
7.	14	9	2	9	7	8
8.	9	7	7	4	10	8

2.2.3   There are three methods of subtraction commonly in use. They
are called the "borrowing," "equal addition," and "decomposition"
methods.

In the borrowing method of subtraction we think of an expanded form of the minuend and subtrahend and use our knowledge of the simpler subtraction facts.

Examples.

(a) $81 = 70 + 11$
      $-16 = 10 + 6$
      $\overline{60 + 5 = 65}$

We think 6 from 11 is 5 and 1 from 7 is 6 so that 16 from 81 is 65.

(b) $56 = 40 + 16$
      $-29 = 20 + 9$
      $\overline{20 + 7 = 27}$

We "borrow" 10 from the 50 so that instead of $56 = 50 + 6$ we have $56 = 40 + 16$. This enables us to easily subtract 9 from 16.

(c) $38 = 30 + 8$
      $-35 = 30 + 5$
      $\overline{0 + 3 = 3}$

Notice that this method is not necessary when the digits of the subtrahend are smaller than or the same as the respective digits of the minuend.

(d) $672 = 600 + 60 + 12$
      $- 35 = 30 + 5$
      $\overline{600 + 30 + 7 = 637 \text{ answer.}}$

(e) $672 = 500 + 160 + 12$
      $- 85 = 80 + 5$
      $\overline{500 + 80 + 7 = 587 \text{ answer.}}$

The difficulty of borrowing 1 from 0 is overcome by thinking 1 from 10. For example, in expanding 502 we might write $502 = 500 + 00 + 2$, or $502 = 400 + 100 + 2$, or $502 = 400 + 90 + 12$, etc.

Examples.

(a) $502 = 400 + 100 + 2$
      $-310 = 300 + 10 + 0$
      $\overline{100 + 90 + 2 = 192 \text{ answer.}}$

(b) $502 = 400 + 90 + 12$
      $-347 = 300 + 40 + 7$
      $\overline{100 + 50 + 5 = 155 \text{ answer.}}$

(c) $7020 = 6000 + 900 + 110 + 10$
      $- 351 = 300 + 50 + 1$
      $\overline{6000 + 600 + 60 + 9 = 6669 \text{ answer.}}$

(d) $2000 = 1000 + 900 + 90 + 10$
      $-1751 = 1000 + 700 + 50 + 1$
      $\overline{0 + 200 + 40 + 9 = 249 \text{ answer.}}$

Practice 2.   Do the following subtractions using the borrowing method. Try to work with a minimum of paper and pencil work.

	(a)	(b)	(c)	(d)	(e)
1.	92	41	89	71	55
	−54	−25	−82	−39	−27
2.	327	564	705	190	922
	− 18	−209	−251	− 47	− 78
3.	750	627	142	875	227
	− 57	− 76	− 75	−367	−158
4.	1234	3705	2136	8207	4001
	− 125	− 607	− 528	− 179	− 783
5.	3710	9200	1005	7000	6082
	−3512	−5031	− 117	−6030	−2705

Answers.

	(a)	(b)	(c)	(d)	(e)
1.	38	16	7	32	28
2.	309	355	454	143	844
3.	693	551	67	508	69
4.	1109	3098	1608	8028	3218
5.	198	4169	888	970	3377

2.2.4   In the equal additions method the same number is added to both the minuend and subtrahend to obtain an easier subtraction. It is usually easiest to add 10 or 100 to both the minuend and subtrahend. However, the number to be added is a matter of convenience in each case.

Examples.

(a) $\begin{array}{r} 81 \\ -16 \\ \hline \end{array}$ We can think: $81 + 5 = 86$
$16 + 5 = 21$
The difference: $65 = 81 - 16$

(b) $\begin{array}{r} 81 \\ -16 \\ \hline \end{array}$ We can think: $81 + 10 = 80 + 11$
$16 + 10 = 20 + 6$
$60 + 5 = 65$ the difference

(c)   672   Can be done: $672 + 100 + 10 = 600 + 170 + 12$
$- 85$ $85 + 100 + 10 = \underline{100 + 90 + 5}$
$500 + 80 + 7 = 587$

(d)   672   Can be done: $672 + 15 = 687$
$- 85$ $85 + 15 = \underline{100}$
587

(e)   4837   Can be done: $4000 + 800 + 130 + 17$ (adding $100 + 10$)
-2769 $\underline{2000 + 800 + 70 + 9}$
$2000 + 0 + 60 + 8 = 2068$

(f)   7053   Can be done: $7000 + 1000 + 150 + 13$ (adding $1000 +$
-4357 $\underline{5000 + 400 + 60 + 7} \quad 100 + 10$)
$2000 + 600 + 90 + 6 = 2696$

Practice 3. Do the following subtractions using the equal additions method. Try to work mentally, writing only the answers.

	(a)	(b)	(c)	(d)	(e)
1.	83	46	97	30	84
	−39	−27	−40	−19	−18
2.	682	422	908	874	320
	− 35	−103	− 59	−697	−175
3.	507	153	720	800	227
	− 38	− 45	−236	−307	−195
4.	2107	5025	8167	4001	8910
	− 720	− 876	− 398	−2107	−3853

Answers.

	(a)	(b)	(c)	(d)	(e)
1.	44	19	57	11	66
2.	647	319	849	177	145
3.	469	108	484	493	32
4.	1109	4149	7769	1894	5057

2.2.5   In the decomposition method we ask ourselves how much must be added to the subtrahend to obtain the minuend. This is done by place positions with the required amounts being borrowed from the place position to the left in the minuend.

Examples.

(a)   81   We think: $6 + ? = 11, 5; 1 + ? = 7, 6$; so that we have
        -16 $5 + 60 = 65$. Note that we borrowed 10 from 80.

(b)   281   We think: $5 + ? = 11, 6; 9 + ? = 17, 8; 1 + ? = 1, 0$. Thus,
       -195 we have 0 hundreds, 8 tens, 6 ones.
               ANSWER. 86.

(c)   1407   We think: $2 + ? = 7, 5; 5 + ? = 10, 5; 6 + ? = 13, 7$; so that
      $-\ 652$ we have 7 hundreds, 5 tens, 5 ones. Thus, $1407 - 652 =$
               755. Notice that we borrowed 100 from 400.

(d)   7241   We think: $6 + ? = 11, 5; 3 + ? = 3, 0; 5 + ? = 12, 7; 2 + ? =$
      -2536 6, 4; so that $7241 - 2536 = 4705$.

Practice 4.   Do the following subtractions using the decomposition method. Write only the answers.

	(a)	(b)	(c)	(d)	(e)
1.	860	327	621	402	231
	$-\ 74$	$-\ 50$	-112	-105	-132
2.	406	151	962	630	341
	$-\ 27$	-107	-574	-257	-295
3.	1347	5210	3837	7051	2463
	$-\ 438$	$-\ 970$	-2778	-2169	-2375
4.	4463	1835	9001	4172	6127
	-1275	$-\ 999$	-7516	-2342	-5579

Answers.

	(a)	(b)	(c)	(d)	(e)
1.	786	277	509	297	99
2.	379	44	388	373	46
3.	909	4240	1059	4882	88
4.	3188	836	1485	1830	548

2.2.6 All three methods discussed above may be involved in doing a given subtraction. With practice, the work can be done from left to right so that answers can be written directly. One should note the various situations in which each method of subtraction is most useful and productive and follow a flexible procedure which will lead to speed and accuracy in subtraction.

The simplest and most commonly used method for checking subtractions is to add the difference to the subtrahend. If this sum is equal to the minuend, then the subtraction is likely to be correct. In conclusion, ordinary subtraction should be done mentally with only the answer being written.

Practice 5.   Use the most convenient method to do the following subtractions:

	(a)	(b)	(c)	(d)	(e)
1.	5207 −2108	2007 − 436	4315 − 647	9210 −9101	4372 −2587
2.	2460 −1671	8243 −7759	6105 −6037	3792 −1993	4010 −3007
3.	1000 − 958	1462 − 975	3104 −2805	6137 −3729	2809 −1819
4.	12,360 − 9,371	49,802 − 9,847	80,496 −64,058	78,936 −77,825	40,001 −39,005

Answers.

	(a)	(b)	(c)	(d)	(e)
1.	3099	1571	3668	109	1785
2.	789	484	68	1799	1003
3.	42	487	299	2408	990
4.	2,989	39,955	16,438	1,111	996

Exercises

1. Find the addend which when added to the given addend will result in the given sum.

(a) $72 + ? = 107$ (b) $36 + ? = 113$ (c) $401 + ? = 520$
(d) $26 + ? = 205$ (e) $120 + ? = 210$ (f) $369 + ? = 778$.

2. A "shortcut" for finding the addend necessary to add to a given addend to result in a given sum is called _____. The _____ is subtracted from the _____ to obtain the _____.

3. In $35 - 29 = 6$, _____ is the subtrahend, _____ is the minuend, and _____ is the difference.

4. In $104 - 37 = 67$, 67 is the _____, 104 the _____, and 37 is the _____.

5. The empty or null set has cardinal number property _____.

6. Since $7 - 7 = 0$, we can say that $7 -$ _____ $= 7$. Thus, subtracting _____ from any natural number results in _____ _____.

7. The three ways in which the symbol "0" is used are illustrated by

    (a) 101 in which "0" is _____ _____.

    (b) $5 + 0 = 5$ in which 0 is a _____.

    (c) 1, 2, 3, . . . , 8, 9, 0 as writing symbols in which case "0" is called a _____.

8. From $18 - 5 = 13$, we know that $18 - 13 =$ _____.

9. Do as indicated:

    (a) $23 + 0 = ?$ (b) $23 - 0 = ?$ (c) $23 - 23 = ?$

    (d) $0 + 23 = ?$ (e) $0 - 23 = ?$ (f) $23 + 23 = ?$

10. Repeat Practice Set 1 mentally until you can find all the differences accurately without error within one minute.

11. The three methods of subtraction discussed were _____, _____, and _____.

12. Repeat Practice Set 5 using each of the methods of subtraction.

13. Find the difference between:

    (a) 769 and 487   (b) 504 and 230   (c) 760 and 345

    (d) 480 and 195   (e) 1025 and 705   (f) 5007 and 928.

14. Subtract

    (a) 945 from 2041   (b) 362 from 972   (c) 604 from 813

    (d) 3032 from 3127   (e) 306 from 791   (f) 913 from 1110.

15. Do the subtractions:

    (a) $2020 - 1600$ (b) $6744 - 3004$ (c) $7012 - 4106$

    (d) $5207 - 315$ (e) $3836 - 3725$ (f) $5180 - 4578$.

16.
(a) 3062	(b) 1904	(c) 8062	(d) 4269	(e) 1030
−2603	− 906	−7070	−3239	− 103

17.
(a) 91,035	(b) 38,521	(c) 10,942	(d) 29,365
−34,126	− 9,031	− 6,847	− 9,656

18.
(a) 101,011	(b) 875,104	(c) 536,491	(d) 910,741
− 82,112	−758,202	−425,381	− 3,870

19. (a)	5,621,001	(b)	8,470,236	(c)	3,526,392
	−4,717,999		−8,389,142		−1,613,473

20. (a)	9,000,635	(b)	4,000,901	(c)	1,382,005
	−7,228,216		− 93,019		− 101,406

Answers.

1. (a) 35   (b) 77   (c) 119   (d) 179   (e) 90   (f) 409.
2. subtraction; subtrahend, minuend, difference.
3. 29, 35, 6.
4. difference, minuend, subtrahend.
5. zero, 0.
6. 0; zero, 0, leaving the natural number unchanged.
7. (a) place holder   (b) number   (c) digit.
8. 5.
9. (a) 23   (b) 23   (c) 0   (d) 23   (e) no answer (as yet)
   (f) 46.
10. −.
11. borrowing, equal additions, decomposition.
12. −.
13. (a) 282   (b) 274   (c) 415   (d) 285   (e) 320   (f) 4079.
14. (a) 1096   (b) 610   (c) 209   (d) 95   (e) 485   (f) 197.
15. (a) 420   (b) 3740   (c) 2906   (d) 4892   (e) 111   (f) 602.
16. (a) 459   (b) 998   (c) 992   (d) 1030   (e) 927.
17. (a) 56,909   (b) 29,490   (c) 4,095   (d) 19,709.
18. (a) 18,899   (b) 116,902   (c) 111,110   (d) 906,871.
19. (a) 903,002   (b) 81,094   (c) 1,912,919.
20. (a) 1,772,419   (b) 3,907,882   (c) 1,280,599.

2.3 The Integers

2.3.1   In the last section we practiced the "mechanics" of subtraction. In doing this chore we also noted that subtraction might be interpreted as a counting of predecessors. Let us pursue this interpretation further.

Suppose we begin with 11 objects and start subtracting, that is "taking away" objects. How many objects can we "take away"? Our intuitive answer might well be 11. On the other hand, our experience might say that if the objects were dollar bills, we could surely go into debt to allow ourselves to "take away" much more than 11 from 11! If we were on the eleventh floor of a building, we might be able to go down into a sub-basement 16 or 17 floors below (see Figure 40).

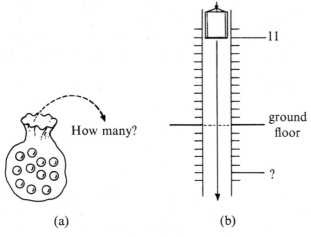

(a)   (b)

FIGURE 40

In our development of subtraction we carefully avoided the "absurd" question of subtracting more than we were given. That is, questions like $11 - 17 = ?$. However, it is a valuable human trait to face embarrassing questions such as this. A further saving grace is that humans invariably find or create answers to such questions. For example, recall our introduction of 0 as a number such that $7 - 7 = 0$ and $7 + 0 = 7$. We extended the natural numbers to include 0 so that the question $7 - 7 = ?$ would have an answer.

Let us begin by noting that our mathematical language thus far consists of the natural numbers and zero with the two operations of addition and subtraction. For convenience consider the number 3. We have three choices of action: we can add a natural number, add or subtract 0, or subtract a natural number from 3. We will proceed with the unit one from which the other numbers were built.

. . .	. . .	. . .	. . .
$3 + 4 = 7$	Four greater than	$0 + 4 = 4$	Four greater than
$3 + 3 = 6$	Three greater than	$0 + 3 = 3$	Three greater than
$3 + 2 = 5$	Two greater than	$0 + 2 = 2$	Two greater than
$3 + 1 = 4$	One greater than	$0 + 1 = 1$	One greater than
$3 + 0 = 3$	The given number	$0 + 0 = 0$	Zero
$3 - 1 = 2$	One less than	$0 - 1 = ?$	One less than
$3 - 2 = 1$	Two less than	$0 - 2 = ?$	Two less than
$3 - 3 = 0$	The number zero	$0 - 3 = ?$	Three less than
$3 - 4 = ?$	?	$0 - 4 = ?$	Four less than
. . .	?	. . .	. . .

Notice that there is an ordering of the numbers described by "**greater than**" and "**less than**." That is, we say that 4 is greater than 3, 3 is **equal to** 3, and 2 is less than 3. If we begin with zero, 0, as a "neutral" element (since adding or subtracting it from a natural number has no effect on the

$$\ldots, 0-4, 0-3, 0-2, 0-1, 0-0, 0+1, 0+2, 0+3, 0+4, \ldots$$

$$\quad\quad ?\quad\quad ?\quad\quad ?\quad\quad ?\quad\quad 0\quad\quad 1\quad\quad 2\quad\quad 3\quad\quad 4$$

FIGURE 41

number), we might observe an interesting and suggestive "pattern" in the writing (Figure 41).

In our rearrangement, we have the set of natural numbers ordered to the right of 0, the "neutral" number 0, and the set of question marks to the left of 0. In order to be consistent, it seems reasonable to expect the set of question marks to have analogous properties as the natural numbers. Of course, as is to be expected, it is terribly awkward to attempt discussion of a set of elements without names. Thus, let us give names to these ideas.

We write $0 - 1 = -1$. That is, the numeral "-1" names a number which is "one whole unit" less than 0. This should suggest that we write: $0 - 2 = -2$, $0 - 3 = -3$, $0 - 4 = -4$, and so on. The prefix symbol "$-$" which we have previously used to indicate subtraction is now called a **negative sign** and distinguishes the numerals naming numbers less than 0. Although the negative sign may seem confusing, it will eventually lead us to considerable simplification.

The new numbers which we have just introduced with the numerals "-1," "-2," "-3," and so forth, are called the **negative integers**. We think of the negative integers as the "opposites" of the natural numbers. To distinguish the new role of the natural numbers as a subset, we now rename them the **positive integers**. The entire set of numbers is called the **integers**. The integers thus consist of the negative integers, zero, and

$$\ldots, -7, -6, -5, -4, -3, -2, -1, 0, \quad 1, \quad 2, \quad 3, \quad 4, \quad 5, \quad 6, \quad 7, \ldots$$

$$\longleftarrow \text{negative integers} \text{—— zero ——} \text{positive integers} \longrightarrow$$

$$\longleftarrow \text{The Integers} \longrightarrow$$

FIGURE 42

the positive integers. The integers are informally referred to as **directed** or **signed whole numbers** (Figure 42).

When the integers are arranged in order, the positive integers can be imagined as shown in Figure 43 to extend indefinitely to the right without end, the negative integers to extend indefinitely to the left without end, and the number zero can be thought of as separating the positive and negative integers. Notice that without the number 0 we would have two units between −1 and 1 while there is one unit between any two other consecutive integers. The positive integers have a least element, 1, but no greatest. The negative integers have a greatest element, −1, but no least. We shall see that with the integers we have extended the set of numbers so that we can not only add any two integers together but can also find the difference between any two integers.

2.3.2 Before proceeding, let us answer now the "absurd" and embarrassing question $11 - 17 = ?$. Since we know $11 - 11 = 0$ and $17 - 11 = 6$,

$$\ldots, -7, -6, -5, -4, -3, -2, -1, 0, 1, 2, 3, 4, 5, 6, 7, 8, 9, 10, 11, 12, \ldots$$

FIGURE 43

$11 - 17$ must be 6 less than 0 or −6. That is, we have $11 - 17 = -6$. We read this "eleven minus seventeen is equal to negative six."

The "blank" spaces in Table 10 can also be filled in. Notice that the numerals should now be thought of as naming integers. Thus, the table can be extended to include both larger and smaller integers. (See Table 12.)

TABLE 12. **Subtraction Facts.**

Subtrahend:		1	2	3	4	5	6	7	8	9	10
Minuend:	1	0	−1	−2	−3	−4	−5	−6	−7	−8	−9
	2	1	0	−1	−2	−3	−4	−5	−6	−7	−8
	3	2	1	0	−1	−2	−3	−4	−5	−6	−7
	4	3	2	1	0	−1	−2	−3	−4	−5	−6
	5	4	3	2	1	0	−1	−2	−3	−4	−5
	6	5	4	3	2	1	0	−1	−2	−3	−4
	7	6	5	4	3	2	1	0	−1	−2	−3
	8	7	6	5	4	3	2	1	0	−1	−2
	9	8	7	6	5	4	3	2	1	0	−1
	10	9	8	7	6	5	4	3	2	1	0

Examples.

(a) To find $4-7=$? we begin with 4 and count 7 predecessors (possible now with the negative integers) to obtain $4-7=-3$, which is read "four minus seven is equal to negative three." Notice how, in reading the symbolism, we distinguish the usage of "−" as a minus, subtraction symbol, and as a negative, prefix symbol.

$$\ldots, -4, -3, -2, -1, 0, 1, 2, 3, 4, 5, \ldots$$

$$-3 \longleftarrow\! 4$$
$$-7$$

(b) To find $2-9=$? we begin at 2 and count 9 predecessors to obtain $2-9=-7$ as indicated in Table 12.

$$\ldots, -8, -7, -6, -5, -4, -3, -2, -1, 0, 1, 2, 3, \ldots$$

$$-7 \longleftarrow\! 2$$
$$-9$$

Since the integers are an extension of the natural numbers, we would expect that the properties and procedures for addition and subtraction should remain unchanged. This is indeed the case.

2.3.3   In the addition of integers, there are four situations to be considered. First, if the integers are both positive, they can be identified with the natural numbers and the addition can be accomplished as before.

Examples.

(a) $32 + 13 = 45$ (b) $201 + 729 = 930$.

Second, if one of the addends is zero, 0, the sum is equal to the other addend.

Examples.

(a) $32 + 0 = 32$ (b) $0 + 17 = 17$
(c) $-16 + 0 = -16$ (d) $0 + (-5) = -5$.

Notice that in Example (d) above we introduced formally a new symbol. The symbols "(" and ")" are called **parentheses** and are used to indicate a grouping or separation of quantities. In our example, the parentheses serve to separate the negative, prefix symbol from the operation symbol "+." They indicate that we have a negative five which we are adding to zero. We read $0 + (-5) = -5$ as "zero plus negative five is equal to negative five."

Third, if the addends are opposite in sign, that is, if one addend is positive and the other negative, we can apply our previous knowledge of addition to obtain the sum. In obtaining the sum we will note the connection between the use of " − " as a negative sign and as a symbol for subtraction. It will be most convenient to develop our thinking by using examples.

Examples.

(a) $-5 + 13 = ?$ can be done by first thinking of a simple sum of natural numbers. Consider $3 + 4 = 7$ can be illustrated by

$$\ldots\ 0,\ 1,\ 2,\ \underset{3\ +\ 4\ =\ 7}{\underbrace{3,\ 4,\ 5,\ 6,\ 7}},\ 8,\ 9,\ 10,\ \ldots$$

We begin with the first addend and count to the right the required number as indicated by the second addend. Now for $-5 + 13 = ?$ we begin with the first addend, -5, and count to the right 13 to obtain the sum 8. Thus, $-5 + 13 = 8$.

$$\ldots,\ -6,\ \underset{-5}{\underbrace{-5},\ -4,\ -3,\ -2,\ -1,\ 0,\ 1,\ 2,\ 3,\ 4,\ 5,\ 6,\ 7,\ \underset{8}{8}},\ 9,\ \ldots$$
$$-5\ \ \ \ \ +\ \ \ \ \ 13\ \ \ \ \ =\ \ \ \ \ 8$$

Now recall that the order of addition was immaterial. That is, $-5 + 13 = 13 + (-5)$. But then $13 + (-5) = 8$. If we represent this sum in a diagram, we note that the sum $13 + (-5) = 13 - 5$, the difference between the positive integers!

$$\ldots,\ -1,\ 0,\ 1,\ 2,\ 3,\ 4,\ 5,\ 6,\ 7,\ \underset{8}{8},\ 9,\ 10,\ 11,\ 12,\ \underset{13}{13},\ 14,\ \ldots$$
$$(-5)$$

(b) $11 + (-7) = ?$ can be done by writing $11 + (-7) = -7 + 11 = 4$ or by noting that $11 + (-7) = 11 - 7 = 4$.

$$\ldots,\ 0,\ 1,\ 2,\ 3,\ \underset{4}{4},\ 5,\ 6,\ 7,\ 8,\ 9,\ 10,\ \underset{11}{11},\ 12,\ \ldots$$
$$4\ \ \ =\ \ \ (-7)\ \ +\ \ 11$$

(c) $-4+4=4+(-4)=4-4=0$. Applying our observations from Example (a) we can "reverse" the order of the addends and also note that adding a negative integer is the same as subtracting the comparable **opposite** positive integer.

$$\ldots, -5, -4, -3, -2, -1, 0, 1, 2, 3, 4, 5, 6, \ldots$$

$$-4 \ + \ 4 \ = \ 0 = (-4) + 4$$

Notice that in writing the relationships $-4+4=4+(-4)=4-4=0$ we are being consistent with what we have observed previously. That is, $4-4=0$ means $4=4+0$, $4+(-4)=0$ must then say that 4 and -4 are **opposites**; $-4+4=0$ requires that $-4=0-4$, which is the case. Furthermore, in writing $4+(-4)=0$ we have $4=0-(-4)$, and $4= -(-4)+0=-(-4)$!

(d) $9+(-13)=-13+9=-4$ or $9+(-13)=9-13=-4$.

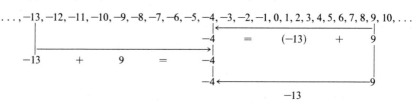

$$\ldots, -13, -12, -11, -10, -9, -8, -7, -6, -5, -4, -3, -2, -1, 0, 1, 2, 3, 4, 5, 6, 7, 8, 9, 10, \ldots$$

(e) $-9+13=13+(-9)=13-9=4$. This example is primarily of interest when compared to Example (d) above. Notice that we have $9-13=-4$ while $13-9=4$. That is, when the **order** of subtraction is reversed the "sign" of the difference is changed.

Fourth, if both the addends are negative, we can relate one of the negative signs to subtraction and consider the problem as if one addend were positive and the operation were subtraction.

Examples.

(a) $-32+(-13)=-32-13=-45$ since we can count 13 predecessors from negative thirty-two. Of course, since the negative integers are the **opposites** of the positive integers, we might expect that addition of negative integers would be exactly analogous to addition of positive integers except for the negative sign. That is, to answer $-32+(-13)=?$ we consider the sum $32+13=45$ and write $-32+(-13)=-45$.

(b) To find $-15+(-5)=?$ we add 15 and 5 to obtain $15+5=20$. Then, $-15+(-5)=-20$.

$$\ldots, 14, 15, 16, 17, 18, 19, 20, 21, \ldots$$

$$15 \ + \ 5 \ = \ 20$$

$$\ldots, -21, -20, -19, -18, -17, -16, -15, -14, -13, \ldots$$

$$-20 \quad = \quad (-5) \quad + \quad -15$$

(c) $-201 + (-729) = -930$ since $201 + 729 = 930$. The sum of two negative integers is obtained by finding the sum of the opposite positive integers and "attaching" a negative sign to the result. The sum of two negative integers will always be negative.

To summarize, to find the sum of two integers:

1. If the integers are positive, we add as before.

2. If one of the integers is zero, the sum is equal to the other integer.

3. If the integers are opposite in sign, we find the difference between the integers. We must be careful to attach the proper "sign" to the sum.

4. If the integers are both negative, we find the sum of the opposite positive integers and attach a negative sign to the result.

Practice 1.   Find the sums mentally.

	(a)	(b)	(c)	(d)
1.	$320 + 62$	$40 + 0$	$-16 + 51$	$-12 + (-29)$
2.	$47 + (-8)$	$0 + (-9)$	$7 + (-7)$	$307 + 95$
3.	$-5 + (-11)$	$-14 + 14$	$37 + 268$	$-17 + 0$
4.	$-18 + (-39)$	$-61 + (-99)$	$-87 + (-3)$	$-19 + (-103)$
5.	$27 + 0$	$-4 + 0$	$0 + (-71)$	$0 + 221$
6.	$13 + (-5)$	$-11 + 91$	$32 + (-32)$	$-99 + 99$
7.	$-16 + 7$	$24 + (-73)$	$-81 + 18$	$37 + (-64)$
8.	$-78 + (-7)$	$-18 + 0$	$36 + (-63)$	$-28 + 28$

Answers.

	(a)	(b)	(c)	(d)		(a)	(b)	(c)	(d)
1.	382	40	35	−41	2.	39	−9	0	402
3.	−16	0	305	−17	4.	−57	−160	−90	−122
5.	27	−4	−71	221	6.	8	80	0	0
7.	−9	−49	−63	−27	8.	−85	−18	−27	−0

2.3.4   It was the "absurd" question of subtracting more than we were given that led us to the extension of the natural numbers to the integers. Now let us consider the consequences of this extension with respect to subtraction. Our first observation is to note that we can find the difference between any two positive integers. That is, we can always find an integer such that when added to a given positive integer the result will be a given sum which is a positive integer.

Examples.

(a) $52 - 27 = 25$ since $52 = 27 + 25$. This situation should be familiar and should not cause any difficulty.

(b) $27 - 52 = ?$ or $27 = 52 + ?$ can be answered by recalling that when the order of subtraction is reversed the "sign" of the difference is changed. Thus, from $52 - 27 = 25$ we have $27 - 52 = -25$.

The result is verified by noting that if $27 - 52 = -25$ then $27 = 52 + (-25) = 52 - 25$. But, if $27 = 52 - 25$ we should have $52 = 25 + 27$ which is indeed the case.

(c)   569   is done   837
      −837   −569
                        268   so that $569 - 837 = -268$.

We have already noted the "zero facts"; however they may be clarified and summarized by the following examples.

Examples.

(a) $7 - 0 = 7$, $0 - 0 = 0$, $-7 - 0 = -7$. When zero is the subtrahend the difference is equal to the minuend. Also, since we have $7 + 0 = 7$, $0 + 0 = 0$, and $-7 + 0 = -7$, we can conclude that when zero is added to or subtracted from any integer, it leaves the integer unchanged.

(b) $7 - 7 = 0$, $2 - 2 = 0$ since these are related to $7 - 0 = 7$ and $2 - 0 = 2$ and are consistent with $7 = 7 + 0$ and $2 = 2 + 0$. When the minuend and subtrahend are equal, the difference is zero.

(c) $0 - 7 = -7$, $0 - (-5) = 5$ since $0 = 7 + (-7) = 7 - 7$, $0 = (-5) + 5 = 5 + (-5) = 5 - 5$. When zero is the minuend, the difference is the negative of the subtrahend.

Notice that in writing $0 - (-5) = 5$ we have $0 + [-(-5)] = 5$ and so $-(-5) = 5$. The symbols "[" and "]" are called **brackets** and serve the same purpose as the parentheses. Now let us consider $0 - 5 = -[-(-5)] = -5$ so that $-[-(-5)] = -5$. The negative of a negative integer is positive and the negative of the negative of a negative integer is negative.

(d) $0 - 0 = 0 + (-0) = 0$ so that $-0 = 0$ and 0 is neither positive nor negative.

With the above observations, we can find the difference between any two integers. Since we have already considered the difference between positive integers and have considered the "zero facts," we will conclude our discussion of subtraction with a few examples in which the minuend, the subtrahend, or both are negative integers.

Examples.

(a) $-14 - 14 = -28$ since we have $-14 = 14 + (-28) = 14 - 28$ and $-14 = 14 - 28$ means $14 = 28 + (-14) = 28 - 14$. Of course, we might have also argued that $-14 - 14 = -14 + (-14)$ which is the negative of the sum $14 + 14 = 28$, that is, $-14 - 14 = -28$.

(b) $17 - (-9) = 17 + [-(-9)] = 17 + 9 = 26$. We might also observe that $17 - (-9) = 26$ means $17 = (-9) + 26 = 26 + (-9) = 26 - 9$ which can be verified by counting.

(c) $17 - (-21) = 17 + [-(-21)] = 17 + 21 = 38$ as above.

(d) $-38 - (-6) = -38 + [-(-6)] = -38 + 6 = -32$. We can easily check $-38 + 6 = -32$ by noting that $-38 + 6 = 6 + (-38) = 6 - 38$ which is equal to the negative of $38 - 6 = 32$.

Practice 2.   Find the differences mentally.

	(a)	(b)	(c)	(d)
1.	$15 - 7$	$7 - 15$	$16 - 0$	$0 - 16$
2.	$9 - 9$	$-8 - 0$	$-11 - 4$	$11 - (-4)$
3.	$0 - (-21)$	$-13 - 13$	$-24 - (-24)$	$23 - 29$
4.	$7 - 17$	$17 - 7$	$47 - 0$	$-47 - 0$
5.	$-6 - (-5)$	$1 - [-(-1)]$	$-10 - 10$	$0 - [- (-7)]$
6.	$-(-11) - 11$	$-5 - (-0)$	$-4 - 9$	$-9 - 4$
7.	$7 - (-25)$	$-25 - 7$	$25 - (-7)$	$-25 - (-7)$
8.	$7 - 25$	$25 - 7$	$-7 - (-25)$	$-7 - 25$

Answers.

	(a)	(b)	(c)	(d)		(a)	(b)	(c)	(d)
1.	8	-8	16	-16	2.	0	-8	-15	15
3.	21	-26	0	-6	4.	-10	10	47	-47
5.	-1	0	-20	-7	6.	0	-5	-13	-13
7.	32	-32	32	-18	8.	-18	18	18	-32

Exercises

1. Give an example of a situation which would suggest the possibility of "taking away" or subtracting more than a given initial or starting amount.

2. Given a natural number, what are the three choices of action that we have discussed thus far?

3. Order the following numerals from smallest to largest:
$5 + 5, 5 + 1, 5 - 4, 5 + 0, 5 + 4, 5 - 2, 5 + 2, 5 - 3, 5 + 3, 5 - 1.$

4. Do as in Exercise 3 with:
    (a) $2 + 1, 3 - 2, 4 + 2, 1 + 1, 5 - 1, 0 + 5, 5 + 2, 2 + 6.$
    (b) $3 + 5, 2 - 0, 2 + 4, 4 + 1, 1 + 0, 7 - 4, 2 + 2, 3 + 4.$

5. Match the numerals in the lettered column with the numbered column so that they name the same number.

    (a) $3 + 7$ 1. $1 + 1$
    (b) $5 - 0$ 2. $9 - 2$
    (c) $2 + 5$ 3. $1 - 3$
    (d) $6 - 8$ 4. $5 + 0$
    (e) $3 - 1$ 5. $7 + 3$

6. Find the missing addends:
    (a) $27 + ? = 39$ (b) $16 + ? = 54$ (c) $51 + ? = 70$
    (d) $33 + ? = 33$ (e) $? + 14 = 31$ (f) $? + 79 = 97$
    (g) $? + 23 = 51$ (h) $? + 97 = 79.$

7. List the fifteen consecutive predecessors to 3.

8. The integers consist of three distinct subsets of numbers. These are called the _____ integers, _____, and the _____ integers.

9. Which of the following statements are true?
    (a) $7 - 11$ is equal to a natural number.
    (b) $11 - 7$ is equal to a positive integer.
    (c) 0 is a positive integer.
    (d) 7 is greater than 11.
    (e) 7 is less than 11.

10. Which of the following statements are true?
    (a) There is no smallest positive integer.
    (b) There is a largest negative integer.
    (c) Every positive integer is at least "two whole units" greater than any negative integer.
    (d) The difference between any two integers is an integer.
    (e) The difference between any two natural numbers is a natural number.

11. Find the differences:
    (a) $8 - 5$ (b) $5 - 8$ (c) $6 - 6$ (d) $6 - 0$ (e) $0 - 6.$

12. Write out how $16 - 23 = -7$ is read.

13. Find the sums:
    (a) $37 + 84$ (b) $0 + 37$ (c) $-64 + 0$ (d) $19 + (-19)$
    (e) $-45 + 45$ (f) $58 + (-61)$ (g) $-36 + 27$ (h) $-21 + (-21).$

14. Write out how $30 + (-17) = 13$ is read. Do the same for $17 + (-30) = -13.$

15. The sum $-12 + 51$ is equal to the related difference _____.

16. Since $51 - 12 = 39$ we have $12 - 51 = ?$. Also, since $51 + 12 = 63$ we have $-51 + (-12) = ?$.

17. Find the sums:
   - (a) $-367 + (-839)$
   - (b) $201 + (-102)$
   - (c) $593 + 709$
   - (d) $-520 + 487$
   - (e) $792 + (-792)$
   - (f) $-4015 + (-286)$.

18. Find the sums:
   - (a) $(-14) + (-63) + 70 + (-4) + 7$.
   - (b) $91 + (-37) + 305 + (-206)$.
   - (c) $43 + 86 + (-9) + 13 + (-33)$.
   - (d) $(-125) + (-362) + (-479) + 800$.

19. Find the differences:
   - (a) $314 - 426$
   - (b) $-207 - 330$
   - (c) $330 - (-207)$
   - (d) $-154 - (-326)$
   - (e) $527 - 527$
   - (f) $-192 - (-87)$.

20. Find the differences:
   - (a) $473 - [-(-743)]$
   - (b) $-[-(-47)] - 28$
   - (c) $-106 - [-(-97)]$
   - (d) $-(-439) - (-182)$
   - (e) $-[-(-207)] - (-314)$
   - (f) $-8065 - (-76)$.

Answers.

1. The temperature can go below freezing. The elevation of ground from sea level might go below sea level.

2. Adding a natural number, adding or subtracting 0, subtracting a natural number.

3. $5 - 4, 5 - 3, 5 - 2, 5 - 1, 5 + 0, 5 + 1, 5 + 2, 5 + 3, 5 + 4, 5 + 5$.

4. (a) $3 - 2, 1 + 1, 2 + 1, 5 - 1, 0 + 5, 4 + 2, 5 + 2, 2 + 6$.
   (b) $1 + 0, 2 - 0, 7 - 4, 2 + 2, 4 + 1, 2 + 4, 3 + 4, 3 + 5$.

5. (a)-5 (b)-4 (c)-2 (d)-3 (e)-1.

6. (a) 12 (b) 38 (c) 19 (d) 0 (e) 17 (f) 18 (g) 28
   (h) -18.

7. $2, 1, 0, -1, -2, -3, -4, -5, -6, -7, -8, -9, -10, -11, -12$.

8. negative, zero, positive.

9. (a) false   (b) true   (c) false   (d) false   (e) true.

10. (a) false   (b) true   (c) true   (d) true   (e) false.

11. (a) 3 (b) -3 (c) 0 (d) 6 (e) -6.

12. Sixteen minus twenty-three is equal to negative seven.

13. (a) 121 (b) 37 (c) -64 (d) 0 (e) 0 (f) -3
    (g) -9 (h) -42.

14. $30 + (-17) = 13$ is read "thirty plus negative seventeen is equal to thirteen." $17 + (-30) = -13$ is read "seventeen plus negative thirty is equal to negative thirteen."

15. $-12 + 51 = 51 - 12.$
16. $12 - 51 = -39; -51 + (-12) = -63.$
17. (a) -1206 (b) 99 (c) 1302 (d) -33 (e) 0 (f) $-4301.$
18. (a) -4 (b) 153 (c) 100 (d) $-166.$
19. (a) -112 (b) -537 (c) 537 (d) 172 (e) 0 (f) $-105.$
20. (a) -270 (b) -75 (c) -203 (d) 621 (e) 107
    (f) $-7989.$

Review Summary

In this chapter we discussed "putting together" and "taking away" operations on sets. When we represent the "putting together" or successive counting of two sets with numerals we call it _____. The numbers being added together are called _____ and the result of addition is called the _____. On the other hand, when we look for an addend which when added to a given addend will result in a given sum, we call it _____. We say that we subtract the _____ from the _____ to obtain the _____. *addition* *addends* *sum* *subtraction* *subtrahend, minuend* *difference*

The simplest additions are often referred to as the basic addition facts. As in learning any activity **PRACTICE** is a necessary chore. In studying addition we noted that the order of addition was immaterial; for example, $3 + 6 =$ _____. Furthermore, we observed that additions could be classified into families and into easy and difficult types. As we progressed to more difficult additions, we used expanded forms of numerals so that we could add groups of fixed sizes separately. For rapid addition, we noted that we might add convenient portions of addends together successively. Grouping by tens was also noted as a useful device. Finally, in using the place positions of the digits in addition, careful spacing and alignment of the partial sums is important. In long additions, answers should be checked for "sense" or the addition should be done again in a different order independently and the two sums compared. *6 + 3*

In subtraction we write $7 - 4 = ?$ meaning $7 =$ _____. That is, the difference is the number such that when *4 + ?*

added to the _____ the sum will equal the _____. As in
addition we began with the simplest subtraction facts. *subtrahend, minuend*
However, we immediately noted two distinctive items:
the use of 0 as a number, the problem of subtracting a
subtrahend greater than the _____. We noted that _____ *minuend, 0*
is the number which results when any natural number is
subtracted from itself. That is, adding _____ to any num- *0*
ber leaves the number unchanged.

In practicing simple subtractions, an auxiliary table
of subtraction facts was found useful. As we studied
subtraction we noted that the order of subtraction was
important; for example, $7 - 4 = 3$ but $4 - 7$ has no natural
number answer. Another relationship observed was that
given a subtraction fact, we can immediately obtain a
related second fact; for example, from $7 - 4 = 3$ we have
_____ $= 4$. The three general methods of subtraction dis- *$7 - 3$*
cussed were called the borrowing, equal additions, and
decomposition methods.

The simplest and most commonly used method for
checking subtraction is to _____ the difference to the *add*
_____. The resulting sum should equal the _____. *subtrahend, minuend*

In our discussion of subtraction we carefully avoided
the "absurd" question of subtracting more than we were
given. In turning to this question we noted that there is an
ordering of numbers which is described by saying that in
comparing any two numbers, one must be greater than,
_____ to, or _____ than the other number. Using addi- *equal, less*
tion and subtraction and beginning with zero, we generated a set of numbers with an interesting and suggestive
pattern in the appearance of their names.

$$\ldots, 0 - 3, 0 - 2, 0 - 1, 0, 0 + 1, 0 + 2, 0 + 3, \ldots$$
$$\ldots, \quad ?, \quad ?, \quad ?, \quad 0, \quad 1, \quad 2, \quad 3, \quad \ldots$$

We gave names to the new ideas and wrote $0 - 1 =$
_____, $0 - 2 =$ _____, $0 - 3 =$ _____, and so forth. *$-1, -2, -3$*
These new number ideas are called the _____ integers. *negative*
The natural numbers are then called the _____ integers. *positive*
The negative and positive integers along with the number
_____ then form a set of numbers called the _____. *zero, integers*
With the integers we have extended the set of numbers
so that we can not only add any two integers but can also
find the _____ between any two integers as an integer. *difference*

In adding integers we considered four situations:

1. If the integers are _____, we add as before.   *positive*
2. If one of the integers is _____, the sum is equal to   *zero*
the other integer.
3. If the integers are opposite in sign, we find the
_____ between the integers and attach the appropriate   *difference*
sign.
4. If the integers are both _____, we find the sum of   *negative*
the opposite positive integers and attach a negative sign
to the sum.

In considering the difference between any two positive
integers we observed that when the order of subtraction
is reversed the "sign" of the difference is also changed.
That is, since $19 - 11 = 8$ we have $11 - 19 =$ _____. To   *−8*
find $317 - 503$ we do $503 - 317 =$ _____. Thus, $317 -$ *186*
$503 =$ _____. The "zero facts" were discussed and we   *−186*
concluded that when zero is added to or subtracted from
any integer, it leaves the integer unchanged. Since $-0 = 0$ *positive,*
we noted that 0 is neither _____ nor _____. In our dis-   *negative*
cussion, we found that $-(-5) =$ _____, $-[-(-5)] =$ *5*
_____. That is, that an even number of negative signs   *−5*
resulted in a positive and that an odd number of negative
signs resulted in a negative. We then concluded our discussion with a few examples in which the minuend, the
subtrahend, or both, were negative integers.

Chapter Exercises (2)

Group I.

1. In $7 + 11 = 18$, the 7 and 11 are called _____ while 18 is called the
_____. The operation symbol "+" indicates _____.
2. Use grouping by tens to find the sum of 102, 37, 78, and 13.
3. Find the following sums:

(a) 840	(b) 17	(c) 204	(d) 798
27	710	107	965
9	825	570	334
204	58	909	287

4. Find the following sums:

(a)	(b)	(c)	(d)
137	3042	4015	4772
704	104	7398	2983
648	80	997	6359
520	975	296	7935

5. Find the following sums:
   (a) $40 + 725 + 6 + 909$
   (b) $475 + 128 + 330 + 382$
   (c) $9017 + 7503 + 1004 + 596$
   (d) $4726 + 8699 + 3997 + 6495.$

6. Find the following sums:

(a)	(b)	(c)	(d)
147	9403	137,000	7,652,381
385	904	10,340	127,048
802	90	805,008	2,595,071
430	109	4,027	6,730,079
595	4006	53,634	40,530
168	607	294,386	5,437,769
700	1403		
275	80		

7. Find the sum of: 340,067,283; 27,924,036; 107,240,831; 7,487,209; 1,036,487,045; and 63,947,872.

8. Find the addends:
   (a) $36 + ? = 56$
   (b) $63 + ? = 72$
   (c) $72 + ? = 81$
   (d) $132 + ? = 153$
   (e) $204 + ? = 337$
   (f) $571 + ? = 830.$

9. In $11 - 7 = 4$, the 7 is called the _____, the 11 the _____, and the 4 the _____. The operation symbol " $-$ " indicates _____.

10. Do as indicated:
   (a) $96 - 0 = ?$
   (b) $96 + 96 = ?$
   (c) $0 - 96 = ?$
   (d) $96 - 96 = ?$
   (e) $0 + 96 = ?$
   (f) $96 + 0 = ?$

11. Find the difference between:
   (a) 401 and 260
   (b) 410 and 206
   (c) 620 and 104
   (d) 572 and 356
   (e) 750 and 695
   (f) 926 and 218.

12. Subtract:
   (a) 307 from 838
   (b) 579 from 611
   (c) 492 from 501
   (d) 260 from 307
   (e) 132 from 1000
   (f) 1027 from 2913.

13.

(a)	(b)	(c)	(d)	(e)
407	281	135	300	356
$-$ 28	$-$173	$-$ 27	$-$ 99	$-$349

14.

(a)	(b)	(c)	(d)
28,361	10,070	7,149	14,058
$-$ 7,942	$-$ 2,680	$-$7,058	$-$ 5,057

15. Do the subtractions:
    (a) 29,307 − 19,412   (b) 80,007 − 1,549
    (c) 21,370 − 16,841   (d) 36,904 − 29,049.

16. (a)   364,208   (b)   287,376   (c)   179,300,471
       −205,009   −278,479   − 26,694,406

17. Order the following numerals from smallest to largest:
    (a) 20 + 0, 20 − 2, 22 − 0, 1 + 22, 22 − 1, 9 + 10.
    (b) VII, IX, VI, XI, V, IV, VIII, X.

18. Find the missing integers:
    (a) 27 + ? = 36   (b) 36 + ? = 27   (c) 27 − ? = 36
    (d) 36 − ? = 27   (e) 36 − 27 = ?   (f) 27 + 36 = ?
    (g) 27 + 0 = ?   (h) 36 − ? = 0   (i) 0 − ? = 63.

19. Which of the following statements are true?
    (a) "Positive integers" is another name for the natural numbers.
    (b) A digit is a number less than ten.
    (c) Zero is a number.
    (d) The integers include negative numbers.
    (e) The negative of a negative number is very negative.

20. Which of the following statements are true?
    (a) The order of addition is immaterial.
    (b) The order of subtraction is immaterial.
    (c) The sum of two integers is an integer.
    (d) The difference between equal integers is zero.
    (e) Zero is neither negative nor positive.

21. Find the sums:
    (a) 16 + (−9)   (b) 47 + 0   (c) −28 + 53
    (d) −29 + 39   (e) −14 + (−47)   (f) 0 + (−46).

22. Find the sums:
    (a) 61 + (−739) + (−300) + 8   (b) 803 + (−148) + 620 + (−48)
    (c) 850 + 835 + (−872) + (−803)
    (d) (−326) + (−62) + (−102) + 310.

23. Find the differences:
    (a) 71 − (−39)   (b) −(−14) − 24   (c) 40 − [−(−15)]
    (d) −(−201) − 146   (e) −364 − [−(−472)]   (f) 276 − [−(−276)].

24. (a)   5,325   (b)   9,364   (c)   14,037   (d)   52,317
       −7,134   −10,191   −15,026   −53,592

Group II.

1. Use grouping by tens to find the sum of 25, 16, 75, 34, and 65.

2. Use expanded numerals to show how one can add 8372, 406, and 725.

3. Find the following sums:

(a) 306	(b) 192	(c) 419	(d) 841
70	476	368	148
625	21	675	700
101	18	327	629

4. Find the following sums:

(a) 570	(b) 683	(c) 6041	(d) 3742
703	4791	70	3179
570	37	719	8794
396	1009	3270	6557

5. Find the following sums:
   (a) $90 + 19 + 901 + 1090$ (b) $682 + 370 + 57 + 71$
   (c) $6294 + 17 + 8375 + 379 + 8030$ (d) $8274 + 9143 + 2736 + 7150$.

6. Find the following sums:

(a) 402	(b) 3659	(c) 30,007	(d) 3,041,680
73	4173	60,392	836,014
549	2849	825	1,385,217
50	9372	1,302	493,760
7	1281	8,485	7,689,548
287	5479	56,071	89,762,306
78	7145		
631	6214		

7. Find the sum of: 18,631,904; 805,250,762; 3,285,004,386; 7,835,045; 21,220,927; and 10,007,948.

8. Find the addends:
   (a) $45 + ? = 54$ (b) $29 + ? = 41$ (c) $78 + ? = 92$
   (d) $364 + ? = 725$ (e) $786 + ? = 875$ (f) $931 + ? = 1020$.

9. Given $34 - 19 = 15$, we know the related subtraction facts
   (a) $34 - 15 = ?$ (b) $19 - 34 = ?$ (c) $15 - 34 = ?$

10. Do as indicated:
    (a) $35 + 0 = ?$ (b) $0 - 35 = ?$ (c) $35 - 35 = ?$
    (d) $35 + 35 = ?$ (e) $0 + 35 = ?$ (f) $35 - 0 = ?$

11. Find the difference between:
    (a) 287 and 109   (b) 901 and 782   (c) 827 and 190
    (d) 615 and 516   (e) 290 and 193   (f) 407 and 318.

12. Subtract:
    (a) 365 from 476   (b) 156 from 240   (c) 281 from 729
    (d) 194 from 590   (e) 87 from 1110   (f) 5082 from 6170.

13. (a) 164	(b) 940	(c) 131	(d) 727	(e) 228
$-$ 67	-574	$-$ 93	-278	-182

14. (a)   63,482   (b)   20,101   (c)   2,541   (d)   19,003
       − 7,373   − 2,121   −2,480   − 9,006

15. Do the subtractions:
    (a) 51,904 − 35,875   (b) 20,100 − 3,259
    (c) 15,002 − 7,483   (d) 45,387 − 44,278.
16. (a)   100,572   (b)   942,479   (c)   283,050,690
       − 90,473   −492,389   − 85,047,791

17. Order the following numerals from smallest to largest:
    (a) 10 + 1, 17 − 3, 10 − 1, 24 − 12, 5 + 5, 6 + 7.
    (b) X, M, I, L, V, D, C (Roman numerals).
18. Find the missing integer:
    (a) 93 − ? = 57   (b) 57 − 93 = ?   (c) 75 + ? = 39
    (d) 39 − 75 = ?   (e) 0 + ? = 93   (f) 75 − ? = 75
    (g) ? + 93 = 57   (h) 39 + 0 = ?   (i) 75 + ? = 0.
19. Which of the following statements are true?
    (a) A numeral stands for the same number in any base.
    (b) Every integer is a natural number.
    (c) The sum of two integers is always a positive integer.
    (d) Zero is greater than −1.
    (e) −[−(−4)] is positive.
20. Which of the following statements are true?
    (a) The sum of any two negative integers is negative.
    (b) The difference between any two positive integers is positive.
    (c) The sum of equal integers of opposite sign is zero.
    (d) Every natural number is an integer.
    (e) −(−1) is less than 0.
21. Find the sums:
    (a) 40 + (−67)   (b) −93 + 17   (c) −52 + (−52)
    (d) −16 + 0   (e) 38 + (−38)   (f) 0 + (−27).
22. Find the sums:
    (a) 945 + (−49) + 793 + 201   (b) −347 + 437 + 107 + (−67)
    (c) 306 + (−76) + (−144) + (−349)
    (d) 325 + (−142) + 774 + (−391).
23. Find the differences:
    (a) −16 − (−24)   (b) 16 − (−0)   (c) −[−(−15)] − 17
    (d) −[−(−10)] − [−(−10)]   (e) −(−87) − [−(−32)]
    (f) −621 − [−(−261)].
24. (a)   3,751   (b)   1,073   (c)   27,192   (d)   101,374
       −9,609   −20,036   −72,591   −210,743

Problem Set (2)

1. Write 231 in an expanded form so that we can "see" that it is
   (a) a multiple of 9 plus the sum of its digits.
   (b) a multiple of 11 plus the sum of its odd-numbered digits less the sum of its even-numbered digits.
Is this true for all positive integers?

2. A famous mathematician, Karl Friedrich Gauss (1777–1855), it is said, confounded his teacher as a youngster by summing the first 100 consecutive natural numbers in less than one minute. By a simple mental process of rearrangement, can you find the sum of the first 100 consecutive natural numbers?

If we begin with 100 and subtract 99 then add 98 and so on: $100 - 99 + 98 - 97 + \cdots$ plus or minus 1, then what will the resulting number equal?

3. Find the set of all three-digit numerals with no zeroes such that if the digits are reversed and the difference of the two numbers thus named are found, this difference will be equal to 792. What multiples are involved in this process?

4. Occasionally, simple observations lead to difficult problems. Christian Goldbach, an eighteenth century mathematician, made the following conjectures:

   (a) Is every even number greater than 4 the sum of two odd primes? Examples: $6 = 3 + 3$, $8 = 3 + 5$.

   (b) Is every odd number greater than 7 the sum of three odd primes? Examples: $9 = 3 + 3 + 3$, $11 = 3 + 3 + 5$.
Represent the consecutive natural numbers from 75 to 100 as the sum of two or three odd primes depending on whether it is even or odd.

Many mathematicians have expended a great deal of work in attempting to prove the conjectures. Although some advances have been made, no complete proof or disproof has ever been published.

CHAPTER 3

Statements and Problems

3.1 Equations

3.1.1   As in ordinary English, mathematical statements can be separated into different kinds of parts. For example, the statement $5 - 2 = 3$ is made up of the symbols "5," "$-$," "2," "$=$," and "3." The statement $13 + 28 = 41$ has the parts 13, 28, 41, and $+$ and $=$. In these examples the parts can be classified into:

1. **Numerals** such as 5, 2, 3, 13, 28, and 41.
2. **Operation symbols** such as $+$ and $-$.
3. **Connective symbols** such as $=$.

In the statement $5 - 2 = 3$ we can say that 5, 2, and 3 are numerals, the symbol "$-$" is an operation symbol, and the symbol "$=$" is a connective symbol.

Beginning with simple numerals we can form more complicated names using operation symbols such as $+$ and $-$. For example, using 7, 11, and 24 we can form $7 + 11$, $24 - 7$, $24 - 11 + 7$, $7 - 11 + 24$, and so forth. If we use **grouping symbols** such as the **parentheses**, "(" ")," and **brackets**, "[" "]," much as the comma and semicolon are used to punctuate a sentence in ordinary English, we can form even more complicated names; for example, $24 + [7 - (11 + 24)]$. Number names formed in this way are called **expressions**. That is, an expression is made up out of numerals, operations, and **grouping** symbols. When we refer to an expression, it usually indicates that we are interested in either finding the simplest numeral for the expression or in analyzing the relationships between the parts which make up the expression.

Examples.

(a) $7 + 11$ and $24 - 7$ are expressions representing 18 and 17, respectively, and indicate that we arrive at these values by applying the operations of addition and subtraction, respectively.

(b) $(7 + 11) - (24 - 7)$ is an expression representing 1. That is, a "fancy" numeral for 1. The parentheses indicate that we first add 7 and 11 to obtain 18; find the difference between 24 and 7 to be 17; then find the difference between the results 18 and 17 to conclude that the expression refers to 1.

(c) $[(7 + 11) - 24] - 7$ tells us to find the sum of 7 and 11; 18; then subtract 24 to obtain -6; and finally to find the difference between this -6 and 7. That is, the expression stands for -13.

Recalling that names of numbers were called numerals, we can say that an expression is a "fancy" numeral. However, expressions often suggest details and actions which a simple numeral cannot. For example, in $1 + 3 + 5$ the expression tells us that we have the sum of the first three consecutive odd numbers. The expression can be rearranged into $(1 + 2) + 3 + (5 - 2)$ and thence to $3 + 3 + 3$ which tells us that the result is a "square" number since the number of addends is equal to one of the equal addends. The simple numeral "9" names this "square." We indicate this conclusion by writing $1 + 3 + 5 = 9$.

3.1.2   When two numerals refer to the same number, we indicate this connection by saying that the numbers they represent are **equal** and use the symbol "$=$" to connect the numerals. If two numerals do not refer to the same number, we say that they are **unequal** and, using a "slash," indicate this by "$\neq$."

Examples.

(a) Equal $0 + 5 = 5$; $1 + 4 = 5$; $4 + 1 = 5$; $1 + 4 = 4 + 1$.
(b) Unequal $3 + 5 \neq 7$; $4 + 3 \neq 1$; $2 + 2 \neq 0$; $5 - 0 \neq 0 - 5$.

If two numerals name different numbers, we can ask whether they are still related in some definite way. We have indeed observed that the integers were ordered and related in a definite way. Given any two numerals, we can say that they name numbers which are related in **exactly one** of the following ways:

(a) One number is **less than** the other; for example, 3 is less than 5. We symbolize this by using the symbol "$<$," $3 < 5$.

(b) The numbers are **equal**; for example, $5 = 5$. (Notice that for convenience in our discussion we are being somewhat vague in our distinction between number and numeral with respect to the use of "equals.")

(c) One number is **greater than** the other; for example, 5 is greater than 3. We symbolize this by using ">" 5 > 3.

The introduction of these symbols, "<," "=," ">," enables us to always relate (connect) and compare any two number names in a specific way. Using the "slash" symbol, "/," we can form the denial of each of these relationships or connections as illustrated in the following examples.

Examples.

(a) $-2 < 0 < 1$ read "negative two is less than zero which is less than one" or simply "zero is **between** negative two and one."

(b) $-2 \neq 2$ read "negative two is not equal to two" since $-2 < 0$ and $2 > 0$ read "negative two is less than zero and two is greater than zero."

(c) $-1 \not< -2$ read "negative one is not less than negative two." Consider $-1 = 0 - 1$ and $(-1) + 1 = 0$, $-2 = 0 - 2$ and $(-2) + 2 = 0$, thus we have $(-1) + 1 = (-2) + 2$ and $-1 = (-2) + 1$ so that $-1 > -2$.

Example (c) above suggests a method for determining whether one number is less than, equal to, or greater than a second number. Recall that we noted the ordering of the integers:

$$\ldots \ , \ 0 - 3, \quad 0 - 2, \quad 0 - 1, \quad 0, \quad 0 + 1, \ 0 + 2, \ 0 + 3, \quad \ldots$$
$$\ldots \ , \quad -3, \quad -2, \quad -1, \quad 0, \quad 1, \quad 2, \quad 3, \quad \ldots$$
$$\ldots \ < \ -3 \ < \ -2 \ < \ -1 \ < \ 0 \ < \ 1 \ < \ 2 \ < \ 3 \ < \ \ldots$$

$\longleftarrow$ ——————— less than ——————— $<$ ——————— greater than ——————— $\longrightarrow$

If a number is greater than a second number, we must have to add a positive integer to the second to obtain a number equal to the first. If a number is less than a second number, we must have to subtract a positive integer from the second to obtain a number equal to the first.

Examples.

(a) $-2 < -1$ since $-2 = -1 - 1$. Also $-1 > -2$ since $-1 = -2 + 1$.
(b) $7 > 3$ since $7 = 3 + 4$. Also $3 < 7$ since $3 = 7 - 4$.

3.1.3   When two numerals are connected by the equal symbol, "=," the resulting statement is called an **equation**. For example, $5 + 2 = 7$ and $5 - 2 = 7$ are called equations but $5 + 2 - 7$ is not. When two numerals or expressions are connected by the greater than or less than symbol, the statement is called an **inequality**. For example, $5 - 2 < 7$ and $5 + 2 > 7$ are called inequalities but $5 - 2 \neq 7$ is not. ($5 - 2 \neq 7$ is read "five minus two is not equal to seven.") Of course, if two numerals or expressions name numbers which are not equal, then they must be related by an inequality.

It should be quite clear from the examples of the previous paragraph that what we say and write may be **true** or may be **false**. The equation $5 + 2 = 7$ is true while $5 - 2 = 7$ is false. The inequality $5 - 2 < 7$ is true while $5 + 2 > 7$ is false. Denying a false statement will result in a true statement; since $5 - 2 = 7$ is false we have $5 - 2 \neq 7$ is true. Since $5 + 2 > 7$ is false, we have $5 + 2 \not> 7$ is true. Given any two numerals, say $5 + 2$ and $5 - 2$, **exactly one** of the following statements are true: $5 + 2 < 5 - 2$, $5 + 2 = 5 - 2$, $5 + 2 > 5 - 2$. ($5 + 2 > 5 - 2$ is true.) If we deny all three statements: $5 + 2 \not< 5 - 2$, $5 + 2 \neq 5 - 2$, $5 + 2 \not> 5 - 2$, then exactly one must be false. ($5 + 2 \not> 5 - 2$ is false.) In mathematics it is just as easy to make false statements as true statements. We will usually be interested in true statements.

Practice 1.

1. Determine which of the following are expressions, which are equations, and which are inequalities.

(a) $3 + 4 = 8$ (b) $3 + 5 - 8$ (c) $3 < 5 - 8$ (d) $3 + 5 > 8$
(e) $7 - 2 < 9$ (f) $7 + 2 = 9$ (g) $7 - 2 + 9$ (h) $7 + 2 > 9$
(i) $9 + 4 - 6$ (j) $9 > 6 - 4$ (k) $9 = 4 + 6$ (l) $9 < 4 + 6$.

2. Which of the equations and inequalities in Practice Exercise 1 are true?

3. Connect (relate) each of the following pairs of numerals with exactly one of $<$, $=$, or $>$ to form a true statement:

(a) $5 + 0$ and $0 - 5$ (b) $3 + 7$ and 9 (c) 0 and $5 - 3$
(d) $3 + 3$ and $7 - 1$ (e) $1 - 4$ and $4 - 1$ (f) $0 + 5$ and $5 - 0$
(g) $3 - 3$ and $0 - 6$ (h) $3 + 5$ and $5 + 3$ (i) $7 - 2$ and $2 + 7$
(j) $3 - (2 + 1)$ and 2 (k) $3 + (2 - 1)$ and 4 (l) $3 - (2 - 1)$ and 0.

4. Find the simplest numeral for the following expressions and form a true equation:

(a) $4 + (2 - 5)$ (b) $4 - (2 + 5)$ (c) $4 - (2 - 5)$ (d) $(4 - 2) - 5$
(e) $(7 - 3) + 4$ (f) $7 - (3 + 4)$ (g) $(3 - 4) + 7$ (h) $3 - (4 + 7)$
(i) $9 + (1 + 6)$ (j) $(1 + 9) + 6$ (k) $6 + (1 - 9)$ (l) $9 - (1 + 6)$.

5. Which of the following statements are true, which are false?

(a) $9 - 5 = 3$ (b) $3 + 6 = 2 + 7$ (c) $6 + 3 \neq 3 + 6$
(d) $1 + 5 = 3 + 3$ (e) $7 + 8 \neq 9 + 3$ (f) $5 + 7 = 4 + 9$
(g) $7 + 0 = 1 + 6$ (h) $3 + 0 \neq 3 - 0$ (i) $3 + 6 = 6 + 3$
(j) $1 + 1 \neq 1 - 1$ (k) $4 + 9 = 7 + 5$ (l) $7 - 5 = 5 - 7$.

6. Which of the following inequalities are true, which are false?

(a) $7 + 2 > 8$ (b) $7 - 2 < 6$ (c) $7 - 2 < 2 - 7$
(d) $7 + 2 > 2 + 7$ (e) $-5 < 0 - 6$ (f) $3 > 6 - 4$
(g) $0 < 1 - 0$ (h) $0 > 1 + 0$.

7. Which of the following equations are true, which are false?

(a) $5 - 5 = 10$ (b) $13 - (6 + 7) = 0$ (c) $0 + 18 = 18$

(d) $-7 + 4 = 3$ (e) $21 - (15 - 6) = 0$ (f) $(7 - 9) + 5 = 3$

(g) $3 + 9 = ?$ (h) $7 + ? = 4$ (i) $27 - ? = 12$

(j) $31 - 15 = ?$ (k) $2 + ? = ? + 2$ (l) $8 - ? = 2 + ?$

Answers.

1. (a) equation   (b) expression   (c) inequality
   (d) inequality   (e) inequality   (f) equation
   (g) expression   (h) inequality   (i) expression
   (j) inequality   (k) equation   (l) inequality.

2. (a) false   (b) —   (c) false   (d) false   (e) true
   (f) true   (g) —   (h) false   (i) —   (j) true
   (k) false   (l) true.

3. (a) $5 + 0 > 0 - 5$ (b) $3 + 7 > 9$ (c) $0 < 5 - 3$
   (d) $3 + 3 = 7 - 1$ (e) $1 - 4 < 4 - 1$ (f) $0 + 5 = 5 - 0$
   (g) $3 - 3 > 0 - 6$ (h) $3 + 5 = 5 + 3$ (i) $7 - 2 < 2 + 7$
   (j) $3 - (2 + 1) < 2$ (k) $3 + (2 - 1) = 4$ (l) $3 - (2 - 1) > 0$.

4. (a) $1 = 4 + (2 - 5)$ (b) $-3 = 4 - (2 + 5)$ (c) $7 = 4 - (2 - 5)$
   (d) $-3 = (4 - 2) - 5$ (e) $8 = (7 - 3) + 4$ (f) $0 = 7 - (3 + 4)$
   (g) $6 = (3 - 4) + 7$ (h) $-8 = 3 - (4 + 7)$ (i) $16 = 9 + (1 + 6)$
   (j) $16 = (1 + 9) + 6$ (k) $-2 = 6 + (1 - 9)$ (l) $2 = 9 - (1 + 6)$.

5. (a) false   (b) true   (c) false   (d) true   (e) true
   (f) false   (g) true   (h) false   (i) true   (j) true
   (k) false   (l) false.

6. (a) true   (b) true   (c) false   (d) false   (e) false
   (f) true   (g) true   (h) false.

7. (a) false   (b) true   (c) true   (d) false   (e) false
   (f) true   (g) through (l) no answers, see following discussion.

3.1.4   The last six questions of Practice Exercise 7 above should puzzle you for the equations are neither true nor false as they stand. If the question marks stand for numerals, then the truth or falsity of the statements would depend upon the particular numeral that the question mark stood for. In 7(g), if ? stands for "12," then $3 + 9 = ?$ would be a true equation. That is, $3 + 9 = 12$ is a true equation. If we write "11" for ? in the equation, then since $3 + 9 \neq 11$, the equation $3 + 9 = 11$ is false. In a similar manner, we could ask "What must ? stand for in the following equations to make each true?"

Answers.

7. (g) If ? is 12 in $3 + 9 = ?$, then the resulting equation $3 + 9 = 12$ is true. If ? stands for any other number, then the equation $3 + 9 = ?$ will be false.

(h) If -3 is written for ? in $7 + ? = 4$, then the resulting equation $7 + (-3) = 4$ is true. If any other number is **substituted** for ? in $7 + ? = 4$, the resulting equation would be false, for example let $? = 3$, then $7 + 3 = 4$ is false.

(i) To have $27 - ? = 12$ result in a true equation we must substitute 15 for ?. Thus, $27 - 15 = 12$ is true. Notice that if $27 - ? = 12$, then $27 = ? + 12$ and $27 - 12 = ?$ so that $? = 15$.

(j) When we write 16 for ? in $31 - 15 = ?$, the resulting equation, $31 - 15 = 16$ is true. When we discover a number which makes an equation true, we say that we have **solved** the equation.

(k) If ? is 7 in $2 + ? = ? + 2$, then the resulting equation $2 + 7 = 7 + 2$ is true. Thus, 7 is a **solution** of $2 + ? = ? + 2$. If ? is 13 in $2 + ? = ? + 2$, then $2 + 13 = 13 + 2$ is true. If the same number is substituted for ? in $2 + ? = ? + 2$, the resulting equation will be true. (Try it!) That is, every number when substituted for both ?'s in $2 + ? = ? + 2$ will result in a true equation. Thus, every number is a solution for $2 + ? = ? + 2$. However, if we substitute a different number for each ? in $2 + ? = ? + 2$, the resulting equation will be false. For example, $2 + 5 = 7 + 2$ is false.

(l) If ? stands for the same number in $8 - ? = 2 + ?$, we can try various numbers to see whether they result in solutions. That is, in true equations. For example, let ? stand for 1, then $8 - 1 = 2 + 1$ or $7 = 3$ which is a false equation. If ? stands for 2, then $8 - 2 = 2 + 2$ which is false. If ? stands for 3, then $8 - 3 = 2 + 3$ or $5 = 5$ which is true. If ? stands for 4, then $8 - 4 = 2 + 4$ or $4 = 6$ which is false. To summarize, we can form a simple table:

?	left	right	true or false
1	7	3	false
2	6	4	false
3	5	5	true
4	4	6	false

Thus, 3 is a solution of $8 - ? = 2 + ?$. Rather than using a judicious trial and error method, we might observe that we can write a somewhat more elegant "mathematical composition" to find the solution.

Given that $8 - ? = 2 + ?$ we must have $8 = (?) + (2 + ?)$. But if $8 = (?) + (2 + ?)$ then $8 = (?) + (? + 2) = (? + ?) + 2$ so that we have $8 - 2 = ? + ?$. Now $8 - 2 = 6$ so that 6 must be twice ? in order that we have a true equation. Thus, $? = 3$ will result in $8 - 3 = 2 + 3$ or $5 = 5$ a true equation and 3 is a solution of $8 - ? = 2 + ?$.

Reflecting on our discussion, we should notice that the ideas in mathematics are revealed in the writing just as English reveals our ideas concerning a situation. We can think of mathematics as a particular language suitable for many special situations. As in any language, however, we must have a suitable "alphabet," "words," "phrases," and "grammar" to enable us to effectively communicate our thoughts.

In using equations it is often convenient to reserve places for numerals. Rather than using the awkward question marks, we commonly use letters from the alphabet. When letters are used in this way they are called **variables**. For example, in Exercise 7 (g)–(l) we could have written:

7. (g) $3 + 9 = N$ (h) $7 + N = 4$ (i) $27 - N = 12$
   (j) $31 - 15 = M$ (k) $2 + A = A + 2$ (l) $8 - K = 2 + K$

where "N," "M," "A," and "K" stand for, or reserve spaces for numerals. Since a letter, such as N, is not a numeral it is sometimes referred to as a **pronumeral** or **literal**. If a letter, that is, a variable occurs in an equation, we are often interested in finding a number which when substituted for the variable will make the equation true. The number which makes such an equation true is then called a **solution** of the equation. For example, $3 + 9 = N$ has the variable N. If we substitute 12 for N, the equation will be true. Thus, 12 is called a solution of $3 + 9 = N$.

Examples.

(a) $N + 12 = 17$ has the solution $N = 5$ since $5 + 12 = 17$ is true. We can also write: If $N + 12 = 17$, then $N = 17 - 12$ so that $N = 5$.

(b) $14 - N = 9$ is true for $N = 5$ so that 5 is a solution of the equation. We can also reason that if $14 - N = 9$ is to be true, we must have $14 = N + 9$ and $14 - 9 = N$ so that $N = 5$.

(c) $N - 23 = 9 + N$ has no solution since we have $N = 23 + (9 + N)$ which leads us to $N = 32 + N$ or $N - N = 32$. That is, $0 = 32$, which is false.

(d) $19 - (N + 7) = 22$ requires that $N + 7 = -3$ in order to be true. But if $N + 7 = -3$, then $N = -10$. Now substituting -10 for N we have

$19 - (-10 + 7) = 19 - (-3) = 19 + 3 = 22$ and $22 = 22$ is true so that $N = -10$ is a solution of the equation $19 - (N + 7) = 22$.

(e) The equation $3 + N = (7 + N) - 4$ is true for any integer N since we have $(3 + N) + 4 = 7 + N$ and $7 + N = 7 + N$ or $N = N$ is always true. Thus, every integer is a solution of $3 + N = (7 + N) - 4$.

Of course, struggling haphazardly to find solutions to equations can be a tedious if not downright discouraging activity. Some equations may have no solution, others may have many solutions. The equations may be quite complicated, there may be two or more different variables involved in one equation. In order to overcome many of these difficulties, it is helpful and practical to study and develop various standard techniques for finding solutions to equations with variables.

As we proceed we will discover that equations with variables are powerful tools for describing and studying many interesting situations.

Exercises

1. In the statement $7 - (9 + 4) = -6$ the symbol "=" is a _____ symbol while "7," "9," and "4" are _____. The symbols "−" and "+" indicate _____ while "(" and ")" indicate grouping and tell us to _____ 9 and 4 first before _____ the sum from 7. The prefix symbol "−" used in writing −6 indicates a _____ number.

2. Describe in ordinary words what the following expressions "say" and find the simplest proper numeral for the expression.
   (a) $(15 - 8) + 3$ (b) $15 - (8 + 3)$
   (c) $9 + [7 - (5 + 1)]$ (d) $[(5 - 2) + 7] - 9$
   (e) $(6 - 2) - (4 + 2)$ (f) $[(6 - 2) - 4] + 2$.

3. Which of the following are expressions, which are equations, which are inequalities?
   (a) $9 - 2 = 2 - 9$ (b) $9 - 2 > 2 - 9$ (c) $9 - 2 < 2 - 9$
   (d) $9 - 2 + 7$ (e) $2 + (9 - 7)$ (f) $9 - 2 = 7$
   (g) $2 - 9 < 7$ (h) $9 - 2 > 0$ (i) $9 - 2 = -(2 - 9)$.

4. Which of the equations and inequalities in Exercise 3 above are true?

5. Rewrite the following inequalities as true equations by adding or subtracting an appropriate positive integer.
   (a) $7 < 12$ (b) $9 > 5$ (c) $-3 < 0$ (d) $-2 > -7$.

6. How many integers are there between the pairs of integers connected by the inequalities in Exercise 5 above? For example, there are 4 between 7 and 12.

7. Write the following as true inequalities:

(a) $4 + 7 \neq 9 - 6$　　(b) $5 - 2 \neq 2 - 5$　　(c) $2 - 4 \neq 5 - 6$

(d) $0 - 1 \neq 1 - 0$　　(e) $4 - 4 \neq 4 + 4$　　(f) $6 + 8 \neq 9 - 1$.

8. Which of the following are equations?

(a) $7 + 6 - N$　　(b) $7 + 6 = N$　　(c) $4 - 1 = 5$

(d) $4 - 1, 5$　　(e) $N = 4$　　(f) 365

(g) $4 - 1 < 5$　　(h) $N + 4 > 3$　　(i) $5 - N = 2$.

9. Rewrite the true inequalities obtained in Exercise 7 above as true equations by adding or subtracting an appropriate positive integer.

10. Which of the following equations are true? False? Which are neither true nor false?

(a) $17 - 9 = 12$　　(b) $9 + 12 = 21$　　(c) $0 - 6 = 6 - 0$

(d) $6 + 0 = 0 + 6$　　(e) $N + 5 = 5 + N$　　(f) $N - 3 = -3 + N$

(g) $7 - 4 = -(4 - 7)$　　(h) $N - 5 = 5 - N$　　(i) $23 + N = 23$

(j) $N + 0 = N$　　(k) $N + 7 = N - 7$　　(l) $A + B = 9 - C$.

11. If $N = 9$ is a true equation, then which of the following equations will be true?

(a) $N - 9 = 0$　　(b) $N + 9 = 0$　　(c) $9 - N = 9$

(d) $9 + N = -9$　　(e) $9 - N = 0$　　(f) $9 + N = 0$

(g) $N - 9 = 9$　　(h) $0 + N = 9$　　(i) $N - 0 = 9$.

12. If $N = 17$ is true, then which of the following equations will be true?

(a) $23 - N = 6$　　(b) $N + 9 = 8$　　(c) $N - 9 = 8$

(d) $N + 15 = 2$　　(e) $N + 34 = 51$　　(f) $11 + N = 6$

(g) $N - 7 = 10$　　(h) $N - 17 = 0$　　(i) $14 = N - 31$.

13. If $N = 6$ is true, then which of the following equations will be false?

(a) $6 - N = 0$　　(b) $0 - N = 6$　　(c) $N - 6 = 0$

(d) $N - 0 = 6$　　(e) $N + 6 = 0$　　(f) $0 + N = 6$

(g) $6 = N - 6$　　(h) $0 = 6 - N$　　(i) $-6 = 0 - N$.

14. Find a number for the variable which will make the equation true.

(a) $N + 5 = 9$　　(b) $4 + M = -2$　　(c) $8 = K + 8$

(d) $16 = 5 + A$　　(e) $S - 11 = 27$　　(f) $7 - T = 3$

(g) $12 = B - 9$　　(h) $-7 = -9 - N$　　(i) $X + 11 = 3$.

15. Solve the following equations and check by substituting in the equation to verify its truth.

(a) $N + 31 = 50$　　(b) $16 + N = 9$　　(c) $37 = 37 + M$

(d) $28 = 2 + M$　　(e) $-31 = K + 31$　　(f) $17 + K = 0$

(g) $-41 + X = 15$　　(h) $64 = -4 + X$　　(i) $Y + 0 = -8$

(j) $11 = 0 + Y$　　(k) $-11 = -15 + T$　　(l) $-9 + T = -9$.

Answers.

1. connective, numerals; operations, add, subtracting; negative.

2. (a) Find the difference between 15 and 8 then add 3; 10.

(b) Subtract the sum of 8 and 3 from 15; 4.

(c) Subtract the sum of 5 and 1 from 7, then add this difference to 9; 10.

(d) Subtract 2 from 5, add 7, then subtract 9; 1.

(e) Subtract 2 from 6, find the sum of 4 and 2, then subtract the sum from the difference; −2.

(f) Subtract 2 from 6, subtract 4 from the difference and then add 2; 2.

3. (a) equation   (b) inequality   (c) inequality
   (d) expression   (e) expression   (f) equation
   (g) inequality   (h) inequality   (i) equation.

4. (a) false   (b) true   (c) false   (d) −   (e) −   (f) true
   (g) true   (h) true   (i) true.

5. (a) $7 = 12 - 5$ (b) $9 = 5 + 4$ (c) $-3 = 0 - 3$
   (d) $-2 = -7 + 5$.

6. (a) 4   (b) 3   (c) 2   (d) 4.

7. (a) $4 + 7 > 9 - 6$ (b) $5 - 2 > 2 - 5$ (c) $2 - 4 < 5 - 6$
   (d) $0 - 1 < 1 - 0$ (e) $4 - 4 < 4 + 4$ (f) $6 + 8 > 9 - 1$.

8. (b), (c), (e), and (i) are equations.

9. (a) $4 + 7 = (9 - 6) + 8$ (b) $5 - 2 = (2 - 5) + 6$
   (c) $2 - 4 = (5 - 6) - 1$ (d) $0 - 1 = (1 - 0) - 2$
   (e) $4 - 4 = (4 + 4) - 8$ (f) $6 + 8 = (9 - 1) + 6$.

10. (a) false   (b) true   (c) false   (d) true   (e) true   (f) true
    (g) true   (h) neither   (i) neither   (j) true   (k) false
    (l) neither.

11. (a), (e), (h), and (i) will be true.

12. (a), (c), (e), (g), and (h) will be true.

13. (b), (e), and (g) will be false.

14. (a) $N = 4$ (b) $M = -6$ (c) $K = 0$ (d) $A = 11$
    (e) $S = 38$ (f) $T = 4$ (g) $B = 21$ (h) $N = -2$
    (i) $X = -8$.

15. (a) $N = 19$, $19 + 31 = 50$ (b) $N = -7$, $16 + (-7) = 9$
    (c) $M = 0$, $37 = 37 + 0$ (d) $M = 26$, $28 = 2 + 26$
    (e) $K = -62$, $-31 = (-62) + 31$ (f) $K = -17$, $17 + (-17) = 0$
    (g) $X = 56$, $-41 + 56 = 15$ (h) $X = 68$, $64 = -4 + 68$
    (i) $Y = -8$, $-8 + 0 = -8$ (j) $Y = 11$, $11 = 0 + 11$
    (k) $T = 4$, $-11 = -15 + 4$ (l) $T = 0$, $-9 + 0 = -9$.

3.2 Descriptions

3.2.1 Using variables we can describe many of the properties of numbers, operations, equations, and general types of situations.

Examples.

(a) Let N stand for any natural number. Then $N + 1$ is the name of the successor of N, and N, $N + 1$, $N + 2$ name three consecutive natural numbers.

(b) Let A be any integer (meaning that A will hold a place for any integer and that any integer may be substituted for A). Then $A + 0 = A$ and $A - 0 = A$ are true.

(c) If A and B are any two integers, then exactly one of the following statements are true: $A < B$, $A = B$, $A > B$.

(d) To describe the sum of the first N consecutive natural numbers, we could write

$$1 + 2 + 3 + \cdots + (N - 2) + (N - 1) + N = \frac{N(N + 1)}{2},$$

where the expression on the right of the equals symbol has yet to be explained and discussed.

Although the study of generalized patterns of computations through the use of variables is usually reserved for that branch of mathematics called **algebra**, we will briefly discuss and develop some of the ideas suggested by the above examples.

In using a variable, notice that there is a restriction placed on the set of numbers which can be substituted for the variable. For example, when we write "Let N stand for any natural number" we restrict our substitutions in, say $N + 1$, to natural numbers like 1, 2, 3, and so forth, and do not allow non-natural numbers like -1, -2, and 0. With the same restriction, the equation $N + 3 = 0$ would have no solution. When we extend the natural numbers to the integers, $N + 3 = 0$ has the solution -3. If we ask "What are the natural numbers $N < 3$?" our answer should be "N can equal 1 or 2." But if we ask "What are the integers $N < 3$?" our answer should be "There are many integers which will make the inequality true. For example, 2, 1, 0, -1, -2, ..." For convenience, the restricted set of numbers which can be substituted for a variable will be called the **permissible set** or **domain** of the variable. When referring to the solutions to equations or inequalities, we call the set of numbers which make an equation or inequality true the **solution set** of the equation or inequality. Notice that the solution set must always be a subset of the permissible set for the variable.

A variable can be used to describe general elements in sets of numbers. For example, our use of N, $N + 1$, $N + 2$ to describe any three consecutive natural numbers for N, an arbitrary natural number. We can describe a number which is "three less than four more than an unknown natural number" by $(N + 4) - 3$. To indicate a way of specifying multiples of natural numbers, let us examine a few examples.

The multiples of two:

2	2	one 2	1(2)
4	$2 + 2$	two 2's	2(2)
6	$2 + 2 + 2$	three 2's	3(2)
8	$2 + 2 + 2 + 2$	four 2's	4(2)
10	$2 + 2 + 2 + 2 + 2$	five 2's	5(2)
.	. . .	. . .	. . .

If N is the number of 2's, we can write $N(2)$ or, since it will cause no ambiguity, $2N$ for any multiple of 2. To obtain eight 2's we set $N = 8$ and have $8(2) = 2(8) = 16$. Notice our careful use of parentheses to avoid writing $82 = 28 = 16$.

The multiples of five:

5	5	one 5	1(5)
10	$5 + 5$	two 5's	2(5)
15	$5 + 5 + 5$	three 5's	3(5)
20	$5 + 5 + 5 + 5$	four 5's	4(5)
25	$5 + 5 + 5 + 5 + 5$	five 5's	5(5)
.	. . .	. . .	. . .

If N is the number of 5's, we can write $N(5)$ or $5N$ for any multiple of 5. For seven 5's we would have $N = 7$ so that $7(5) = 35$. Thus, if N is any natural number, we can describe the multiples of the natural numbers with

$$2N \text{ is a multiple of 2,}$$
$$3N \text{ is a multiple of 3,}$$
$$4N \text{ is a multiple of 4,}$$
$$. . .$$

Recalling that the even numbers were the same as the multiples of 2 we have for any natural number N, $2N$ is an even number. Can we describe an odd number? Yes; if $2N$ is even, then $2N - 1$ is odd. Of course we could have written $2N + 1$, but then would $2N + 1 = 1$ for some natural number N? (No.)

3.2.2   When variables occur in equations, the equations are always true, only true for certain substitutions, or always false for any number in the permissible set for the variable.

Examples.   For N any integer,

(a) $N + 0 = N$ is always true regardless of the integer substituted for N.

(b) $N + 3 = 0$ is true only for $N = -3$. Otherwise the equation is false. For example, if $N = 0$, then $N + 3 = 0$ is false.

(c) $5N - 1 = 7$ is always false regardless of the integer substituted for N.

For convenience, we name these three types of equations:

(a) A **universally true** equation (or **identically true** equation) is any equation which is true for every substitution of a number from its permissible set. For example, for A and B integers $A + B = B + A$ is a universally true equation.

(b) A **conditional** equation (or **conditionally true** equation) is any equation which can be made true and also false by substitutions from its permissible set. For example, $3 - N = 5$ is true for $N = -2$ and false for $N = 0$, where the permissible set is the set of integers.

(c) A **universally false** equation is any equation which is false for every substitution from its permissible set. For example, if N is a natural number, $3 - N = 5$ is a universally false equation. If K is any integer, then $3K = 7$ is a universally false equation.

3.2.3 Using a few universally true equations, we can describe the properties of addition and subtraction of integers. These are briefly summarized as follows:

Properties of Addition and Subtraction of Integers

1. If A and B are integers, then there are always integers S and D such that $A + B = S$ and $A + D = B$ $(D = B - A)$. This is called the **closure property** of addition and subtraction of integers.

Examples.

(a) If $A = 8$ and $B = 3$, then $8 + 3 = 11$ so that $S = 11$ and also since $A + (-5) = B$, we have $D = -5$.

(b) If $A = 5$ and $B = -7$, then $A + B = -2 = S$ and $5 + D = -7$ for $D = -12$.

2. If A and B are integers, then $A + B = B + A$. This is called the **commutative property** of addition of integers.

Examples.

(a) $7 + 2 = 2 + 7$ (b) $14 + (-26) = -26 + 14$.

3. If A and B are integers, then $A - B = -(B - A)$. This is called the **anticommutative property** of subtraction of integers.

Examples.

(a) $7 - 2 = -(2 - 7)$ (b) $14 - (-26) = -(-26 - 14)$
(c) $-9 - 5 = -[5 - (-9)]$ (d) $-3 - (-7) = -[-7 - (-3)]$
(e) If we set $A = 0$ and $B < 0$, for example $0 - (-7)$, we have
$0 - (-7) = -(7 - 0) = -(-7) = 7$. That is, $-(-C) = C$ for every integer C.

4. If A, B, and C are integers, then $A + (B + C) = (A + B) + C$. This is called the **associative property** of addition of integers.

Examples.

(a) $4 + (6 + 9) = (4 + 6) + 9$.
(b) $-7 + [2 + (-4)] = (-7 + 2) + (-4)$.
(c) $5 + (-5 + 9) = [5 + (-5)] + 9$.
(d) But $4 - (7 - 9) \neq (4 - 7) - 9$. That is, **subtraction is not associative** in general. Of course, we might rewrite a subtraction as the addition of integers with the appropriate changes: $4 - (7 - 9) = 4 + [-(7 - 9)] = 4 + (9 - 7) = 4 + [9 + (-7)] = (4 + 9) + (-7)$. Now we could note that $4 - (7 - 9) = (4 - 7) + 9$. That is, $A - (B - C) = (A - B) + C$. Also, $(A - B) - C = A - (B + C)$.

5. If A is any integer, then $A + 0 = A$. The number 0 is called the **identity** of addition of integers.

Examples.

(a) $14 + 0 = 14$ (b) $-6 + 0 = -6$ (c) $0 + 0 = 0$
(d) Notice that we have $14 = 14 - 0$, $-6 = -6 - 0$, $0 = -0$ so that for any integer A, $A - 0 = A$.

6. If A is any integer, then there is another integer I such that $A + I = 0$. Notice that $I = -A$. The number I is called the **inverse** of A under addition of integers.

Examples.

(a) If $A = 21$, then since $21 + (-21) = 0$ we have $I = -21$.
(b) If $A = -7$, then since $-7 + 7 = 0$, $I = 7$.
(c) If $A = 7$, then $I = -7$ so that we can note that an integer and its negative are inverses of each other under addition of integers.

Learning to use variables and to recognize the "patterns" in writing is an important and practical part of developing mathematical skills and understanding. According to the famous British mathematician and philosopher, Alfred North Whitehead (1861–1947), the symbols in mathematics have not been introduced to make things incomprehensible and difficult; . . . "On the contrary they have invariably been introduced to make things easy." . . . , ". . . the symbolism is invariably an immense simplification." . . . ". . . it represents an analysis of the ideas of the subject and an almost pictorial representation of their relations to each other."

Practice 1.

1. Use the variable N to write mathematical expressions for the following:
 (a) A natural number which is seven more than three less than N.
 (b) Three less than a multiple of seven.
 (c) Five less a multiple of three.
 (d) Three consecutive odd numbers.
 (e) An element in the set of numerals used in counting by 7's beginning with 3.
 (f) An element in the set of numerals used in counting by 4's beginning with 7.
2. Do as in Practice Exercise 1 with:
 (a) Three more than a natural number is equal to eleven.
 (b) Four less than a number is greater than nine.
 (c) Two more than a multiple of five is less than eight.
 (d) The set of odd numbers between 10 and 20.
 (e) Five more than a number is between −5 and 5.
 (f) Two less than a number is less than 5 which is less than two more than the number.
3. Determine which of the following equations are universally true, conditionally true, or universally false; if N is an integer such that $-4 < N < 4$.
 (a) $N + 3 = 0$ (b) $N - 3 = 2$ (c) $N - 0 = N$
 (d) $N + 3 = 2$ (e) $2 - N = N - 2$ (f) $N + 2 = 2 + N$
 (g) $5 - N = N - 5$.
4. Determine which of the properties of addition or subtraction is best illustrated by each of the following equations.
 (a) $29 + 0 = 29$ (b) $1 + (3 + 5) = (1 + 3) + 5$
 (c) $15 + 0 = 0 + 15$ (d) $-7 + 9 = 2$

(e) $9 - 7 = -(7 - 9)$ (f) $-7 + 7 = 7 + (-7)$
(g) $15 = 0 + 15$ (h) $24 - 24 = 0$
(i) $-3 + 3 = 0$ (j) $(-5 + 2) + (-4) = -5 + (2 - 4)$
(k) $-9 - 2 = -(2 + 9)$ (l) $59 + 14 = 73$.

Answers.

1. (a) $(N - 3) + 7$ (b) $7N - 3$ (c) $5 - 3N$
   (d) $2N - 1, 2N + 1, 2N + 3$ (e) $7N - 4$ (f) $4N + 3$.
2. (a) $N + 3 = 11$ (b) $N - 4 > 9$ (c) $5N + 2 < 8$
   (d) $10 < 2N - 1 < 20$ (e) $-5 < N + 5 < 5$
   (f) $N - 2 < 5 < N + 2$.
3. (a) conditional   (b) universally false   (c) universally true
   (d) conditional   (e) conditional   (f) universally true
   (g) universally false.
4. (a) identity   (b) associative   (c) commutative
   (d) closure   (e) anticommutative   (f) commutative
   (g) identity   (h) inverse   (i) inverse
   (j) associative   (k) anticommutative   (l) closure.

3.2.4   We have noted that finding solutions to (conditional) equations can be a tedious, if not downright discouraging, activity, if done by the method of guessing. Thus, rather than guessing solutions and checking, let us consider developing a more efficient and well regulated procedure for solving equations. How do we begin? By studying a few simple and easy examples.

Example 1.   To study the process for solving $N + 9 = 131$.

120   121   122   123   124   125   126   127   128   129   130   131   132

$$N \qquad + \qquad 9 \qquad = \qquad 131$$

We observe that 131 is 9 more than N. If we subtract 9 from both sides of the equation, $N + 9 = 131$, then we would be "undoing" what adding the 9 has done to N. That is, we can write $(N + 9) - 9 = 131 - 9$. But $(N + 9) - 9 = N + (9 - 9) = N$ and $131 - 9 = 122$ so that $N = 122$ must be true. Checking, $122 + 9 = 131$ is true, so that $N = 122$ is, in fact, a solution of $N + 9 = 131$.

Notice the steps taken:

   (a) In order to "isolate" N by itself we subtracted 9, the amount which had been added to N.

   (b) To compensate for our subtraction of 9 on the left we subtracted the same amount, 9, from the right. That is, we "acted" in the same way on both sides of the equation.

(c) We applied some known properties of addition and subtraction to obtain N on the left and 122 on the right.

(d) Knowing that the equation must be true to have a solution, we concluded that $N = 122$ and checked to verify our finding.

Example 2. To study the process for solving $N - 21 = 36$.

36   38   40   42   44   46   48   50   52   54   56   58   60   62   64

36   = (-21) + N

Observe that we can write $N - 21 = N + (-21) = (-21) + N$.

If we notice that the subtraction can be changed to the addition of the inverse element, then we can apply our observations from Example 1 to solve this equation. That is, we "isolate" the variable by "undoing" what has been done. Thus, we have $[N + (-21)] - (-21) = N + (-21 + 21) = N$ and $36 - (-21) = 36 + 21 = 57$ so that $N = 57$. Checking, $57 - 21 = 36$ is true so that $N = 57$ is a solution of $N - 21 = 36$.

On the other hand, can we "undo" subtraction? Yes, by adding! Thus, we add as much as has been subtracted to obtain $(N - 21) + 21 = N + (-21 + 21) = N + 0 = N$ and $36 + 21 = 57$ so that we have $N = 57$.

Notice the steps taken:

(a) In order to "undo" subtraction we added.

(b) This action of ours "isolated" the variable.

(c) Acting the same way on both sides of the equation, we used known properties of addition and subtraction to obtain a solution of the equation.

(d) Checking: if $N = 57$, then $N - 21 = 36$ is true so that $N = 57$ is in fact a solution of $N - 21 = 36$.

Example 3. To study the process for solving $23 - N = 14$.

12   13   14   15   16   17   18   19   20   21   22   23   24   25   26   27

14   = $(-N)$ +   23

We might avoid the issue by noting that $23 - N = 23 + (-N) = -N + 23$ so that we have $-N + 23 = 14$ and $-N = 14 - 23 = -9$ so $N = 9$ is a solution of $23 - N = 14$.

However, for this example, let us consider our work step-by-step to determine "what goes on."

(a) We are given the equation $23 - N = 14$ to solve.

(b) We can "undo" the subtraction by adding:
$$(23 - N) + N = 14 + N.$$
The same "unknown" amount is added on both sides of the equation.

(c) We can then apply our knowledge of addition and subtraction to obtain
$$23 + (-N + N) = 14 + N.$$

(d) But $-N + N = 0$ for any integer, so that we have
$$23 + 0 = 14 + N.$$

(e) And since $23 + 0 = 23$, we can write
$$23 = 14 + N.$$

(f) Now "undoing" the addition by subtracting
$$23 - 14 = (14 + N) - 14.$$

(g) We can manipulate the expressions, using the properties of addition and subtraction to obtain
$$9 = N.$$

(h) But, if $N = 9$, we have
$$23 - 9 = 14 \text{ is a true equation!}$$

(i) Thus, $N = 9$ is a solution of $23 - N = 14$.

What have we noted in the examples? Are useful principles and ideas suggested in our discussion? Can we "pick out" and summarize the important ideas and procedures?

First, is there a general "pattern" to these examples?

(a) We have a given conditional equation to solve.

(b) We try to "isolate" the variable.

(c) Subtraction "undoes" addition and addition "undoes" subtraction.

(d) We must "act" in the same way on both sides of an equation.

(e) Known properties of addition and subtraction can be applied to the expressions.

(f) Once the variable has been "isolated" we check to verify that we have found a solution to the given equation.

Second, is there an organization, a succession of steps which can be followed in solving an equation? Briefly, to save space, we might have written Examples 1 through 3 as follows:

Example 1.   Solve $N + 9 = 131$.

WORK.
$$(N + 9) - 9 = 131 - 9$$
$$N + (9 - 9) = 122$$
$$N + 0 = 122$$
$$N = 122 \text{ solution.}$$

CHECK.
$$122 + 9 = 131 \text{ is true.}$$

Example 2.   Solve $N - 21 = 36$.

WORK.
$$(N - 21) + 21 = 36 + 21$$
$$N + [(-21) + 21] = 57$$
$$N + 0 = 57$$
$$N = 57 \text{ solution.}$$

CHECK.
$$57 - 21 = 36 \text{ is true.}$$

Example 3.   Solve $23 - N = 14$.

WORK.
$$(23 - N) + N = 14 + N$$
$$23 + [(-N) + N] = 14 + N$$
$$23 + 0 = 14 + N$$
$$23 = 14 + N$$
$$23 - 14 = (N + 14) - 14$$
$$9 = N + (14 - 14)$$
$$9 = N + 0$$
$$9 = N \text{ or } N = 9 \text{ solution.}$$

CHECK.
$$23 - 9 = 14 \text{ is true.}$$

In each example we obtained a succession of equations. Each successive equation was obtained from the preceding equation by using universally true properties of operations and equations. Thus, when any one of the equations in such a succession of equations is true, the others are also. If any one of the equations is false, the others in the succession will also be false. (Providing, of course, that the steps in our reasoning have been correct.) The equations will all be true or all be false together. When two or more equations are related in this way we say that they are **equivalent**. Thus, in solving equations, we can proceed by looking for simpler equivalent equations which might lead to a solution.

Third, have we used definite principles in solving the conditional equations? Yes, two general principles can be stated.

The Principle of Equal Addition: If A, B, and C are numbers and $A = B$, then $A + C = B + C$.

Examples.

(a) $2 + 3 = 5$ so that $(2 + 3) + 9 = 5 + 9$.
(b) If $N - 7 = 14$, then $(N - 7) + 7 = 14 + 7$.

The Principle of Equal Subtraction: If A, B, and C are numbers and $A = B$, then $A - C = B - C$.

Examples.

(a) $2 + 3 = 5$ so that $(2 + 3) - 9 = 5 - 9$.
(b) If $N + 7 = 14$, then $(N + 7) - 7 = 14 - 7$.

As a final example, we illustrated how the solution of a given conditional equation might be written and justified.

Example 4. To solve $7 - (N - 12) = 37$ and give justifications for each step in the solution.

The Equations	The Justifications
$7 - (N - 12) = 37$	The given equation.
$[7 - (N - 12)] + (N - 12) = 37 + (N - 12)$	Equal addition.
$7 + [-(N - 12) + (N - 12)] = (N - 12) + 37$	Subtracting is the same as adding the negative, the associative, and commutative properties of addition.
$7 + 0 = N + (-12 + 37)$	Inverse and associative properties.
$7 = N + 25$	Identity and closure of addition.
$7 - 25 = (N + 25) - 25$	Equal subtraction.
$-18 = N + (25 - 25)$	Closure and associative properties.
$-18 = N + 0$	Inverse.
$N = -18$	Identity.
$7 - (-18 - 12) = 37$	Checking.
$7 - (-30) = 37$	Closure.
$7 + 30 = 37$	Subtraction.
$37 = 37$	A true equation.
$N = -18$	The solution of the given equation.

Practice 2. Give a justification (as in Example 4) for each step in the following step-by-step solutions.

1. Solve $(N + 9) - 7 = 2$ _____
   $[(N + 9) - 7] + 7 = 2 + 7$ _____
   $(N + 9) + (-7 + 7) = 9$ _____

$(N + 9) + 0 = 9$ _____

$(N + 9) = 9$ _____

$(N + 9) - 9 = 9 - 9$ _____

$N + (9 - 9) = 0$ _____

$N + 0 = 0$ _____

$N = 0$ _____

$(0 + 9) - 7 = 2$ _____

$9 - 7 = 2$ _____

$2 = 2$ _____

$N = 0$ _____

2. Solve $8 + (6 - N) = 17$ _____

$(6 - N) + 8 = 17$ _____

$[(6 - N) + 8] - 8 = 17 - 8$ _____

$(6 - N) + (8 - 8) = 9$ _____

$(6 - N) + 0 = 9$ _____

$6 - N = 9$ _____

$-N + 6 = 9$ _____

$(-N + 6) - 6 = 9 - 6$ _____

$-N + (6 - 6) = 3$ _____

$-N + 0 = 3$ _____

$-N = 3$ _____

$N = -3$ _____

$8 + [6 - (-3)] = 17$ _____

$8 + (6 + 3) = 17$ _____

$8 + 9 = 17$ _____

$17 = 17$ _____

$N = -3$ _____

3. Solve $5 - (3 + N) = 11$ _____

$[5 - (3 + N)] + (3 + N) = 11 + (3 + N)$ _____

$5 + [-(3 + N) + (3 + N)] = (11 + 3) + N$ _____

$5 + 0 = 14 + N$ _____

$5 = 14 + N$ _____

$5 - 14 = (14 + N) - 14$ _____

$-9 = (N + 14) - 14$ _____

$-9 = N + (14 - 14)$ _____

$-9 = N + 0$ _____

$-9 = N$ _____

$5 - [3 + (-9)] = 11$ _____

$5 - (-6) = 11$ _____

$5 + 6 = 11$ _____

$11 = 11$ _____

$N = -9$ _____

Answers.

1. Given; Equal addition; Associative and closure; Inverse; Identity; Equal subtraction; Associative and inverse; Inverse; Identity; Checking by substitution; Closure; Closure (subtraction); and a true equation; Solution.

2. Given; Commutative; Equal subtraction; Associative and closure; Inverse; Identity; Anticommutative; Equal subtraction; Associative and closure; Inverse; Identity; (Negative of a negative); Checking; Subtraction of a negative; Closure; Closure; True equation; Solution.

3. Given; Equal addition; Associative; Inverse and closure; Identity; Equal subtraction; Closure and commutative; Associative; Inverse; Identity; Checking (substitution); Closure; Subtraction of negative into sum; Closure; True equation; Solution.

Although justifications are helpful in understanding the steps in a sequence of equivalent equations leading to a solution of a conditional equation, justifications can be given only after a step has already been taken. The "key" to solving an equation lies in observing the "pattern" in an equation. The motivation comes from understanding what is meant by a solution of an equation and the steps in solving an equation are determined by the wish to "isolate" the variable on one side of the equation. Finally, skill in solving equations for variables comes from **PRACTICE** in solving them.

Practice 3. Solve the following equations.

	(a)	(b)	(c)	(d)
1.	$N + 3 = 8$	$N + 8 = 3$	$N + 8 = 8$	$N + 32 = 70$
2.	$5 + N = 9$	$7 + N = 5$	$9 + N = 9$	$17 + N = 71$
3.	$N - 3 = 8$	$N - 8 = 3$	$N - 8 = 8$	$N - 32 = 70$
4.	$N - 5 = -3$	$N + 5 = -3$	$N - 8 = -8$	$N - 3 = -5$
5.	$3 - N = 8$	$8 - N = 3$	$8 - N = 8$	$-3 + N = 8$
6.	$-9 - N = 12$	$9 - N = -12$	$-3 - N = -8$	$-12 - N = -9$

7. (a) $(N + 4) + 2 = 7$ (b) $5 + (N + 7) = 16$
   (c) $(N + 4) - 7 = 9$ (d) $9 - (5 + N) = 11.$

8. (a) $(7 - N) + 9 = 4$ (b) $-6 - (N + 9) = 21$
   (c) $11 - (8 - N) = 7$ (d) $(N - 5) - 11 = -30.$

9. (a) $21 = 11 - (N + 2)$ (b) $-8 = 14 - (21 - N)$
   (c) $11 - 15 = N - 7$ (d) $(5 - N) + 7 = 0.$

10. (a) $8 = (N - 8) - 8$ (b) $(16 - 7) + 5 = 13 - N$
   (c) $21 - (-N + 7) = -9$ (d) $-18 + 9 = (13 - 4) - (18 - N).$

Answers.

	(a)	(b)	(c)	(d)		(a)	(b)	(c)	(d)
1.	5	−5	0	38	2.	4	−2	0	54
3.	11	11	16	102	4.	2	−8	0	−2
5.	−5	5	0	11	6.	−21	21	5	−3
7.	1	4	12	−7	8.	12	−36	4	−14
9.	−12	−1	−3	12	10.	24	−1	−23	0

3.2.5   When two numerals or expressions name numbers which are not equal, then we have noted that they must be related by an inequality. Just as with equations, we can use variables in inequalities to describe various situations. Inequalities may also be universally true, conditional, or universally false. When an inequality is conditional, we can ask "For what elements in the permissible set, will the inequality be true?" When we have answered this question, we say that we have **solved** the inequality. Our procedure and "point of view" in studying conditional inequalities is quite similar to our study of equations. From this study, we could enunciate two analogous Principles of Addition and Subtraction for inequalities.

The Principle of Equal Addition: If A, B, and C are numbers and $A < B$, then $A + B < B + C$.

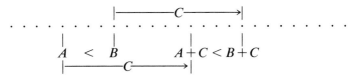

Examples.

(a) $3 < 7$ so that $3 + 10 < 7 + 10$.

(b) If $N - 7 < 14$, then $(N - 7) + 7 < 14 + 7$.

The Principle of Equal Subtraction: If A, B, and C are numbers and $A < B$, then $A - C < B - C$.

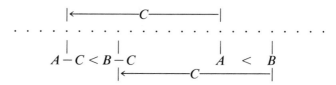

Examples.

   (a) $3 < 7$ so that $3 - 10 < 7 - 10$.
   (b) If $N + 7 < 14$, then $(N + 7) - 7 < 14 - 7$.

Of course, if $A < B$, then we have $B > A$ and analogous statements concerning equal addition and subtraction for the greater than relation. For three numbers we might have the "triple" inequality $A < B < C$ (which is read "B is between A and C" or "A is less than B and B is less than C"). We can treat this "triple" inequality as two separate inequalities: $A < B$ **and** $B < C$.

On occasion we wish to write that "A is less than **or** equal to B" or, alternatively, that "A is greater than **or** equal to B." These two statements can be symbolized by combining our previous symbols to $A \leq B$ and $A \geq B$, respectively.

With the above observations concerning inequalities, many interesting situations may be described and studied. Since we must move on, however, we conclude this section with a few examples and leave the further study of inequalities for the reader to pursue.

Examples.

   (a) To solve $N + 9 < 16$ for N, a natural number.
SOLUTION.

$N + 9 < 16$	Given.
$(N + 9) - 9 < 16 - 9$	Equal subtraction.
$N + (9 - 9) < 7$	Associative and closure.
$N < 7$	Inverse and identity.

Thus, N can be any natural number less than 7. That is, the solution set of the inequality consists of the six natural numbers: 1, 2, 3, 4, 5, and 6.

   (b) To solve $N - 7 \geq -6$ for N, a natural number.
SOLUTION. By equal addition we have $N \geq 1$ so that any natural number will make the inequality true. That is, the solution set is equal to the permissible set and the inequality is universally true for N, a natural number.

   (c) If N is a natural number, then solve $N + 5 < 4$.
SOLUTION. By equal subtraction we have $N < -1$ which is universally false in the natural numbers so that the solution set of the inequality is empty or null in the permissible set of N.

   (d) To solve $7 \leq N - 3 < 9$ for N, an integer.

SOLUTION. We can separate the "triple" inequality into

$$7 \leq N - 3 \quad \text{and} \quad N - 3 < 9$$
$$7 + 3 \leq N \quad \text{and} \quad N < 9 + 3$$

so that $10 \leq N < 12$.

Thus, the solution set of the inequality consists of the two integers 10 and 11.

Exercises

1. When a letter is used in an expression or equation to hold a place for a number, we call it a _____. The set of numbers which can be substituted for a variable is called the _____ set for the variable.

2. If a number, when _____ for a variable in an equation, makes the equation true, then we call the number a _____ of the equation and the process of finding this number _____ the equation.

3. Use the variable N to write an expression, equation, or inequality which describes the following:

(a) The sum of three consecutive multiples of five.

(b) The difference between the Nth multiple of seven and the Nth multiple of three.

(c) Nine less a number is equal to five more than three.

(d) Two more than a number is between negative seven and eleven.

4. Do as in Exercise 3 with:

(a) Nine less than a number added to five.

(b) Four subtracted from two more than a number.

(c) Seven less than a multiple of three is greater than zero.

(d) Twenty-six subtracted from a number is equal to the negative of the number added to thirty-one.

5. If N is a natural number greater than 10, then determine which of the following are universally true, conditional, or universally false.

(a) $N - 7 = 4$ (b) $N + 7 = 4$ (c) $N - 7 \geq 4$
(d) $N - 7 \leq 4$ (e) $7 - N = 4$ (f) $-4 > 7 - N$.

6. If the permissible set for the variables is the integers, then determine which of the following are universally true, which are conditional, and which are universally false.

(a) $3 + N = 5 + N$ (b) $A + 4 = 4 + A$
(c) $N - A = A - N$ (d) $N - 2 = 2 - N$
(e) $N + 2 = -(N - 2)$ (f) $N - 7 = A + N$.

7. Name the property of addition or subtraction which justifies the truth of each of the following equations.

(a) $-N + 5 = 5 + (-N)$ (b) $(N + 3) - (N + 3) = 0$
(c) $(N + 5) - 3 = N + (5 - 3)$ (d) $N - 5 = -(5 - N)$
(e) $(N + 11) + 0 = N + 11$
(f) $[(3 + N) + 7] + 5 = (3 + N) + (7 + 5)$.

8. If $A = 3$, $B = 8$, and $C = 11$, then determine the truth or falsity of the following equations:

(a) $C - A = B + 6$ (b) $A + 5 = B - 1$
(c) $C = B - (B - 11)$ (d) $A + (B - C) = 0$
(e) $A + (C - B) = 0$ (f) $19 - A = -[3 - (B + C)]$.

9. What must be added to or subtracted from both sides of each of the following equations in order to "isolate" the variable N?

(a) $N + 17 = 23$ (b) $14 + N = 9$ (c) $N - 27 = 35$
(d) $-15 + N = 64$ (e) $11 - N = 5$ (f) $-(6 - N) = 15$.

10. Which of the following pairs of equations are equivalent?

(a) $N + 5 = 7$ and $2 = -N$ (b) $N + 5 = 9$ and $-9 = -5 - N$
(c) $7 + N = 23$ and $N + 0 = 30$ (d) $N - 7 = 23$ and $N = 30$
(e) $N - 3 = 11$ and $N - 14 = 0$ (f) $N + 5 = 17$ and $N - 5 = 12$.

11. Which of the following pairs of equations are equivalent?

(a) $N + 5 = 0$ and $N = -5$.
(b) $13 - N = 9$ and $N - 13 = -9$.
(c) $8 + N = 4 - N$ and $-2 = N$.
(d) $8 - (5 - N) = 4$ and $N + 3 = 4$.
(e) $-14 = -8 + N$ and $N = -6$.
(f) $8 - (5 - N) = 4$ and $3 - N = 2$.

12. Give a justification for each step in the following:

(a) $(7 + N) - 40 = 13$ Given equation.
(b) $[(7 + N) - 40] + 40 = 13 + 40$ _____
(c) $(7 + N) + (-40 + 40) = 53$ _____
(d) $(7 + N) + 0 = 53$ _____
(e) $7 + N = 53$ _____
(f) $N + 7 = 53$ _____
(g) $(N + 7) - 7 = 53 - 7$ _____
(h) $N + (7 - 7) = 46$ _____
(i) $N + 0 = 46$ _____
(j) $N = 46$ _____

13. Give a justification for each step in the following:

(a) $(11 - N) + 15 = 36$ Given equation.
(b) $15 + (11 - N) = 36$ _____
(c) $(15 + 11) - N = 36$ _____
(d) $26 - N = 36$ _____
(e) $(26 - N) + N = 36 + N$ _____
(f) $26 + (-N + N) = 36 + N$ _____

(g) $26 + 0 = 36 + N$ _____

(h) $26 = 36 + N$ _____

(i) $26 - 36 = (N + 36) - 36$ _____

(j) $-10 = N + (36 - 36)$ _____

(k) $-10 = N + 0$ _____

(l) $N = -10$ _____

14. In which of the following equations is $N = 7$ a solution?

(a) $23 - N = 16$ (b) $N - 13 = 6$

(c) $39 + N = 45$ (d) $N + 61 = 68$

(e) $(15 + N) - 9 = 17$ (f) $19 - (38 + N) = -12$

(g) $(18 - N) + 9 = 20$ (h) $21 - (N - 8) = 6$

(i) $11 + (43 - N) = 47$.

15. Solve the following equations.

(a) $96 = N + 18$ (b) $N + 63 = 49$ (c) $0 = 14 + N$

(d) $84 + N = 84$ (e) $0 + N = 10$ (f) $100 + N = 1000$.

16. Solve the following equations.

(a) $N - 36 = 47$ (b) $N - 94 = 0$ (c) $-16 = N - 9$

(d) $18 - N = 0$ (e) $13 = 9 - N$ (f) $-N - 31 = 56$.

17. Solve the following equations.

(a) $(N + 13) + 9 = 27$ (b) $(N + 59) - 16 = 38$

(c) $45 + (N - 8) = 37$ (d) $14 - (N - 62) = 83$

(e) $57 = (N - 14) - 38$ (f) $31 = 38 - (7 + N)$.

18. Solve the following inequalities, listing the complete solution set. Assume a permissible set of integers.

(a) $(17 - N) + 5 \le 22 < -N + 26$ (b) $9 < 21 - (8 - N) \le 15$.

Answers.

1. variable; permissible (or domain).

2. substituted, solution, solving.

3. (a) $(5N - 5) + 5N + (5N + 5)$ (b) $7N - 3N$

    (c) $9 - N = 3 + 5$ (d) $-7 < N + 2 < 11$.

4. (a) $(N - 9) + 5$ (b) $(N + 2) - 4$ (c) $3N - 7 > 0$

    (d) $N - 26 = -N + 31$.

5. (a) conditional   (b) universally false   (c) universally true

    (d) conditional   (e) universally false   (f) universally true.

6. (a) universally false   (b) universally true   (c) conditional

    (d) conditional   (e) conditional   (f) conditional.

7. (a) commutative   (b) inverse   (c) associative

    (d) anticommutative   (e) identity   (f) associative.

8. (a) false   (b) false   (c) true   (d) true   (e) false   (f) true.

9. (a) subtract 17   (b) subtract 14   (c) add 27

    (d) add 15   (e) add N and subtract 5   (f) add 6.

10. (a) not equivalent   (b) equivalent   (c) not equivalent
    (d) equivalent   (e) equivalent   (f) not equivalent.
11. (a) equivalent   (b) equivalent   (c) equivalent
    (d) equivalent   (e) equivalent   (f) equivalent.
12. (a) −   (b) equal addition   (c) associative and closure
    (d) inverse   (e) identity   (f) commutative
    (g) equal subtraction   (h) associative and closure
    (i) inverse   (j) identity.
13. (a) −   (b) commutative   (c) associative   (d) closure
    (e) equal addition   (f) associative   (g) inverse
    (h) identity   (i) equal subtraction   (j) closure and associative
    (k) inverse   (l) identity.
14. $N = 7$ is a solution in (a), (d), (g), and (i).
15. (a) 78   (b) −14   (c) −14   (d) 0   (e) 10   (f) 900.
16. (a) 83   (b) 94   (c) −7   (d) 18   (e) −4   (f) −87.
17. (a) 5   (b) −5   (c) 0   (d) −7   (e) 109   (f) 0.
18. (a) $22 \leq 22 + N < 26$ so that $0 \leq N < 4$ and the solution set consists of 0, 1, 2, 3.

(b) $-4 < N \leq 2$ so that the solution set consists of −3, −2, −1, 0, 1, and 2.

3.3 Problems

3.3.1   What is a problem? How do they occur? Most problems occur in real situations in which we ask questions. For example, we may be concerned with the cost of operating an automobile. What kind of an auto? Under what conditions of operation? For how long? Once we have asked the proper questions, we are in a position to look for and gather information and facts to provide answers. The ability to ask just the "right" questions and the skill to answer them are two of the most useful tools which can be developed.

Thus far we have been working mostly with the mathematical symbols used in stating problems rather than with problems as they occur naturally. Problems are often described in ordinary English. Translating them into mathematical terms may simplify their solution. Consider, for example:

1. Nine members of a club were absent from a meeting. If the club has 42 members, how many members attended the meeting?

2. Mr. Jones earned $9,650 during the year. He paid out $1,806 in taxes and $2,045 in retirement and insurance funds. How much did Mr. Jones have left for his normal living expenses?

3. How much more is the sum of 16 and 21 than the difference?

After reading the problems carefully, the next thing to do is **not** to anticipate an answer immediately or jump to too rapid a conclusion. Read each problem again. Look for an overall idea in the problem. Observe that there are words and phrases which suggest the following kinds of parts:

1. Numerals and variables.
2. Mathematical operations.
3. Connections and relationships.
4. General terms which "set the stage" for the problem.

The next step is to concentrate on **one problem** and to read it again. Look for the mathematical parts of the problem. Note the numerals given; assign a letter name to each variable suggested in the problem. Look for key words and phrases which indicate the operations involved in the problem.

ADDITION is usually suggested by words such as:
sum, combine, plus, increased by, total, and, how many, all, together.
SUBTRACTION is usually suggested by words such as:
difference, more than, less than, larger, smaller, from, take away.

Now look for connectives such as "is" and "equals." Of course, one must be "sensitive" to inequalities which often appear as sums and differences. Rephrase the problem and simplify it into its essential parts. That is, write the problem in a "mathematical language" form. The next step is to describe the problem in mathematical symbols. That is, in equation (or inequality) form. Now, once the equations (or inequalities) can be solved, the problem can usually be answered.

To illustrate this general procedure, let us consider further the foregoing problems. Note that there are no specific rules which we follow except those of common sense and observation.

1. Nine members of a club were absent from a meeting. If the club has 42 members, how many members attended the meeting?

(a) Notice the word "nine" and the "42." The variable suggested is "members." Let M stand for the unknown number of members who attended the meeting.

(b) "How many" might tell us that the sum of the absentees and M equals 42. That is, $9 + M = 42$. Alternatively, we might note that the "club has 42 members" and "nine were absent" indicates that the difference between 42 and 9 must equal the number of members who attended. That is, $42 - 9 = M$.

(c) Now we must make a decision. Which equation or alternative to take? But the equations are equivalent and both are easy to solve. That is, $M = 33$.

(d) On checking, since $9 + 33 = 42$ is true and makes "sense," we conclude that 33 members attended the meeting.

2. Mr. Jones earned $9,650 during the year. He paid out $1,806 in taxes and $2,045 in retirement and insurance funds. How much did Mr. Jones have left for his normal living expenses?

(a) The quantities mentioned are 9,650, 1,806, and 2,045. The variable suggested is "normal living expenses." Let N stand for "normal living expenses."

(b) There are three separate sentences involved in the problem. Consider:

> Total: $9,650.
> Paid out: $1,806 and $2,045.
> Had left: N.

(c) Look at the simpler problem: Mr. Jones paid out $1,806 and $2,045. How much did he pay out?

$$\$1,806 + \$2,045 = \$3,851 \text{ paid out.}$$

(d) How much did he have left? $9,650 less $3,851 equals N.

(e) Given $\$9,650 - \$3,851 = N$ we have $N = \$5,799$.

(f) Answer: Mr. Jones had $5,799 left for his normal living expenses.

3. How much more is the sum of 16 and 21 than the difference?

(a) The numbers involved are 16 and 21. If we are to find how much more the sum is than the difference, then we must first find the sum and the difference.

(b) Let S stand for the sum: $S = 16 + 21 = 37$. Let D stand for the difference: $D = 21 - 16 = 5$. (Note that we are *assuming* the positive difference.)

(c) Now the sum, S, less the difference, D, must equal "how much more." Let M stand for "how much more."

(d) $S - D = M$ and $S = 37$, $D = 5$ so that $37 - 5 = M$.

(e) $M = 32$ and so the sum of 16 and 21 is 32 more than the (positive) difference.

Ordinarily we would not write our "thinking" to the extent shown above. However, a careful beginning and step-by-step procedure will pay high dividends in both speed and correct solutions in the long run. In an abbreviated form the above problems might appear as follows:

1. 42 is the sum of M and 9.
   $42 = M + 9$, $M = 42 - 9 = 33$.
   Answer: 33 members attended.
2. Total: $9,650.
   Paid out: $\$1,806 + \$2,045 = \$3,851$.
   Had left: $\$9,650 - \$3,851 = N$, $N = \$5,799$.
   Answer: $5,799 left.

3. Sum: $16 + 21 = 37$.
   Difference: $21 - 16 = 5$.
   Sum is $37 - 5 = M$ more than the difference.
   Answer: $M = 32$ more.

Practice 1.   Solve the following problems.

1. A baseball team played 163 games during the season. If they won 86 games and 7 games were not completed on account of the weather or darkness, how many games did they lose?

2. Bill who is 28 years old is 12 years older than Sam. How old is Sam?

3. Two bowlers in "match play" rolled three lines each. If bowler "A" rolled 221, 186, and 237 and bowler "B" rolled 199, 214, and 224, then which bowler won the match and by how many pins?

4. In an election for councilman in a certain town there were three candidates: Mr. Allan who received 862 votes, Mr. Baker who received 528 votes, and Mr. Charles who received 318 votes. Did Mr. Allan receive a majority of the votes cast?

4. An airplane takes off from an airport at 985 feet elevation. How many feet must the airplane rise if it is to clear a mountain pass at 4,565 feet elevation by 500 feet?

6. It took Joe 4 hours longer to do his homework than Sally. Sally took 3 hours to do her homework. How long did it take Joe to do his homework?

7. Two bowling teams rolled the following series:
   Team A: 182, 208, 196, 173, 224.
   Team B: 194, 159, 235, 160, 241.
Which team won and by how many total pins?

8. If 17 more than a certain number is equal to 25 less than 168, then what is the certain number?

Answers.

1. 70 games   2. 16 years old   3. "A" won by 7 pins   4. Yes
5. 4,080 feet   6. 7 hours   7. Team B by 6 pins   8. 126.

3.3.2   Since problems arise naturally from our external surroundings, they have been of interest to mathematicians throughout history. A problem, which has been called the "inventory of a household," appeared in the Ahmes Papyrus (about 1650 B.C.) and was stated somewhat as follows:

There were seven houses; in each house are seven cats; each cat kills seven mice; each mouse would have eaten seven ears of wheat;

each ear of wheat will produce seven grains of wheat. What is the total of all of these?

An example of a problem from the *Greek Anthology* compiled by Metrodorus (about 500) was given as follows:

The three Graces were carrying baskets of apples, and in each was the same number. The nine Muses met them and asked each for apples and they gave the same number to each Muse and the nine Muses and the three Graces each had the same number. How many apples did each Grace give and how many did each have?

The Chinese were interested in problems of pursuit. The following problem probably originates from the sixth century:

A man who had stolen a horse rode away on his back. When he had gone 38 miles the owner discovered the theft and pursued the thief for 150 miles. He than returned being unable to overtake the thief. When he turned back the thief was riding 23 miles ahead of him. If he had continued in his pursuit without turning back, then in how many miles would he have overtaken the thief?

Leonardo of Pisa (about 1170–1250), better known as Fibonacci (meaning the "son of Bonaccio"), stated a problem of the "Apples and the Gatekeeper":

A man went into an orchard which had seven gates, and while there took a certain number of apples. When he left, he gave one more than half the apples he had to the first gate guard. To the second guard at the second gate he gave half of his remaining apples and one apple more. He did the same at each of the remaining five gates and left the orchard with just one apple. How many apples did he take in the orchard?

A more contemporary type of problem might be given as follows:

Miss Allan was very sensitive about her age and tried to keep it a secret. However, liking parties, she held a birthday party one year and on being questioned by one of her guests she said: "If you take the difference between the sum of this year and the year of my birth and twice the year of my tenth birthday, then the result will be 21." How old was Miss Allan?

Of course, solving recreational problems of the above kind should not be a final end. However, we learn to solve more useful and difficult problems by studying simpler and more routine problems. It is often helpful to follow a general procedure in solving problems which are already stated in ordinary English.

To Solve a Problem.

1. **Read** the problem slowly and carefully. **Reread** the problem without trying to solve it until you are completely familiar with it.

2. Paraphrase and translate the problem into simplified mathematical language. Cross out the nonessential parts, determine what is **GIVEN**, and be certain of what the problem **REQUIRES**.

3. Determine the numerals and assign letter names to all variables. Look for given relationships. Translate the mathematical language into mathematical symbols. The statements will usually be in the form of equations and/or inequalities. Check to be sure that the statements reflect the same essential meaning as the original written problem.

4. Examine the mathematical statements and decide on a course of action, devise a **PLAN**. Determine what operations to perform to solve for the desired variables. **ACT**: perform the operations, carry out the plan. Find **SOLUTIONS**.

5. Translate your solutions into an **ANSWER** to the original problem. Does the answer seem reasonable? **CHECK**.

Of course, solving problems is not a simple matter of following a set of rules or procedures. It takes confidence, patience, desire, intuition, hard work, and oftentimes sheer luck to solve hard problems. However, solving a difficult problem independently leads to satisfaction and self-esteem. Success in solving problems leads to further gratifications and insights. Finally, the way to learn to solve problems is to solve them! (From the easy ones to harder ones and thence to the most difficult challenges.)

Example 1. During the week Bill worked 7 hours more than Sam. Sam worked 5 hours less than John. John worked 46 hours during the week. How many hours did Bill work during the week?

SOLUTION. Have you read the problem carefully?
How many statements are there in the problem?
What numerals are involved in the problem?
What are the names of the people involved?
What have they done?
What are we looking for?
Translate the problem.
Name the variables.
Write the equations.
Let B stand for the number of hours Bill worked.
S stand for the hours Sam worked.
J stand for the hours John worked.

Bill worked 7 hours more than Sam: $B = S + 7$.
Sam worked 5 hours less than John: $S = J - 5$.
John worked 46 hours: $J = 46$.
Question: $B = ?$
Eliminate J and S to obtain B.
$S = 46 - 5 = 41; B = 41 + 7 = 48$.
   ANSWER. Bill worked 48 hours during the week.
   CHECK. $48 = 41 + 7$ and $41 = 46 - 5$ are both true.

Example 2.   If Bill deposits $5 in his bank account and Sam withdraws
$7 from his account, then the difference in their bank accounts would be
$31. Sam has more than Bill in his bank account. What is the difference
in their bank accounts?

   SOLUTION.   Have you read the problem carefully?
What is the topic in the problem?
Is there a "shift" in time?
What is given now?
What will be the situation after?
What do we want to find?
Can we restate the problem?
What are the numerals? Variables?
What is given? What is desired?
Bill deposits $5: $B + 5$.
Sam withdraws $7: $S - 7$.
The difference is: $(S - 7) - (B + 5) = 31$.
(Since Sam has more than Bill: $(S - 7) > (B + 5)$).
The difference before? $S - B$.
What can we do? Work with the equation:
$(S - 7) - (B + 5) = [(S - 7) - B] - 5 = [(S - B) - 7] - 5$.
$\qquad\qquad = (S - B) - (7 + 5) = (S - B) - 12 = 31$.
What do we have? $S - B = 31 + 12 = 43$.
But that is the difference we are looking for!
   ANSWER.   The difference now is $43.
   CHECKING. $43 - (7 + 5) = 43 - 12 = 31$.

Example 3.   Mr. and Mrs. Anderson celebrated their fiftieth wedding
anniversary with a family party. Mr. Anderson observed that he had been
married twenty-six years more than the number of years he had been
single. How old was Mr. Anderson when he was married?

SOLUTION.   Have you read the problem carefully?
What was the party about?
What fact is given in the first sentence?
What are the two parts of Mr. Anderson's life?
How are the parts connected?
What is given?
Married 50 years. 50 is 26 more than the number of single years. $50 = S + 26$ so that $S = 24$.
   ANSWER.   Mr. Anderson was 24 years old when he was married. Does the answer make "sense"?

3.3.3   Once we have solved a problem it is nice to be recognized and be able to have others appreciate it. In ordinary circumstances in a classroom or on a job, a problem should be carefully written up for **presentation**. Credit for solving problems comes from the presentation as well as the skill required in solving the problem. The presentation or layout will vary in different situations; however, certain items are common in all good forms.

Presenting a Problem.

   1. Give a **reference** or title to the problem.
   2. **State** and give an introduction to the problem.
   3. Present the **solution** in an orderly and neat way.
   4. State the **answer** carefully. Identify it clearly.
   5. **Check** if required. Give further references if necessary.
   6. **Identify** yourself. Take the credit!

```
#Reference                                    Identification
     Statement of the problem . . .
        Solving the problem . . .
                                              Answer . . .

     (Check or references)
#Reference
     Statement of the next problem . . .
        Solving the problem . . .
                                              Answer . . .

     (Check or references)
```

FIGURE 44

The preceding examples might be presented as follows. We will not restate the problems to conserve space and will assume that a #reference is sufficient.

Example 1.   (Statement)

SOLUTION.   Let B, S, and J stand for the hours worked. Then, $B = S + 7$, $S = J - 5$, and $J = 46$. Thus, $B = (46 - 5) + 7 = 48$.
ANSWER.   Bill worked 48 hours.

Example 2.   (Statement)

SOLUTION.   Let D be the difference now. Let B and S be the amounts now. Then, $S - B = D$, $(S - 7) - (B + 5) = 31$, $(S - B) - 12 = 31$ so that $D = 43$.
ANSWER.   The difference is $43.

Example 3.   (Statement)

SOLUTION.   Let S be the years he was single. We have $50 = S + 26$, $S = 24$.
ANSWER.   Mr. Anderson was 24 years old.

Exercises

Remark.   The following "problems" are primarily routine exercises to give practice in developing a technique and understanding of the procedures useful in solving problems. For more difficult and challenging problems see the problem sets located at the end of each chapter.

1. A salesman keeps a record of his transportation mileage for his expense account. During a certain week he traveled 210 miles on Monday, 186 miles on Tuesday, 197 miles on Wednesday, 208 miles on Thursday, and 155 miles on Friday. What was his mileage for the week?

2. A college enrolled 4,582 students at the beginning of the semester and had 3,394 students still enrolled at the end of the semester. How many students withdrew or dropped out during the semester?

3. A college library began the year with 26,384 volumes on its shelves. It acquired 2,368 volumes but 139 volumes were lost during the year. How many volumes were available for the library shelves at the end of the year?

4. A store sold merchandise totaling $1,365 during a certain week.

If the store's net profit was $470 for the week, then what was the total cost of the merchandise sold?

5. A cashier at a theater kept a record of her sales by noting the serial numbers of the tickets sold. She sold adult tickets from one roll beginning with number 1250 and at the end of the evening the ticket number was 1628. Student tickets of a different color began with 2400 and at the end of the evening the ticket number on the same roll was 2638. Children's tickets began with number 1625 and at the end of the evening was 1801. What was the total attendance at the theater for the evening?

6. Mr. Smith owned a five-year-old sedan. He used it for ordinary commuting to and from work as well as for weekend trips. He paid a nominal insurance premium of $132 per year and a license fee of $24 per year. His garage bill for one year was $203 and his gasoline and oil charges came to $287. Miscellaneous costs, such as parking tickets and a new cushion, came to $38. Without considering depreciation or tax deductions, how much did it cost Mr. Smith to operate his auto for one year?

7. An elevator starting on the twenty-first floor of a building went down six floors, then up fourteen floors to the top floor of the building. How many floors does the building have?

8. John opened a savings account with an initial deposit of $37. He deposited $5 less than his initial deposit the following month and $5 less than that in his third deposit. The month after that, John withdrew $18. How much did he have in his savings account after his withdrawal?

9. In a tennis match, David Roe beat Bill Sayer by sets of 4–6, 6–4, 9–7. How many games did David lose?

10. The town of Gurney had a population of 2,136 at the beginning of the year. There were 39 births during the year. At the end of the year the population was 2,242. If there were 28 deaths during the year, did new people move into Gurney during the year?

11. Together, Mr. and Mrs. Jones earned $12,586 in one year. If Mr. Jones earned $4,090 more than Mrs. Jones did during the year, then how much did Mrs. Jones earn?

12. Mr. Willis paid $3,426 for a new car. If the base price of the car was advertised as $2,882 and the taxes were $296, then how much did Mr. Willis pay for "extras" and service charges?

13. James is twelve years older than Sue who is nine years younger than David. Who is older, James or David? If David is twenty-seven, then how old is James?

14. Bill had the following expenses in going to school for one semester:

    $245   for tuition.

    $47   for books and stationery.

$350   for housing.

$410   for food.

$96   for laundry and personal items.

$142   for transportation and miscellaneous items.

Bill's bank balance was $2,210 at the beginning of the semester. If all of his expenses were drawn from his bank balance with no deposits, how much did he have left in the bank at the end of the semester?

15. Mrs. Stevens charged a blanket costing fourteen dollars, a dress costing twenty-one dollars, and towels costing eight dollars to her account at the department store. There were additional service and tax charges of three dollars. She had a credit balance of seven dollars from her previous statement. What was the amount of her statement after the charges?

16. If the sum of two numbers is twelve more than their difference and the difference between the numbers is equal to five, then what are the two numbers?

17. One number is six more than a second number and a third number is four less than the sum of the first two numbers. The sum of the three numbers is twenty. Find the three numbers.

18. If the sum of the digits in a two-digit numeral is equal to twelve and the difference between the ten's digit and the one's digit is four, then what is the two-digit numeral?

19. Take any three-digit numeral such that the difference between the hundred's digit and the one's digit is more than one. Form a new numeral by reversing the order of the digits. Find the difference between the two numbers. Reverse the order of the digits in this difference. Find the sum of the last two numbers.

20. Find two natural numbers such that each number is a sum of six's, their difference a sum of eight's and their sum a sum of nine's.

Answers.

1. 956 miles.	11. $4,248.
2. 1,188 students.	12. $248.
3. 28,613 volumes.	13. James; 30 years.
4. $895.	14. $920.
5. 792.	15. $39.
6. $684.	16. 6 and 11.
7. 29 floors.	17. 3, 8, and 9.
8. $78.	18. 84.
9. 17 games.	19. 1,089.
10. Yes, 95 people.	20. 6 and 30 (others).

Review Summary

As in ordinary English, mathematical statements can be separated into different kinds of parts. For example, the expression $7 + [5 - (9 + 1)]$ is made up of the symbols "7," "5," "9," "1" called _____; the symbols *numerals* "+" and "−" called _____ symbols; and the _____ *operation,* symbols "[," "]," "(," ")." When two numerals or *grouping* expressions name the same number, we can indicate this connection by using the symbol "=" and by saying that they are _____. Given any two numerals or expressions, *equal* we know that they are related in exactly one of the following ways: 1. One numeral names a number _____ *less* _____ the other, indicated by $<$; 2. One numeral *than* names a number _____ _____ the other, indicated by *equal to* $=$; 3. One numeral names a number _____ _____ the *greater than* other, indicated by $>$. If an integer is greater than a second integer, we must add a positive integer to the second to obtain a number equal to the first. If an integer is less than a second integer, we must subtract a positive integer from the second to obtain a number equal to the first.

When two numerals or expressions are connected by $=$, we call the resulting statement an _____. When *equation* connected by $<$ or $>$ we say that two expressions or numerals form an _____. Of course, what we say and *inequality* write may be true or may be false. The equation $7 - 2 = 5$ is _____ while the inequality $7 - 2 < 5$ is _____. If we *true, false* deny the equation, that is, $7 + 2 \neq 5$, then it must be _____. If we deny the inequality, $7 - 2 \nless 5$, then the *false* resulting statement is _____. *true*

In using equations and inequalities it is often convenient to reserve places for numerals. When we use symbols in this way, usually letters, we call them _____. *variables* Of course, when a variable appears in an equation, the equation may be neither true nor false. If, when a number is substituted for a variable in an equation, the equation is true, then the number is called a _____ of the equation. *solution*

Using variables we can describe many of the properties of numbers, operations, equations, and general types of situations. For example, the statement "Bill is three years older than Sam" could be described by $B = S + \_\_\_$ *3* while "Bill is less than three years older than Sam" can be described by $B < S + 3$. In using a variable, the restricted set of numbers which can be $\_\_\_$ for the *substituted* variable was called the permissible set or domain for the variable. When referring to the set of numbers which makes an equation or inequality true, the set was called the $\_\_\_$ set of the equation. We noted that the *solution* solution set of an equation was always a subset of the permissible set for the variable.

To develop our mathematical language, we discussed a way of specifying multiples of natural numbers. If N is any natural number, then $7N$ is a multiple of $\_\_\_$. Three consecutive numbers three less than a *7* multiple of seven could be specified by $7N - 3, 7N + 4$, and $7N + 11$.

When variables occur in equations, the equations are always true, only true for certain substitutions, or always false for any number in the $\_\_\_$ set for the variable. *permissible* These three types of equations were called universally $\_\_\_$ equations, $\_\_\_$ equations, and universally *true,* $\_\_\_$ equations, respectively. *conditional* *false*

Using variables in equations we can describe many of *false* the general properties of operations on numbers. For addition and subtraction these can be summarized by:

1. If A and B are integers, then there are always integers S and D such that $A + B = S$ and $A + D = B$. $A + D = B$ is more commonly written $D = \_\_\_$. *$B - A$* This property is called $\_\_\_$. *closure*

2. If A and B are integers, then $A + B = B + A$. This is called the $\_\_\_$ property of addition. *commutative*

3. If A and B are integers, then $A - B = -(B - A)$. This is called the $\_\_\_$ property of subtraction. *anticommu-* *tative*

4. If $A, B,$ and C are integers, then $A + (B + C)$ *tative* $= (A + B) + C$. This is called the $\_\_\_$ property of *associative* addition. However, subtraction is not, in general, associative.

5. If A is any integer, then $A + 0 = A$. The $\_\_\_$ 0 *number* is called the $\_\_\_$ element of addition of integers. *identity*

6. If A is any integer, then there is another integer $-A$ such that $A + (-A) = \_\_\_$. The number $-A$ is *0*

called the _____ of A under addition of integers.   *inverse*

Rather than guessing solutions to equations, we carefully discussed and studied a few simple and easy examples. From the patterns developed in the examples, we noted that:

(a) We try to "isolate" the variable.

(b) Subtraction "undoes" addition and addition "undoes" subtraction.

(c) We "act" in the same way on both sides of an equation.

(d) Our actions are based on known properties of addition and subtraction of integers.

(e) Once the variable is "isolated" we check to make certain that we have found a solution to the equation.

In solving an equation, we noted that we wrote a succession of equations. Each successive equation was obtained from the preceding equation by using universally true properties of operations and equations. When any one of the equations is true, the others are also. If any one of the equations is false, the others will also be false. The equations will all be true or all be false together. Two or more equations related in this way are said to be _____. Thus, in solving an equation, we often   *equivalent*
look for simpler equivalent equations which lead to a
_____. Given the equation $(N + 7) - 13 = 5$, we can   *solution*
obtain the equivalent equation $N + 7 = 18$ which, in
turn, leads us to the equation $N =$ _____. Thus, $N = 11$ *11*
is a solution of the given equation. Check: $(11 + 7) - 13$
$= 5$ is true.

In obtaining equivalent equations, we applied two general principles:

The Principle of Equal Addition: If A, B, and C are
numbers and $A = B$, then $A + C =$ _____.   *$B + C$*

The Principle of Equal Subtraction: If A, B, and C
are numbers and $A = B$, then $A - C =$ _____.   *$B - C$*

Although in ordinary practice in solving equations we only sketch the key steps and assume that the steps can be justified, writing the justifications for each step in the solution of a conditional equation can help us to understand the processes and principles used in its solution. For example, to solve the equation $(N + 7) - 13$ $= 5$, we can write:

The Equations	The Justifications	
$(N + 7) - 13 = 5$	Given equation.	
$[(N + 7) - 13] + 13$		
$\quad = 5 + 13$	_____.	*Equal*
$(N + 7) + (-13 + 13)$		*addition*
$\quad =$ _____	_____ and closure.	*18, Associative*
$(N + 7) +$ _____ $= 18$	_____.	*0, Inverse*
$N + 7 = 18$		*Identity*
$(N + 7)$ _____ $= 18$ _____	_____.	*-7, -7*
$N + (7 - 7) = 11$	Equal subtraction.	*Associative,*
$N + 0 = 11$	_____ and _____.	*closure*
$N = 11$	Inverse.	
$(11 + 7) - 13 = 5$	Identity.	
$18 - 13 = 5$	Checking.	
$5 = 5$	Closure.	
	A true equation (closure).	

Similar procedures can be used in studying conditional inequalities. Two analogous principles of addition and subtraction for inequalities were that:

If A, B, and C are numbers and $A < B$, then
$$A + B < B + C \text{ and } A - C < B - C.$$

Problems do not just "happen" by themselves, they occur as the result of asking questions. The ability to ask good questions and the skill to answer them are two of the most useful tools which can be developed. Once a problem has been stated in ordinary English a regular procedure for solving the problem is often helpful. A first principle is to READ a problem carefully. To concentrate on the problem, to re-read it, to dissect it into its separate mathematical parts, to THINK of the problem in "mathematical language" form, these are the common-sense procedures used in solving problems. To solve problems, we can ask certain common questions:

What is GIVEN?
What is REQUIRED?
What RELATIONSHIPS are given?
What can we DO? How can we ACT?
Have we ANSWERED the problem?
Does it make SENSE? Can we CHECK?

Of course, solving problems is not a simple matter of following a set of rules or procedures. The way to learn to solve problems is to solve them. From the easy ones to the more difficult and challenging problems.

Once a problem has been solved, full credit and recognition can come only with a proper presentation of the problem. Problems should be identified, described; the solution to a problem should be explained, answers clearly identified; and finally a person who solves a problem should identify himself and be recognized.

Chapter Exercises (3)

Group I.

1. Write an expression using the following symbols exactly once so that the expression is equal to 2.

    (a) 18, 7, 23, +, −, ( ).

    (b) 18, 8, 8, +, −, ( ).

2. Which of the following are expressions, which are equations, and which are inequalities?

    (a) $7 + 7 + 7$ (b) $2 + 4 = 3$

    (c) $2 + 4 > 3$ (d) $7 = 7$

    (e) $[(2 + 4) - 3] < 3$ (f) $(N - 27) + 11$

    (g) $5 - [7 - (-3)]$ (h) $2N = N + N$

    (i) $(9 + 1) < (11 - 0)$.

3. Which of the equations and inequalities in Exercise 2 are true?

4. Connect (relate) each of the following pairs of numerals with exactly one of $<$, $=$, or $>$ to form a true statement.

    (a) $5 + 7$ and $12 - 5$ (b) 16 and $8 + 8$ (c) $1 + 3 + 5$ and 10

    (d) -7 and 0   (e) 10 and -1 (f) $5 - 9$ and $9 - 13$

    (g) $2 + 0$ and $2 - 0$ (h) 7 and $3 + 4$ (i) $8 - 1$ and $8 + 1$.

5. Which of the following equations are true, which are false, which are neither true nor false?

    (a) $9 - (5 - 3) = 12 - 5$ (b) $A - B = B - A$

    (c) $13 - (7 + 5) = 11$ (d) $8 + N = N - 8$

    (e) $11 - N = 7 + N$ (f) $5 + (N - 6) = -(1 - N)$.

6. If $N = 13$ is true, then which of the following equations will be true?

    (a) $N + 17 = 30$ (b) $N - 17 = 30$ (c) $17 - N = 30$

    (d) $N - 8 = 21$ (e) $21 - 8 = N$ (f) $N + 5 = 8$.

7. If $N = 21$ is true, then which of the following equations will be false?

    (a) $9 = 30 - N$ (b) $N - 9 = 30$ (c) $9 + N = 30$

    (d) $N - 21 = 0$ (e) $N + 21 = 0$ (f) $-17 = -(N - 4)$.

8. Using N as the variable, express the following in mathematical symbols:

    (a) Eight more than a given number.

    (b) Three less than a given number.

(c) Eight more than three less than a given number.

(d) Eight more than three less than a given number is equal to eleven less than twenty-three.

9. Match the descriptions in the numbered column with the lettered column so that they best describe the properties illustrated.

(a) $A + 0 = A$ 1. Anticommutative.

(b) If $A = B$, then $A - C = B - C$ 2. Associative.

(c) $A + (B + C) = (A + B) + C$ 3. Identity.

(d) $A - B = -(B - A)$ 4. Equal addition.

(e) If $A = B$, then $A + C = B + C$ 5. Equal subtraction.

10. Which of the following equations are equivalent to $N = 3$?

(a) $N + 7 = 10$ (b) $N - 7 = 10$ (c) $7 - N = 4$

(d) $7 = 4 + N$ (e) $(N + 7) - 7 = 3$ (f) $(N - 7) - 7 = 3$.

11. If $N = 7$, $M = -4$, and $K = 8$, then determine the truth or falsity of the following equations.

(a) $N - M = K + 3$ (b) $M - K = N - 3$

(c) $K + N - M = 11$ (d) $(M - K) - 5 = N$

(e) $K + M + 3 = N$ (f) $-(M + 0) = N - K$.

12. Find a justification for each step in the following:

(a) $18 - N = 11$ Given equation.

(b) $(18 - N) + N = 11 + N$ _____

(c) $18 + (-N + N) = 11 + N$ _____

(d) $18 + 0 = 11 + N$ _____

(e) $18 = 11 + N$ _____

(f) $18 - 11 = (N + 11) - 11$ _____

(g) $7 = N + (11 - 11)$ _____

(h) $7 = N + 0$ _____

(i) $7 = N$ _____

(j) $18 - 7 = 11$ _____

(k) $11 = 11$ _____

(l) $N = 7$ _____

13. State what must be added to or subtracted from both sides of each of the following equations in order to "isolate" the variable N.

(a) $20 + N = 13$ (b) $7 = 27 + N$ (c) $N - 38 = 42$

(d) $N + 11 = -51$ (e) $36 = -11 + N$ (f) $27 - N = -7$.

14. Which of the following pairs of equations are equivalent?

(a) $N + (5 - 5) = 7$ and $N = 7$ (b) $5 - N = 13$ and $N - 5 = 13$

(c) $5 + N = 9$ and $9 = N + 5$ (d) $(N + 6) - 18 = 35$ and $N + 6 = 53$

(e) $7 - (3 + N) = 21$ and $4 + N = 21$ (f) $(7 - N) + 3 = 9$ and $N = 1$.

15. Solve the following equations.

(a) $N + 81 = 107$ (b) $108 = N + 98$ (c) $68 + N = 36$

(d) $N - 52 = 63$ (e) $18 = N - 21$ (f) $N - 65 = -47$.

16. Solve the following equations.

(a) $47 - (N + 13) = 34$ (b) $26 = (7 - N) + 55$

(c) $30 - (-N + 41) = -57$ (d) $93 - (54 - N) = 51$.

17. Determine the truth or falsity of the following statements.

(a) The symbol "=" is an operation symbol.

(b) "$13 + 28$" is a numeral.

(c) 356 is an equation.

(d) $-1 > 0$ is true.

(e) $-3 < -2 < -1$.

(f) $13 = 28$ is an equation.

(g) The equation $A + B = 0$ is universally true.

(h) The equation $N + 5 = 11$ has an integer solution.

(i) Subtraction is associative.

(j) The permissible set of a variable is a subset of the solution set of an equation.

18. Translate the following into mathematical symbols.

(a) If we take away three points from Bill's score, then his score will be Sam's score increased by nine points.

(b) The U.S. OSO I satellite launched March 7, 1962 weighed 173 pounds more than the U.S. Tiros IV satellite launched February 8, 1962.

(c) The estimated production of tobacco in the U.S. in 1962 was 2,261,243 thousands of pounds. This was 1,891,243 thousands of pounds more than was the estimated production of tobacco in the U.S.S.R. in 1962.

Solving the following problems using a "regular" procedure. After solving, present the problem in a well-organized, neat, and clear way.

19. An All-American halfback in a football game gained 191 yards on fourteen carries, lost 12 yards on five carries, and was stopped for no-gain on three carries. How many times did he carry the ball and what was his net gain for the game?

20. If the membership in two social clubs are counted together, there are eighty-four people. If the difference in membership is counted, it amounts to twelve people. If there are no people who belong to both clubs, then how many people are in each club?

21. Joe was told to check the stock of certain items in a storage area. He was given the following records:

May 8: checked inventory; 3,648 in stock.

May 10: sales and shipment; 963 items.

May 12: purchased and put in stock; 750 items.

May 14: sales and shipment; 1,347 items.

How many of the items should there be in the storage area?

22. A family man made four hundred seventy-two dollars in take-home

pay per month. In making out a monthly budget, he figured out the following list: Rent $95, Food $110, Utilities $37, Auto (with payments) $127, Other monthly payments $36, Miscellaneous needs $40. If he followed his budget exactly, how much could he save each month for insurance, retirement, emergencies, and savings?

23. The towns of Action, Beacon, Carson, and Denine are connected to each other by a network of roads.

Town to Town	Road Mileage
Action to Beacon	17
Action to Carson	25
Action to Denine	22
Beacon to Carson	16
Beacon to Denine	29
Carson to Denine	9

Mr. Williams, who is in Action, wishes to visit the other three towns. If he stops and stays in the last town (the fourth), what is the shortest route he can take through the three towns? What is the longest route? Will he end by staying in the same town taking the shortest and the longest routes?

24. If two more than a multiple of three is greater than twenty and four less than the multiple of three is less than twenty, then find the multiple of three.

Group II.

1. Write two distinct expressions using the following symbols exactly once so that the expressions are both equal to 5:
$$3, 4, 5, 7, -, -, +, (\ ), [\ ].$$

2. Which of the following are expressions, which are equations, and which are inequalities?

(a) $3 + 8 - 2$ (b) $3 + 8 = 2$ (c) $3 + 2 < 8$
(d) $A = B$ (e) $3 + 8 > 2$ (f) $A + (B - C)$
(g) $3 + (8 - 2)$ (h) $A + 3 = 5$ (i) $A < 3 - 5.$

3. Which of the equations and inequalities in Exercise 2 are true?

4. Connect (relate) each of the following pairs of numerals with exactly one of $<, =, >$ to form a true statement.

(a) 16 and $10 + 6$ (b) N and $N - 1$
(c) N and $N + 1$ (d) $0 + 2$ and $0 - 2$
(e) $0 - 2$ and $-2 + 0$ (f) $3 - 9$ and 6
(g) 101 and 110   (h) $12 - 7$ and $32 - 27$
(i) $16 + 7$ and 32.

5. Which of the following equations are true, which are false, which are neither true nor false?

(a) $N + 5 = 5 + N$ (b) $0 - N = N - 0$
(c) $(23 - 17) - 79 = 73$ (d) $9 + (7 - 9) = 7$
(e) $-(-5 + 9) = 4$ (f) $-(N - 1) = 7 - (6 + N)$.

6. If $N = 9$ is true, then which of the following equations will be true?
    (a) $N + 9 = 0$ (b) $N - 9 = 0$ (c) $12 - N = 21$
    (d) $21 - N = 11$ (e) $12 - 21 = -N$ (f) $N + 3 = 21$.

7. If $N = 11$ is true, then which of the following equations will be false?
    (a) $19 + N = 20$ (b) $19 - N = 18$
    (c) $N - 19 = -8$ (d) $N + 9 = 31 - N$
    (e) $N - 6 = -(16 - N)$ (f) $23 - 12 = -N$.

8. Using N as the variable, express the following in mathematical symbols.
    (a) Take five away from a given number.
    (b) A given number and twelve.
    (c) Take five away from a given number and twelve.
    (d) Take five away from a given number and twelve and the result is ten less than seventeen.

9. Match the descriptions in the numbered column with the lettered column so that they best describe the properties illustrated.
    (a) $A + B = B + A$ 1. Equal addition.
    (b) Since $1 + 1 = 2, 1 + 1 + 1 = 2 + 1$ 2. Equal subtraction.
    (c) If $A = B, A - 3 = B - 3$ 3. Commutative.
    (d) $A - A = 0$ 4. Associative.
    (e) $3 + (7 + 4) = (3 + 7) + 4$ 5. Inverse.

10. Which of the following equations are equivalent to $N = 7$?
    (a) $N - 7 = 0$ (b) $3 + N = 4$ (c) $10 = N - 3$
    (d) $-7 = -(0 - N)$ (e) $4 - N = 11$ (f) $4 - 11 = -N$.

11. If $A = 5$, $B = -9$, and $C = 4$, then determine the truth or falsity of the following equations.
    (a) $A + C = -B$ (b) $A - B = C$ (c) $B + C = A$
    (d) $A + B - C = 0$ (e) $-(A - C) = B + 10$ (f) $2 - B = C + A$.

12. Find a justification for each step in the following:
    (a) $27 = -(8 - N)$ Given equation.
    (b) $27 + (8 - N) = -(8 - N) + (8 - N)$ _____
    (c) $(27 + 8) - N = 0$ _____
    (d) $35 - N = 0$ _____
    (e) $(35 - N) + N = 0 + N$ _____
    (f) $35 + (-N + N) = N$ _____
    (g) $35 + 0 = N$ _____
    (h) $35 = N$ _____
    (i) $27 = -(8 - 35)$ _____
    (j) $27 = -(-27)$ _____
    (k) $27 = 27$ _____
    (l) $N = 35$ _____

13. State what must be added to or subtracted from both sides of each of the following equations in order to "isolate" the variable N.

(a) $19 = 37 + N$ (b) $N + 9 = 23$ (c) $-7 + N = 16$
(d) $-31 = N + 7$ (e) $N - 9 = -5$ (f) $17 - N = 25$.

14. Which of the following pairs of equations are equivalent?

(a) $17 = N$ and $N + 0 = 17$ (b) $-(N - 4) = 7$ and $3 = N$
(c) $14 - N = 11$ and $N - 11 = 14$ (d) $N - 4 = 7$ and $-3 = -N$
(e) $1 - (5 - N) = 13$ and $N - 4 = 8$
(f) $(1 - 5) - N = 13$ and $13 + 4 = -N$.

15. Solve the following equations.

(a) $43 + N = 51$ (b) $-87 = N - 93$ (c) $N + 24 = 13$
(d) $N - 71 = 38$ (e) $60 = N - 57$ (f) $19 - N = -47$.

16. Solve the following equations.

(a) $69 - (N + 96) = 0$ (b) $74 = 30 - (N - 44)$
(c) $29 + (18 - N) = -47$ (d) $52 - N = -(85 - 39)$.

17. Determine the truth or falsity of the following statements.

(a) $8 - 11$ is an equation.
(b) $8 = 11$ is true.
(c) $11 = N - 7$ is an inequality.
(d) Equations are always true or false.
(e) In $8 + 11$, the $+$ indicates an operation.
(f) "536" is a numeral.
(g) The equation $A - B = D$ means $A = B + D$.
(h) Equivalent conditional equations have the same solutions.
(i) If $A < B$ and $B < C$, then $A < C$.
(j) The inverse of a negative integer is positive under addition.

18. Translate the following into mathematical symbols.

(a) If the discount on the auto was one hundred eighty dollars, then it would have cost ninety dollars more than my present auto.

(b) On December 31, 1962 there were ten more member states in the United Nations than the number of original charter members added to itself.

(c) Early estimates of the world's coffee crop in 1962 was placed at 65,932,000 bags. This was 6,277,000 bags less than the previous crop.

Solve the following problems using a "regular" procedure. After solving, present the problem in a well-organized, neat, and clear way.

19. Bill gave his week's paycheck to his wife Sue who spent twenty-four dollars for groceries, twenty-three dollars for the rent, and paid a sixteen-dollar debt. If Sue had nine dollars left, how large was Bill's paycheck?

20. A mathematics class had thirty-four students. Nine of these students were also taking English. If the English class had twenty-eight students in it, then how many students were in the two classes together?

21. A golfing foursome carded the following scores in four rounds of golf:

Round:	I	II	III	IV
Arny	74	78	75	81
Cook	75	76	83	79
Nick	82	74	79	80
Vern	77	77	81	77

Which of the golfers carded the lowest score for the four rounds of golf? In which round did the foursome have the lowest total score?

22. The clock time in New York is three hours later than in San Francisco. Mr. Jones, who is in San Francisco, wants to call his wife in New York on the phone at 5:00 P.M. New York time. If it is 9:00 A.M. in San Francisco, how many hours should Mr. Jones wait before calling New York?

23. If we wish to go from point A to point E in the maze depicted in Figure 45, which route would be the shortest and which the longest?

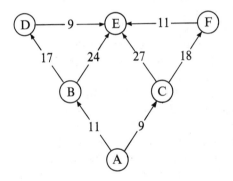

FIGURE 45

24. If the sum of a certain fixed multiple of five and seven is between two less than fourteen and four more than thirty-two, then find the multiples of five and seven.

Problem Set (3)

1. Solve the problem from the *Greek Anthology*:
The three Graces were carrying baskets of apples, and in each was the same number. The nine Muses met them and asked each for apples and they gave the same number to each Muse and the nine Muses and the three Graces each had the same number. How many apples did each Grace give and how many did each have?

2. Solve the Chinese pursuit problem:

A man who had stolen a horse rode away on its back. When he had gone 38 miles the owner discovered the theft and pursued the thief for 150 miles. He then returned being unable to overtake the thief. When he turned back the thief was riding 23 miles ahead of him. If he had continued in his pursuit without turning back, then in how many miles would he have overtaken the thief?

3. Solve the "Apples and the Gatekeeper" problem:

A man went into an orchard which had seven gates, and while there took a certain number of apples. When he left, he gave one more than half the apples he had to the first gate guard. To the second guard at the second gate he gave half of his remaining apples and one apple more. He did the same at each of the remaining five gates and left the orchard with just one apple. How many apples did he take in the orchard?

4. Solve the "contemporary" problem:

Miss Allan was very sensitive about her age and tried to keep it a secret. However, liking parties, she held a birthday party one year and on being questioned by one of her guests she said: "If you take the difference between the sum of this year and the year of my birth and twice the year of my tenth birthday, then the result will be 21." How old was Miss Allan?

CHAPTER 4

Multiplication

4.1 Factors and Products

4.1.1   In our brief excursion into the natural numbers in Chapter 1, we noted that we could select subsets of the natural numbers by considering arrangements of elements in rows with the same number of elements in each row. For example, five rows with the same number of elements as illustrated in Figure 46. We called subsets selected in this

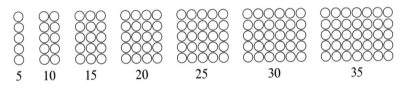

FIGURE 46

way **multiples** of the fixed number of rows. Furthermore, we noted that counting columns would result in 1, 2, 3, . . . columns. That is, if we had three columns of fives, we called this "three fives" and indicated this idea by writing 3 × 5 or 3(5) but **not** 35. The number of rows and the number of columns are called **factors** of the multiple.

$$5 \quad \times \quad 7 \quad = \quad 35$$
Factor   Factor   Multiple   (of both 5 and of 7)

Examples.

(a)   In $7 \times 9 = 63$ we can interpret 63 as both a multiple of 7 and of 9. We say that 7 and 9 are factors of 63.

(b) $33 = (3)(11)$ tells us that 33 is a multiple of 3 and of 11; 3 and 11 are called factors of 33.

(c)   If $M = (A)(B)$, where M, A, and B stand for numbers, then we can say that *M* is a multiple of *A* and of *B* and that *A* and *B* are factors of *M*.

In our discussion of multiples we emphasized the number properties of the situation rather than the operation involved. Observing that multiples can be interpreted as the counting of sets of a fixed cardinal size, we can reinterpret this situation as a repeated addition operation. That is, when we write $7 \times 6 = 42$ we can think of the "7" as indicating the number of addends "6" which are added together to obtain the sum $42: 6+6+6+6+6+6+6=42$. When interpreted in this way, we call the result a **product** and the operation **multiplication**. That is, multiplication of integers is a "shortcut" operation for finding the sum of repeated additions of the same addend. One of the equal addends is called the **multiplicand** while the number of times the multiplicand is added to itself is called the **multiplier**. We read $6 \times 4 = 24$ as "six times four is equal to twenty-four." In $6 \times 4 = 24$, 6 is the multiplier, 4 is the multiplicand, and 24 is called the product.

$$5 \quad \times \quad 7 \quad = \quad 35$$
Multiplier   Multiplicand   Product

We also write,   7   **Multiplicand**

(Multiplication sign) $\times$ 5   **Multiplier**

35   **Product**

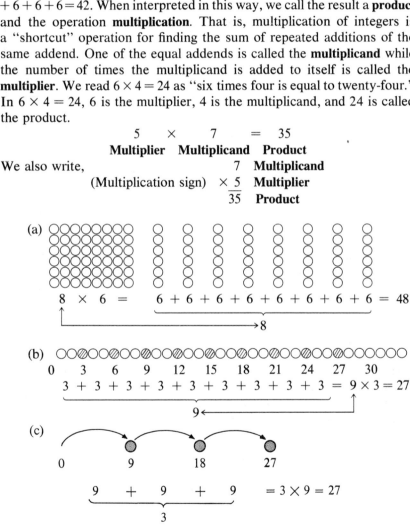

FIGURE 47

As with addition and subtraction, we begin with the simpler basic multiplication facts. These should be practiced until they become automatic. Observe that we can interpret Table 13 in two distinct ways: (1) As a table of multiples, and (2) as a table of products. As multiples, the marginal entries are factors and the entries in the body of the table are multiples of the marginal entries in the row and column. As products, the left-hand marginal entries are thought of as the multipliers and the top marginal entries as the multiplicands with the products in the body of Table 13.

TABLE 13.   **Basic Multiplication Facts.**

×	1	2	3	4	5	6	7	8	9	10
1	1	2	3	4	5	6	7	8	9	10
2	2	4	6	8	10	12	14	16	18	20
3	3	6	9	12	15	18	21	24	27	30
4	4	8	12	16	20	24	28	32	36	40
5	5	10	15	20	25	30	35	40	45	50
6	6	12	18	24	30	36	42	48	54	60
7	7	14	21	28	35	42	49	56	63	70
8	8	16	24	32	40	48	56	64	72	80
9	9	18	27	36	45	54	63	72	81	90
10	10	20	30	40	50	60	70	80	90	100

For convenience we will often refer to the marginal entries in the table as factors, while the entries in the body of the table will be called products. Notice that the main diagonal entries from upper left to lower right are "square" numbers. We should also observe that rows and columns are "paired"; that is, if the marginal entries are the same, then the row and column entries are the same. Also note that the entries in a row or column are all even or alternate between odd and even. (Why?) Multiples of five always "end" (have a one's digit of) in "0" or "5" while the multiples of ten always end in "0." Many further observations might be made.

Certain basic products usually cause difficulties. Do Practice Set 1 until there is no hesitation in giving the correct products.

Practice 1.	(a)	(b)	(c)	(d)	(e)	(f)
1.	9	7	9	3	5	8
	×5	×7	×4	×9	×9	×3
2.	6	8	4	9	8	5
	×7	×5	×9	×7	×6	×7

3.   9   7   8   6   7   4
       ×8   ×4   ×9   ×8   ×5   ×7

4.   4   3   7   6   8   7
       ×8   ×8   ×6   ×9   ×4   ×8

5.   9   5   8   7   9   8
       ×3   ×8   ×8   ×9   ×6   ×7

Answers.	(a)	(b)	(c)	(d)	(e)	(f)
1.	45	49	36	27	45	24
2.	42	40	36	63	48	35
3.	72	28	72	48	35	28
4.	32	24	42	54	32	56
5.	27	40	64	63	54	56

4.1.2 In multiplication, as in addition, the **commutative** and **associative** properties are true. For example, $5 \times 7 = 7 \times 5$ and $2 \times (5 \times 7) = (2 \times 5) \times 7$. That is, if A, B, and C are positive integers, then $A \times B = B \times A$ and $A \times (B \times C) = (A \times B) \times C$. The order of multiplication is immaterial and we need only consider one arrangement of factors forming a product.

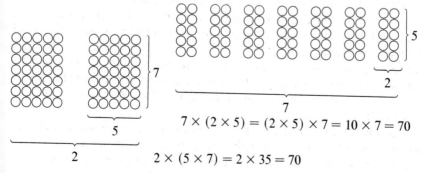

5    $5 \times 7 = 35$ $7 \times 5 = 35$

FIGURE 48

$7 \times (2 \times 5) = (2 \times 5) \times 7 = 10 \times 7 = 70$

$2 \times (5 \times 7) = 2 \times 35 = 70$

FIGURE 49

In terms of addition, the commutative and associative properties of multiplication are not so obvious. For example, $5 \times 7 = 7 \times 5$ would mean that the sum of five sevens must equal the sum of seven fives. When we write $2 \times (5 \times 7) = (2 \times 5) \times 7$ in terms of addition, we would have $(7+7+7+7+7) + (7+7+7+7+7) = (5+5) + (5+5) + (5+5) + (5+5) + (5+5) + (5+5) + (5+5)$ where we have assumed the commutative property of multiplication on the right. It should be quite evident why multiplication is an advantageous "shortcut" for addition.

By far the most important property of multiplication is, however, a property which connects addition to multiplication. The idea is illustrated in Figures 50 and 51. This joint property of addition and multiplication is

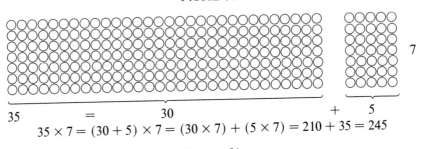

$$(3 \times 5) + (7 \times 5) \qquad = \qquad (3+7) \times 5$$

FIGURE 50

$$35 \times 7 = (30+5) \times 7 = (30 \times 7) + (5 \times 7) = 210 + 35 = 245$$

FIGURE 51

called the **distributive** property of multiplication over addition. For example, if we wish to find the sum of the products 3×5 and 7×5 we could first find the products and then sum the results: $(3 \times 5) + (7 \times 5) = 15 + 35 = 50$. On the other hand, if we notice that both products are multiples of 5, we could reason that the sum of the multiples of 5 would result in the same total: $3(5) + 7(5) = (3+7)(5) = 10(5) = 50$. Conversely, if we have a product such that one of the factors could be written as a sum, then we might reason that the product could be "split" into two separate products. For example, $35 \times 7 = (30+5) \times 7 = (30 \times 7) + (5 \times 7) = 210 + 35$.

The **distributive** property of multiplication over addition will enable us to show how any two positive integers can be multiplied to obtain a product. Using variables, this universally true property of multiplication over addition is stated as: If A, B, and C are positive integers, then $(A + B) \times C = (A \times C) + (B \times C)$. Also, $C \times (A + B) = (C \times A) + (C \times B)$.

Examples.

(a) $(17 \times 9) + (8 \times 9) = (17 + 8) \times 9 = 25 \times 9$.
(b) $25 \times 9 = (20 + 5) \times 9 = (20 \times 9) + (5 \times 9)$.
(c) $32(9) + 18(9) = (32 + 18)\,(9) = 50(9)$.

Zero and one, 0 and 1, are of special interest in multiplication. Re-calling that 0 was the identity element for addition, $N + 0 = N$ for any integer N, we observe that 1 plays a similar role in multiplication: $N \times 1 = N$ for any integer N. Thus, we call one, 1, the **identity** element of multiplication. If we note that adding any number of zeroes together, $0 + 0 + \cdots + 0$, will result in zero, we have $N \times 0 = 0$ for any integer N. In ordinary English, we might express these properties as:
"Any multiple of one is equal to that multiple."
"Any multiple of zero is zero."

Examples.

(a) $6 \times 1 = 1 + 1 + 1 + 1 + 1 + 1 = 6$.
(b) $452 \times 1 = \underbrace{1 + 1 + \cdots + 1}_{452} = 452$.

(c) $6 \times 0 = 0 + 0 + 0 + 0 + 0 + 0 = 0$.
(d) $452 \times 0 = \underbrace{0 + 0 + \cdots + 0}_{452} = 0$.

Since multiplication is commutative, we can write
$1 \times N = N \times 1 = N$ and $0 \times N = N \times 0 = 0$.
In ordinary English, we can say that:
"One times any integer is equal to that integer."
"Zero times any integer is zero."

Examples.

(a) $1 \times \underbrace{6}_{1} = 6$.

(b) $1 \times \underbrace{452}_{1} = 452$.

(c) $0 \times 6 = 0$. (Notice why the number zero was difficult to interpret and understand.)

(d) $0 \times 452 = 0$. (We add "no" 452's together to obtain 0.)

Although the above properties of zero and one appear to be extremely simple and "obvious," ignoring and/or forgetting them can lead to many errors and subsequent confusion.

4.1.3 Before proceeding to the general question of multiplying two factors to obtain a product, let us consider briefly the special case of multiplying by 10, 100, 1000, and so forth. For example, $152 \times 10 = 152 \times (1 \text{ ten} + 0 \text{ ones}) = (152 \times 1) \text{ tens} + (152 \times 0) \text{ ones} = 152 \text{ tens} + 0 \text{ ones} = 1520$. Notice that we expand the numeral, apply the distributive property, then use the properties of 1 and 0. Since multiplication is commutative, we have $10 \times 152 = 152 \times 10 = 1520$. A few observations should make it evident that

Examples.

(a) $742 \times 10 = 7420$ (b) $742 \times 100 = 74200$

(c) $\begin{array}{r} 365 \\ \times\ 10 \\ \hline 3650 \end{array}$ (d) $\begin{array}{r} 365 \\ \times\ 100 \\ \hline 36500 \end{array}$ (e) $\begin{array}{r} 365 \\ \times\ 1000 \\ \hline 365000 \end{array}$

multiplying by 10, 100, 1000, and so forth, is an extremely simple process; we simply "shift" the place positions of the digits to the left the same number of places as there are zeroes.

Practice 2.

1. Name the property illustrated by each of the following equations.
    (a) $3 \times (7 \times 4) = (3 \times 7) \times 4$ (b) $3 \times (7+4) = (3 \times 7) + (3 \times 4)$
    (c) $3 \times (7 \times 4) = (7 \times 4) \times 3$ (d) $(7+4) \times 3 = (7 \times 3) + (4 \times 3)$
    (e) $(7 \times 4) \times 3 = 7 \times (4 \times 3)$ (f) $(4 \times 3) \times 7 = 7 \times (4 \times 3)$.
2. Find the value of N in each of the following equations so that the equations will be true.
    (a) $5 \times N = 5$ (b) $5 \times N = 0$ (c) $N \times 1 = 7$
    (d) $0 \times 7 = N$ (e) $1 \times 9 = N$ (f) $N \times 0 = 0$.
3. Do as in Practice Exercise 2:
    (a) $1 \times 1 = N$ (b) $1 \times 0 = N$ (c) $0 \times 0 = N$
    (d) $0 \times N = 0$ (e) $1 \times N = 1$ (f) $1 \times N = 0$.
4. Find the products:
    (a) 36×10 (b) 36×1000 (c) 100×36

(d) 102×100 (e) 10×81 (f) 1×5219
(g) 100×300 (h) 500×1000 (i) 904×1.

5. Find the products:
(a) $3 \times (7 \times 0)$ (b) $(9 \times 1) \times 4$ (c) $3 \times (10 \times 7)$
(d) $(100 \times 1) \times 6$ (e) $10 \times (100 \times 1)$ (f) $70 \times (0 \times 10)$
(g) $5 \times (1 \times 0)$ (h) $(9 \times 3) \times 1$ (i) $(1000 \times 100) \times 10$.

6. Find the products:
(a) $7 \times (0 + 5)$ (b) $0 \times (5 + 8)$ (c) $(10 + 2) \times 1$
(d) $(9 + 1) \times 8$ (e) $3 \times (100 + 1)$ (f) $(3 + 6) \times 9$
(g) $1 \times (10 + 0)$ (h) $5 \times (1 + 100)$ (i) $(4 + 1) \times 0$.

7. Find the products:
(a) $6 \times (100 + 10 + 1)$.
(b) $[3 \times (4 \times 10)] + (3 \times 7)$.
(c) $[7 \times (1 \times 100)] + [7 \times (3 \times 10)] + [7 \times (5 \times 1)]$.
(d) $9 \times [(8 \times 100) + (0 \times 10) + (7 \times 1)]$.

Answers.

1. (a) Associative   (b) Distributive   (c) Commutative
   (d) Distributive   (e) Associative   (f) Commutative.
2. (a) 1   (b) 0   (c) 7   (d) 0   (e) 9   (f) Any number.
3. (a) 1   (b) 0   (c) 0   (d) Any number   (e) 1   (f) 0.
4. (a) 360   (b) 36000   (c) 3600   (d) 10200   (e) 810
   (f) 5219   (g) 30000   (h) 500,000   (i) 904.
5. (a) 0   (b) 36   (c) 210   (d) 600   (e) 1000   (f) 0
   (g) 0   (h) 27   (i) 1,000,000.
6. (a) 35   (b) 0   (c) 12   (d) 80   (e) 303   (f) 81   (g) 10
   (h) 505   (i) 0.
7. (a) 666   (b) 141   (c) 945   (d) 7263.

4.1.4   Historically many different, awkward, and cumbersome-appearing methods were devised for multiplication. The "lattice" method dates back to the early Hindus and, except for its time consuming construction, is quite sound. The method consists of constructing a rectangular "lattice" as shown in Figure 52. The multiplication of 3516 by 194 was, for example, found by constructing a four-by-three rectangle with the multiplicand written along the top row and the multiplier along the right margin. The single-digit products were entered into the diagonally divided squares. Beginning with the left-hand digits we have $1 \times 3 = 3$ in the top left square, $1 \times 5 = 5$ in the square to its right, and so on. Note the blanks left where no entry is needed. In the second row of squares we have $9 \times 3 = 27$, $9 \times 5 = 45$, and so forth. After the squares have been completed as shown, the entries are added along the diagonals from lower

multiplicand

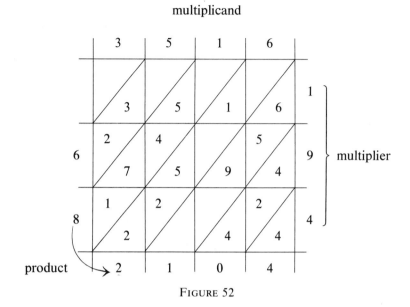

FIGURE 52

left to upper right. The product then appears along the left and bottom margins (as the sum). That is, $194 \times 3516 = 682,104$.

Napier's "Bones" was a device invented by a Scotch mathematician. John Napier (1550–1617), to take advantage of the "lattice" method of multiplication. The flat wooden rods, called "bones," had successive multiples of the digits inscribed on them for ease in obtaining products.

The ancient Egyptians used a method of doubling or duplication to obtain products. In this method one must know the successive products obtained by using 2 repeatedly as a factor. For example, 2, $2 \times 2 = 4$, $2 \times 4 = 8$, $2 \times 8 = 16$, and so forth. Furthermore, one must be able to express any numeral in terms of a sum of these products. That is, $13 = 1 + 4 + 8$ and $27 = 1 + 2 + 8 + 16$.

To find the product of 56 and 13, we might proceed as follows: $56 \times 13 = 56 \times (1 + 4 + 8) = (56 \times 1) + (56 \times 4) + (56 \times 8) = 56 + [(56 \times 2) \times 2] + ([(56 \times 2) \times 2] \times 2)$. We can tabulate the products of 56 with 2:

$$
\begin{array}{ll}
56 & 56 \\
56 \times 2 = 112 & \\
112 \times 2 = 224 & 224 \\
224 \times 2 = 448 & 448 \\
& \overline{} \\
56 \times 13 = & \overline{728}
\end{array}
$$

The doubling method has its virtue in that only a few facts need be known and that the process of doubling is quite simple. In fact the method has never been completely lost and is probably still in use.

Our contemporary method of multiplication is based on the expansion of decimal numerals and the application of the distributive property of multiplication. We first consider a one-digit multiplier with multiplicands of two or more digits. For example, $8 \times 47 = 376$ and $6 \times 293 = 1758$.

Examples.

(a) $8 \times 47 = 8 \times (40 + 7) = (8 \times 40) + (8 \times 7) = 320 + 56 = 376.$

Or
$$\begin{array}{r} 47 \\ \times\ 8 \\ \hline 56 \\ 320 \\ \hline 376 \end{array}$$

$$= \quad 4 \text{ tens} + \quad 7 \text{ ones}$$
$$\underline{\qquad\qquad 8 \qquad\qquad}$$
$$32 \text{ tens} + 56 \text{ ones} = 3 \text{ hundreds} + (2 + 5) \text{ tens} + 6 \text{ ones}$$
$$= 376$$

The single-digit products "32 tens" and "56 ones" are called **partial products**.

(b) $6 \times 293 = 6 \times (200 + 90 + 3) = (6 \times 200) + (6 \times 90) + (6 \times 3)$
$$= (1200) + (540) + (18) = 1758.$$

Or
$$\begin{array}{r} 293 \\ \times\ 6 \\ \hline 18 \\ 540 \\ 1200 \\ \hline 1758 \end{array}$$

$$= \quad 2 \text{ hundreds} + \quad 9 \text{ tens} + \quad 3 \text{ ones}$$
$$\underline{\qquad\qquad\qquad 6 \qquad\qquad\qquad}$$
$$12 \text{ hundreds} + 54 \text{ tens} + 18 \text{ ones}$$
$$= 1 \text{ thousands} + (2 + 5) \text{ hundreds} + (4 + 1) \text{ tens} + 8 \text{ ones}$$
$$= 1758$$

(c)
$$\begin{array}{r} 7\ 0\ 1\ 5 \\ \times \qquad 9 \\ \hline 4\ 5 \\ 9\ 0 \\ 0\ 0\ 0 \\ 6\ 3\ 0\ 0\ 0 \\ \hline 6\ 3\ 1\ 3\ 5 \end{array}$$

Notice the alignment of the digits and the result of adding 9×0 hundreds. The multiplication can easily be abbreviated by "carrying" the next higher place digit in each step of the multiplication.

$$\begin{array}{r} 7\ 0\ 1\ 5 \\ \times \qquad 9 \\ \hline 5 \\ 3 \\ 1 \\ 6\ 3 \\ \hline 6\ 3\ 1\ 3\ 5 \end{array}$$

"carry" four.
$9 + 4 = 13$, "carry" one.
$0 + 1 = 1$.
$9 \times 7 = 63$.

$$\begin{array}{r} 7\ 0\ 1\ 5 \quad \text{(multiplicand)} \\ \times \qquad 9 \quad \text{(multiplier)} \\ \hline 6\ 3\ 1\ 3\ 5 \quad \text{(product)} \end{array}$$

(d) $\begin{array}{|c|c|c|c|}\hline 3 & 1 & 7 & 0 \\\hline\end{array}$ is abbreviated to

$$
\times \quad\quad\quad 7
$$

```
(d)  |3|1|7|0|   is abbreviated to      |3|1|7|0|  (multiplicand)
   × |   |   | 7|                     × |   |   | 7|  (multiplier)
     |   |   | 0|                      |2|2|1|9|0|  (product)
     |   | 9 |  |
     | 1 |   |  |
   2 | 2 |   |  |
   2 | 2 | 1 | 9 | 0
```

Practice 3. *   "Carry" mentally and write only the products.

	(a)	(b)	(c)	(d)	(e)
1.	81 6	72 4	60 5	94 2	53 7
2.	37 4	95 3	86 7	45 9	67 5
3.	49 7	90 9	58 8	37 8	89 6
4.	513 3	732 4	481 7	962 2	835 6
5.	850 8	362 7	874 9	409 6	145 5
6.	7140 4	8302 2	3619 7	5397 6	2091 9
7.	6347 3	4089 5	1736 9	5591 7	9586 8
8.	3 × 74	6 × 85	9 × 92	8 × 83	5 × 27
9.	2 × 752	9 × 791	8 × 105	4 × 477	7 × 769
10.	3 × 5170	7 × 9672	4 × 7510	9 × 9605	8 × 8769

* Note: The multiplication sign, "×," has been omitted as understood.

Answers.

	(a)	(b)	(c)	(d)	(e)
1.	486	288	300	188	371
2.	148	285	602	405	335
3.	343	810	464	296	534

4.	1539	2928	3367	1924	5010
5.	6800	2534	7866	2454	725
6.	28560	16604	25333	32382	18819
7.	19041	20445	15624	39137	76688
8.	222	510	828	664	135
9.	1504	7119	840	1908	5383
10.	15510	67704	30040	86445	70152

4.1.5   In order to multiply by numbers with two or more "places" in their numerals, we repeat the process of expansion and apply the distributive property twice. Place positions of the digits must be carefully observed and single-digit products should be automatic for rapid and accurate multiplication.

Examples.

(a) $52 \times 37 = (50 + 2) \times 37 = (50 \times 37) + (2 \times 37)$
$= [50 \times (30 + 7)] + [2 \times (30 + 7)]$
$= [(50 \times 30) + (50 \times 7)] + [(2 \times 30) + (2 \times 7)]$
$= [1500 + 350] + [60 + 14] = 1850 + 74 = 1924.$

Or   37   which can be thought of as:
$\times 52$

74	37		37		
1850	$\times 50$		$\times 2$		
1924	1850	+	74	=	1924

The single-digit products, 1850 and 74, are called **partial products** for 52×37.

(b)   481   multiplicand
$\times 69$ multiplier
4329   partial product: $9 \times 481 = 4329$.
2886   partial product: (6×481) tens $= 2886$ tens.
33189   product: $4329 + 28860 = 33189$.

(c) $69 \times 481 = (60 + 9) \times 481 = (60 \times 481) + (9 \times 481)$
$= 28860 + 4329 = 33189.$

Or rewriting: $9 \times 481 = 4329$ ⎫
$60 \times 481 = 28860$ ⎬ partial products.
$69 \times 481 = 33189$ product is the sum.

(d)

		5	3	8	0		Notice the effect of the digit 0 in shifting the
	$\times$		2	7	6		place positions of the partial products.
		3	2	2	8	0	
	3	7	6	6	0		
1	0	7	6	0			
1	4	8	4	8	8	0	

(e)

```
      | 4 | 9 | 0 | 1 |
  × |   | 7 | 5 | 0 |
  ---------------------
      |   |   |   | 0 |
  | 2 | 4 | 5 | 0 | 5 |
3 | 4 | 3 | 0 | 7 |
3 | 6 | 7 | 5 | 7 | 5 | 0 |
```

Proper place positioning of the digits in the partial products and the final product must be carefully observed.

Practice 4. Write only the partial products and products.

	(a)	(b)	(c)	(d)	(e)
1.	72	56	81	37	90
	32	45	79	60	51
2.	48	16	52	71	93
	82	26	90	45	93
3.	13	65	54	97	40
	81	28	39	76	80
4.	901	841	258	439	340
	67	47	25	80	62
5.	528	908	457	379	380
	61	70	35	42	61
6.	741	954	176	105	890
	329	630	761	487	2$ $8
7.	271 × 507	930 × 891	268 × 814	504 × 752	739 × 426
8.	683 × 753	628 × 296	905 × 370	714 × 869	174 × 341
9.	509 × 645	463 × 906	815 × 290	258 × 813	647 × 523
10.	7123	4805	6921	3850	6479
	457	624	309	380	817
11.	6059	2791	4035	7483	8132
	1562	6219	7921	3057	6981
12.	3150	7900	1005	4060	2181
	4051	6890	7211	1009	1900

Answers.

	(a)	(b)	(c)	(d)	(e)
1.	2304	2520	6399	2220	4590
2.	3936	416	4680	3195	8649

3.	1,053	1,820	2,106	7,372	3,200
4.	60,367	39,527	6,450	35,120	21,080
5.	32,208	63,560	15,995	15,918	23,180
6.	243,789	601,020	133,936	51,135	265,220
7.	137,397	828,630	218,152	379,008	314,814
8.	514,299	185,888	334,850	620,466	59,334
9.	328,305	419,478	236,350	209,754	338,381
10.	3,255,211	2,998,320	2,138,589	1,463,000	5,293,343
11.	9,464,158	17,357,229	31,961,235	22,875,531	56,769,492
12.	12,760,650	54,431,000	7,247,055	4,096,540	4,143,900

4.1.6 Observation and study of the practice problems should suggest possibilities for many refinements. When zero occurs in a multiplicand, the partial products are simplified by noting that $N \times 0 = 0$. Be careful to avoid the common error of incorrect place positioning of the digits in a partial product.

Examples.

(a)
```
  70402      The first partial product:    70402
×    39                                  ×     9
------                                   -------
633618                                        18
211206                                         0
------                                        36
2745678                                        0
                                              63
                                         -------
                                         633618
```

```
             The second partial product:    70402
                                          ×     30
                                          -------
                                                6
                                                0
                                               12
                                                0
                                               21
                                          -------
                                          2112060
```

(b)
```
  70003
×    62
------
140006
420018
-------
4340186
```

(c)
```
  73500     can be abbreviated since
×    94
------
294000      73500 = 735 × 100 and
661500
-------
6909000         735
              × 94
              -----
              2940
              6615
              -----
              69090 × 100 = 6909000
```

When zeroes occur in a multiplier, the number of partial products is reduced. Note that the partial products are aligned so that the right-hand digit is directly below the digit of the multiplier used to obtain it.

Examples.

(a)
```
    583    can be abbreviated to:        583
  × 205                                × 205
   2915                                 2915
    000                                 1166
   1166                                119515
  119515
```

(b)
```
   1825    Notice that the alignment of the partial products is
 × 4003    especially important.
   5475
  7300
  7305475
```

(c)
```
    407005
  ×   1004
   1628020
   407005
  408633020
```

When zeroes occur at the "end" of the multiplicand or multiplier, the zeroes can be separated from the multiplication process and reintroduced into the product after a simplified multiplication has been accomplished.

Examples.

(a)
```
  37200    is accomplished by noting that:
 × 420
```
$$420 \times 37200 = (42 \times 10) \times (372 \times 100)$$
$$= (42 \times 372) \times (10 \times 100)$$
$$= 15{,}624 \times 1000 = 15{,}624{,}000.$$

In an abbreviated form we could write:
```
    37200
  × 420
     744
    1488
  15624000
```

(b)   8 0 4 0 0 0
        × 2 0 1 0 0
        _____
            8 0 4
    1 6 0 8
    _____
    1 6,1 6 0,4 0 0,0 0 0
                    ‿‿‿‿‿
            five zeroes.

(c)   5 6 3 0 0
        ×   4 7 0 0 0 0
        _____
        3 9 4 1
    2 2 5 2
    _____
    2 6,4 6 1,0 0 0,0 0 0
                ‿‿‿‿‿‿
            six zeroes.

Exercises

1. Subsets of the natural numbers selected by considering arrangements of elements in sets with a fixed number of rows were called _____ of the number of rows. The number of rows and the number of columns in such an arrangement were called _____. If we reinterpret the situation as a repeated addition of a fixed cardinal number, we call the resulting "shortcut" operation _____ and the result of the operation a _____.

2. In $9 \times 7 = 63$ the 9 is called the _____, the 7 the _____, and 63 the _____ when considered as a multiplication operation.

3. Since $1 \times 24 = 2 \times 12 = 3 \times 8 = 4 \times 6 = 24$, 24 can be thought of as a multiple (or product) with the paired factors: _____ and _____, _____ and _____, _____ and _____, _____ and _____. The **prime factors** of 24 are _____ and _____.

4. Describe the successive multiples of nine in terms of the digits appearing in the one's place position; the ten's place position.

5. Write an equation describing the factors and multiples suggested by the following arrangements:

(a) 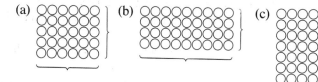   (b)   (c)

6. Rearrange the multiples of Exercise 5 so that all of the factors appearing will be prime. (There may be more than two factors.)

7. Write an equation which describes the important property illustrated by the arrangement below:

8. Find the value of N in each of the following equations so that the equation will be true.

(a) $7 \times N = 0$ (b) $1 \times N = 7$ (c) $7 \times 1 = N$
(d) $N \times 7 = 7$ (e) $0 = 7 \times N$ (f) $1 = N \times 1$.

9. Find the products:

(a) $(31 \times 1) \times 1000$ (b) $20 \times (300 + 5)$ (c) $10 \times (100 \times 0)$
(d) $(70 + 8) \times 5$ (e) $(47 \times 1) \times 9$ (f) $14 \times (9 + 0)$.

10. Find the products:

(a) $74 \times (300 + 80 + 4)$ (b) $29 \times (500 + 60 + 7)$
(c) $(600 + 50 + 9) \times 87$ (d) $(900 + 10 + 0) \times 56$.

11. Find the product of 735 and 27 by the "lattice" method; by the doubling method.

12. Find the value of N in each of the following equations so that the equation will be true.

(a) $7 \times N = 35$ (b) $9 \times 11 = N$ (c) $N \times 16 = 48$
(d) $37 \times 64 = N$ (e) $85 \times N = 255$ (f) $19 \times 76 = N$.

13. Find the products:

(a)	3104	(b)	81002	(c)	50107	(d)	73010
	× 92		× 503		× 710		× 6400

(e)	40029	(f)	210101	(g)	370592	(h)	400001
	× 1010		× 9110		× 1200		× 7956

14. Do as indicated:

(a) Multiply 1760 by 503   (b) Find 250 times 404
(c) $21 \times 2{,}000{,}000 = ?$ (d) What is 80 times 90 equal to?

15. Do as indicated:

(a) What is the product of ninety-nine and three hundred?

(b) What must sixty-four be multiplied by in order to result in a product equal to zero?

(c) What must thirty-six be multiplied by in order to result in the product thirty-six?

(d) If the last three digits "on the right" of a product are zeroes, then what can we say about one of the factors?

16. A man works eight hours each working day, five days each week, forty weeks each year. How many hours does he work in one year?

17. There are sixty seconds in each minute and sixty minutes in each hour. How many seconds are there in the twenty-four hour day?

18. In a closed course endurance run an auto averaged 74 miles per hour for 53 hours. How many miles did the auto cover?

19. If the product of two factors is an odd number, what can you say about the factors? If the product is even, what can you say about at least one of the factors?

20. An auto dealer sold three thousand five hundred autos during a certain year. If the average profit on each auto sold was two hundred fifty-two dollars, what was the dealer's total profit for the year?

21. The velocity of light is approximately 186,000 miles per second. How far will light travel in one hour?

22. Boxes of goods stored in a warehouse are arranged in neat rows. If there are 110 boxes in each row, 1010 rows, and the boxes are stacked 101 boxes high, then how many boxes of goods are stored in the warehouse?

23. A satellite travels approximately 28,000 miles in one revolution about the earth. If one revolution takes two hours, how far will the satellite have traveled in one day?

24. If the "square" of the sum of the digits of a two-digit numeral is equal to four times the product of the digits, then what can you say about the two-digit numeral?

Answers.

1. multiples; factors; multiplication, product.
2. multiplier, multiplicand, product.
3. 1 and 24, 2 and 12, 3 and 8, 4 and 6; 2 and 3.
4. The one's digits precess by ones: 9, 8, 7, and so on. The ten's digits increase by ones: 0, 1, 2, and so on.
5. (a) $6 \times 5 = 30$ (b) $9 \times 4 = 36$ (c) $10 \times 7 = 70$.
6. (a) $30 = 2 \times (3 \times 5)$ (b) $36 = (2 \times 2) \times (3 \times 3)$
   (c) $70 = 2 \times (5 \times 7)$.
7. $(9 + 4) \times 3 = (9 \times 3) + (4 \times 3) = 13 \times 3$.
8. (a) 0   (b) 7   (c) 7   (d) 1   (e) 0   (f) 1.
9. (a) 31,000   (b) 6100   (c) 0   (d) 390   (e) 423
   (f) 126.
10. (a) 28,416   (b) 16,443   (c) 57,333   (d) 50,960.

11. The "lattice" method:

	7	3	5	
1	1		1	2
	4	6		
	4	2	3	7
9	9	1	5	
	8	4	5	

Doubling method:

$$735 \times 27 = 735 \times (1 + 2 + 8 + 16)$$

735	735
$735 \times 2 = 1470$	1470
$1470 \times 2 = 2940$	
$2940 \times 2 = 5880$	5880
$5880 \times 2 = 11760$	11760
Product:	19845

Product: 19,845

12. (a) 5   (b) 99   (c) 3   (d) 2368   (e) 3   (f) 1444.
13. (a) 285,568   (b) 40,744,006   (c) 35,575,970
    (d) 467,264,000   (e) 40,429,290   (f) 1,914,020,110
    (g) 444,710,400   (h) 3,182,407,956.
14. (a) 885,280   (b) 101,000   (c) 42,000,000   (d) 7,200.
15. (a) 29,700   (b) 0   (c) 1   (d) There must be a factor of 1000.
16. 1600 hours.
17. 86,400 seconds.
18. 3922 miles.
19. They must both be odd; At least one even.
20. $882,000.
21. 669,600,000 miles.
22. 11,221,100 boxes.
23. 336,000 miles.
24. The two digits are the same, that is, 11, 22, 33, and so forth.

4.2 Rounding, Estimating, and Checking

4.2.1   In calculating with large values it is common sense to approximate or estimate answers. As an old Persian proverb says, "One pound of learning requires ten pounds of common sense to apply it." For example, if we are told that 516 people each contributed 28 dollars to a certain charity, we could quickly estimate the total funds contributed by these people by reasoning as follows:

516 is just a "little" larger than 500; 28 is "almost" 30; $500 \times 30 = 15,000$ so that "about" $15,000 was contributed.

Of course, we cannot be certain just how "close" our estimate is to the exact amount. In approximating or estimating values, it is desirable to "**round off**" numerals to name the nearest multiple of 10, 100, 1000, and so forth. The population of California in 1960 was 15,717,204. We might round this to the nearest multiple of 1000 which would be 15,717,000. To the nearest 10,000 the population estimate would be 15,720,000. Notice the use of "place holding" zeroes.

Examples.

   (a) 516 rounded to the nearest multiple of 10 is 520.

   510   511   512   513   514   515   516   517   518   519   520
   510   516   520
   |←————————————6————————————→|←————————4————————→|

   (b) 516 rounded to the nearest multiple of 100 is 500.

   500   510   520   530   540   550   560   570   580   590   600
   500 < 516   <   600
   |←16→|←————————————————84————————————————→|

   (c) 2,374 rounded to the nearest multiple of 10 is 2,370.

   2,370   <   2,374   <   2,380
   |←————4————→|←——————————6——————————→|

   (d) 2,374 rounded to the nearest multiple of 100 is 2,400.

   2,300   <   2,374   <   2,400
   |←——————————74——————————→|←——————————26————————→|

   (e) 2,374 rounded to the nearest multiple of 1000 is 2,000.

   2,000   <   2,374   <   3,000
   |←——————————374——————————→|←——————————626————————→|

   (f) To round 275 to the nearest multiple of 10 requires a special **convention** or agreement. A common convention is to round to the even digit. Thus, we round 275 to 280.

   270   271   272   273   274   275   276   277   278   279   280
   270   275   280
   |←————————————5————————————→|←————————5————————→|

   In rounding numerals we say that we "**round up**" or "**round down**" according to whether the rounded numeral is larger than or smaller than the given numeral. That is, 516 rounded up to 520 and 516 rounded down to 510. In Example (d) above we have rounded 2,374 up to 2,400 while in Example (e) we have rounded 2,374 down to 2,000.

   If the digit in the place position to be rounded is 0, 1, 2, 3, or 4 we round down. If the digit is 6, 7, 8, or 9 we round up. In rounding up, if the digit to the left is a 9, we add and "carry" the "1" to the next place position to the left leaving a 0. If the digit in the place position to be rounded is a 5, we agree to round to the even digit. That is, we round up if the digit to the left is odd and round down if the digit to the left is even (including 0). In computations this will tend to lessen the errors.

Examples.

    (a) Rounding to the nearest multiple of 10:

        231 rounded down to 230.   237 rounded up to 240.

        296 rounded up to 300.   235 rounded up to 240.

        205 rounded down to 200.   245 rounded down to 240.

    (b) Rounding to the nearest multiple of 100:

        12,647 rounded down to 12,600.

        27,577 rounded up to 27,600.

        5,961 rounded up to 6,000.

        68,750 rounded up to 68,800.

        9,027 rounded down to 9,000.

        125,090 rounded up to 125,100.

    (c) 36,257 rounded to the nearest multiple of 100 is 36,300.

    36,257 rounded to a multiple of 100 using our convention or agreement is 36,200.

Notice that in rounding, the digits to the right of the place position to be rounded are replaced zeroes. In rounding we **lose information** since the zeroes to the right are merely place holders. We describe the number of digits giving us information by saying that they are **significant** digits. The number of significant digits in a numeral is usually determined by counting the number of digits from the first nonzero digit on the left to the last nonzero digit on the right. (For integers.)

Examples.

    (a) 240 has 2 significant digits.

    (b) 6,000 has 1 significant digit.

    (c) 12,600 has 3 significant digits.

    (d) 20,310 has 4 significant digits.

    (e) 375,407 has 6 significant digits.

Of course, the above are primarily conventions and agreements of common sense. In rounding 5,961 to the nearest multiple of 100 we obtain 6,000. The zero in the hundred's place actually is giving us information. In rounding to estimate the product of 516×28 we can round up to guarantee an estimate which is larger than the actual product or round down to guarantee a product which is smaller than the actual product. That is, we can obtain **high** and **low estimates** of difficult products rapidly by rounding appropriately.

Examples.

(a) To estimate 516 × 28 we can obtain a
high estimate: 516 × 30 = 15,480.
low estimate: 516 × 20 = 10,320.
actual product: 516 × 28 = 14,448.

(b) To estimate 476 × 93,708 we can obtain a
high estimate: 500 × 93,708 = 46,854,000.
low estimate: 400 × 93,708 = 37,483,200.
actual product: 476 × 93,708 = 44,605,008.

4.2.2 On occasion we calculate the exact product and then round the result to a certain number of significant digits. For example, we might compute 516 × 28 = 14,448 and then round the answer to three significant digits: 14,400. Or, we might begin at the left, higher place, digits and round the partial products "as we go."

```
  516
×  28
  103
   40
    1
14400
```
We first note that 20 × 500 = 10,000 so that the place positions are established. The first partial product from the left is 2 × 51 = 102 and we add 1 from 2 × 6 = 12. The second partial product is 8 × 5 = 40. The third partial product is a "carry" from 8 × 16 = 128. Summing the rounded partial products, we have 14,400, the product to three significant digits.

If we wish the product of 476 × 93,708 to three significant digits, we could do the calculations with one more, that is, four, significant digits, and then round the result to three significant digits:

```
  93,710          or, working from the left:      93,710
×    476                                         ×    476
 562300                          (4 × 9)       36000,000
   6560                          (4 × 3)             120
   3748                          (4 × 7)              28
44600000  (rounded)              (7 × 9)             630
                                 (7 × 3)              21
                                 (7 × 7)               5
                                 (6 × 9)              54
                                 (6 × 3)               2
                                               44,600,000  (rounded)
```

Thus, the answer to three significant digits is obtained directly as 44,600,000. Notice the importance of careful place positioning of digits in the partial products, especially when working from the left.

Practice 1.

1. Round to the nearest multiple of 10.
    (a) 974   (b) 1,362   (c) 509   (d) 12,096
    (e) 3,875   (f) 5,725   (g) 39,010   (h) 4,996
    (i) 70,901   (j) 18,465.

2. Round to the nearest multiple of 100.
    (a) 1,362   (b) 12,096   (c) 5,725   (d) 39,010
    (e) 4,996   (f) 3,557   (g) 38,453   (h) 8,962
    (i) 72,075   (j) 9,600.

3. Determine the number of significant digits in:
    (a) 2,401   (b) 10,400   (c) 25,000   (d) 93,365
    (e) 50,000.

4. Round to 3 significant digits:
    (a) 1,362   (b) 12,096   (c) 39,010   (d) 4,996
    (e) 3,557   (f) 8,962   (g) 38,453   (h) 72,075
    (i) 7,001   (j) 1,010.

5. Round the multipliers to one significant digit both up and down to obtain a high and a low estimate of the following products. Indicate which estimate is closest to the actual product.
    (a) 74×398 (b) $39 \times 1,627$ (c) $127 \times 91,367$
    (d) $379 \times 18,402$ (e) $928 \times 51,070$ (f) $1,704 \times 81,920$.

Answers.

1. (a) 970   (b) 1,360   (c) 510   (d) 12,100
    (e) 3,880   (f) 5,720   (g) 39,010   (h) 5,000
    (i) 70,900   (j) 18,460.

2. (a) 1,400   (b) 12,100   (c) 5,700   (d) 39,000
    (e) 5,000   (f) 3,600   (g) 38,400   (h) 9,000
    (i) 72,100   (j) 9,600.

3. (a) 4   (b) 3   (c) 2   (d) 5   (e) 1.

4. (a) 1,360   (b) 12,100   (c) 39,000   (d) 5,000
    (e) 3,560   (f) 8,960   (g) 38,400   (h) 72,100
    (i) 7,000   (j) 1,010.

5. (a) high: 31,840; low: 27,860; low estimate is closer.
    (b) high: 65,080; low: 48,810; high estimate is closer.
    (c) high: 18,273,400; low: 9,136,700; low is closer.
    (d) high: 7,360,800; low: 5,520,600; high is closer.
    (e) high: 51,070,000; low: 45,963,000; low is closer.
    (f) high: 163,840,000; low: 81,920,000; high is closer.

4.2.3 In working with factors and products, estimates and approximations are helpful but not a very reliable check on actual answers. An instructive technique which was originally developed for checking multiplications done on a counting board is called the "casting out the nines" check. "Casting out nines" is based on the fact that every number may be expressed as a multiple of nine and the sum of its digits less all multiples of nine.

Examples.

(a) $122 = 1(100) + 2(10) + 2(1) = 1(99+1) + 2(9+1) + 2(1)$
    $= 1(99) + 2(9) + (1+2+2) = 13(9) + 5$
    $= \text{(a multiple of 9)} + \text{(sum of the digits)}.$

(b) $576 = 5(99+1) + 7(9+1) + 6(1) = 62(9) + (5+7+6)$
    $= 62(9) + 18 = 64(9) + 0.$

(c) $1{,}536 = 1(999+1) + 5(99+1) + 3(9+1) + 6$
    $= \text{(a multiple of 9)} + (1+5+3+6)$

but $1 + 5 + 3 + 6 = 9 + 6$ so that we have
$$1{,}536 = \text{(a multiple of 9)} + 6.$$

(d) $207{,}625 = \text{(a multiple of 9)} + (2+7+6+2+5)$
    $= \text{(a multiple of 9)} + 22$

but $22 = 2(9) + 4$ so that we can write
$$207{,}625 = \text{(a multiple of 9)} + 4.$$

The sum of the digits in a numeral less all multiples of nine is called the **excess of nines** in the given numeral. For example, the excess of nines in 122 is 5, in 576 is 0, in 1,536 is 6, and in 207,625 it is 4.

Now, consider the product $122 \times 1{,}536$:

$122 \times 1{,}536 = [\text{(a multiple of 9)} + 5] \times [\text{(a multiple of 9)} + 6]$
    $= \text{(a multiple of 9)} + (5 \times 6)$
    $= \text{(a multiple of 9)} + 30$
    $= \text{(a multiple of 9)} + 3, \text{ since } 30 = 3(9) + 3.$

Thus, if the multiplication is done correctly, then the excess of nines in the product should equal the excess in the product of the excesses of the factors.

$$1{,}536 = \text{(a multiple of 9)} + 6$$
$$\underline{\times \quad 122} = \text{(a multiple of 9)} + 5$$
$$3072 \qquad\qquad\qquad \overline{30} = 3(9) + 3, \text{ excess is 3.}$$
$$3072$$
$$\underline{1536}$$
$$\overline{187392} = \text{(a multiple of 9)} + 3, \text{ excess is 3.}$$

Examples.

(a)   207,625   excess: 4
    ×   576   excess: 0
    ‾‾‾‾‾‾‾‾‾‾‾‾‾‾‾‾‾
      1245750   0   excess: 0
      1453375
      1038125
    ‾‾‾‾‾‾‾‾‾‾‾
      119592000   excess: 0   since $1+1+9+5+9+2=27=3(9)$.

Thus, since the excesses check, the product is likely to be correct.

(b)   731,401   excess: 7
      × 1,623   excess: 3
    ‾‾‾‾‾‾‾‾‾‾‾‾‾‾‾‾‾‾‾‾
      2 194 203   21   excess: 3
      14 628 02
      438 840 6
      731 401
    ‾‾‾‾‾‾‾‾‾‾‾‾‾
      1,187,063,823   excess: 3.

Since the excesses are equal, the answer is most likely correct.

Notice that in finding the excess we can "drop" multiples of 9: $1+1+8+7+6+3+8+2+3$ can be rearranged to $(1+1+7)+(6+3) + (8+8+2) + 3$ where we need only note the excess 3 at the end.

This "casting out nines" check is, however, not infallible since any rearrangement (transposition) of digits in a numeral would still result in the same excess. For example, in Example (b) above, 1,178,603,832 would have the same excess 3. Since transpositions are not too common and the check is rapid and easy, it is useful. A "casting out nines" check can also be developed for addition and for subtraction.

Exercises

1. Use common sense to "roughly" estimate the following products:
   (a) 498 × 72   (b) 687 × 189   (c) 3,507 × 28,065.
2. Round the following to the nearest multiple of 100:
   (a) 92,527   (b) 47,172   (c) 16,450   (d) 36,759   (e) 104,095.
3. Round the following to the nearest multiple of 1000:
   (a) 7,158,306   (b) 365,925   (c) 21,009,508   (d) 140,750.
4. Round each of the numerals in Exercise 2 to two significant digits.
5. Round each of the numerals in Exercise 3 to three significant digits.
6. Round the multipliers to one significant digit both up and down to

obtain a high and a low estimate of the following products:

(a) 5,307
$\times$ 527

(b) 7,081
$\times$ 379

(c) 39,645
$\times$ 1,507

(d) 625,475
$\times$ 9,857

7. Find the products for the multiplications in Exercise 6 to three significant digits by rounding the partial products to four digits and then the product to three.

8. Find the exact products for the multiplications in Exercise 6 and check by "casting out nines."

9. Given the addition:

14,653
32,974
17,328
35,465
90,333
48,901
25,694
+ 13,007
───────
278,355

work out a method for checking the addition by casting out nines and comparing the excesses of nines in the addends with the excess of nines in the sum.

10. Show that any numeral formed by using zeroes and the other nine digits exactly once names a number which is a multiple of nine. That is, its excess of nines is 0. (Use an example.)

11. Use an example to show that if the digits in any given numeral are rearranged to form a new numeral and that if the new number named is subtracted from the given number, then the resulting number will be a multiple of 9.

12. A large house has two rectangular floors with dimensions of 37 feet by 48 feet and 32 feet by 42 feet. Find the total floor area of the house to the nearest one hundred square feet.

13. The borough of Manhattan in New York had a population of 1,698,281 according to the 1960 census. If the average per capita income was $2,684 per year, then what was the gross (total) income of the population of Manhattan for the year to the nearest $100,000?

14. A rocket travels at 19,645 miles per hour for 832 hours in outer space. How far has it traveled to three significant digits?

15. A rectangular swimming pool with a level bottom is 4 feet deep and measures 18 by 24 feet. A cubic foot of water weighs approximately 64 pounds. What is the total weight of water in the pool rounded to 1,000's of pounds when the pool is filled?

Answers.

1. (a) 35,000   (b) 140,000   (c) 120,000,000 or 90,000,000.

2. (a) 92,500   (b) 47,200   (c) 16,400   (d) 36,800
  (e) 104,100.
3. (a) 7,158,000   (b) 366,000   (c) 21,010,000   (d) 141,000.
4. (a) 92,000   (b) 47,000   (c) 16,000   (d) 37,000
  (e) 100,000.
5. (a) 7,160,000   (b) 366,000   (c) 21,000,000   (d) 141,000.
6. (a) high: 3,184,200   (b) high: 2,832,400
      low: 2,653,500   low: 2,124,300
  (c) high: 79,290,000   (d) high: 6,254,750,000
      low: 39,645,000   low: 5,629,275,000.
7. (a) 2,800,000   (b) 2,680,000   (c) 59,700,000
  (d) 6,160,000,000.
8. (a) 2,796,789 excess 3   (b) 2,683,699 excess 7
  (c) 59,745,015 excess 0   (d) 6,165,307,075 excess 4.
9. Excess of the sum of the excesses of the addends should equal
the excess of the sum: $1 + 7 + 3 + 5 + 0 + 4 + 8 + 2$, excess 3 while
278,355 has excess 3.
  10. 1023456789 has excess $(1 + 8) + (2 + 7) + (3 + 6) + (4 + 5) + 9$
$= 5(9)$ equal to 0 so that it is a multiple of 9.
  11. Let $abcd$ be a four-digit numeral, then we have
      $abcd = $ (a multiple of 9) $ + (a + b + c + d)$ and
      $cabd = $ (a multiple of 9) $ + (a + b + c + d)$ so the difference is
      (a multiple of 9) $ + 0$.
12. 3,100 square feet.
13. $4,658,200,000.
14. 16,300,000 miles.
15. 110,000 pounds (111,000 to the nearest 1,000 pounds.)

4.3 Integers and Signs

4.3.1   Thus far in our discussion of multiplication we have only considered products of positive integers and zero. We now ask: "How can
we interpret and multiply together negative integers?"

Recall that we interpreted multiplication as a "shortcut" for finding
the sum of repeated additions of the same number. For example,
$8 \times 6 = 6 + 6 + 6 + 6 + 6 + 6 + 6 + 6 = 48$. Suppose the number were a
negative integer, say -6. We could add -6 to itself 8 times and obtain
$(-6) + (-6) + (-6) + (-6) + (-6) + (-6) + (-6) + (-6) = -48$.
It should seem reasonable and consistent with our previous interpretation to write this as $8 \times (-6) = -48$.

Examples.

(a)

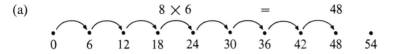

$$8 \times 6 \qquad = \qquad 48$$

0   6   12   18   24   30   36   42   48   54

(b) -48 $=$ $8 \times (-6)$

-54 -48 -42 -36 -30 -24 -18 -12 -6 0

(c) $-12 = 4 \times (-3)$ $4 \times 3 = 12$

-15 -12 -9 -6 -3 0   3   6   9   12   15

Now consider the equation with $N = 4 \times (-3)$; if we add 12 we have $N + 12 = [4 \times (-3)] + 12$. But since $12 = 4 \times 3$ we can write that $N + 12 = [4 \times (-3)] + (4 \times 3) = 4 \times (-3 + 3) = 4 \times 0 = 0$. With $N + 12 = 0$ we must have $N = -12$ so that $4 \times (-3) = -12$ and our interpretation is consistent with what we would expect in an equation.

Example. If $N = 8 \times (-6)$ we choose to add $48 = 8 \times 6$ to both sides of the equation:

$$
\begin{aligned}
N + 48 &= [8 \times (-6)] + (8 \times 6) && \text{Equal addition.} \\
&= 8 \times (-6 + 6) && \text{Distributive.} \\
&= 8 \times 0 && \text{Inverse.} \\
&= 0 && \text{Zero factor.}
\end{aligned}
$$

Then $N + 48 = 0$ so that $N = -48$ and
$$8 \times (-6) = -48.$$

If the commutative property is to be true for multiplication, then we must have $4 \times (-3) = (-3) \times 4 = -12$ and also $8 \times (-6) = (-6) \times 8 = -48$.

Observing that when one of two factors in a multiplication is negative, the product is negative, we can immediately note that what we have said is also true for $3 \times (-4)$ and $(-4) \times 3$: $3 \times (-4) = (-4) \times 3 = -12$. Furthermore, a negative product would be obtained as the negative of the product of two positive factors: $-(3 \times 4) = -(4 \times 3) = -12$.

To summarize, we have
$$4 \times (-3) = (-3) \times 4 = 3 \times (-4) = (-4) \times 3 = -(3 \times 4) = -(4 \times 3) = -12.$$

Also,
$$8 \times (-6) = (-6) \times 8 = 6 \times (-8) = (-8) \times 6 = -(6 \times 8) = -(8 \times 6) = -48.$$
In general, if A and B are positive integers, then
$$A \times (-B) = (-B) \times A = B \times (-A) = (-A) \times B = -(A \times B) = -(B \times A)$$
is universally true.

Examples.

(a) $7 \times (-5) = (-5) \times 7 = 5 \times (-7) = (-7) \times 5 = -(7 \times 5) = -(5 \times 7)$
$= -35.$
That is, any one of the multiplications, say, $5 \times (-7)$, has the product
-35: $5 \times (-7) = -35.$

(b) For $A = 15$ and $B = 12$ we have
$$15 \times (-12) = -180 \, , \, (-12) \times 15 = -180 \, , \, 12 \times (-15) = -180$$
$$(-15) \times 12 = -180 \, , \, -(15 \times 12) = -180 \, , \, -(12 \times 15) = -180.$$

In ordinary English we might say: "When one of two factors in a multiplication is negative, then the product is the negative of the product of the two positive factors."

If N is any integer we might write $N \times (-5) = -(5 \times N)$. Suppose $N = -3$, then we would have $(-3) \times (-5) = -[5 \times (-3)]$. But $-[5 \times (-3)] = -[-(5 \times 3)] = -(-15) = 15$. Does this make "sense"? Can we justify writing $(-3) \times (-5) = 15$? Consider the following:

If $(-3) \times (-5) = 15$, then $[(-3) \times (-5)] - 15 = 0.$

But
$$\begin{aligned}[(-3) \times (-5)] - 15 &= [(-3) \times (-5)] + (-15) \\ &= [(-3) \times (-5)] + [(-3) \times 5] \\ &= (-3) \times [(-5) + 5] \\ &= (-3) \times 0 \\ &= 0.\end{aligned}$$

Thus, our conjecture does make "sense." Since our choice of integers was quite arbitrary, we should be able to conclude that for any two negative integers their product will be positive. That is, the product of two negative integers is the same as the product of the positive factors.

Examples.

(a) $(-8) \times (-6) = 8 \times 6 = 48.$
(b) $(-7) \times (-5) = 7 \times 5 = 35.$
(c) $(-1) \times (-9) = 1 \times 9 = 9.$
(d) $(-15) \times (-12) = 15 \times 12 = 180.$

In general, if A and B are positive integers, then
$(-A) \times (-B) = A \times B$ is universally true.

4.3.2   In our discussion of the integers with respect to subtraction we asserted that "The negative of a negative integer is positive and the negative of the negative of a negative integer is negative." That is, the product of an even number of negative integers is positive and the product of an odd number of negative integers is negative.

Examples.

(a) $(-6) \times (3 \times 7) = (-6) \times 21 = -126.$

(b) $[(-6) \times (-3)] \times 7 = (6 \times 3) \times 7 = 18 \times 7 = 126.$

(c) $(-6) \times [(-3) \times (-7)] = (-6) \times (3 \times 7) = -126.$

(d) $(-6) \times (3 \times 7) = 6 \times [(-3) \times 7] = 6 \times [3 \times (-7)]$
$$= -[6 \times (3 \times 7)] = -126.$$

(e) If A, B, and C are positive integers, we have
$(-A) \times (B \times C) = A \times (-B \times C) = A \times (B \times -C) = -(A \times B \times C)$
and $(-A) \times (-B \times C) = (-A) \times (B \times -C) = A \times (-B \times -C)$
$= A \times B \times C$ and $(-A) \times (-B \times -C) = (-A) \times (B \times C) =$
$-(A \times B \times C).$

In a product, if the number of negative factors is odd, the product is negative. If the number of negative factors is even, the product is positive. Thus, to find the product of any number of integers we need only count the evenness or oddness of the number of negative signs, find the positive product of the factors (without regard to sign), then attach the appropriate sign to the products. We note that every negative integer can be thought of as the product of -1 and the opposite positive integer. Thus, in any product, we can separate consideration of positive or negative from the value of the product.

Examples.

(a) $(-7) \times (-4) = [(-1) \times 7] \times [(-1) \times 4] = [(-1) \times (-1)] \times$
(7×4)
$$= 1 \times 28 = 28.$$

(b) $[(-37) \times 8] \times [(-13) \times (-4)] = [(-1) \times (-1) \times (-1)] \times$
$(37 \times 8 \times 13 \times 4).$
Three negative factors so product will be negative.
$37 \times 8 = 296$; $13 \times 4 = 52$; $296 \times 52 = 15{,}392$ so that the product is $-15{,}392.$

(c) $(-2) \times [(-57) \times (-1) \times (-20)].$
Four negative factors so product will be positive.
$57 \times 20 = 1140$; $2 \times 1140 = 2280$ is the product.

(d) $[15 \times (-5)] \times [1 \times ([-19] \times [-30])]$
Three negative factors so product will be negative.

$15 \times 5 = 75$; $19 \times 30 = 570$; $75 \times 570 = 42{,}750$ so that the product is $-42{,}750$.

   (e) $47 \times [(-93) \times (0 \times 65)]$.

One negative factor, but notice the zero!

Product is 0.

Practice 1.

   1. Given $N = 9 \times (-7)$. Show by using equal addition and the distributive property of multiplication that $N = -63$.

   2. Do as in Practice Exercise 1; given $N = (-5) \times (-8)$ then $N = 40$.

   3. Find the value of N in each of the following equations so that the equation will be true.

   (a) $5 \times N = -5$ (b) $-5 \times N = -5$ (c) $-5 \times N = 5$
   (d) $9 \times (-4) = N$ (e) $(-9) \times (-6) = N$ (f) $-N \times 7 = 7$
   (g) $N \times (-1) = -1$ (h) $N \times (-1) = 1$ (i) $(-1) \times (-1) = N$
   (j) $1 \times N = -1$ (k) $-5 \times 0 = N$ (l) $-7 \times N = 0$.

   4. Find the products:

   (a) $8 \times (-10)$ (b) -13×6 (c) $-27 \times (-8)$
   (d) $(-9) \times (-9)$ (e) $10 \times (-10)$ (f) $(-1) \times 100$
   (g) $53 \times (-39)$ (h) $-(41 \times 80)$ (i) $(-41) \times 80$
   (j) $(-97) \times (-27)$ (k) $-[(-52) \times 41]$ (l) $-[(-12) \times (-68)]$.

   5. Find the products:

   (a) $17 \times [(-5) \times 8]$ (b) $(-9) \times [6 \times (-7)]$
   (c) $22 \times [(-3) \times (-15)]$ (d) $-[4 \times (-5)] \times 6$
   (e) $[(-11) \times 30] \times (-13)$ (f) $[(-19) \times (-2)] \times (-1)$.

   6. Find the products:

   (a) $-[(-4) \times (-1)] \times [(-7) \times 3]$.
   (b) $-[5 \times (-9)] \times [-(3 \times 8)]$.
   (c) $[(-17) \times 31] \times [10 \times (-4)]$.
   (d) $-(-[6 \times (-1)] \times 20) \times (-79)$.

Answers.

   1. $N + 63 = [9 \times (-7)] + 63$
           $= [9 \times (-7)] + (9 \times 7)$
           $= 9 \times [(-7) + 7]$
      $N + 63 = 9 \times 0 = 0$
           $N = -63$.

   2. $N - 40 = [(-5) \times (-8)] - 40$
           $= [(-5) \times (-8)] + [(-5) \times 8]$
           $= (-5) \times (-8 + 8)$
      $N - 40 = -5 \times 0 = 0$
           $N = 40$.

3. (a) −1   (b) 1   (c) −1   (d) −36   (e) 54   (f) −1
   (g) 1   (h) −1   (i) 1   (j) −1   (k) 0   (l) 0.
4. (a) −80   (b) −78   (c) 216   (d) 81   (e) −100   (f) −100
   (g) −2067   (h) −3280   (i) −3280   (j) 2619   (k) 2132
   (l) −816.
5. (a) −680   (b) 378   (c) 990   (d) 120   (e) 4290   (f) −38.
6. (a) 84   (b) −1080   (c) 21,080   (d) 9480.

4.3.3 Using a few universally true equations, we can describe the properties of multiplication of integers. These are briefly summarized as follows:

Properties of Multiplication of Integers

1. If A and B are integers, then there is always an integer P such that $A \times B = P$. This is called the **closure property** of multiplication of integers.

Examples.

(a) If $A = 9$ and $B = 3$, then since $9 \times 3 = 27$ we have $P = 27$.
(b) If $A = -9$ and $B = 3$, we have $-9 \times 3 = -27$ and $P = -27$.
(c) If $A = -9$ and $B = -3$, we have $-9 \times (-3) = 27$ and $P = 27$.

2. If A and B are integers, then $A \times B = B \times A$. This is the **commutative property** of multiplication of integers.

Examples.

(a) $3 \times 9 = 9 \times 3$ (b) $5 \times (-9) = (-9) \times 5$.

3. If A, B, and C are integers, then $A \times (B \times C) = (A \times B) \times C$. This is the **associative property** of multiplication of integers.

Examples.

(a) $3 \times (5 \times 9) = (3 \times 5) \times 9$.
(b) $-3 \times (5 \times 9) = [(-3) \times 5] \times 9$.
(c) $-3 \times [(-5) \times (-9)] = [(-3) \times (-5)] \times (-9)$.
(d) $-3 \times [(-5) \times 9] = [(-3) \times (-5)] \times 9$.

4. If A, B, and C are integers, then $(A + B) \times C = (A \times C) + (B \times C)$ and $C \times (A + B) = (C \times A) + (C \times B)$. This is the **distributive property** of multiplication over addition.

Examples.

(a) $(5 + 7) \times 9 = (5 \times 9) + (7 \times 9)$.
(b) $(-3) \times (5 + 7) = [(-3) \times 5] + [(-3) \times 7]$.
(c) $9 \times [(-5) + 7] = [9 \times (-5)] + (9 \times 7)$.
(d) $(-9) \times [5 + (-7)] = [(-9) \times 5] + [(-9) \times (-7)]$.

5. If A is an integer, then $1 \times A = A \times 1 = A$. The number 1 is called the **identity** element of multiplication of integers.

Examples.

(a) If $A = 9$, $1 \times 9 = 9 \times 1 = 9$.
(b) If $A = -9$, $1 \times (-9) = (-9) \times 1 = -9$.

6. If A is any integer, then $0 \times A = A \times 0 = 0$. Since this property is true only for the integer 0, it is often referred to as the **zero property**.

Examples.

(a) If $A = 9$, $0 \times 9 = 9 \times 0 = 0$.
(b) If $A = -9$, $0 \times (-9) = (-9) \times 0 = 0$.

7. If A and B are positive integers, then $A \times (-B) = (-A) \times B = -(A \times B)$ and $(-A) \times (-B) = A \times B$. These are called the **Laws of Signs** for multiplication of integers.

Examples.

(a) If $A = 4$, and $B = 8$, then $4 \times (-8) = (-4) \times 8 = -(4 \times 8)$ and $(-4) \times (-8) = 4 \times 8$.
(b) If $A = 7$ and $B = 3$, then $7 \times (-3) = (-7) \times 3 = -(7 \times 3)$ and $(-7) \times (-3) = 7 \times 3$.

4.3.4   Of course, memorizing a set of properties or rules should not be an end in itself. Just as in learning English or any other language, we must observe and recognize not only the need but also the usefulness of the properties and rules.

We have noted that by far the most important property of multiplication is the distributive property. As a matter of fact, this property underlies our very form of writing numerals.

Examples.

(a) $3204 = 3(1000) + 2(100) + 0(10) + 4(1)$
$= 30(100) + 2(100) + 0(1) + 4(1)$
$= (30 + 2)\ (100) + (0 + 4)\ (1)$
$= 32(100) + 4(1)$, and so forth.

(b) $3204 = 3(999 + 1) + 2(99 + 1) + 0(9 + 1) + 4(1)$
$= (\text{a multiple of } 9) + (3 + 2 + 0 + 4)$.

(c) $3204 = 3(1001 - 1) + 2(99 + 1) + 0(11 - 1) + 4(1)$
$= 3[91(11) - 1] + 2[9(11) + 1] + 0(11 - 1) + 4(1)$
$= (\text{a multiple of } 11) + (2 + 4 - 3 - 0)$.

We have not mentioned the distributive property of multiplication over subtraction. However, we have noted that subtraction can be expressed as a sum of integers. For example, $9 - 5 = 9 + (-5)$. Thus, we should expect that multiplication will be distributive over subtraction.

Examples.

(a) $7 \times (9 - 5) = 7 \times [9 + (-5)] = (7 \times 9) + [7 \times (-5)]$
$= (7 \times 9) + [-(7 \times 5)] = (7 \times 9) - (7 \times 5)$.

(b) $(11 - 17) \times 6 = [11 + (-17)] \times 6 = (11 \times 6) + [(-17) \times 6]$
$= (11 \times 6) + [-(17 \times 6)] = (11 \times 6) - (17 \times 6)$.

From the above examples, it should be evident that multiplication is indeed distributive over subtraction. In general, if A, B, and C are integers, we have
$A \times (B - C) = (A \times B) - (A \times C)$ and $(B - C) \times A = (B \times A) - (C \times A)$.
Notice the use of parentheses and brackets in "carrying" our discussion through to its end.

The use of punctuation, parentheses, and brackets is just as important in mathematical statements as it is in any other language. In discussing statements in Chapter 3, we noted that expressions were formed out of numerals, symbols for operations, and grouping symbols. When given an expression, we are often interested in finding the simplest numeral for the value of the expression. For example, $24 + [7 - (11 + 24)]$ is another "fancy" name for -4.

Examples.

(a) $6 \times ([9 + (7 \times 4)] - 2) = 6 \times ([9 + 28] - 2) = 6 \times (37 - 2)$
$= 6 \times 35 = 210$. We proceed from the simple "inner" computations and

work "outward" step-by-step: $7 \times 4 = 28$, $9 + 28 = 37$, $37 - 2 = 35$, and $6 \times 35 = 210$.

(b) $(-3) \times ([5 \times (7 - 4)] + 9) = -72$ since $7 - 4 = 3$, $5 \times 3 = 15$, $15 + 9 = 24$, and $-3 \times 24 = -72$.

(c) $([([(3 + 4) \times 5] - 6) \times 7] - 8) \times 9 = 1755$ since working from the "inner" simpler expressions "outward" we have $3 + 4 = 7$, $7 \times 5 = 35$, $35 - 6 = 29$, $29 \times 7 = 203$, $203 - 8 = 195$, and $195 \times 9 = 1755$.

In discussing the multiplication of numbers expressed by two-digit numerals, we applied the distributive property twice. The "patterns" involved in the manipulations and conclusions in such situations can lead to powerful descriptive devices in mathematics. Look for the "patterns" in the following examples.

Examples.

(a) $37 \times 58 = (30 + 7) \times (50 + 8) = [(30 + 7) \times 50] + [(30 + 7) \times 8]$
$= [(30 \times 50) + (7 \times 50)] + [(30 \times 8) + (7 \times 8)]$
$= (30 \times 50) + [(7 \times 50) + (30 \times 8)] + (7 \times 8)$.

(b) $(9 + 7) \times (2 + 5) = [(9 + 7) \times 2] + [(9 + 7) \times 5]$
$= (9 \times 2) + (7 \times 2) + (9 \times 5) + (7 \times 5)$.

(c) $(9 + 2) \times (9 + 2) = (9 \times 9) + (2 \times 9) + (9 \times 2) + (2 \times 2)$
$= (9 \times 9) + [2 \times (2 \times 9)] + (2 \times 2)$.

(d) $(9 - 2) \times (9 - 2) = [(9 - 2) \times 9] - [(9 - 2) \times 2]$
$= (9 \times 9) - (2 \times 9) - (9 \times 2) + (2 \times 2)$
$= (9 \times 9) - [2 \times (2 \times 9)] + (2 \times 2)$.

(e) $(9 + 2) \times (9 - 2) = (9 \times 9) + (2 \times 9) - (9 \times 2) - (2 \times 2)$
$= (9 \times 9) - (2 \times 2)$.

4.3.5   In concluding this chapter we return to an earlier consideration; if A and B are integers, then to find $P = A \times B$. Suppose that we are given P and are asked to find A or B. For example, given $P = 54$ and $A = 6$ in $P = A \times B$, then can we find B? Since we have $6 \times B = 54$, the answer is yes, $B = 9$.

Examples.

(a) $7 \times B = 84$ has $B = 12$ as a solution since $7 \times 12 = 84$.

(b) $3 \times (N + 5) = 54$ can be solved by noting that
$3 \times (N + 5) = (3 \times N) + (3 \times 5) = 54$ so that $3 \times N = 54 - 15 = 39$ and $N = 13$ since $3 \times (13 + 5) = 3 \times 18 = 54$.

(c) $(N - 7) \times 9 = 18$ can be solved by noting that $(N - 7) \times 9 = (N \times 9) - (7 \times 9) = 18$ so that $N \times 9 = 81$ and $N = 9$ since $(9 - 7) \times 9 = 2 \times 9 = 18$.

(d) $3 \times (N + 5) = 0$ can be solved by observing that if $P = 0$ in $A \times B = P$, then $A = 0$ or $B = 0$. Thus, since $3 \neq 0$ we must have $N + 5 = 0$ and $N = -5$.

(e) $(N - 7) \times (N + 5) = 0$ can be solved by noting that $N - 7 = 0$ or $N + 5 = 0$ so that $N = 7$ or $N = -5$. Checking: if $N = 7$ we have $(7 - 7) \times (7 + 5) = 0 \times 12 = 0$ and if $N = -5$ we have $[(-5) - 7] \times [(-5) + 5] = (-12) \times 0 = 0$.

Practice 2.

1. Name the property which is best illustrated by each of the following equations:

(a) $15 \times (9 + 5) = (9 + 5) \times 15$
(b) $15 \times (9 \times 5) = (15 \times 9) \times 5$
(c) $15 \times (9 \times 5) = 675$
(d) $15 \times (9 - 5) = (15 \times 9) - (15 \times 5)$
(e) $1 \times (9 \times 5) = 9 \times 5$
(f) $3 \times [(-5) \times 9] = -[3 \times (5 \times 9)]$
(g) $15 \times (0 \times 5) = 0$
(h) $(3 + 9) \times 7 = (3 \times 7) + (9 \times 7)$.

2. Find the simplest numeral for:

(a) $([7 - (4 - 9)] + 3) \times 6$ (b) $(3 \times [(4 + 1) \times (5 - 2)]) - 10$
(c) $2 + ([(7 \times 3) - 10] \times 3)$
(d) $[(7 + 6) \times (9 - 3)] - [(7 \times 6) + (3 \times 9)]$.

3. Find the products:

(a) $3 \times [(-7) + 5]$ (b) $(-3) \times [(-7) + 5]$
(c) $[-(11 - 2)] \times 13$ (d) $3 \times (7 - 5)$
(e) $(-3) \times [(-7) - 5]$ (f) $[(-13) + 11] \times (-2)$
(g) $(-3) \times (7 + 5)$ (h) $(2 - 11) \times 13$
(i) $[-(2 - 11)] \times (-13)$ (j) $3 \times [(-7) - 5]$
(k) $(2 + 11) \times (-13)$ (l) $[(-11) - 2] \times (-13)$.

4. Find the products:

(a) $(13 + 9) \times (7 + 34)$ (b) $(37 + 56) \times (18 + 24)$
(c) $(13 + 9) \times (13 + 9)$ (d) $(7 + 34) \times (7 + 34)$
(e) $(13 - 9) \times (13 - 9)$ (f) $(7 - 34) \times (7 - 34)$
(g) $(13 + 9) \times (13 - 9)$ (h) $(7 + 34) \times (7 - 34)$
(i) $(13 + 9) \times (7 - 34)$ (j) $(7 + 34) \times (13 - 9)$.

5. Solve the following equations for N:

(a) $13 \times N = 52$ (b) $N \times 27 = 297$
(c) $8 \times (N + 14) = 40$ (d) $(N - 6) \times (11 + 7) = 36$
(e) $(5 + 8) \times (2N - 6) = 0$ (f) $(N + 9) \times (4 - N) = 0$
(g) $[(N + 4) \times 7] \times 16 = 0$ (h) $12 = [3 \times (N - 5)] \times (7 - 3)$.

Answers.

1. (a) commutative   (b) associative   (c) closure
   (d) distributive   (e) identity   (f) signs   (g) zero
   (h) distributive.
2. (a) 90   (b) 35   (c) 35   (d) 9.
3. (a) −6   (b) 6   (c) −117   (d) 6   (e) 36   (f) 4
   (g) −36   (h) −117   (i) −117   (j) −36   (k) −169
   (l) 169.
4. (a) 902   (b) 3906   (c) 484   (d) 1681   (e) 16
   (f) 729   (g) 88   (h) −1107   (i) −594   (j) 164.
5. (a) 4   (b) 11   (c) −9   (d) 8   (e) 3   (f) 4 or −9
   (g) −4   (h) 6.

Exercises

1. The product of 7 and −13, written $7 \times (-13) = -91$, can be interpreted as the sum of _____ addends, each addend equal to _____.

2. Verify that $7 \times (-13) = -91$ by setting $N = 7 \times (-13)$ and solving for N by applying appropriate properties of multiplication and equations.

3. State the five multiplication facts associated with $7 \times (-13) = -91$.

4. Verify that $(-7) \times (-13) = 91$ by setting $N = (-7) \times (-13)$ and solving for N by applying appropriate properties of multiplication and equations.

5. Separate the following products into the product of two products, one product having only −1 as factors and the other having only positive factors.

   (a) $[3 \times (-6)] \times (-5)$ (b) $(-9) \times [(-3) \times (-14)]$
   (c) $[(-8) \times 7] \times [4 \times (-3)]$
   (d) $[(-1) \times (-8)] \times [(-7) \times (-7)]$.

6. Find the value of N in each of the following equations so that the equation will be true.

   (a) $N \times 1 = -1$ (b) $-1 \times N = 1$ (c) $N = -1 \times 0$
   (d) $3 \times N = -9$ (e) $-7 \times (-4) = N$ (f) $N \times (-7) = 0$.

7. Find the products:

   (a) $(-11) \times 13$ (b) $59 \times (-73)$ (c) $(-59) \times (-13)$
   (d) $28 \times [(-14) \times 6]$ (e) $(-6) \times [17 \times (-41)]$
   (f) $[(-30) \times (-17)] \times (-6)$.

8. Find the products:

   (a) $(-85) \times (50 \times [(-19) \times (-31)])$.
   (b) $[64 \times (-23)] \times [(-85) \times (-74)]$.

    (c) $([(-57) \times 36] \times 18) \times (-42)$.

    (d) $-[(-49) \times (-49)] \times [19 \times (-19)]$.

9. Match the descriptions in the numbered column with the lettered column so that they best describe the properties illustrated.

    (a) $[15 \times (-6)] \times 28 = -[15 \times (6 \times 28)]$ 1. closure

    (b) $[15 \times (-6)] \times 28 = 15 \times [(-6) \times 28)]$ 2. identity

    (c) $[15 \times (-6)] \times 1 = 15 \times (-6)$ 3. commutative

    (d) $[15 + (-6)] \times 28 = (15 \times 28) + [(-6) \times 28]$ 4. distributive

    (e) $[15 \times (-6)] \times 28 = -2520$ 5. associative

    (f) $[15 \times 0] \times 28 = 0$ 6. zero

    (g) $[15 \times (-6)] \times 28 = 28 \times [15 \times (-6)]$ 7. signs

10. Find the simplest numeral for:

    (a) $-[12 \times (27 - 13)] \times [6 + (-7)]$.

    (b) $[(-61) + (47 - 70)] \times [(17 + 36) \times (-28)]$.

    (c) $[(24 + 19) \times (75 - 41)] \times [(52 - 30) \times (47 + 11)]$.

11. Find the products:

    (a) $(79 + 18) \times (36 + 52)$ (b) $(36 + 52) \times (36 + 52)$

    (c) $(79 - 18) \times (79 - 18)$ (d) $(79 - 18) \times (36 + 52)$

    (e) $(79 - 18) \times (79 + 18)$ (f) $(79 - 18) \times (36 - 52)$.

12. Solve the following equations for the variable.

    (a) $(N - 16) \times 17 = 34$ (b) $24 = (-6) \times (9 - N)$

    (c) $35 \times (3N + 18) = 0$ (d) $(20 - 5N) \times (2N + 12) = 0$.

13. If twice the negative of a number is added to sixteen and the sum is multiplied by three, then the product is six less than twenty-four. Find the number.

14. A wristwatch cost three times as much as a pen and pencil set. The pen and pencil set cost four dollars more than a certain book. If the book cost six dollars, then how much did the wristwatch cost?

15. If a number is added to and subtracted from seventeen, then the product of the sum times the difference is equal to eight multiplied by itself. Find the possible numbers.

Answers.

    1. $7; -13$.

    2. $-$.

    3. $(-13) \times 7 = (-7) \times 13 = 13 \times (-7) = -(13 \times 7)$
                                       $= -(7 \times 13)$.

    4. $-$.

    5. (a) $[(-1) \times (-1)] \times [3 \times (6 \times 5)]$.

       (b) $[(-1) \times (-1) \times (-1)] \times [9 \times (3 \times 14)]$.

       (c) $[(-1) \times (-1)] \times [(8 \times 7) \times (4 \times 3)]$.

       (d) $[(-1) \times (-1) \times (-1) \times (-1)] \times [8 \times (7 \times 7)]$.

6. (a) −1   (b) −1   (c) 0   (d) −3   (e) 28   (f) 0.
7. (a) −143   (b) −4307   (c) 767   (d) −2352   (e) 4182
   (f) −3060.
8. (a) −2,503,250   (b) −9,258,880   (c) 1,551,312
   (d) 886,761.
9. (a) −7,   (b) −5,   (c) −2,   (d) −4,   (e) −1,   (f) −6,
   (g) −3.
10. (a) 168   (b) 124,656   (c) 1,865,512.
11. (a) 8536   (b) 7744   (c) 3721   (d) 5368   (e) 5917
    (f) −976.
12. (a) 18   (b) 13   (c) −6   (d) 4 or −6.
13. 5.
14. $30.
15. 15 or −15.

Review Summary

In this chapter we began by interpreting the multiples of numbers as repeated additions of the same addends. As an operation we call this _____ where one of the equal addends is called the _____ and the number of times the multiplicand is added to itself is called the _____. The result of the operation is then called the _____. For convenience we often refer to the multiplicand and multiplier as factors of the product. In $11 \times 17 = 187$ the product is _____ while 11 is called the _____ and 17 the _____. But 11 and 17 may be referred to as _____ of the product 187.   *multiplication* *multiplicand* *multiplier* *product* *187* *multiplier,* *multiplicand* *factors*

In studying the basic multiplication facts, we observed various interesting patterns. In multiplication, just as in addition, the _____ and _____ properties are true. However, the most important property to be noted is called the _____ property of multiplication over addition. For example, $9 \times (37 + 14) =$ _____ + _____. Using this property in conjunction with expanded numerals we discussed the general problem of multiplying two factors to find their product.   *commutative,* *associative* *distributive* *$9 \times 37,$* *9×14*

Two numbers of special interest in multiplication are zero and one, 0 and 1. Since $N \times 1 = 1 \times N = N$ for any integer N, we call 1 the _____ element of multiplication. Since $N \times 0 = 0 \times N =$ _____, we noted that 0 "annihilates" any factor N in a product. The special   *identity* *0*

cases in multiplying by 10, 100, 1000, and so forth, were observed to be quite simple. In multiplying 256 by 10 we simple "shift" the place positions of the digits in 256 to the _____ one place to obtain _____. The   *left, 2560*
(left or right)

product $1000 \times 256 =$ _____ since there are three zeroes   *256000*
in 1000.

Historically, many different methods were devised for doing multiplications. We discussed two methods called the "lattice" method and the doubling or duplication method. Our contemporary method for multiplication is, however, based directly on the expansion of numerals and the _____ property of multiplication.   *distributive*
For example, $46 \times 83 = (40 + 6) \times 83$
$$= (40 \times 83) + (6 \times 83)$$
$$= 3320 + 498 = 3818.$$
In computations we use the following form:

3076 is the _____.   *multiplicand*
$\times \ \underline{280}$ is the _____.   *multiplier*

$$\left. \begin{array}{l} 0 \\ 24608 \\ 6152 \end{array} \right\} \text{are} \ \underline{\hspace{1cm}} \ \underline{\hspace{1cm}}.$$ *partial*
    products
$\overline{861280}$ is the _____.   *product*

In calculating with large values it is common sense to approximate or estimate answers. We often "round numerals to name multiples of 10, 100, 1000, and so forth. For example, 5,367 rounded to the nearest multiple of ten is _____ while to the nearest 1000 is   *5,370*
_____. In rounding 5,367 to 5,370 we say that we have   *5,000*
rounded 5,367 up to 5,370 and in rounding 5,367 to 5,360 we have rounded down. In rounding 5,367 to 5,000 we lose information. We indicate the number of digits in a numeral giving us information by saying that they are significant digits. The number of _____   *significant*
digits in a numeral can usually be determined by counting the number of digits from the first nonzero digit on the left to the last nonzero digit on the right. For example, 310,700 has _____ significant digits. Of course, rounding   *four*
and estimating is primarily a matter of convention and agreement. What we must do is use our common sense in each situation.

We can obtain high and low estimates of difficult products by rounding appropriately. To estimate

3,936 × 48,600 we might round both factors to one significant digit and estimate the product to be 4,000 × 50,000 = _____. Of course, this would be a very rough estimate with only one significant digit in the product. A high and low estimate could be obtained by rounding 3,936 _____ and _____ to 4,000 and 3,900, respectively. In this event we would have 4,000 × 48,600 = _____ and 3,900 × 48,600 = _____ respectively. The actual product of 3,936 and 48,600 is _____.

200,000,000

up, down
194,400,000
189,540,000
191,289,600

The product of 3,936 and 48,600 can be checked by "casting out nines." That is, by computing the excess of nines in 3,936, which is _____, and in 48,600, which is _____, and finally in the product. If the excess in the product of the excesses equals the excess in the product, then the product is likely to be correct. For example,

3

0

$$527,451 \quad \text{has excess} \text{_____.}$$
$$\times \ \ 6,042 \quad \text{has excess} \text{_____.}$$

6
3

```
  1054902
 2109804
31647060
```

_____ has excess _____.

18, 0

3186858942   has excess _____.

0

Since the excesses are both 0, the product is likely to be correct.

Applying our interpretation of multiplication as a repeated addition, we concluded that 8 × (−6) = −48. To verify our conclusion we set $N = 8 \times (-6)$ and showed that N must then equal −48 by applying known properties of multiplication and of equations.

To verify 17 × (−34) = −578 we set $N = 17 \times (-34)$. Since 578 = 17 × 34 we can write:
$$N + 578 = [17 \times (-34)] + (17 \times 34) \text{ by } \text{_____.}$$
$$= 17 \times [(-34) + 34] \text{ by the } \text{_____.}$$
$$= 17 \times 0 \text{ by the inverse property.}$$
$$N + 578 = 0 \text{ by the property of zero.}$$
Solving for N in $N + 578 = 0$, we have $N = $ _____.
Thus, 17 × (−34) = −578.

equal
addition
distributive
property
−578

In general, we concluded that when one of two factors in a multiplication is negative, then the product must be _____. Similarly, if two factors are negative, then the product must be _____. That is, the product of an even number of negative integers is positive and the product of an odd number of negative integers is negative. For

negative
positive

example, the product $(-15) \times 9 \times (-42) \times (-7) =$ _____   *−39,690*
while $(-15) \times 9 \times 42 \times (-7) =$ _____.   *39,690*

The properties of multiplication of integers can be summarized and illustrated by the following examples:

1. Since for any two integers A and B we have an integer P such that $A \times B = P$, we say that multiplication is _____. That is, for 7×5 we have $P =$ _____.   *closed, 35*

2. Since for any two integers A and B we have $A \times B = B \times A$, we say that multiplication is _____.   *commutative*
That is, $7 \times 5 =$ _____.   *5 × 7*

3. Since for any three integers A, B, and C we have $A \times (B \times C) = (A \times B) \times C$, we say that multiplication is _____. That is, $7 \times (5 \times 3) =$ _____.   *associative,*
    (7 × 5) × 3

4. Since for any three integers A, B, and C we have $A \times (B + C) = (A \times B) + (A \times C)$, we say that multiplication is _____. That is, $7 \times (5 + 3) =$ _____.   *distributive,*
    (7 × 5) +
    (7 × 3)

5. Since for any integer A we have $1 \times A = A \times 1 = A$, we call the number 1 the _____ element of multiplication. That is, $7 \times 1 = 1 \times 7 =$ _____.   *identity*
    7

6. Since for any integer A we have $0 \times A = A \times 0 = 0$, we call this a property of _____. That is, $7 \times 0 = 0 \times 7 =$ _____.   *zero*
    0

7. Since for any two positive integers A and B we have $A \times (-B) = (-A) \times B = -(A \times B)$ and $(-A) \times (-B) = A \times B$, we call these the Laws of _____ for multiplication of integers. That is, $7 \times (-5) = (-7) \times 5 =$ _____   *Signs*
    −34 or
and $(-7) \times (-5) =$ _____.   *−(7 × 5)*
    35 or 7 × 5

The use of proper parentheses and brackets in mathematical statements is just as important as punctuation in any other language. In finding the simplest numeral for an expression involving parentheses and brackets we begin with the simple "inner" computations and work "outward." This process enables us to combine parts one-by-one until we finally have eliminated all possible complications. For example, $150 - [(7 + [(8 \times 3) - 4])$
$\times 5] = 150 - [(7 + [$_____$ - 4]) \times 5] = 150 - [(7 +$ *24*
_____$) \times 5] = 150 - [$_____$ \times 5] = 150 -$_____ $=$ *20, 27, 135*
_____.   *15*

In concluding the chapter we observed that we could now inquire into the solution of a variety of equations. For example, the equation $17 \times N = 153$ has the solution

$N =$ _____. The equation $5 \times (2N + 10) = 30$ has the   9
solution $N =$ _____. Finally, the equation $(2N - 10) \times$ -2
$(N + 3) = 0$ has two solutions, $N =$ _____ and $N =$ 5
_____. -3

Chapter Exercises (4)

Group I.

   1. Multiplication is a "shortcut" operation for finding the _____ of
repeated additions of the same _____. One of the equal addends is
called the _____ while the number of times an addend is added to itself
is called the _____. The result is called the _____.
   2. The number 15 can be thought of as the product of the paired
positive integers 1 and 15 as well as of _____ and _____.
   3. Express the following numbers as products of prime factors:
      (a) 42   (b) 91   (c) 165.
   4. Find the products:
      (a) $300 \times (1 \times 47)$ (b) $(15 \times 6) \times (0 \times 84)$
      (c) $[69 \times (10 \times 7)] \times 100$ (d) $(70 - 31) \times 26$
      (e) $50 \times (300 + 4000)$ (f) $(20 + 3) \times (60 + 8)$.
   5. Find the product of 42 and 137 by the
      (a) "lattice" method   (b) doubling method.
   6. Find the products:
      (a)   2635   (b)   4107   (c)   91004
          $\times\ \ \ 42$ $\times\ 357$ $\times\ \ \ 860$

      (d)   57300   (e)   140601   (f)   821563
          $\times\ 8030$ $\times\ \ 6501$ $\times\ \ \ \ 278$

   7. Check the products of Exercise 6 by "casting out nines."
   8. Do as indicated:
      (a) Find 504 times 145   (b) Multiply 4321 by 101
      (c) $30{,}000 \times 700{,}000 = ?$ (d) What is the product of 36 and 54?
   9. Round the products of Exercise 6 to three significant digits.
   10. Round 847,563 to the nearest multiple of 1,000. Round 847,563
down to two significant digits.
   11. Estimate the following products by rounding both multiplier and
multiplicand to one significant digit.
      (a)   3,475   (b)   6,503   (c)   9,785   (d)   4,391
          $\times\ \ 762$ $\times\ \ 157$ $\times\ \ 509$ $\times\ \ 952$

12. Round the multipliers of Exercise 11 to one significant digit both up and down to obtain a high and a low estimate of the products.

13. Find the products:

(a) $431 \times (-207)$ (b) $(-395) \times (-138)$ (c) $(-614) \times 527$

(d) $(-109) \times (-96)$ (e) $(-740) \times 208$ (f) $(-116) \times (-823)$.

14. Check the products of Exercise 13 by "casting out nines."

15. Find the products:

(a) $(-12) \times [20 \times (-20)]$ (b) $[9 \times (-107)] \times [(-250) \times 16]$

(c) $[(-31) \times 29] \times 36$ (d) $[(-300) \times (-14)] \times [105 \times (-7)]$.

16. Find the simplest numeral for:

(a) $[9 \times (16 - 47)] \times [(92 + 9) \times 5]$.

(b) $([(23 \times 18) - 391] \times 30) + 19$.

(c) $[7 + (9 \times 11)] - ([13 - (15 - 17)] \times 19)$.

(d) $[-(6 \times 11) + (-7)] \times [(24 - 37) \times (-18)]$.

17. Match the descriptions in the numbered column with the lettered column so that they best describe the properties illustrated.

(a) $A \times 0 = 0$ 1. commutative

(b) $A \times (B \times C) = (A \times B) \times C$ 2. identity

(c) $A \times (B + C) = (A \times B) + (A \times C)$ 3. closure

(d) $A \times B = B \times A$ 4. associative

(e) $A \times 1 = A$ 5. zero

(f) $(-A) \times (-B) = A \times B$ 6. signs

(g) $A \times B = P$ 7. distributive

18. Solve the following equations for the variable.

(a) $3 \times [N \times (-7)] = -42$ (b) $N + 4 = 7 \times (17 - 9)$

(c) $(2N - 3) \times 11 = 27 + 6$ (d) $(12 - 7) \times (21 + N) = 25$

(e) $(N + 2) \times (3 - N) = N - 10$

(f) $[(4 \times 7) + 28] \times (7N - 35) = 0$.

19. Bill's father opened a savings account for Bill on his sixth birthday with a deposit of five dollars. Every month thereafter Bill deposited five dollars in his account. Without considering the interest, how much was in Bill's account on the day before his eighteenth birthday?

20. Bill said "If my one dollar bills were tens, then I would have twice as much from them as I have in tens and fives." Bill had one ten and two fives. How many one dollar bills did Bill have?

21. The New England state of Connecticut averages 508 people on each of its 4,999 square miles of land area. What is the population of Connecticut to the nearest multiple of 10,000?

22. Sam was two years less than three times Bill's age. The sum of their ages was seventy. How old was Sam?

Group II.

1. A multiple of a number can be thought of as the number _____ to

itself a certain number of times. The two numbers used in forming a multiple are called _____ while the multiple is often called a _____.

2. The number 39 can be thought of as a multiple of _____ and of _____ as well as of 1 and 39.

3. Express the following numbers as products of prime factors.
   (a) 75   (b) 119   (c) 130.

4. Find the products:
   (a) $(47 + 74) \times 107$ (b) $(305 \times 0) \times (190 \times 7)$
   (c) $(10 + 600) \times 5000$ (d) $(39 \times 1) \times 800$
   (e) $(30 - 5) \times (80 - 9)$ (f) $25 \times [4 \times (19 \times 2)]$.

5. Find the product of 37 and 745 by the
   (a) "lattice" method   (b) doubling method.

6. Find the products:

   (a)   4718   (b)   2069   (c)   37010
       ×   36   × 548   ×   709

   (d)   41900   (e)   234007   (f)   869155
       × 9044   ×   3025   ×   716

7. Check the products of Exercise 6 by "casting out nines."

8. Do as indicated:
   (a) Multiply 6040 by 807   (b) $150,000 \times 20,000 = ?$
   (c) Find 843 times 202   (d) What is the product of 51 and 18?

9. Round the products of Exercise 6 to three significant digits.

10. Round 754,529 to a multiple of 1,000. Round 754,529 up to two significant digits.

11. Estimate the following products by rounding both factors to one significant digit.

    (a)   4,705   (b)   7,521   (c)   9,612   (d)   2,463
        ×   728   ×   452   ×   903   ×   982

12. Round the multipliers of Exercise 11 to one significant digit both up and down to obtain a high and a low estimate of the products.

13. Find the products:
    (a) $(-710) \times 104$ (b) $(-465) \times (-216)$
    (c) $861 \times (-127)$ (d) $(-49) \times (-760)$
    (e) $618 \times (-280)$ (f) $(-491) \times (-395)$.

14. Check the products of Exercise 13 by "casting out nines."

15. Find the products:
    (a) $(34) \times [(-16) \times (-70)]$.
    (b) $[29 \times (-320)] \times [17 \times (-610)]$.
    (c) $[51 \times 37] \times (-44)$.
    (d) $[(-500) \times (-50)] \times [(-5) \times 505]$.

16. Find the simplest numeral for:
  (a) $[(61 - 39) \times 21] \times [17 \times (80 - 103)]$.
  (b) $([640 - (28 \times 43)] \times 60) + 1{,}098$.
  (c) $[(14 \times 51) + (-408)] + ([(32 - 18) + 75] \times 2)$.
  (d) $[(-83) - (41 \times 6)] \times [98 \times (51 - 53)]$.

17. Match the descriptions in the numbered column with the lettered column so that they best describe the properties illustrated.

  (a) $M \times (N \times K) = (M \times N) \times K$ 1. commutative
  (b) $M \times N = P$ 2. identity
  (c) $1 \times K = K$ 3. closure
  (d) $M \times (N - K) = (M \times N) - (M \times K)$ 4. associative
  (e) $0 \times K = 0$ 5. zero
  (f) $M \times N = (-M) \times (-N)$ 6. signs
  (g) $M \times N = N \times M$ 7. distributive

18. Solve the following equations for the variable.
  (a) $(-5) \times [4 \times N] = 60$ (b) $19 + 3N = (3 + N) \times 5$
  (c) $13 \times (2N + 7) = 72 - 7$ (d) $2 \times (N + 14) = N - 2$
  (e) $(N - 5) \times (1 - N) = 3 \times (2N - 3)$
  (f) $5N \times (3N - 15) = 0$.

19. One foot is twelve inches and one yard is three feet. There are 1,760 yards in a mile. How many inches are there in a mile?

20. The sum of two consecutive multiples of a positive integer is equal to 35. Find the three possible pairs of multiples.

21. A bank teller at the end of a day was supposed to have a balance of $8,490. Her credit and debit lists were:

Credit	Debit	Total
1,376	768	15,020
792	509	−6,548
4,085	2,953	8,472 balance.
370	1,060	
596	397	
7,801	861	
15,020	6,548	

Can you find a simple error the teller might have made? If so, indicate the possible correction.

22. If sound travels at 1,078 feet per second, then how many feet will it travel in one minute to the nearest 1,000 feet?

Problem Set (4)

1. If three consecutive odd numbered digits, in order from smallest to largest, form a numeral which names a number 555 more than the sum

of the three consecutive even numbered digits, each one larger than the odd numbered digits, then what is the three-digit numeral?

2. If the product of the sum and the difference of the digits of a two-digit numeral is 9, then what are the possible two-digit numerals?

3. Using examples and a discussion, show that the smallest factor other than 1 of any positive integer is a prime.

4. (a) If A, B, C, and D are distinct digits such that they form the product as shown:

$$
\begin{array}{r}
ABC \\
\times\ CA \\
\hline
ABC \\
CDA \\
\hline
CCAC
\end{array}
$$

then find the digits A, B, C, and D.

(*Hint.* Use expanded numerals and remember "carrying.")

(b) If A, B, C, D, and E are distinct nonzero digits such that they form the product as shown:

$$
\begin{array}{r}
ABC \\
\times\ CC \\
\hline
BCDC \\
BCDC \\
\hline
BDAEC
\end{array}
$$

then find the digits A, B, C, D, and E.

5. Since multiplication can be interpreted as a repeated addition process, it should be clear that if $A = B$ and C is any integer, then $A \times C = B \times C$.

(a) Since if $A > B$ there must be a positive integer C such that $A = B + C$, show that for any positive integer D we must have if $A > B$ and $D > 0$, then $A \times D > B \times D$.

(b) Show that if $A > B$ and $D < 0$, then $A \times D < B \times D$.

CHAPTER 5

Division

5.1 Quotients and Remainders

5.1.1   In practicing to find products such as $5 \times 7 = N$, we might practice the related problem $K \times 7 = 35$. That is, rather than looking for the product of two factors, we could look for the factor which when multiplied by a given factor results in a given product.

Examples.

(a) $5 \times 7 = N$ means $\underbrace{7 + 7 + 7 + 7 + 7}_{5} = N$.

(b) $K \times 7 = 35$ means $\underbrace{7 + 7 + 7 + 7 + 7}_{K} = 35$.

(c) For $K \times 7 = 35$ we might write: $0 = 35 \underbrace{- 7 - 7 - 7 - 7 - 7}_{K}$.

In multiplication we asked "What is the product when we multiply a multiplicand with a given multiplier?" That is, if we added a multiplicand to itself the "multiplier" number of times, we obtained the product. Now we ask the "inverse" question, "What must a multiplier be equal to in order to result in a given product when multiplying a given multiplicand?" That is, how many times can we subtract a given multiplicand from a given product? We can think of this new question as posing a repeated subtraction problem. This process is then called **division**. Instead of writing $N \times 7 = 35$ we write $35 \div 7 = N$ or $\frac{35}{7} = N$. We read "$35 \div 7 = N$" as "Thirty-five **divided by** seven is equal to N."

Division is a "shortcut" operation for finding how many times we can subtract a fixed subtrahend from a given minuend. To distinguish this operation from addition, subtraction, and multiplication we introduce some new names for the numbers involved. The given "product" is now called the **dividend**. The "factor" is now the **divisor** and the result, the "factor" which we obtain, is called the **quotient**. We say that we "divide the dividend by the divisor to obtain the quotient." It should be evident that the quotient times the divisor must then equal the dividend.

$$35 \div 7 = 5$$
Dividend   Divisor   Quotient

Dividend: $\dfrac{35}{7} = 5$ **Quotient.**
Divisor:

As with addition, subtraction, and multiplication, we begin with the simplest division facts. These should be practiced until they become automatic. Because of our interpretation, the basic division facts appear exactly like the basic multiplication facts. In Table 14 the left-hand marginal entries are divisors, the entries in the body of the table are the dividends, and the top marginal entries are the quotients. We enter the table with the given divisor and look along the row to the right until we find the dividend. Going to the top of the column we find the quotient of the given dividend divided by the given divisor.

TABLE 14. **Basic Division Facts.**

Quotients:		1	2	3	4	5	6	7	8	9	10
Divisors:	1	1	2	3	4	5	6	7	8	9	10
	2	4	4	6	8	10	12	14	16	18	20
	3	3	6	9	12	15	18	21	24	27	30
	4	4	8	12	16	20	24	28	32	36	40
	5	5	10	15	20	25	30	35	40	45	50
	6	6	12	18	24	30	36	42	48	54	60
	7	7	14	21	28	35	42	49	56	63	70
	8	8	16	24	32	40	48	56	64	72	80
	9	9	18	27	36	45	54	63	72	81	90

Examples.

(a) $63 \div 9 = N$ is done by entering the table at 9 on the margin, "moving" along the row to "63" and reading the quotient $N = 7$ at the top of the column. Of course we could "work the problem out" by noting that this is the same as writing $63 = N \times 9 = 9 \times N$. That is,

$$\underbrace{9 + 9 + \cdots + 9}_{N} = 63.$$

Subtracting successive nines from both sides of the equation, we have

$$\underbrace{9 + 9 + \cdots + 9}_{N-1} = 63 - \underbrace{9}_{1}$$

$$\underbrace{9 + 9 + \cdots + 9}_{N-2} = (63 - 9) - 9 = 63 - \underbrace{(2 \times 9)}_{2}$$

$$\underbrace{\cdots\cdots\cdots 0}_{N-7} = 63 - \underbrace{(7 \times 9)}_{7}$$

Thus, $N = 7$ the number of nines that we subtracted from 63.

(b) $54 \div 6 = N$ is done by entering the table at 6, moving to 54, then reading the quotient $N = 9$ at the top. To "work it out" we might arrange subtractions as follows:

$$
\begin{array}{rl}
54 & \text{is the given dividend.} \\
-\ 6 & \text{subtracting one 6.} \\
\hline
48 & \\
\end{array}
$$

$$
\begin{array}{rl}
-30 & \text{subtracting five more 6's.} \\
\hline
18 & \\
\end{array}
$$

$$
\begin{array}{rl}
-18 & \text{subtracting three more 6's.} \\
\hline
0 & \\
\end{array}
$$

Since we have subtracted $1 + 5 + 3 = 9$ sixes, $N = 9$.
The computation is often arranged in the following form:

$$
\begin{array}{rl}
& 9 \quad \text{quotient.} \\
\text{divisor:} \quad 6\overline{)54} & \text{dividend.} \\
\underline{54} & 9 \times 6 \text{ to be subtracted.} \\
0 & \text{called the } \textbf{remainder.}
\end{array}
$$

Certain division facts seem to cause more difficulty than others. In order to develop facility in using numbers we must first develop automatic and rapid responses to fundamental number situations. Repeat the following practice set of simple division facts until they can be done without error within one minute.

Practice 1. Do the following mentally, giving quotients only.

	(a)	(b)	(c)	(d)	(e)	(f)	(g)	(h)
1.	$9\overline{)63}$	$6\overline{)48}$	$7\overline{)56}$	$5\overline{)45}$	$8\overline{)72}$	$9\overline{)81}$	$7\overline{)28}$	$5\overline{)35}$
2.	$3\overline{)21}$	$8\overline{)24}$	$9\overline{)54}$	$3\overline{)15}$	$4\overline{)28}$	$6\overline{)42}$	$3\overline{)18}$	$8\overline{)64}$
3.	$7\overline{)42}$	$5\overline{)40}$	$3\overline{)27}$	$9\overline{)72}$	$8\overline{)32}$	$3\overline{)24}$	$6\overline{)18}$	$7\overline{)35}$
4.	$8\overline{)48}$	$7\overline{)49}$	$4\overline{)36}$	$7\overline{)21}$	$9\overline{)27}$	$6\overline{)30}$	$4\overline{)32}$	$9\overline{)36}$
5.	$8\overline{)56}$	$7\overline{)63}$	$9\overline{)45}$	$6\overline{)36}$	$4\overline{)24}$	$6\overline{)54}$	$8\overline{)40}$	$6\overline{)24}$

Answers.

	(a)	(b)	(c)	(d)	(e)	(f)	(g)	(h)
1.	7	8	8	9	9	9	4	7
2.	7	3	6	5	7	7	6	8
3.	6	8	9	8	4	8	3	5
4.	6	7	9	3	3	5	8	4
5.	7	9	5	6	6	9	5	4

5.1.2 In practicing simple divisions, it should soon become apparent that certain dividends are "missing." That is, in dividing by, say 4, we have only included as dividends exact multiples of 4. There is no reason why we couldn't consider a dividend of, say 27, when dividing by 4. However, we would then have an added problem. We would have to concede that there is no integer N such that $27 = N \times 4$. Leaving this problem for the next chapter, we can overcome the difficulty by introducing a new number indicated by R: $27 = (N \times 4) + R, 0 \leq R < 4$. The introduction of R enables us to retain the equality while looking for the largest multiple of the divisor less than or equal to the dividend. The number R is called the **remainder** and is always less than the divisor. For example, $27 = (6 \times 4) + 3$ so that the quotient is 6 and the remainder is 3 (which is less than the divisor 4). The various forms used in division are illustrated in the following examples.

Examples.

(a) $43 \div 5$ is more commonly indicated by:

   (i) $\dfrac{43}{5} = 8 + \dfrac{3}{5}$ (ii) $43 = (8 \times 5) + 3$ (iii) $5)\overline{43}$ 8 R3

$$\begin{array}{r} 40 \\ \hline 3 \end{array}$$

(b) $51 \div 8$ is written:

$$
\begin{array}{r}
6 \quad \text{quotient} \\
\text{divisor: } 8)\overline{51} \quad \text{dividend} \\
48 \quad (6 \times 8) \\
\hline
3 \quad \text{remainder}
\end{array}
$$

(c) $9)\overline{7}$ 0 R7

$$\begin{array}{r} 0 \\ \hline 7 \end{array}$$

(d) $3)\overline{26}$ 8 R2

$$\begin{array}{r} 24 \\ \hline 2 \end{array}$$

The **quotient** in a division operation names the largest multiple of the divisor which can be subtracted from the dividend with a **remainder** greater than or equal to zero and less than the divisor. Note especially that when the dividend is less than the divisor the quotient is zero and the remainder equal to the dividend. Each of the four forms used to describe division above has its proper place in writing.

The use of "÷" emphasizes the operation of division and dates from the latter half of the seventeenth century. It may have arisen from the use of a colon,":," by the German philosopher and mathematician Gottfried Wilhelm von Leibniz (1646–1716) for division.

The use of the bar, " – ," to indicate division dates back to the sixth century and the Hindus. Although the use of this symbol with the dividend and divisor above and below the bar causes some difficulties in setting type for mass printing, it is a preferred form of writing since it leads suggestively to a further extension of numbers and to the development of manipulations with numerals.

The product form, for example, $43 = (8 \times 5) + 3$, suggests the close connection between division and multiplication. The form is called the **division algorithm** and can be stated using variables as:

Given any integers A and B with $A \neq 0$, there are integers Q and R such that $B = (Q \times A) + R$, $0 \leq R <$ the positive value corresponding to A.

By "the positive value corresponding to any number N" we mean that if $N \geq 0$ then we select N and if $N < 0$ then we select $-N > 0$ for our value. For example, if $N = 3$, the positive value corresponding to N is 3, while if $N = -3$, the positive value corresponding to N is $-N = -(-3) = 3$. The positive value corresponding to a number N is called the **absolute value** of N.

Mathematical procedures such as that described by $B = (Q \times A) + R$ are called algorithms. Other examples are the principles of equal addition and of equal subtraction. We have used the distributive property of multiplication over addition, $C \times (A + B) = (C \times A) + (C \times B)$, as an algorithm for computing products. **Algorithms**, that is, mathematical procedures used in computations to obtain results, have played important roles in the historical development of arithmetical computations. Euclid (about 300 B.C.), who is more popularly known for his exposition of geometry, used the division algorithm extensively in his study of numbers.

Finally, the computational form, illustrated in Examples (c) and (d) above, offers the organization and format which appears most suitable for finding quotients and remainders.

Practice 2. Find the quotient and remainder without the use of paper or pencil.

	(a)	(b)	(c)	(d)	(e)	(f)	(g)	(h)
1.	27 ÷ 5	19 ÷ 7	40 ÷ 9	11 ÷ 3	3 ÷ 4	61 ÷ 8	69 ÷ 7	22 ÷ 5
2.	8 ÷ 7	30 ÷ 4	62 ÷ 7	32 ÷ 5	70 ÷ 8	35 ÷ 4	18 ÷ 8	85 ÷ 9

3. $\dfrac{37}{6}$ $\dfrac{43}{5}$ $\dfrac{57}{9}$ $\dfrac{75}{8}$ $\dfrac{11}{2}$ $\dfrac{51}{6}$ $\dfrac{16}{3}$ $\dfrac{19}{7}$

4. $\dfrac{7}{8}$ $\dfrac{48}{9}$ $\dfrac{69}{9}$ $\dfrac{55}{7}$ $\dfrac{23}{6}$ $\dfrac{26}{3}$ $\dfrac{22}{7}$ $\dfrac{17}{4}$

5. $3\overline{)29}$ $7\overline{)20}$ $6\overline{)1}$ $9\overline{)76}$ $3\overline{)20}$ $8\overline{)38}$ $5\overline{)39}$ $7\overline{)48}$

Answers.

	(a)	(b)	(c)	(d)	(e)	(f)	(g)	(h)
1.	5R2	2R5	4R4	3R2	0R3	7R5	9R6	4R2
2.	1R1	7R2	8R6	6R2	8R6	8R3	2R2	9R4
3.	6R1	8R3	6R3	9R3	5R1	8R3	5R1	2R5
4.	0R7	5R3	7R6	7R6	3R5	8R2	3R1	4R1
5.	9R2	2R6	0R1	8R4	6R2	4R6	7R4	6R6

5.1.3   To extend our discussion of division to quotients with two or more digits, we observe that, since $6 \div 3 = 2$ means $6 = 2 \times 3$, we can multiply both sides of the latter equation by 10 to obtain $60 = (2 \times 3) \times 10 = 20 \times 3$ or, in division form, $60 \div 3 = 20$. Given that $28 \div 4 = 7$, we can write $280 \div 4 = 70$. Since we have $8 \div 2 = 4$, we can obtain $800 \div 2 = 400$. That is, multiplying a dividend by 10, 100, 1,000, and so forth, simply means that the quotient in turn is multiplied by 10, 100, 1,000, and so forth.

Since we can work in both directions with an equation, we can immediately note that given $60 = 20 \times 3$ we have $60 \div 20 = 3$. But $6 \div 2 = 3$ so that $60 \div 20 = 6 \div 2$. We also have $280 \div 70 = 28 \div 7$ and $800 \div 400 = 8 \div 4$. That is, when both dividend and divisor terminate in zeroes, we can separate the factors of 10, 100, 1,000, and so forth, which are common in both and simplify the division process somewhat.

Furthermore, since division can be interpreted as a successive subtraction process, we can expand a dividend and subtract convenient multiples of the divisor from the addends of the expanded dividend. For example, $64 \div 3$ can be thought of as $(60 + 4) \div 3$ so that we can easily subtract $20 \times 3 = 60$ from the addend 60 and $1 \times 3 = 3$ from the addend 4. Thus, $(60 + 4) = (20 + 1)3 + 1$ and the quotient is $21R1$. The idea can be expressed by $64 \div 3 = (60 + 4) \div 3 = (60 \div 3) + (4 \div 3)$. That is, division is **distributive** from the right to the left (but **not** from the left to the right).

Examples.

(a) $420 \div 6$ is the same as $(42 \times 10) \div 6$ so that, since $42 \div 6 = 7$, we have $420 \div 6 = 70$. For computation, we write:

$$\begin{array}{r} 70 \quad \text{quotient.} \\ 6\overline{)420} \\ \underline{42} \quad (7 \times 6) \\ 00 \end{array}$$

(b) $560 \div 70$ has a factor of 10 in both dividend and divisor so that we can think, $560 \div 70 = 56 \div 7 = 8$.

(c) $91 \div 7$ can be done by noticing that $91 = 70 + 21$ so that $91 \div 7 = (70 \div 7) + (21 \div 7) = 10 + 3 = 13$. That is, we can subtract 10 sevens, then 3 more sevens to exhaust 91.

(d) $64 \div 3$ is written for computation as:

$$\begin{array}{r} 21 \; R1 \\ 3\overline{)64} \\ \underline{6} \quad (2 \times 3) \\ 4 \\ \underline{3} \quad (1 \times 3) \\ 1 \; \text{remainder.} \end{array}$$

Our thinking might proceed as follows: 3 into 6 is 2 (tens); 2 times 3 is 6 (tens); 6 from 6 is zero; bring down the 4, 3 into 4 is 1; 1 times 3 is 3 from 4 is 1; remainder 1.

(e) $74 \div 4$ is arranged:

$$\begin{array}{r} 18 \; R2 \\ 4\overline{)74} \\ \underline{4} \quad (1 \times 4) \\ 34 \quad \text{difference } 74 - 40. \\ \underline{32} \quad (8 \times 4) \\ 2 \quad \text{difference and remainder.} \end{array}$$

Our thinking might be: 4 into 7 is 1 (tens); 1 times 4 is 4 (tens); 4 from 7 is 3, bring down 4; 4 into 34 is 8, 8 times 4 is 32; 32 from 34 is 2, the remainder.

(f)

$$\begin{array}{r} 40 \; R5 \\ 8\overline{)325} \\ \underline{32} \quad (4 \times 8)\text{tens.} \\ 05 \quad (325 - 320) \\ \underline{0} \quad (0 \times 8) \\ 5 \quad (5 - 0) \text{ remainder.} \end{array}$$

We might think: 8 into 32 is 4; 4 times 8 is 32; 32 less 32 is 0; bring down the 5; 8 into 5 is 0; 0 times 8 is 0; 0 from 5 is 5, remainder less than 8.

(g)

$$\begin{array}{r} 1208 \quad \text{quotient.} \\ 6\overline{)7248} \\ \underline{6} \quad (1 \times 6)\text{thousands.} \\ 12 \quad (72 - 60)\text{hundreds.} \\ \underline{12} \quad (2 \times 6)\text{hundreds.} \\ 04 \quad (12 - 12)\text{hundreds, "bring down 4 tens."} \\ \underline{0} \quad (0 \times 6)\text{tens.} \\ 48 \quad (4 - 0)\text{tens, "bring down 8 ones."} \\ \underline{48} \quad (8 \times 6)\text{ones.} \\ 0 \quad (48 - 48) \text{ remainder.} \end{array}$$

Notice that the division is accomplished by successively subtracting multiples of the divisor from the dividend and what is "left over." The digits in the quotient are obtained by finding the largest multiple of the divisor less than or equal to the one- or two-digit number indicated in the dividend or what is "left over."

(h)   941 R3   (i)   1008 R3
    5)4708   9)9075
     45   9
     ――   ――
     20   07
     20   0
     ――   ――
      8   75
      5   72
     ―   ――
      3   3

Practice should enable one to do all divisions by a one-digit divisor in the following abbreviated form. The differences in the subtractions should be "carried" mentally to the next dividend until a remainder less than the divisor is obtained.

Examples.

(a)   21 R1   We can think: 3 into 6 is 2 with no "carry";
    3)64   3 into 4 is 1 with remainder 1.

(b)   18 R2   We can think: 4 into 7 is 1 with 3 to "carry";
    4)74   4 into 34 is 8 with remainder 2.

(c)   13 R0   We can think: 7 into 9 is 1 with 2 to "carry";
    7)91   7 into 21 is 3 with 0 remainder.

(d)   40 R5   Think: 8 into 32 is 4, "carry" 0; 8 into 5 is 0,
    8)325   remainder 5.

(e)   1208 R0   Think: 6 into 7 is 1, "carry" 1; 6 into 12 is 2,
    6)7248   "carry" 0; 6 into 48 is 8, don't forget the
                        place-holding 0; remainder 0.

(f)   941 R3   Think: 5 into 47 is 9 and 2 to "carry"; 5 into 20
    5)4708   is 4, no "carry"; 5 into 8 is 1 with remainder
                        3.

(g)   1008 R3   Think: 9 into 9 is 1; zero; zero; 9 into 75 is 8,
    9)9075   72, "carry" 3, the remainder.

Practice set 3 which follows is arranged in order of difficulty. The divisions should be done mentally and practiced until only the quotients and remainders need be written. Check by multiplying the quotient by the divisor and adding the remainder to see that the result is equal to the dividend.

Practice 3.   Write only the quotients and remainders.

	(a)	(b)	(c)	(d)	(e)	(f)
1.	7)217	6)304	2)167	9)726	4)289	8)409
2.	5)250	3)213	7)772	3)278	8)564	9)549
3.	2)134	6)253	9)302	5)468	7)513	6)409
4.	8)960	4)523	7)627	3)913	8)275	9)109
5.	5)4603	9)2898	6)3250	8)4257	3)1712	7)4711
6.	4)1100	7)8517	2)6543	9)8300	7)3919	6)3894
7.	6)34167	2)14101	9)23360	5)54073	4)26318	8)62128
8.	7)32746	9)51876	3)81715	8)45471	6)50004	7)41062

Answers:

	(a)	(b)	(c)	(d)	(e)	(f)
1.	31R0	50R4	83R1	80R6	72R1	51R1
2.	50R0	71R0	110R2	92R2	70R4	61R0
3.	67R0	42R1	33R5	93R3	73R2	68R1
4.	120R0	130R3	89R4	304R1	34R3	12R1
5.	920R3	322R0	541R4	532R1	570R2	673R0
6.	275R0	1216R5	3271R1	922R2	559R6	649R0
7.	5694R3	7050R1	2595R5	10814R3	6579R2	7766R0
8.	4678R0	5764R0	27238R1	5683R7	8334R0	5866R0

5.1.4   Division with divisors of two or more digits presents some difficulties. Consider $741 \div 38$. Our previous experience might suggest that 3 into 7 is 2, but $2 \times 38 = 76$ so that we cannot subtract 76 from 74 without a negative difference. Although 30 divides into 741 at least 20 times, our actual divisor of 38 does not. We can overcome this difficulty in two ways:

1. Remember that division is the successive subtraction of multiples of the divisor from the dividend.

2. Mentally round the divisor up to a slightly larger numeral to estimate the quotient.

To divide 741 by 38 we think 741 divided by 40:

$$\begin{array}{r} 1 \\ 38\overline{)741} \\ 38 \\ \hline 36 \end{array}$$ Think 40 into 74 is 1 and $1 \times 38 = 38$ so that $74 - 38 = 36$ which is smaller than the divisor 38.

$$\begin{array}{r} 19 \\ 38\overline{)741} \\ 38 \\ \hline 361 \\ 342 \\ \hline 19 \end{array}$$ Bring down the 1 to form 361; 4 into 36 is 9; $9 \times 38 = 342$ and $361 - 342 = 19$ which is less than 38. Since 19 is less than 38, 19 is the remainder.

Division was rarely used in ancient times except when the divisor was small. The Egyptians avoided the difficulties by a system of doubling. For example, to divide 741 by 38 we list the doubles as shown:

$$\begin{array}{rr} 1/ & 38 \\ 2/ & 76 \\ 4 & 152 \\ 8 & 304 \\ 16/ & 608 \end{array}$$

Since $741 = 608 + 76 + 38 + 19 = 16(38) + 2(38) + 1(38) + 19$ we have $741 = (16 + 2 + 1)38 + 19$ and the quotient is 19 with remainder 19.

It is not surprising that Fibonacci, whom we have previously mentioned, described a method of division called the "galley" or "scratch" method. Leonardo of Pisa, called Fibonacci, was the son of a commercial agent who traveled the Orient and Northern Africa as a merchant representative of the flourishing Italian city of Pisa. Leonardo, in his travels with his father, came in contact with the Hindu and Arabic culture of the time. Indeed, his writing of the *Liber Abaci* (1220) was one of the means whereby the Hindu-Arabic system of numerals was introduced into Western Europe.

To divide 5261 by 43 the work is arranged as shown below:

9
5̸2̸61 (1
4̸3̸

The divisor is written below the dividend as shown. The first digit of the quotient is written to the right of the dividend. We then subtract the product of this first digit and the divisor from the left-hand digits of the dividend, writing the difference above the dividend. As we "use" the digits, we cross them out.

1
9
5̸2̸6̸1 (12
4̸3̸3̸
4

We begin the second step by writing the divisor below and one place to the right under the dividend. The next digit in the quotient is obtained and written to the right of the first digit in the quotient. The product ($2 \times 43 = 86$) is computed and subtracted from what remains of the dividend. The digits are "scratched" as we use them.

	We begin again by writing the divisor below and one
̸1̸1̸	
9̸2̸5	place to the right under the dividend. The next digit in
5̸2̸6̸1̸ (122	the quotient is obtained and the product is subtracted
4̸3̸3̸3	from what remains of the dividend. The digits are
4̸4	"scratched" as they are used. Since what remains, 15, is
	less than the divisor, the process is completed.

The numerals remaining in the scheme without being scratched out name the quotient 122 and the remainder 15.

5.1.5   Our present division scheme called "long division" was first introduced in the fifteenth century. It appeared in an arithmetic manuscript published in Florence, Italy, in 1491, a year before Columbus "sailed the ocean blue" to America. In "long division" we estimate the quotient one digit at a time and successively subtract the product of the estimate and the divisor from the dividend. The most common error is in estimating the quotient digit. The following examples describe the method of "long division."

Examples.

(a)

$$
\begin{array}{r} 1 \\ 43)\overline{5261} \\ 43 \\ \hline 9 \end{array}
\qquad
\begin{array}{r} 12 \\ 43)\overline{5261} \\ 43 \\ \hline 96 \\ 86 \\ \hline 10 \end{array}
\qquad
\begin{array}{r} 122\ R15 \\ 43)\overline{5261} \\ 43 \\ \hline 96 \\ 86 \\ \hline 101 \\ 86 \\ \hline 15 \end{array}
$$

In this example, it is clear that 43 goes "into" 52 once. Also, 43 "into" 96 and 43 "into" 101 are quite evidently two's.

(b)

$$
\begin{array}{r} 8 \\ 93)\overline{7526} \\ 744 \\ \hline 8 \end{array}
\qquad
\begin{array}{r} 80\ R86 \\ 93)\overline{7526} \\ 744 \\ \hline 86 \end{array}
$$

We might estimate by thinking 9 "into" 75 is 8. Since $86 < 93$ the division "ends" with the remainder 86.

(c)

$$
\begin{array}{r} 4 \\ 84)\overline{3705} \\ 336 \\ \hline 34 \end{array}
\qquad
\begin{array}{r} 44\ R9 \\ 84)\overline{3705} \\ 336 \\ \hline 345 \\ 336 \\ \hline 9 \end{array}
$$

We can estimate that 8 "into" 37 is 4.

(d)

$$
\begin{array}{r}
2 \\
28\overline{)81645} \\
\underline{56} \\
25
\end{array}
\qquad
\begin{array}{r}
2\cancel{8} \\
28\overline{)81645} \\
\underline{56} \\
256 \\
\underline{224} \\
32 \\
\underline{28} \\
4
\end{array}
\qquad
\begin{array}{r}
291 \\
28\overline{)81645} \\
\underline{56} \\
256 \\
\underline{252} \\
44 \\
\underline{28} \\
16
\end{array}
\qquad
\begin{array}{r}
2915 \; R25 \\
28\overline{)81645} \\
\underline{56} \\
256 \\
\underline{252} \\
44 \\
\underline{28} \\
165 \\
\underline{140} \\
25
\end{array}
$$

In this example, we can mentally round 28 to 30 and estimate 3 into 8 is 2. In the second step, when we estimate 3 into 25 is 8 we find that the difference 32 is greater than 28. Thus, we must subtract one more 28 from the 256. That is, $9 \times 28 = 252$ from 256 rather than the original estimate of $8 \times 28 = 224$. Notice how this error in the estimate can be corrected easily in writing.

(e)

$$
\begin{array}{r}
1 \\
420\overline{)53710} \\
\underline{420} \\
117
\end{array}
\qquad
\begin{array}{r}
12 \\
420\overline{)53710} \\
\underline{420} \\
1171 \\
\underline{840} \\
331
\end{array}
\qquad
\begin{array}{r}
7 \\
12\cancel{8} \; R370 \\
420\overline{)53710} \\
\underline{420} \\
1171 \\
\underline{840} \\
3310 \\
\cancel{3360} \\
\underline{2940} \\
370
\end{array}
$$

We must be careful in the placement of the first digit of the quotient in long divisions. In this example, it is easy to estimate 42 into 53. Then 4 into 11, but note our error in thinking 4 into 33. Since 3360 is too large, we must reduce our estimate by one.

(f)

$$
\begin{array}{r}
7 \\
\cancel{6}0,072 \; R328 \\
576\overline{)40,361,800} \\
\underline{34\;56} \\
5\;80 \\
\underline{5\;76} \\
41\;80 \\
\underline{40\;32} \\
1\;480 \\
\underline{1\;152} \\
328
\end{array}
$$

Of course, in actual practice we do not copy over each step. The completed work might look like the last step in each example.

In this example, we estimated with 6 into 40 as 6 but discovered that we could subtract one more 576 from the 4036 in the first step. Observe the need for careful alignment and spacing of digits in the work. Since 576 will not divide into 41 or 418, we insert zeroes in the quotient.

(g)

$$
\begin{array}{r}
3{,}800\ R307 \\
7164\overline{)27{,}223{,}507} \\
21{,}492 \\
\overline{5\ 731\ 5} \\
5\ 731\ 2 \\
\overline{307}
\end{array}
$$

Notice the placement of the first digit of the quotient. Count the digits from the left in the dividend above which the first digit in the quotient is placed and compare this number with the number of digits in the divisor.

Practice 4. Find the quotients and remainders.

	(a)	(b)	(c)	(d)	(e)
1.	$56\overline{)243}$	$87\overline{)630}$	$42\overline{)397}$	$96\overline{)504}$	$71\overline{)436}$
2.	$17\overline{)151}$	$34\overline{)271}$	$23\overline{)184}$	$83\overline{)581}$	$62\overline{)523}$
3.	$38\overline{)394}$	$48\overline{)706}$	$84\overline{)965}$	$51\overline{)573}$	$18\overline{)378}$
4.	$91\overline{)6377}$	$54\overline{)1630}$	$72\overline{)2381}$	$67\overline{)1367}$	$45\overline{)9500}$
5.	$82\overline{)2706}$	$66\overline{)1195}$	$57\overline{)1254}$	$73\overline{)5110}$	$32\overline{)1058}$
6.	$45\overline{)1227}$	$77\overline{)4928}$	$89\overline{)5789}$	$27\overline{)1839}$	$19\overline{)1706}$
7.	$39\overline{)2474}$	$67\overline{)5400}$	$51\overline{)4233}$	$94\overline{)9127}$	$61\overline{)3045}$
8.	$18\overline{)73530}$	$82\overline{)96842}$	$47\overline{)79917}$	$18\overline{)90367}$	$92\overline{)18032}$
9.	$44\overline{)11836}$	$39\overline{)88150}$	$57\overline{)95247}$	$63\overline{)93456}$	$29\overline{)49040}$
10.	$76\overline{)15000}$	$99\overline{)63169}$	$15\overline{)54016}$	$38\overline{)11286}$	$64\overline{)74816}$

Answers.

	(a)	(b)	(c)	(d)	(e)
1.	4R19	7R21	9R19	5R24	6R10
2.	8R15	7R33	8R0	7R0	8R27
3.	10R14	14R34	11R41	11R12	21R0
4.	70R7	30R10	33R5	20R27	211R5
5.	33R0	18R7	22R0	70R0	33R2
6.	27R12	64R0	65R4	67R30	89R15
7.	63R17	80R40	83R0	97R9	49R56
8.	4085R0	1181R0	1700R17	5020R7	196R0
9.	269R0	2260R10	1671R0	1483R27	1691R1
10.	197R28	638R7	3601R1	297R0	1169R0

5.1.6 As the number of digits in the dividend and divisor become larger, checking division by multiplying the divisor by the quotient becomes increasingly awkward. In this event, "casting out nines" is a useful method for checking division.

Examples.

(a) Checking by multiplying quotient times the divisor:

$$
\begin{array}{r}
14\ R34 \\
48)\overline{706}
\end{array}
\qquad
\begin{array}{rl}
\text{check:} & 48 \quad \text{divisor.} \\
\times 14 & \text{quotient.} \\
\hline
192 & \\
48 & \\
\hline
672 + 34 = 706 & \text{the dividend.}
\end{array}
$$

(b) Checking by multiplying the quotient times the divisor:

$$
\begin{array}{r}
1483\ R27 \\
63)\overline{93456}
\end{array}
\qquad
\begin{array}{rl}
\text{check:} & 1483 \\
\times\ 63 & \\
\hline
4449 & \\
8898 & \\
\hline
93429 + 27 = 93456 & \text{the dividend.}
\end{array}
$$

(c) Checking by "casting out nines":

$$
\begin{array}{r}
1483\ R27 \\
63)\overline{93456}
\end{array}
\qquad
\begin{array}{rl}
\text{check:} & 1483 \text{ has excess } 7 \\
& 63 \text{ has excess } \underline{0} \\
& 0
\end{array}
$$

remainder 27 has excess 0, sum excess is 0.
93456 has excess 0.

(d) Checking by "casting out nines":

$$
\begin{array}{r}
1691\ R1 \\
29)\overline{49040}
\end{array}
\qquad
\begin{array}{rl}
\text{check:} & 1691 \text{ excess } \ \ 8 \\
& 29 \text{ excess } \ \underline{2} \\
& 16 \text{ excess } 7
\end{array}
$$

remainder 1 excess $\qquad\qquad\quad \underline{1}$

sum $\overline{8}$ excess 8.

49040 excess 8.

5.1.7   In divisions with large divisors and dividends, placement of the first digit of the quotient may cause difficulties as well as the determination of the numbers of digits to be expected in the quotient. A close review of the examples previously given should suggest a procedure for the placement of the first left-hand digit of the quotient.

If the left-hand digit of the dividend is larger than the left-hand digit of the divisor, place the first digit of the quotient above the digit in the dividend which is the same number of places from the left as are in the divisor.

If the left-hand digit of the dividend is smaller than the left-hand digit of the divisor, place the first digit of the quotient above the digit in the dividend which is one more place from the left than are in the divisor.

If the left-hand digits of the dividend and the divisor are the same, then the second digits are used in the same way to determine the placing of the first digit of the quotient.

Once the first digit in the quotient has been placed, each additional digit in the dividend below indicates an additional digit in the quotient.

For the impatient, but careful person in a "hurry" to do division, a further abbreviation of "long division" is possible by omitting the products obtained in multiplying the digits of the quotient and the divisor. The product is "carried" mentally while the subtraction is accomplished and the differences alone are recorded. The following examples illustrate the method.

Examples.

(a) Rather than

$$
\begin{array}{r}
5020\ R7 \\
18)\overline{90367} \\
90 \\
\hline
036 \\
36 \\
\hline
07 \\
0 \\
\hline
7
\end{array}
$$

we write

$$
\begin{array}{r}
5020\ R7 \\
18)\overline{90367} \\
036 \\
07
\end{array}
$$

(b) Rather than

$$
\begin{array}{r}
1169 \\
64)\overline{74816} \\
64 \\
\hline
108 \\
64 \\
\hline
441 \\
384 \\
\hline
576 \\
576 \\
\hline
0
\end{array}
$$

we write

$$
\begin{array}{r}
1169 \\
64)\overline{74816} \\
108 \\
441 \\
576 \\
0
\end{array}
$$

(c)

$$
\begin{array}{r}
127\ R370 \\
420)\overline{53710} \\
1171 \\
3310 \\
370
\end{array}
$$

(d)

$$
\begin{array}{r}
2{,}071\ R785 \\
2705)\overline{5{,}602{,}840} \\
192\ 84 \\
3\ 490 \\
785
\end{array}
$$

5.1.8 Of course, in divisions with large numbers, we may not be interested in exact quotients but only in estimates and/or approximations.

In this case, we can round the dividend and divisor to one more than the required number of significant digits and proceed with the simplified division. (Note: For some computations the dividend should be carried to two more significant digits than required.) The resulting quotient is then rounded again to the specified number of significant digits.

Examples.

(a) Find the quotient of 5,602,840 divided by 2,705 to two significant digits.

$$
\begin{array}{r}
2{,}070 \\
2{,}700\overline{)5{,}600{,}000} \\
5{,}400 \\
\hline
200\ 00 \\
189\ 00 \\
\hline
11\ 00
\end{array}
$$

We round both dividend and divisor to three significant digits and carry the division out until we have three significant digits, completing the quotient with zeroes. Finally we round the quotient to the required two significant digits: 2,100.

(b) Divide 7,031,685 by 873 and obtain the quotient to three significant digits.

$$
\begin{array}{r}
8{,}050 \\
873\overline{)7{,}032{,}000} \\
6{,}984 \\
\hline
48\ 00 \\
43\ 65
\end{array}
$$

Note that the divisor is retained since it is to three significant digits. We terminate the division when the required number of significant digits have been determined for the quotient. The quotient to three significant digits is 8,050.

(c) What is the quotient, to three significant digits, of 36,417 divided into 7,463,509,147?

$$
\begin{array}{r}
204{,}900 \\
36{,}420\overline{)7{,}464{,}000{,}000} \\
7\ 284\ 0 \\
\hline
180\ 000 \\
145\ 680 \\
\hline
34\ 320\ 0 \\
32\ 778\ 0
\end{array}
$$

ANSWER: 205,000.

Practice 5.

(A) Find the quotient and remainder. Check by either multiplying the quotient and divisor or by "casting out nines."

	(a)	(b)	(c)
1.	456)97,186	218)137,804	781)749,350
2.	630)3,438,194	576)42,048,714	803)16,341,290
3.	1670)7,182,708	3614)8,200,052	9722)65,293,472
4.	7518)7,420,266	2145)15,103,000	6874)4,763,939

(B) Find the quotients to two significant digits.

	(a)	(b)	(c)
5.	3647)10,725,936	1736)12,627,689	5587)5,989,628
6.	4372)160,982,431	8445)483,138,963	2778)54,726,785

Answers.

	(a)	(b)	(c)
1.	213R58	632R28	959R371
2.	5,457R284	73,001R138	20,350R240
3.	4,301R38	2,268R3500	6,716R520
4.	987R0	7,041R55	693R257
5.	2,900	7,300	1,100
6.	37,000	57,000	20,000

Exercises

1. A "shortcut" operation for finding how many times we can subtract a fixed subtrahend from a given minuend is called _____. The given "minuend" is then called the _____, the fixed "subtrahend" is called the _____, and the result, the number of times we can subtract the "subtrahend," is called the _____.

2. Because of our interpretation, division can be thought of as an "inverse" operation to _____. Thus, the basic division facts appear exactly like the basic _____ facts.

3. We can "work out" $56 \div 7$ by _____ 8 sevens from _____.

4. In dividing 32 by 5 we obtain a quotient _____ and _____ 2.

5. Match the numbered descriptions so that they best describe the

forms in the lettered column.

(a) $75 = (8 \times 9) + 3$ 1. computational form.
(b) $75 \div 9 = 8\ R3$ 2. division algorithm.
(c) $\dfrac{75}{7} = 8 + \dfrac{3}{9}$ 3. extension and manipulation.
                                     4. division operation.
(d) $\begin{array}{r} 8\ R3 \\ 9\overline{)75} \\ 72 \\ \hline 3 \end{array}$

6. (a) If a dividend is multiplied by 10, the _____ is also multiplied by 10.

(b) If a dividend and a divisor both have a factor of 10, then the _____ appearing in the dividend and divisor can both be omitted to simplify the division.

(c) Division is _____ from the right to the left, but not from the left to the right.

7. To divide 146 by 12 we can expand $146 = 120 +$ _____. Now, $120 =$ _____(12) and _____ $= 2(12) +$ _____ so that $146 \div 12 =$ _____ R _____.

8. Write only the quotients and remainders.

(a)	(b)	(c)	(d)
$8\overline{)3616}$	$5\overline{)7152}$	$9\overline{)1409}$	$6\overline{)2341}$

(e)	(f)	(g)	(h)
$3\overline{)71000}$	$7\overline{)40703}$	$4\overline{)41236}$	$2\overline{)99999}$

9. Divide 697 by 53 using the   (a) Egyptian doubling method, (b) "galley" or "scratch" method.

10. Find the quotients and remainders.

(a)	(b)	(c)	(d)
$60\overline{)38,470}$	$11\overline{)57,106}$	$35\overline{)27,803}$	$49\overline{)99,524}$

11. Check the divisions of Exercise 10 by multiplying the quotient times the divisor and adding the remainder.

12. Do the divisions:

(a)	(b)	(c)	(d)
$406\overline{)37,964}$	$761\overline{)84,093}$	$258\overline{)57,380}$	$540\overline{)219,764}$

13. Check the divisions of Exercise 12 by "casting out nines."

14. Do the following divisions using the abbreviated "hurry up" method of long division.

(a)	(b)	(c)
$1483\overline{)29,865,058}$	$3701\overline{)21,600,482}$	$8025\overline{)65,477,300}$

15. Check the divisions of Exercise 14 by "casting out nines."
16. Find the quotients to three significant digits:

(a) $64,307\overline{)8,604,490,352}$ (b) $48,452\overline{)9,785,573,918}$

17. Find the exact quotients and remainders for the divisions of Exercise 16.
18. Check the divisions of Exercise 17 by "casting out nines."
19. Six men rented a hunting cabin for 8 weeks at $45 per week. What was each man's share of the rent?
20. An inheritance of $39,240 is to be shared by six people. Three of the people are each to receive twice what each of the other three receive. How much is the double share?
21. Seven gross of peanuts are to be divided equally among twenty-one monkeys. One gross is equal to twelve dozen. How many peanuts do each of the monkeys receive?
22. The area of the United States is 3,615,211 square miles including 66,237 square miles of inland water. The estimated (1962) population of the United States was 185,822,000. How many people, on the average, were there per square mile of land area in the United States in 1962?

Answers.

1. division, dividend, divisor, quotient.
2. multiplication; multiplication.
3. subtracting, 56.
4. 6, remainder.
5. *a*-2, *b*-4, *c*-3, *d*-1.
6. (a) quotient   (b) zero   (c) distributive.
7. 26; 10, 26, 2, 12, 2.
8. (a) $452R0$ (b) $1,430R2$ (c) $156R5$ (d) $390R1$
   (e) $23,666R2$ (f) $5,814R5$ (g) $10,309R0$ (h) $49,999R1$
9. (a) 1/   53   (b) 1̸
        2   106   1̸6̸8
        4/   212   6̸9̸7̸ (13
        8/   424   5̸3̸3̸
                            5̸
        $697 = 424 + 212 + 53 + 8$
            $= (8 + 4 + 1)53 + 8.$
        Quotient: 13.
        Remainder: 8.
10. (a) $641R10$ (b) $5,191R5$ (c) $794R13$ (d) $2,031R5.$
11. −.
12. (a) $93R206$ (b) $110R383$ (c) $222R104$ (d) $406R524.$

13. Excesses in dividends: (a) 2   (b) 6   (c) 5   (d) 2.
14. (a) 20,138R404   (b) 5,836R1,446   (c) 8,159R1,325.
15. Excesses in dividends: (a) 7   (b) 5   (c) 5.
16. (a) 134,000   (b) 202,000.
17. (a) 133,803R20,831   (b) 201,964R14,190.
18. Excesses in dividends: (a) 5   (b) 8.
19. $60.
20. $8,720.
21. 48 peanuts.
22. 52 people ("plus").

5.2 Factors and Primes

5.2.1 The operation of division is probably more important as a tool to compare and relate numbers than as an operation. As we have noted, Euclid used the idea of the **division algorithm**, $B = (Q \times A) + R$, in his study of numbers. Since Euclid did not have our modern symbolism to represent numbers and operations, he was forced to use geometric figures and lengthy discussions to illustrate and describe his ideas. Even with these handicaps, Euclid in his *Elements* showed remarkable insight and penetration into the fundamental properties of numbers.

Euclid's famous *Elements* is, next to the Bible, probably the most successful and widely studied book in the history of the Western world. More than a thousand editions have appeared in print and much of our school geometry has been taken, often literally, from the *Elements*. The first English version (1570) of the *Elements* is attributed to Sir Henry Billingsley who later became Lord Mayor of London. Books VII through IX of the *Elements* are devoted to the study of numbers; not to the computational techniques but more to the study of the factors and "decomposition" of composite numbers.

Let us begin with a consideration of the **division algorithm**. Given any integers A and B, with $A \neq 0$, there are integers Q and R such that $B = (Q \times A) + R, 0 \leq R <$ the positive value corresponding to A.

Thus far we have called B the dividend, A the divisor, Q the quotient, and R the remainder. Since we will now be more interested in comparing and relating numbers, it will be convenient to introduce a few more special descriptive terms. When B is a **multiple** of A so that $B = Q \times A$ for some integer Q with $R = 0$, we say that B is **divisible** by A (with remainder zero) and that A is a **factor** of B. For example, we have $35 = 5 \times 7$ so that we can say that 35 is divisible by 7 and that 7 is a factor of 35. Notice also that 5 is a factor of 35 and that 35 is divisible by 5. We have already described 35 as a multiple of 5 and of 7. Recall also that in our brief discussion of the natural numbers we described the **prime** and **composite** numbers in terms of multiples. With the above terminology we can say that a prime number is any positive integer (greater than one) which is **not** divisible by any integers other than 1 and itself. Now a composite number is any positive integer which is not a prime, or any positive integer which **is** divisible by some positive integer other than 1 or itself. We have also noted the following very fundamental and important property of the positive integers:

Every composite number, no matter how large, can be expressed as (**decomposed** into) a product of primes. That is, every positive integer other than 1 can be described by a product of factors that are prime.

Examples.

(a) Which of the following integers are multiples of 7?
GIVEN. 8, 13, 14, 17, 21, 27, 34, 42, 70.
By division we note that 14, 21, 42, and 70 are multiples of 7. By the same reasoning, 7 is a factor of 14, 21, 42, and 70, and 14, 21, 42, and 70 are divisible by 7. We also often say that 7 is a **divisor** of 14, 21, 42, and 70. The integers 8, 13, 17, 27, and 34 are not related to 7 in the above described ways since they "leave" a nonzero remainder upon division by 7.

(b) Which of the following integers are divisible by 9?
GIVEN. 3, 6, 9, 19, 27, 34, 54, 61, 63.
By division we have 9, 27, 54, and 63 are divisible by 9 and thus multiples of 9. Our previous discussion of numbers has, however, already suggested a quick method for determining the divisibility of any number by 9. Recall "casting out nines," 9 is thus a factor of any integer whose excess of nines is zero. Since the excess of nines in 3, 6, 19, 34, and 61 is not zero, these integers are not divisible by 9 and leave nonzero remainders on division by 9.

(c) Which of the following integers are primes, which are composites?
GIVEN. 2, 3, 4, 8, 9, 14, 17, 21, 23, 27.
The integers 2, 3, 17, and 23 are primes since they are not divisible by any positive integers other than 1 and themselves. The integers 4, 8, 9, 14, 21, and 27 are composites since they are not primes. Observe that $4 = 2 \times 2$, $8 = 2 \times (2 \times 2)$, $9 = 3 \times 3$, $14 = 2 \times 7$, $21 = 3 \times 7$, and $27 = 3 \times (3 \times 3)$. Every one of these latter composite numbers are thus expressible as products of primes.

(d) List the first fifteen prime numbers less than 50.
Recalling the *sieve of Eratosthenes*, we have 2, 3, 5, 7, 11, 13, 17, 19, 23, 29, 31, 37, 41, 43, and 47. We should get to know these first fifteen primes like "comfortable friends" for they can be just as valuable and helpful in many mathematical situations.

(e) Express (decompose) the following integers as products of primes: 42; 99; 364; 1,173; 5,390.

We proceed by dividing by the successive primes to determine the prime factors of the integer.

42 is divisible by 2, quotient is 21 which is in turn divisible by 3, quotient is 7, a prime. Thus, $42 = 2 \times (3 \times 7)$.

99 being odd is not divisible by 2; 3 divides 99 with no remainder, quotient is 33 which is also divisible by 3. The resulting quotient is 11, a prime. Thus, $99 = 3 \times (3 \times 11)$.

364 being even is divisible by 2, quotient 182. 182 is divisible by 2, quotient 91. Now 91 is odd and clearly not divisible by 3 or 5 (Why?). But 91 is divisible by 7 with quotient 13 which is prime. Thus, $364 = 2 \times [2 \times (7 \times 13)]$.

1,173 on dividing by 3 results in a quotient of 391 with remainder 0. 391 is clearly not divisible by 3 or 5 so we try dividing by 7; 7 into 391 is 55 with remainder 6, so 7 is not a factor of 391. 11 is easily seen as not being a divisor of 391 (Why?). We try 13 which results in a quotient of 30 with remainder 1. Going on to 17 we find that 391 is a multiple of 17: $391 = 17 \times 23$. But 23 is also a prime. Thus, $1,173 = 3 \times 17 \times 23$. Note that since multiplication is both commutative and associative, we can omit the parentheses (and brackets) without causing any confusion or difficulties.

5,390 is clearly divisible by 10 (Why?) which is the product of 2 and 5. The quotient, 539, is tested for a factor of 3 which is not a divisor. Since 539 is clearly not divisible by 5, we try 7; 7 divides 539 with quotient 77 which is easy to factor into 7 and 11. Thus, $5,390 = 2 \times 5 \times 7 \times 7 \times 11$.

The above procedure is illustrated in computational form as follows:

$$
\begin{array}{c}
7 \\
\overline{3)21} \\
\overline{2)42} = 2 \times 3 \times 7.
\end{array}
\qquad
\begin{array}{c}
11 \\
\overline{3)33} \\
\overline{3)99} = 3 \times 3 \times 11.
\end{array}
\qquad
\begin{array}{c}
13 \\
\overline{7)91} \\
\overline{2)182} \\
\overline{2)364} = 2 \times 2 \times 7 \times 13.
\end{array}
$$

$$
\begin{array}{c}
23 \\
\overline{17)391} \\
\overline{3)1,173} = 3 \times 17 \times 23.
\end{array}
\qquad
\begin{array}{c}
77 = 7 \times 11 \\
\overline{7)539} \\
2 \times 5 = \overline{10)5,390} = 2 \times 5 \times 7 \times 7 \times 11.
\end{array}
$$

(f) The **divisors** of an integer are the set of prime and composite integers which divide the integer with remainder zero. Notice that the prime factors form a subset of the divisors of an integer and can be used to find the remaining divisors. Find the sets of divisors of 42, 99, and 364.

$42 = 2 \times 3 \times 7$ so that the divisors of 42 are 1, 2, 3, 6, 7, 14, 21, and 42. Observe that $6 = 2 \times 3$, $14 = 2 \times 7$, $21 = 3 \times 7$.

$99 = 3 \times 3 \times 11$ so that the divisors of 99 are 1, 3, 9, 11, 33, and 99.
Notice that $9 = 3 \times 3$, $33 = 3 \times 11$.

$364 = 2 \times 2 \times 7 \times 13$ so that the divisors of 364 are 1, 2, 4, 7, 13, 14, 26, 28, 52, 91, 182, and 364. The work can be arranged in an orderly manner as follows:

$$364 = 2 \times 2 \times 7 \times 13; \text{ we have 1 and 364.}$$

Primes: 2, 7, 13.

Composites: $2 \times 2 = 4$ $2 \times 2 \times 7 = 28$
$2 \times 7 = 14$ $2 \times 2 \times 13 = 52$
$2 \times 13 = 26$ $2 \times 7 \times 13 = 182.$
$7 \times 13 = 91$

The set of divisors: 1, 2, 4, 7, 13, 14, 26, 28, 52, 91, 182, and 364.

Practice 1.

1. (a) Which of the following are multiples of 3?
   5, 8, 12, 15, 21, 29, 33, 35, 47, 57, 72, 105.
   (b) Which of the following are multiples of 11?
   21, 33, 56, 77, 92, 101, 121, 153, 154, 222, 242.
   (c) Which of the following are multiples of 17?
   34, 89, 102, 134, 153, 170, 239, 340, 461, 850.
2. (a) Which of the following are divisible by 8?
   12, 18, 24, 36, 44, 56, 72, 96, 106, 156, 248.
   (b) Which of the following are divisible by 13?
   23, 31, 39, 60, 78, 93, 104, 117, 127, 130, 273.
   (c) Which of the following are divisible by 19?
   19, 27, 57, 75, 95, 123, 133, 153, 171, 209.
3. Express (decompose) the following as products of primes:
   (a) 56   (b) 90   (c) 231   (d) 275   (e) 935   (f) 4,199.
4. Find the sets of divisors of:
   (a) 56   (b) 90   (c) 231   (d) 275   (e) 935   (f) 4,199.

Answers.

1. (a) 12, 15, 21, 33, 57, 72, 105.
   (b) 33, 77, 121, 154, 242.
   (c) 34, 102, 153, 170, 340, 850.
2. (a) 24, 56, 72, 96, 248.
   (b) 39, 78, 104, 117, 130, 273.
   (c) 19, 57, 95, 133, 171, 209.
3. (a) $56 = 2 \times 2 \times 2 \times 7$ (b) $90 = 2 \times 3 \times 3 \times 5$
   (c) $231 = 3 \times 7 \times 11$ (d) $275 = 5 \times 5 \times 11$
   (e) $935 = 5 \times 11 \times 17$ (f) $4{,}199 = 13 \times 17 \times 19.$

4. (a) 1, 2, 4, 7, 8, 14, 28, 56.
    (b) 1, 2, 3, 5, 6, 9, 10, 15, 18, 30, 45, 90.
    (c) 1, 3, 7, 11, 21, 33, 77, 231.
    (d) 1, 5, 11, 25, 55, 275.
    (e) 1, 5, 11, 17, 55, 85, 187, 935.
    (f) 1, 13, 17, 19, 221, 247, 323, 4199.

5.2.2 When we decompose a number into a product of factors we say that we are **factoring** the number. If the factors are all prime, we say that we have decomposed the number into its prime factors. In the factoring process it is evident that a knowledge of the divisibility of a number by a given factor would be helpful. The following observations concerning the divisibility of numbers by small factors can easily be verified:

1. Every even number is divisible by 2; that is, every number with a digit in the one's place which is divisible by 2. For example, 316, 530, but not 247.

2. If the excess of nines of a numeral is divisible by 3, then the number is divisible by 3. For example, 546 has excess 6 which is divisible by 3 so that 546 is divisible by 3.

3. Since every multiple of 100 is divisible by 4, if the ten's and one's digits form a numeral (naming a number) divisible by 4, then the number is divisible by 4. For example, 356 is divisible by 4 since 56 is divisible by 4. The number 441 is not divisible by 4 since 41 is not divisible by 4. In a large number, such as 53,612, it is a definite advantage to be able to check 12 and say that 53,612 is divisible by 4.

4. Every numeral with a one's digit of "0" or "5" names a number which is divisible by 5. For example, 73,645 is divisible by 5. But, 105,361 is not divisible by 5.

5. Every number which is divisible by both 2 and 3 is divisible by 6. That is, any even number with an excess of nines divisible by 3 is divisible by 6. For example, since 546 is both even and has excess 6 which is divisible by 3, it is divisible by 6. However, 537 is not divisible by 6 since it is odd. The number 272 is not divisible by 6 since its excess 2 is not divisible by 3.

6. Checking the divisibility of a number by 7 is best done by actual mental division.

7. Since every multiple of 1,000 is divisible by 8, a number will be divisible by 8 if the digits in the hundred's, ten's, and one's places form a numeral which names a number divisible by 8. For example, 784,344 is divisible by 8 since 344 is divisible by 8.

8. A number is divisible by 9 if its excess of nines is 0. For example, 23,715 has excess 0 so it is divisible by 9.

9. Every numeral with a 0 in the one's place names a number divisible by 10. For example, 78,640 is divisible by 10.

10. An excess of elevens test for divisibility by 11 can be stated by noting the following:

$$3,146 = 3(1000) + 1(100) + 4(10) + 6$$
$$= 3(1001 - 1) + 1(99 + 1) + 4(11 - 1) + 6$$
$$= (\text{a multiple of } 11) + (6 + 1 - 4 - 3).$$

The excess of elevens in a numeral equals the excess of elevens in the difference between the sum of the odd numbered place digits and the sum of the even numbered place digits counting from the right of the numeral.

For example, in 73,516 we have $(6 + 5 + 7) = 18$ and $(1 + 3) = 4$ so that $18 - 4 = 14$, then $4 - 1 = 3$ is the excess of elevens in 73,516. In 793,265 the excess of elevens is $(5 + 2 + 9) - (6 + 3 + 7) = 16 - 16 = 0$.

Now, it should be quite evident that if the excess of elevens is 0, then the number must be divisible by 11. For example, 3,146 and 793,265 are both divisible by 11. But 73,516 is not divisible by 11.

Practice 2.

1. Apply the preceding observations to determine the divisibility of the following by factors 2 through 11.
(a) 245   (b) 264   (c) 330   (d) 2,310   (e) 2,520.

2. Find the largest factor less than 12 in each of the following:
(a) 623   (b) 158   (c) 355   (d) 603   (e) 291
(f) 498   (g) 292   (h) 583   (i) 472   (j) 610.

3. Find the smallest prime factor in each of the following:
(a) 1,007   (b) 1,829   (c) 1,067   (d) 2,047   (e) 2,627
(f) 1,027   (g) 2,117   (h) 2,747   (i) 1,037   (j) 3,569.

4. Factor the following into products of primes.
(a) 2,499   (b) 9,295   (c) 6,992   (d) 3,509   (e) 17,205.

Answers.

1. (a) 5, 7   (b) 2, 3, 4, 6, 8, 11   (c) 2, 3, 5, 6, 10, 11
(d) 2, 3, 5, 6, 7, 10, 11   (e) 2, 3, 4, 5, 6, 7, 8, 9, 10.

2. (a) 7   (b) 2   (c) 5   (d) 9   (e) 3   (f) 6   (g) 4
(h) 11   (i) 8   (j) 10.

3. (a) 19   (b) 31   (c) 11   (d) 23   (e) 37
(f) 13   (g) 29   (h) 41   (i) 17   (j) 43.

4. (a) $3 \times 7 \times 7 \times 17$ (b) $5 \times 11 \times 13 \times 13$
(c) $2 \times 2 \times 2 \times 2 \times 19 \times 23$ (d) $11 \times 11 \times 29$
(e) $3 \times 5 \times 31 \times 37$.

5.2.3   As we proceed, we will find it useful to know how to compare and relate numbers in a variety of ways. For example, given the pair of numbers 66 and 78. How can we compare them? How can we combine them? What is common between them? What "contains" them? Let us write down a few immediate observations:

(a) They are both positive, even integers with $66 < 78$.

(b) They are both divisible by 2; by 3; by 6.

(c) $66 = 2 \times 3 \times 11$ and $78 = 2 \times 3 \times 13$.

(d) The divisors of 66 are 1, 2, 3, 6, 11, 22, 33, and 66. The divisors of 78 are 1, 2, 3, 6, 13, 26, 39, and 78.

(e) They have the **common factors** 1, 2, 3, and 6. The largest factor common to both numbers is 6. That is, the **greatest common divisor** or **highest common factor** of 66 and 78 is 6.

(f) $66 \times 78 = 5{,}148$ is a (common) multiple which contains both 66 and 78 as divisors (or factors). There are many such multiples which contain both 66 and 78 as factors. The smallest or **lowest common multiple** which contains both 66 and 78 as factors is 858 (which is considerably smaller than 5,148).

Since the last two observations are of frequent use, the ideas are given proper names. The largest factor common to a set of numbers is called the **greatest common divisor** or **highest common factor** of the set of numbers. The smallest multiple which contains each number in a set of numbers as a factor is called the **lowest common multiple** of the set of numbers.

Let us begin examining these two ideas with pairs of numbers. The lowest common multiple (often abbreviated as LCM) of two numbers can be determined by first noting that since it is a multiple of both, it must be as large as either of the numbers. Next, the LCM must contain as a factor every divisor of either given number. If we express the two given numbers as products of primes, then the LCM must be the product of all of the factors of one of the numbers times the factors of the other number which have not appeared as factors in the first number.

Examples.

(a) To find the LCM of 306 and 476:

We decompose 306 and 476 into products of primes: $306 = 2 \times 3 \times 3 \times 17$ and $476 = 2 \times 2 \times 7 \times 17$.

We begin with $306 = 2 \times 3 \times 3 \times 17$ and multiply this by 2×7 since we must have a factor of 2×2 and also of 7 in the multiple. Thus, $306 \times 14 = 4{,}284$ is the LCM.

(b) To find the LCM of 520 and 1,235:
$$520 = 2 \times 2 \times 2 \times 5 \times 13 \text{ and } 1{,}235 = 5 \times 13 \times 19.$$
Thus, the LCM must equal
$$2 \times 2 \times 2 \times 5 \times 13 \times 19 = 8 \times 1{,}235 = 9{,}880.$$

(c) To find the LCM of 306 and 476 we can arrange the work as follows:

2	306	476
2	153	238
3	153	119
3	51	119
	17	119
		7

We successively divide by prime divisors of one or both numbers. If a divisor does not divide both remainders, we "bring down" the remainder which is not divisible.

LCM is equal to $2 \times 2 \times 3 \times 3 \times 17 \times 7 = 4{,}284.$

(d) To find the LCM of 520 and 1,235 we have

5	520	1,235
2	104	247
2	52	247
2	26	247
	13	247
		19

LCM is equal to
$$5 \times 2 \times 2 \times 2 \times 13 \times 19 = 9{,}880.$$

The greatest common divisor (often abbreviated as GCD) or highest common factor (often abbreviated as HCF) of two numbers can be determined by first noting that it must be a divisor (or factor) of both numbers. Next, the GCD must be the largest such factor. If we express the two given numbers as products of primes, then the GCD must be the product of the factors common to both numbers.

Examples.

(a) To find the GCD of 306 and 476:
$$306 = 2 \times 3 \times 3 \times 17 \text{ and } 476 = 2 \times 2 \times 7 \times 17.$$
The factors common to both are $2 \times 17 = 34.$
Thus, 34 is the GCD of 306 and 476.

(b) To find the GCD of 520 and 1,235:
$$520 = 2 \times 2 \times 2 \times 5 \times 13 \text{ and } 1{,}235 = 5 \times 13 \times 19.$$

The factors common to both are $5 \times 13 = 65$.

Thus, 65 is the GCD of 520 and 1,235.

(c) We can find the GCD of two numbers by a process of successive divisions:

(i)
$$\begin{array}{r} 1 \\ 306\overline{)476} \\ 306 \quad 1 \\ \overline{170)306} \\ 170 \quad 1 \\ \overline{136)170} \\ 136 \quad 4 \\ \text{GCD } \overline{34)136} \\ 136 \\ \overline{0} \end{array}$$

(ii)
$$\begin{array}{r} 2 \\ 520\overline{)1235} \\ 1040 \quad 2 \\ \overline{195)520} \\ 390 \quad 1 \\ \overline{130)195} \\ 130 \quad 2 \\ \text{GCD } \overline{65)130} \\ 130 \\ \overline{0} \end{array}$$

The larger number is divided by the smaller, then the smaller by the remainder. Each successive divisor is divided by the remainder until a remainder of 0 is obtained. The last divisor is then the GCD.

(d) Find the GCD of 306 and 1,235.

$$\begin{array}{r} 4 \\ 306\overline{)1235} \\ 1224 \quad 27 \\ \overline{11)306} \\ 297 \quad 1 \\ \overline{9)11} \\ 9 \quad 4 \\ \overline{2)9} \\ 8 \quad 2 \\ \overline{1)2} \\ 2 \\ \overline{0} \end{array}$$

The GCD is 1. That is, the numbers 306 and 1,235 have no factors other than 1 in common (in integers). When two numbers are related in this way, we say that they are **relatively prime** to each other.

Notice that the **lowest common multiple is the smallest number which contains** both of two numbers as factors and the **greatest common divisor is the largest common factor included** as divisors in two numbers. When two numbers have a greatest common divisor of 1, we say that they are **relatively prime** to each other. Two relatively prime numbers have a lowest common multiple which is the product of the two numbers. The fundamental property of numbers which leads us to these ideas is that:

Every composite number greater than one, no matter how large, can be decomposed into a product of primes.

Practice 3. Find the lowest common multiple and the greatest common divisor for each of the following pairs of numbers. Indicate with an RP those which are relatively prime.

	(a)	(b)	(c)
1.	6 and 9	4 and 12	12 and 30
2.	8 and 12	15 and 20	21 and 22
3.	6 and 21	18 and 27	24 and 42
4.	36 and 45	30 and 49	56 and 84
5.	42 and 50	66 and 84	195 and 315
6.	60 and 90	63 and 105	131 and 143
7.	420 and 1176	507 and 595	286 and 363
8.	224 and 675	3,630 and 10,890	1,309 and 7,735

Answers.

	(a)	(b)	(c)
1. LCM	18	12	60
GCD	3	2	6
2. LCM	24	60	462
GCD	4	5	1 RP
3. LCM	42	54	168
GCD	3	9	6
4. LCM	180	1,470	168
GCD	9	1 RP	28
5. LCM	1,050	924	4,095
GCD	2	6	15
6. LCM	180	315	18,733
GCD	30	21	1 RP
7. LCM	5,880	301,665	9,438
GCD	84	1 RP	11
8. LCM	151,200	10,890	85,085
GCD	1 RP	3,630	119

5.2.4   The above ideas can be readily extended to sets of three or more numbers. Each number is factored into a product of primes and the factors examined and combined to form the LCM and GCD. To be relatively prime, however, every pair of numbers in a set of three or more numbers must be relatively prime. Thus, even if the GCD of a set of three or more numbers is one, the set of numbers may not form a relatively prime set. To organize and reduce the work involved, the set of numbers to be tested may be arranged as shown in the following examples and the divisions may be accomplished successively.

Examples.   To find the LCM and GCD of a set of numbers:

(a) GIVEN. 8, 12, and 20.

/2	8	12	20
/2	4	6	10
	2	3	5

When a divisor divides all the numbers, we place a mark to indicate this factor for the GCD.

LCM $2 \times 2 \times 2 \times 3 \times 5 = 120$.
GCD $2 \times 2 = 4$.

(b) GIVEN. 6, 21, and 35.

3	6	21	35
7	2	7	35
	2	1	5

When a divisor does not divide a number, we "bring it down" unchanged. Every divisor must divide at least one of the numbers or remainders.

LCM $3 \times 7 \times 2 \times 5 = 210$.
GCD 1.

Notice that the set of numbers are not relatively prime since 6 and 21 have the common factor 3; also 21 and 35 have a common factor 7. The pair of numbers 6 and 35 are relatively prime.

(c) GIVEN. 17, 22, 63, and 65.

2	17	22	63	65
5	17	11	63	65
3	17	11	63	13
3	17	11	21	13
	17	11	7	13

LCM $2 \times 5 \times 3 \times 3 \times 17 \times 11 \times 7 \times 13 = 1,531,530$.
GCD 1.

The set is a relatively prime set.

(d) GIVEN. 18, 30, 42, and 54.

/2	18	30	42	54
/3	9	15	21	27
3	3	5	7	9
	1	5	7	3

LCM $2 \times 3 \times 3 \times 5 \times 7 \times 3 = 1,890$.
GCD $2 \times 3 = 6$.

(e) GIVEN. 120, 210, and 315.

/3	120	210	315
/5	40	70	105
7	8	14	21
2	8	2	3
	4	1	3

LCM $3 \times 5 \times 7 \times 2 \times 4 \times 3 = 2{,}520.$
GCD $3 \times 5 = 15.$

(f) GIVEN. 140, 210, 245, 420, and 525.

/5	140	210	245	420	525
2	28	42	49	84	105
/7	14	21	49	42	105
3	2	3	7	6	15
2	2	1	7	2	5
	1	1	7	1	5

LCM 14,700.
GCD 35.

Practice 4.   Find the LCM and GCD for each of the following sets of numbers.

1. 7; 15; 21
2. 6; 9; 18; 27
3. 8; 16; 24; 28
4. 14; 21; 35; 42
5. 15; 27; 33; 45
6. 16; 24; 56; 72
7. 2; 3; 4; 6; 8; 9; 12
8. 18; 72; 90; 126; 198
9. 240; 300; 420; 450
10. 770; 1155; 1925.

Answers.	LCM	GCD		LCM	GCD
1.	105	1	6.	3,204	8
2.	54	3	7.	72	1
3.	336	4	8.	27,720	18
4.	210	7	9.	25,200	30
5.	1,485	3	10.	16,170	385

Exercises

1. When $R = 0$ in the division algorithm $B = (Q \times A) + R$, the numbers represented by A and B are said to be related in certain ways. We say that B is a _____ of A and that A is a _____ of B; _____ is also called a divisor of B and _____ is divisible by _____.

2. Complete the following sentences:
    (a) A prime number is _____.
    (b) A composite number is _____.
3. Every _____ number, no matter how large, can be decomposed into a product of _____.
4. Given the set of integers
$$13, 16, 21, 25, 33, 36, 43, 49, 54, 57, 66, 67.$$
    (a) Which are multiples of 3?
    (b) Which are multiples of 6?
    (c) Which are divisible by 8?
    (d) Which are divisible by 11?
    (e) Which are prime numbers?
5. Decompose the following integers into products of primes.
    (a) 360   (b) 450   (c) 945   (d) 1,078   (e) 1,573.
6. Find the sets of divisors of:
    (a) 33   (b) 43   (c) 52   (d) 54   (e) 210.
7. Find the largest factor less than 12 in each of the following:
    (a) 102   (b) 132   (c) 175   (d) 234   (e) 425.
8. Find the smallest prime factor in each of the following:
    (a) 2,197   (b) 1,547   (c) 5,589   (d) 1,045   (e) 5,491.
9. Factor the following numbers into products of primes
    (a) 900   (b) 3,234   (c) 1,053   (d) 6,545   (e) 20,677.
10. The _____ _____ _____ is the smallest number which contains each number in a set of numbers as a factor while the _____ _____ _____ is the largest number which is contained or included in each number in a set of numbers as a factor.
11. Find the lowest common multiple and the greatest common divisor for each of the following pairs of numbers.
    (a) 2 and 3   (b) 3 and 8   (c) 2 and 4   (d) 2 and 9
    (e) 4 and 6   (f) 6 and 9   (g) 2 and 6   (h) 3 and 4
    (i) 3 and 7   (j) 8 and 9   (k) 5 and 6   (l) 6 and 8
    (m) 3 and 7   (n) 3 and 6   (o) 4 and 9.
12. Which of the pairs of numbers in Exercise 11 are relatively prime?
13. Find the LCM and GCD for each of the following pairs of numbers.
    (a) 14 and 21   (b) 12 and 42   (c) 15 and 18
    (d) 20 and 35   (e) 26 and 91   (f) 24 and 54
    (g) 33 and 63   (h) 35 and 56.
14. Find the LCM and GCD for each of the following sets of numbers.
    (a) 5, 7, 10, 14, 15, 21   (b) 12, 30, 36, 84
    (c) 18, 27, 45, 72   (d) 165, 210, 195, 150.
15. One of the prime factors of 4,403 is 17. Find the other prime factors of the number.

16. What is the smallest number containing 6, 7, and 15 among its set of divisors?

17. What is the greatest common divisor of two consecutive positive integers?

18. If the lowest common multiple of two numbers is 630 and the greatest common divisor is 18, then what are the two numbers?

19. In comparing two freight elevators in a warehouse, we know that elevator A has a capacity of 27 tons and elevator B has a capacity of 45 tons. If both elevators operate at full capacity on each trip from a loading dock to warehouse floor, then: (a) what is the smallest common load of freight that the two elevators will move? That is, what is the smallest tonnage that should be used in comparing their operation? (b) how many trips will each elevator make in moving this common load of freight?

20. A small compact car and a standard American sedan race around an oval track beginning at a common starting point together. If the compact takes 9 minutes to go around the oval and the sedan takes 6 minutes for one circuit, then how long will it take for the two cars to pass each other at precisely the point at which they started?

Answers.

1. multiple, factor, A (and Q), B, A (and Q).

2. (a) A prime number is any positive integer which has exactly two divisors, 1 and itself.

   (b) A composite number is any positive integer which is not a prime.

3. composite, primes.

4. (a) 21, 33, 36, 54, 57, 66   (b) 36, 54, 66   (c) 16
   (d) 33, 66   (e) 13, 43, 67.

5. (a) $2 \times 2 \times 2 \times 3 \times 3 \times 5$ (b) $2 \times 3 \times 3 \times 5 \times 5$
   (c) $3 \times 3 \times 3 \times 5 \times 7$ (d) $2 \times 7 \times 7 \times 11$
   (e) $11 \times 11 \times 13$.

6. (a) 1, 3, 11, 33   (b) 1, 43   (c) 1, 2, 4, 13, 26, 52
   (d) 1, 2, 3, 6, 9, 18, 27, 54
   (e) 1, 2, 3, 5, 6, 7, 10, 14, 15, 21, 30, 35, 42, 70, 105, 210.

7. (a) 6   (b) 11   (c) 7   (d) 9   (e) 5.

8. (a) 13   (b) 7   (c) 11   (d) 5   (e) 17.

9. (a) $2 \times 2 \times 3 \times 3 \times 5 \times 5$ (b) $2 \times 3 \times 7 \times 7 \times 11$
   (c) $3 \times 3 \times 3 \times 3 \times 13$ (d) $5 \times 7 \times 11 \times 17$
   (e) $23 \times 29 \times 31$.

10. lowest common multiple, greatest common divisor.

11.

	(a)	(b)	(c)	(d)	(e)	(f)	(g)	(h)
LCM	6	24	4	18	12	18	6	12

GCD	1	1	2	1	2	3	2	1
	(i)	(j)	(k)	(l)	(m)	(n)	(o)	
LCM	21	72	30	24	21	6	36	
GCD	1	1	1	2	1	3	1	

12. (a), (b), (d), (h), (i), (j), (k), (m), and (o).

13.

	(a)	(b)	(c)	(d)	(e)	(f)	(g)	(h)
LCM	42	84	90	140	182	216	693	280
GCD	7	6	3	5	13	6	3	7

14.

	(a)	(b)	(c)	(d)
LCM	210	1,260	1,080	150,150
GCD	1	6	9	15

15. 7 and 37.
16. 210.
17. 1.
18. 90 and 126.
19. (a) 135 tons   (b) A: 5 trips; B: 3 trips.
20. 18 minutes.

5.3 Combined Operations

5.3.1   Thus far we have considered primarily the mechanics of division with positive integers and a few properties of the positive integers as revealed by the division algorithm with remainder equal to zero. In this section we will consider four further questions:

1. How can we extend the division operation to include the negative integers?

2. What are the properties of the division operation?

3. How can we handle situations requiring the combined operations of addition, subtraction, multiplication, and division?

4. What "new" tools do we have for solving conditional equations?

Here, again, let us return to the **division algorithm** which we have found so useful. For our purposes, we will identify the division algorithm with the equivalent bar form of describing division:

Given any integers A and B, with $A \neq 0$, there are integers Q and R such that $\dfrac{B}{A} = Q + \dfrac{R}{A}$, $0 \leq R <$ the absolute value of A.

This latter bar form is read "B divided by A is equal to the quotient Q plus the remainder R divided by A." Notice that the remainder R divided by A can only be an "indicated" division unless $R = 0$. If we "go through the motions" of dividing, we will clearly have a quotient 0 and remainder R again. That is, for $0 \leq R <$ the absolute value of A, we have $\dfrac{R}{A} = 0 + \dfrac{R}{A}$.

Now, for simplicity, let us consider an example where A is a divisor of

B so that $R = 0$. Let $B = 21$ and $A = 3$ so that we have $\dfrac{21}{3} = 7 + \dfrac{0}{3}$. That is, $21 = (7 \times 3) + 0$. Since 21 divided by 3 is exactly equal to 7, we must also have $\dfrac{0}{3} = 0$, that is, $0 = 0 \times 3$. We must be careful, however, not to conclude from $0 = 0 \times 3$ that $\dfrac{0}{0} = 3$ for then in the division $\dfrac{45}{5} = 9 + \dfrac{0}{5}$ we have $\dfrac{0}{5} = 0$ and $0 = 0 \times 5$ so that we might conclude $\dfrac{0}{0} = 5$ and obtain $3 = 5$. The conclusion that we can reach from the above discussion is that zero divided by any number other than zero must equal zero: $\dfrac{0}{A} = 0$ for all $A \neq 0$. Note the importance of $A \neq 0$. **No divisor may equal zero.** For example, if we were to allow, say $\dfrac{3}{0} = N$, then we would have $3 = 0 \times N$ so that $3 = 0$.

Suppose $A = -3$ and $B = 21$, then we will have $\dfrac{21}{-3} = Q + \dfrac{R}{-3}$ or $21 = Q(-3) + R$. But we know that for $Q = -7$, $21 = (-7)(-3) + 0$. That is, $\dfrac{21}{-3} = -7$. Suppose $A = 3$ and $B = -21$, then $\dfrac{-21}{3} = Q$ and $-21 = Q(3)$ so that $Q = -7$. If $A = -3$ and $B = -21$, we have $\dfrac{-21}{-3} = Q$ and $-21 = Q(-3)$ so that $Q = 7$. These examples seem to suggest that the properties of division with respect to the negative sign are quite comparable to those of multiplication with respect to the negative sign.

Examples.

    (a) To find $18 \div (-2)$:

        We write this in the more suggestive form: $\dfrac{18}{-2} = Q$.

        Then $18 = Q(-2)$ whence $Q = -9$.
        Thus, $18 \div (-2) = -9$.

    (b) To find $(-24) \div 6$:

        We write this as $\dfrac{-24}{6} = Q$ which is equivalent to writing $-24 = Q(6)$ so that $Q = -4$.
        Thus, $(-24) \div 6 = -4$.

    (c) To find $(-84) \div (-12)$:

        $\dfrac{-84}{-12} = Q$ is equivalent to writing $-84 = Q(-12)$.
        Thus, $Q = 7$ and $(-84) \div (-12) = 7$.

5.3.2   In the division algorithm, if we have $B = 23$ and $A = 5$, then $23 = (Q \times 5) + R$ and $\frac{23}{5} = Q + \frac{R}{5}$. From our study of division we know that $Q = 4$ and $R = 3$ so that we have $\frac{23}{5} = 4 + \frac{3}{5}$. Suppose $B = 23$ and $A = -5$, then $23 = [Q \times (-5)] + R$ or $\frac{23}{-5} = Q + \frac{R}{-5}$. Now by the division algorithm we also have that $0 \leq R < 5$ (the absolute value of A) so that (applying the principle of equal subtraction) we can write $23 - R = [Q \times (-5)]$. If $R = 3$, then $20 = Q \times (-5)$ and $Q = -4$ so that $\frac{23}{-5} = (-4) + \left(\frac{3}{-5}\right)$. That is, we might conclude that 23 divided by -5 has a quotient equal to -4 with remainder 3 divided by -5. Consider the indicated division of the remainder 3 by -5 in the form $\frac{3}{-5} = Q$. Although we must concede that this Q could not be an integer, we might continue and write $3 = Q \times (-5)$ and say to ourselves that Q must be negative. That is, $\frac{3}{-5} < 0$. If $B = -23$ and $A = 5$, we have $-23 = (Q \times 5) + R, 0 \leq R < 5$. Now, $-23 - R = Q \times 5$ and for $R = 2$ we have $-25 = Q \times 5$ so that $Q = -5$. That is, $\frac{-23}{5} = (-5) + \left(\frac{2}{5}\right)$. This tells us that -23 divided by 5 is equal to -5 plus the remainder 2 divided by 5. If we continue and write $\frac{2}{5} = Q$ and $2 = Q \times 5$, then we could very well conclude that this latter Q must be positive, although not an integer, that is, $\frac{2}{5} > 0$. Finally, for $B = -23$ and $A = -5$, we have $-23 = [Q \times (-5)] + R$ so that $-23 - R = Q \times (-5)$. Let $R = 2$, then $-25 = Q \times (-5)$ and $Q = 5$. Thus, -23 divided by -5 equals 5 with remainder 2 divided by -5, that is, $\frac{-23}{-5} = 5 + \left(\frac{2}{-5}\right)$. From our previous comments, $\frac{2}{-5} < 0$.

Examples.

(a) $25 \div (-11)$.   Write $25 = [Q \times (-11)] + R$ so that $25 - R = Q \times (-11)$ and for $R = 3$, $22 = Q \times (-11)$ and $Q = -2$.

$\frac{25}{-11} = (-2) + \left(\frac{3}{-11}\right)$ where $\frac{3}{-11} < 0$.

(b) $(-39) \div 7$.   Write $-39 = (Q \times 7) + R$
$$-39 - R = Q \times 7 \text{ and for } R = 3,$$
$$-42 = Q \times 7 \text{ and } Q = -6.$$

$\dfrac{-39}{7} = (-6) + \left(\dfrac{3}{7}\right)$, where $\dfrac{3}{7} > 0$.

(c) $(-59) \div (-13)$.   Write $-59 - R = Q \times (-13)$ and for $R = 6$
$$-65 = Q \times (-13) \text{ and } Q = 5.$$

$\dfrac{-59}{-13} = 5 + \left(\dfrac{6}{-13}\right)$ where $\dfrac{6}{-13} < 0$.

How can we extend the division operation to include the negative integers? We begin with the division algorithm and examine a few well-chosen examples. First, if the remainder $R = 0$, observations lead us to the following conclusions:

(a) If the dividend is positive and the divisor negative, then the quotient is negative.

(b) If the dividend is negative and the divisor positive, then the quotient is negative.

(c) If both the dividend and divisor are negative, then the quotient is positive.

Incidentally, if the dividend is zero, then the quotient is zero. Finally, we note the importance of a divisor being "nonzero." That is, no divisor may equal zero.

Now, if $R \neq 0$, the sign of the quotient is as we would expect from the above observations. Since $0 \leq R <$ the absolute value of the divisor, by a judicious choice of R and the application of the principle of equal subtraction to the division algorithm, we can "reduce" the division to one with no remainder. That is, the dividend less the remainder is set equal to the greatest multiple of the divisor less than the dividend.

Thus, we can extend the division operation to include all integers, negative as well as positive. Of course, we are now faced with the question of what is meant by "R divided by A," where $0 \leq R <$ the absolute value of A. We will consider this question in the next chapter.

Practice 1.   Find the quotients and remainders.

	(a)	(b)	(c)	(d)
1.	$15 \div (-3)$	$12 \div (-6)$	$(-32) \div 4$	$(-56) \div 7$
2.	$(-16) \div (-8)$	$(-10) \div 2$	$28 \div (-7)$	$(-72) \div (-6)$
3.	$52 \div (-13)$	$(-36) \div (-9)$	$(-63) \div (-9)$	$(-78) \div 13$
4.	$46 \div (-8)$	$(-39) \div 17$	$(-52) \div (-8)$	$(-23) \div 6$
5.	$(-35) \div 4$	$28 \div (-5)$	$43 \div (-7)$	$(-57) \div (-11)$
6.	$(-74) \div (-9)$	$(-25) \div 7$	$37 \div (-10)$	$(-93) \div (-12)$

Answers.

	(a)	(b)	(c)	(d)		(a)	(b)	(c)	(d)
1.	-5	-2	-8	-8	2.	2	-5	-4	12
3.	-4	4	7	-6	4.	$-5R6$	$-3R12$	$7R4$	$-4R1$
5.	$-9R1$	$-5R3$	$-6R1$	$6R9$	6.	$9R7$	$-4R3$	$-3R7$	$8R3$

5.3.3   What are the properties of the division operation? To discuss this question, recall our interpretation of division as an operation in which we look for a factor, the quotient, which when multiplied by a given factor, the divisor, will result in a given product, the dividend. That is, when we write $B \div A = Q$ or $\dfrac{B}{A} = Q$ we mean $A \times Q = B$. We observed that if A were not a divisor (a factor) of B, then the quotient could not be an integer. Because of this, some of the properties of division cannot be discussed adequately until we have disposed of the "embarrassing" problem.

By introducing the remainder R and using the division algorithm, $B = (Q \times A) + R$, we developed computational methods for division and examined a few properties of the positive integers. In the process certain properties of division were noted. These can be summarized as follows:

1. If $B \div A = Q$, then $(B \times C) \div (A \times C) = Q$ for all $C \neq 0$.

 Or, if $\dfrac{B}{A} = Q$, then $\dfrac{B \times C}{A \times C} = Q$ for all $C \neq 0$.

Examples.

(a) $12 \div 4 = 3$ so that $(12 \times 7) \div (4 \times 7) = 3$; $C = 7$.

(b) $\dfrac{48}{6} = 8$ so that $\dfrac{480}{60} = 8$; $C = 10$.

2. If $A \neq B$, then $B \div A \neq A \div B$; or, $\dfrac{B}{A} \neq \dfrac{A}{B}$. That is, division is **not commutative.**

Examples.

(a) $12 \div 4 = 3$ but $4 \div 12$ is not an integer!

(b) $\dfrac{48}{6} = 8$ but we are "embarrassed" by $\dfrac{6}{48} = N$,

3. In general, $A \div (B \div C) \neq (A \div B) \div C$ or $\dfrac{A}{\frac{B}{C}} \neq \dfrac{\frac{A}{B}}{C}$.

That is, in general, division is **not associative**.

Examples.

(a) $24 \div (6 \div 2) = 24 \div 3 = 8$, whereas $(24 \div 6) \div 2 = 4 \div 2 = 2$.

(b) $\dfrac{30}{\frac{10}{2}} = \dfrac{30}{5} = 6$ but $\dfrac{\frac{30}{10}}{2} = \dfrac{3}{2} = 1 + \dfrac{1}{2}$ where $\dfrac{1}{2}$ is not an integer.

4. $(B + C) \div A = (B \div A) + (C \div A)$ or $\dfrac{B + C}{A} = \dfrac{B}{A} + \dfrac{C}{A}$.

$(B - C) \div A = (B \div A) - (C \div A)$ or $\dfrac{B - C}{A} = \dfrac{B}{A} - \dfrac{C}{A}$.

That is, division is **distributive** from the "right to the left." (But not from the "left to the right.")

Examples.

(a) $(21 + 6) \div 3 = 27 \div 3 = 9$
$(21 \div 3) + (6 \div 3) = 7 + 2 = 9$
$(21 + 6) \div 3 = (21 \div 3) + (6 \div 3)$.

(b) $\dfrac{54 - 18}{6} = \dfrac{36}{6} = 6$ and $\dfrac{54}{6} - \dfrac{18}{6} = 9 - 3 = 6$
$\dfrac{54 - 18}{6} = \dfrac{54}{6} - \dfrac{18}{6}$.

5. $A \div 1 = A$ for all A and, for $A \neq 0$ we have $A \div A = 1$. Alternatively, we write:
$\dfrac{A}{1} = A$ for all A and, for $A \neq 0$ we have $\dfrac{A}{A} = 1$.

Examples.

(a) $7 \div 1 = 7$ and $7 \div 7 = 1$.
(b) $\dfrac{19}{1} = 19$ and $\dfrac{19}{19} = 1$.

6. $0 \div A = 0$ for $A \neq 0$ and we cannot divide by 0.

Examples.

(a) $0 \div 7 = 0$ but $7 \div 0$ is not meaningful (not defined).

(b) $\frac{0}{7} = 0$ but $\frac{7}{0}$ is not defined (not allowed).

7. If A, B, and C are numbers with $A \neq 0$, then $(B \div A) \times C = B \times (C \div A) = (B \times C) \div A$ or $\frac{B}{A} \times C = B \times \frac{C}{A} = \frac{B \times C}{A}$. This property connects multiplication and division. It can be verified by setting $\frac{B}{A} = D$ and $\frac{C}{A} = E$, then applying our interpretation of division as an "inverse" operation to multiplication.

Examples.

(a) $(24 \div 3) \times 6 = 8 \times 6$; $24 \times (6 \div 3) = 24 \times 2$; $(24 \times 6) \div 3 = 144 \div 3$; $8 \times 6 = 24 \times 2 = 144 \div 3 = 48$; $(24 \div 3) \times 6 = 24 \times (6 \div 3) = (24 \times 6) \div 3$.

(b) $\frac{56}{7} \times 21 = 8 \times 21 = 168$; $56 \times \frac{21}{7} = 56 \times 3 = 168$;

$\frac{56 \times 21}{7} = \frac{1176}{7} = 168$;

$\frac{56}{7} \times 21 = 56 \times \frac{21}{7} = \frac{56 \times 21}{7}$.

8. If A and B are both positive integers, we have

(a) $B \div A > 0$ or $\frac{B}{A} > 0$ (b) $B \div (-A) < 0$ or $\frac{B}{-A} < 0$

(c) $(-B) \div A < 0$ or $\frac{-B}{A} < 0$ (d) $(-B) \div (-A) > 0$ or $\frac{-B}{-A} > 0$.

Examples.

(a) $9 \div 3 > 0$ or $\frac{9}{3} > 0$ (b) $9 \div (-3) < 0$ or $\frac{9}{-3} < 0$

(c) $(-9) \div 3 < 0$ or $\frac{-9}{3} < 0$ (d) $(-9) \div (-3) > 0$ or $\frac{-9}{-3} > 0$.

5.3.4   Thus far we have emphasized the separate operations of addition, subtraction, multiplication, and division of integers. Most computations in elementary arithmetic consist of combinations of these four operations; hence, these are called the **fundamental arithmetical operations**. Beginning with simple counting we developed addition. Reverse, that is, "undo" it, and we have subtraction. Repeat the addition and we have multiplication. Repeat the subtraction and we have division. Or, reverse, that is, "undo" multiplication, and we have division.

In writing expressions and mathematical statements we introduced the parentheses and brackets as grouping symbols to indicate the order or succession in which operations were to be accomplished. For example, $7 \times (11 + 5) = N$ and $(7 \times 11) + 5 = M$. With the parentheses, it should be quite clear what the order of operations should be. That is, $7 \times (11 + 5) = 7 \times 16 = 112 = N$ while $(7 \times 11) + 5 = 77 + 5 = 82 = M$. Without the parentheses we have $7 \times 11 + 5$. Should we multiply first or add first? Since there are only two possibilities in $7 \times 11 + 5$, it should be quite simple to agree on a convention or rule so that we can omit the parentheses and still avoid confusion (and disagreement). To escape a multitude of agreements and rules for each separate situation, the following general conventions have been adopted.

Conventions for the Order of Operations

1. Parentheses, brackets, and grouping symbols have "precedence" and require that the work "inside" the grouping symbols be done first.

Examples.

(a) $11 - (7 + 5) = 11 - 12 = -1$.
(b) $(11 - 7) + 5 = 4 + 5 = 9$.

2. Multiplication and division are to be done before addition and subtraction unless grouping symbols indicate otherwise.

Examples.

(a) $9 + 3 \times 7 = 9 + 21 = 30$ while $(9 + 3) \times 7 = 12 \times 7 = 84$.
(b) $9 + 6 \div 3 - 5 \times 4 = 9 + 2 - 20 = -9$
while $[(9 + 6) \div 3 - 5] \times 4 = [15 \div 3 - 5] \times 4 = [5 - 5] \times 4 = 0$.

3. The bar symbol used to indicate division is considered to have the additional effect of parentheses. That is, operations indicated in the dividend and divisor are to be done first before the division indicated by the bar.

Examples.

(a) $\dfrac{7+5}{7-5} = \dfrac{12}{2} = 6$ (b) $\dfrac{18}{9-3} + 2 = \dfrac{18}{6} + 2 = 3 + 2 = 5.$

4. The properties of the operations involved must be observed. Note particularly that division is not commutative or associative and that subtraction is anticommutative. The "normal" order of work is written from left to right.

Examples.

(a) $(18 \div 6) \div 3 = 3 \div 3 = 1$ while $18 \div (6 \div 3) = 18 \div 2 = 9.$
(b) $6 - 8 \div 2 = 6 - 4 = 2$ while $8 \div 2 - 6 = 4 - 6 = -2.$

Further examples.

(a) $\dfrac{7 \times 11 + 5}{45 - 4} = \dfrac{77 + 5}{41} = \dfrac{82}{41} = 2.$

(b) $15 - 12 \div 3 = 15 - 4 = 11$ while $(15 - 12) \div 3 = 3 \div 3 = 1.$

(c) $28 \div 4 + 3 = 7 + 3 = 10$ while $28 \div (4 + 3) = 28 \div 7 = 4.$

(d) $4 + 6 \times 9 = 4 + 54 = 58$ while $(4 + 6) \times 9 = 10 \times 9 = 90.$

(e) $64 \div 4 + 5 \times 3 - (9 - 5) \times 2 = 16 + 15 - 4 \times 2 = 16 + 15 - 8 = 31 - 8$
$= 23.$

(f) $\dfrac{36 - \dfrac{48}{6}}{(9 - 7) \times 7} = \dfrac{36 - 8}{2 \times 7} = \dfrac{28}{14} = 2.$

(g) $3 + \dfrac{11 - 4}{2 + 5} - 6 \times 3 = 3 + \dfrac{7}{7} - 18 = 3 + 1 - 18 = 4 - 18 = -14.$

(h) $\dfrac{\dfrac{6}{3} + \dfrac{15}{5}}{\dfrac{28}{4} - \dfrac{4}{2}} = \dfrac{2 + 3}{7 - 2} = \dfrac{5}{5} = 1.$

(i) $32 \div (5 + 3) - (3 \times 7 - 4 \times 5) = 32 \div 8 - (21 - 20) = 4 - 1 = 3.$

(j) $\dfrac{42}{1 + 5} - \dfrac{6}{3} + 4 + \left(\dfrac{12}{4} - \dfrac{6}{3}\right) \times 5 = \dfrac{42}{6} - 2 + 4 + (3 - 2) \times 5$
$= 7 - 2 + 4 + 1 \times 5 = 7 - 2 + 4 + 5 = 5 + 4 + 5 = 14.$

Practice 2.   Find the simplest numeral for:

	(a)	(b)	(c)
1.	$9 \times 4 - 7$	$8 + 3 \times 5$	$18 + 6 \div 2$

2. $12 \div 6 - 2$ $9 \times (4 - 7)$ $(8 \times 3) \times 5$

3. $(18 + 6) \div 2$ $12 \div (6 - 2)$ $3 \times 4 \div 2$

4. $\dfrac{9 + 11}{5}$ $\dfrac{16 + 12}{4}$ $\dfrac{19 - 4}{3}$

5. $\dfrac{18 - 3}{3}$ $\dfrac{42}{3 + 4}$ $\dfrac{56}{6 + 2}$

6. $\dfrac{5 \times 3 + 6}{7}$ $\dfrac{36}{\dfrac{9}{3} + 6}$ $\dfrac{\dfrac{28}{2}}{11 - 4}$

7. $\dfrac{16}{2} \times (4 + 5)$ $(3 \times 8 - 4) \div 4$ $(2 \times 9 - 7 \times 3) \times \left(\dfrac{3 - 9}{2}\right)$.

8. (a) $27 \div (3 + 6) + (7 - 1) \times 2$.
    (b) $5 - 6 \div 3 + 4 \times 7 - 1$.
    (c) $2 \times 8 - (9 + 3) \div 4$.

9. (a) $\dfrac{38}{2} \times 3 - 5 \times (4 + 3) + \dfrac{9 + 3}{3}$

    (b) $\dfrac{7 + 11}{11 - 9} + \dfrac{36 - 10}{10 + 3}$ (c) $\dfrac{2 \times 7}{1 + 1} - \dfrac{15 - 3}{3 \times 2}$.

10. (a) $\dfrac{3 + \dfrac{18}{2}}{\dfrac{12}{3} - 10}$ (b) $\dfrac{\dfrac{6}{3} - \dfrac{4}{2}}{\dfrac{8}{4} + \dfrac{6}{3}}$ (c) $\dfrac{\dfrac{15}{3} - 2}{1 - \dfrac{16}{4}}$.

Answers.

	(a)	(b)	(c)
1.	29	23	21
2.	0	−27	60
3.	12	3	6
4.	4	7	5
5.	5	6	7
6.	3	4	2
7.	72	5	9
8.	6	30	13
9.	26	11	5
10.	−2	0	−1

5.3.5   We must know how to compute with numbers, but the most important and probably the most useful aspect of working with numbers is knowing how to "set up" problems, when to do a computation, and what computation to do. In many situations machines and special devices are available to do computations, but they need direction and must be "set up" to do any given problem.

Let us now ask "What new tools do we have for solving conditional equations which arise out of problem situations?" We might answer, "We can now multiply and divide with numbers." Will we recognize the situations in which these operations arise? Consider the following examples:

1. When nineteen more than a number is divided into seven equal parts, the result is eight. Find the number.

2. If seven more than a number is equal to thirteen times five less than the number, then what is the number?

3. In complaining about the cost of living, Mr. Smith commented that two years after moving into their present apartment the rent had been raised fifteen dollars and that since then the rent had been doubled. If Mr. Smith is now paying $120 per month for rent, how much was the rent when he first moved in?

4. A small cooperative venture operated by seven men for one year had total expense costs amounting to $1,600. At the end of the year, however, each of the seven had made a profit of $500. What was the total income of the cooperative venture for the year?

Recalling our discussion of problem solving in Chapter 3 we should read each problem carefully. (Review 3.3 on Problems!) Our interest in each problem will be not only to solve the problem but also to determine any new techniques that we can apply to future problems.

Example 1. When nineteen more than a number is divided into seven equal parts, the result is eight. Find the number.

SOLUTION. Let N be the number.

$\dfrac{N + 19}{7} = 8$, solve for N.

$N + 19 = 7 \times 8 = 56$; $N = 56 - 19 = 37$.

ANSWER. The number is 37.

DISCUSSION. The phrase "divided into seven equal parts" must mean that 7 times one of the parts must equal 19 more than the number. But, in an equation, this must mean that we can multiply both sides of the equation by this amount. That is, multiplication and division are "inverse" operations.

Example 2. If seven more than a number is equal to thirteen times five less than the number, then what is the number?

SOLUTION. Let N be the number.

$N + 7 = 13 \times (N - 5)$, solve for N.
$N + 7 = 13 \times N - 13 \times 5$; $7 + 13 \times 5 = 13 \times N - N$;
$7 + 65 = (13 - 1) \times N$; $72 = 12N$; $N = 6$.

ANSWER.   The number is 6.

DISCUSSION.   Once the equation is "set up" by careful translation of the problem, we can apply the distributive property and then equal addition and subtraction. Using the distributive property again, we isolate the variable N. Notice how we have used our conventions concerning the order of operations. Given the equation $72 = 12N$, we should recognize the value of $N = 6$. However, is there a "principle" involved? What are the mechanics for isolating N?

Example 3.   In complaining about the cost of living, Mr. Smith commented that two years after moving into their present apartment the rent had been raised fifteen dollars and that since then the rent had been doubled. If Mr. Smith is now paying one hundred twenty dollars per month for rent, how much was the rent when he first moved in?

SOLUTION.   Let R be the rent when he first moved in.
$2 \times (R + 15) = 120$, solve for R.
$R + 15 = \dfrac{120}{2}$; $R = 60 - 15 = 45$.

ANSWER.   The rent was $45.

DISCUSSION.   Notice the importance of reading completely through the problem. Eliminate all unnecessary words, write the problem in "mathematical language." Rather than using the distributive property, we apply division first to isolate the variable R.

Example 4.   A small cooperative venture operated by seven men for one year had total expense costs amounting to $1,600. At the end of the year, however, each of the seven had made a profit of $500. What was the total income of the cooperative venture for the year?

SOLUTION.   Let T be the total income.
$T - 1,600$ is the total profit.
$\dfrac{T - 1,600}{7} = 500$, solve for T.
$T - 1,600 = 7 \times 500 = 3,500$; $T = 3,500 + 1,600 = 5,100$.

ANSWER.   The total income was $5,100.

DISCUSSION.   Notice the distinctions and relationships between total income, total cost, and total expenses. Observe the similarity between this problem in its "pattern" to Example 1.

What have we noted in the above examples? Are useful principles and ideas suggested? Can we "pick out" new ideas and techniques?
Consider the four conditional equations:

1. $\dfrac{N + 19}{7} = 8.$

2. $N + 7 = 13 \times (N - 5)$.

3. $2 \times (R + 15) = 120$.

4. $\dfrac{T - 1600}{7} = 500$.

5.3.6 Our procedure in "setting up" each problem is still based on a careful reading of the problem and previously discussed techniques. Our method for solving the equations is still motivated by the idea that we must "isolate" the desired variable. The equations, however, now involve multiplication and division. Have we used "new" principles in solving these equations? Yes, two further general principles can be stated.

The Principle of Equal Multiplication: If A, B, and C are numbers and $A = B$, then $A \times C = B \times C$.

Examples.

(a) $2 + 3 = 5$ so that $(2 + 3) \times 9 = 5 \times 9$.

(b) If $\dfrac{N}{7} = 14$, then $\dfrac{N}{7} \times 7 = 14 \times 7$.

The Principle of Equal Division: If A, B, and C are numbers with $C \neq 0$ and $A = B$, then $\dfrac{A}{C} = \dfrac{B}{C}$.

Examples.

(a) $9 + 3 = 12$ so that $\dfrac{3 + 9}{4} = \dfrac{12}{4}$.

(b) If $7N = 14$, then $\dfrac{7N}{7} = \dfrac{14}{7}$.

We apply the above principles to equations in order to "isolate" variables and state the principle as a justification for our action. For example,

1. Since $\dfrac{N + 19}{7} = 8$, we have $\left(\dfrac{N + 19}{7}\right) \times 7 = 8 \times 7$ and we can now write $\dfrac{(N + 19) \times 7}{7} = (N + 19) \times \dfrac{7}{7} = (N + 19) \times 1 = (N + 19)$. Thus, $N + 19 = 8 \times 7 = 56$.

2. Given $N + 7 = 13 \times (N - 5)$, we have $N + 7 = 13N - 65$ and $12N = 72$. Now, $\dfrac{12N}{12} = \dfrac{72}{12}$ so that $N = 6$.

3. $2 \times (R + 15) = 120$ so that $\dfrac{2 \times (R + 15)}{2} = \dfrac{120}{2}$ and $R + 15 = 60$.

4. $\dfrac{T - 1{,}600}{7} = 500$ so that $\left(\dfrac{T - 1{,}600}{7}\right) \times 7 = 500 \times 7$ and $(T - 1{,}600)$

$\times \dfrac{7}{7} = T - 1{,}600 = 3{,}500$.

Notice how, in solving the conditional equations, we use "inverse" operations. That is,

(a) subtraction to "undo" addition: $(N + 4) - 4 = N.$
(b) addition to "undo" subtraction: $(N - 7) + 7 = N.$

(c) division to "undo" multiplication: $\dfrac{5 \times N}{5} = N.$

(d) multiplication to "undo" division: $\dfrac{N}{9} \times 9 = N.$

When two operations are related in this way, we say that they are **inverse operations**. Sometimes the same number is involved in a pair of inverse operations; in this event, we can often omit both operations. When this is done correctly, it is often called **cancellation**. Our examples (a), (b), (c), and (d) above are instances of this.

Practice 3.   Solve the following equations.

(a)	(b)	(c)
1. $\dfrac{N}{7} = 9$	$\dfrac{6}{N} = 2$	$\dfrac{N + 3}{5} = 12$
2. $8N = 64$	$\dfrac{9N}{5} = 27$	$\dfrac{2N - 4}{17} = 6$
3. $3 \times (N + 7) = 18$	$4 \times \dfrac{5}{N} = 2$	$\dfrac{N}{3} \times (6 + 11) = 34$
4. $\dfrac{5 - N}{11} = 3$	$\dfrac{30}{6 + N} = 3$	$\dfrac{3 + 4N}{1 - 8} = 3$
5. $3N + 7 = \dfrac{6}{2} - 5$	$\dfrac{5N}{12} = \dfrac{15}{3}$	$\dfrac{6}{8 - 2N} = 3$
6. $\dfrac{15}{N} - 3 = \dfrac{5 - 1}{2}$	$\dfrac{42}{6 \times (N + 1)} = 1$	$\dfrac{N + 5}{7 - N} = 1$
7. $\dfrac{4 \times (5 + N)}{7} = 8$	$\dfrac{12 \times (N - 5)}{15} = 4$	$\dfrac{6 + \dfrac{3N}{2}}{8} = 9$

8. $\dfrac{\dfrac{6N}{5} - 18}{3} = 2$ $\dfrac{\dfrac{7N}{3} - 4}{2 + 13} = 3$ $\dfrac{3 \times (5N + 7)}{22} = \dfrac{6}{2}$

9. $\dfrac{14 \times (N - 1)}{N \times (N - 1)} = 7$ $\dfrac{3N + 8}{7} = 3N - 4$

$\dfrac{(21 + 3N) \times (N - 5)}{6} = 5 \times (N - 5)$

10. $(2 + N) \times (N - 2) = 21$ $\dfrac{3N - 7}{10 + N} = 2$ $N \times (N + 1) = 12$

Answers.

	(a)	(b)	(c)
1.	63	3	57
2.	8	15	53
3.	−1	10	6
4.	−28	4	−6
5.	−3	12	3
6.	3	6	1
7.	9	10	44
8.	20	21	3
9.	2	2	3
10.	5 and −5	27	3 and −4

Exercises

1. Write out the statement for the division algorithm.

2. 0 divided by any number $A \neq 0$ is _____ but any number divided by 0 is _____.

3. In a division:

(a) If the dividend and divisor are both positive, then the quotient is _____.

(b) If the dividend or divisor, but not both, are negative, then the quotient is _____.

(c) If both the dividend and the divisor are negative, then the quotient is _____.

4. Find the quotients:

(a) $12 \div (-4)$ (b) $(-38) \div (-19)$ (c) $(-42) \div 6$

(d) $34 \div 17$ (e) $\dfrac{36}{9}$ (f) $\dfrac{56}{-7}$ (g) $\dfrac{-45}{3}$ (h) $\dfrac{-54}{-9}$.

5. Match the numbered column of examples with the lettered column of descriptions so that they best illustrate the properties described.

(a) If $\dfrac{B}{A} = Q$, $\dfrac{B \times C}{A \times C} = Q$ for $C \neq 0$

1. $\dfrac{24}{6} \neq \dfrac{\frac{24}{6}}{2}$

(b) If $A \neq B$, $B \div A \neq A \div B$

2. $\dfrac{37}{1} = 37$ and $\dfrac{37}{37} = 1$

(c) $\dfrac{A}{\frac{B}{C}} \neq \dfrac{\frac{A}{B}}{C}$

3. $\dfrac{18}{6} = 3$ so that $\dfrac{54}{18} = 3$

(d) $\dfrac{B + C}{A} = \dfrac{B}{A} + \dfrac{C}{A}$

4. $\dfrac{9}{4} \times 12 = 9 \times \dfrac{12}{4} = \dfrac{9 \times 12}{4}$

(e) $\dfrac{A}{1} = A$ and $\dfrac{A}{A} = 1$

5. $12 \div 3 \neq 3 \div 12$

(f) $\dfrac{B}{A} \times C = B \times \dfrac{C}{A} = \dfrac{B \times C}{A}$

6. $\dfrac{13 + 17}{6} = \dfrac{13}{6} + \dfrac{17}{6}$

6. Write out in your own words the conventions for the order of doing operations in expressions.

7. Find the simplest numeral for:

(a) $\dfrac{8 \times 5 - 7}{7 + 4}$ (b) $\dfrac{(6 + 9) \times 2}{3}$ (c) $7 \times \left(4 - \dfrac{15}{2 + 3}\right)$

(d) $\dfrac{18 - 5}{5 + 8}$ (e) $7 \times 3 - \dfrac{28}{7}$ (f) $\dfrac{11 \times 6 + 4}{4 + 2 \times 5}$.

8. Find the simplest numeral for:

(a) $\dfrac{18}{2} + 4 \times 7 - \dfrac{5 \times (9 - 7)}{3 + 2}$ (b) $\dfrac{\frac{16}{4} \times (3 + 12)}{\frac{72 - 4}{4 + 13}}$

(c) $12 - \dfrac{12}{8 - \dfrac{6}{6 - \frac{6}{2}}}$ (d) $\dfrac{\frac{\frac{18}{3} + 2}{4} + 7}{1 + \dfrac{6}{1 + \frac{6}{3}}}$.

9. What is the inverse operation of:
   (a) addition?   (b) subtraction?   (c) division?
   (d) multiplication?

10. Solve the following equations.

(a) $\dfrac{2N + 7}{5} = 17$ (b) $\dfrac{3 \times (6 - N)}{8} = 12$ (c) $5 + \dfrac{4N}{7} = 13$

(d) $\dfrac{15}{N + 9} = 3$ (e) $\dfrac{\frac{N}{2} + 6}{7} = 3$ (f) $\dfrac{5N + 6}{6 - N} = 7$.

11. Solve the following equations.

(a) $\dfrac{5 \times \left(3 - \dfrac{N}{5}\right)}{9 + 5N} = 1$ (b) $\dfrac{24 - \dfrac{42}{N+7}}{9} = 2.$

12. A small company paid $7 on each of 936 shares of stock. What was the total amount paid by the company?

13. If a ton (2,000 pounds) of coal is divided equally among the families in a certain village, each family will receive 50 pounds of coal. How many families are there in the village?

14. Mr. Smith was five years more than three times his son's age. If his son was four years younger than his daughter who was 17, then how old was Mr. Smith?

15. The quotient of the ten's digit of a two-digit numeral divided by the one's digit is three. The product of the digits is twelve. Find the two-digit numeral.

16. When six more than three times a number is divided by two less than the number, the resulting quotient is four. Find the number.

Answers.

1. $-$.
2. 0, not defined (or meaningless).
3. (a) positive   (b) negative   (c) positive.
4. (a) -3 (b) 2   (c) -7 (d) 2   (e) 4   (f) -8
   (g) -15 (h) 6.
5. (a)-3, (b)-5, (c)-1, (d)-6, (e)-2, (f)-4.
6. $-$.
7. (a) 3   (b) 10   (c) 7   (d) 1   (e) 17   (f) 5.
8. (a) 35   (b) 15   (c) 10   (d) 3.
9. (a) subtraction   (b) addition   (c) multiplication
   (d) division.
10. (a) 39   (b) -26 (c) 14   (d) -4 (e) 30   (f) 3.
11. (a) 1   (b) 0.
12. $6,552.
13. 40 families.
14. 44 years old.
15. 62.
16. 14.

Review Summary

In multiplication we asked what is the product when we multiplied a multiplicand with a multiplier. In this chapter we asked the "inverse" question, what must a multiplier be equal to in order to result in a given product when multiplying a given multiplicand?

Division is a "shortcut" operation for finding how many times we can _____ a fixed subtrahend from a   *subtract* given minuend. The fixed subtrahend is then called the _____ and the given minuend the _____. The number of   *divisor,* times we can subtract the divisor from the dividend is   *dividend* then called the _____. It should be evident that the quo-   *quotient* tient times the _____ must then equal the _____. In   *divisor,* writing $45 \div 9 = 5$, the 45 is the _____, the 9 is the _____,   *dividend* and 5 is the _____.   *dividend,*
divisor,
quotient

Although simple divisions can be "worked out" by   *dividend,* counting successive subtractions, when divisors are   *divisor,* not exact factors of dividends we have to concede that   *quotient* there is no integer which is an exact quotient in the division. We overcame this difficulty by introducing a new number, called the _____. Four different forms   *remainder* were introduced in writing and indicating divisions:

(i) $45 \div 9 = 5$ emphasizes the operation of division.

(ii) $\frac{57}{9} = 6 + \frac{3}{9}$ leads to an extension of numbers and the manipulation of numerals.

(iii) $65 = (7 \times 9) + 2$ suggests the close connection between division and multiplication.

(iv)   8   offers the organization and format most
$9\overline{)77}$ suitable for computations.
     $\frac{72}{5}$

In extending our discussion of division to quotients with two or more digits, we observed that multiplying a dividend by 10, 100, 1,000, and so forth, simply means that the _____ in turn is multiplied by 10, 100,   *quotient* 1,000, and so forth. When both dividend and divisor are multiplied by 10, 100, 1,000, and so forth, the quotient remains unchanged. Since division can be interpreted as a successive subtraction process, we can expand a dividend and subtract convenient multiples of the _____   *divisor* from the expanded parts. That is, division is distributive from the right to the left. After doing a division, we can check our work by _____ the quotient by the divisor   *multiplying* and _____ the remainder to the product to see if the   *adding* result is the same as the _____.   *dividend*

In extending division to divisors with two or more digits we observed two important ideas:

1. Remember that division is the _____ of multiples   *subtraction* of the divisor from the dividend.

2. Mentally round the divisor to a slightly _____   *larger* numeral to estimate the quotient.

Historically, division was rarely used except when the divisor was small. The Egyptians avoided some difficulties by a system of doubling. Another device used for division was called the "galley" or "scratch" method of division. Our present method of "long division" was introduced in the fifteenth century. We estimate the quotient one digit at a time and successively _____ the   *subtract* product of the estimate and the _____ from the _____.   *divisor,* The most common error is in estimating the quotient   *dividend* digit. For lengthy divisions involving large numerals, we can check by a method of "casting out nines."

Once we had discussed the computational aspects of division, we noted that the operation of division is probably more important as a tool to compare and relate numbers than as a computation in its own right. We then began with a consideration of the division algorithm:

Given any integers A and B, with $A \neq 0$, there are integers Q and R such that $B =$ _____, $0 \leq R <$ the $Q \times A + R$ positive value corresponding to A.

When B is a multiple of A so that $B = Q \times A$ with $R = 0$, we say that B is _____ by A and that A is a factor,   *divisible* or a divisor, of B. Our first observation was that a prime number was any positive integer (other than 1) which _____ divisible by any integer other than _____   *is not, 1*
(is or is not)
and _____. A composite number is any positive integer   *itself* which is not a prime. A fundamental property of the positive integers is that every positive integer other than 1 can be described by a product of factors that are prime. For example, the prime factors of 30 are 2, _____, and   *3* _____. The divisors of 30, on the other hand, are 1, 2, 3,   *5* _____, _____, _____, _____, and 30. We noted that   *5, 6, 10, 15* the set of prime factors of an integer is a subset of the set of divisors of the integer.

When we decompose a number into a product of factors we say that we are factoring the number. In factoring a number, knowledge of the divisibility of

the number by a given factor is helpful. Tests of divisibility can be devised. A few simple tests are:

(a) A number is divisible by 2 if it is _____.   *even*

(b) Every number divisible by 5 must "end" in
the digit _____ or _____ at the right.   *0, 5*

(c) A number is divisible by 9 if its _____ _____   *excess of*
_____ is 0.   *nines*

In relating numbers, the largest factor common to a
set of numbers is called the _____ _____ _____ or   *greatest com-*
highest common factor of the set of numbers. The   *mon divisor*
smallest number which contains each number in a set of
numbers as a divisor is called the _____ _____ _____   *lowest   com-*
of the set of numbers. For example, the lowest common   *mon multiple*
multiple of 54 and 60 is _____ while the greatest   *540*
common divisor is _____. If the greatest common divisor   *6*
between two numbers is 1, we say that the two numbers
are relatively prime to each other. Two _____ _____   *relatively*
numbers have a lowest common multiple which is the   *prime*
product of the two numbers.

Continuing with our study, we asked how we could
extend the division operation to include the negative
integers. Here again we used the division algorithm
to examine the possibilities. Starting with simple examples, we concluded that we can extend division to
include the negative as well as positive integers. Putting
aside the "embarrassing" question of remainders, we
noted that:

(a) If the dividend is positive and the divisor
negative, then the quotient is _____.   *negative*

(b) If the dividend is negative and the divisor
positive, then the quotient is _____.   *negative*

(c) If both the dividend and divisor are negative,
then the quotient is _____.   *positive*

(d) If the dividend is zero, then the quotient is
_____. However, no _____ may equal zero.   *zero, divisor*

In summary, we can say that division_____ commuta-   *is not*
(is or is not)

tive, _____ associative, but _____ distributive from the   *is not, is*
(is or is not)   (is or is not)

right to the left. Two further useful properties of division
were:

1. If $\dfrac{B}{A} = Q$, then $\dfrac{B \times C}{A \times C} = Q$ for all $C \neq 0$.

7. In general, $\dfrac{B}{A} \times C = B \times \dfrac{C}{A} = \dfrac{B \times C}{A}$.

The four operations that we have studied thus far are called the fundamental arithmetical operations since they are the operations used most commonly in elementary arithmetical work. In considering the four operations together we found that there was a need for conventions or rules to avoid confusion and disagreement as to the order in which operations should be done. Four general conventions for the order of operations were stated. Very briefly, these were that:

1. Grouping symbols indicate a "first preference" in the order of work.

2. Multiplication and division are to be done before addition and subtraction.

3. The bar symbol of division is considered to have the effect of parentheses.

4. The "normal" order of work is from left to right.

We concluded the chapter by noting that we must know how to compute with numbers, but that the most important and probably the most useful aspect of working with numbers lay in learning how to "set up" problems, when to do computations, and then what computations to do. With examples we illustrated and discussed procedures and two "new" principles which could be used in solving conditional equations. These were called the principles of equal multiplication and equal division.

Chapter Exercises (5)

Group I.

1. Division is a "shortcut" operation for finding a factor which when _____ by a given factor will result in a given product. The given product is then called the _____, the given factor the _____, and the factor which we find is called the _____.

2. If a divisor is not an exact factor of a dividend, the division will result in a _____. The remainder is always greater than or equal to zero and less than the _____.

3. Find the quotients and remainders.

(a) $37 \div 5$ (b) $52 \div 4$ (c) $79 \div 8$

(d) $\dfrac{46}{7}$ (e) $\dfrac{61}{5}$ (f) $\dfrac{95}{9}$

(g) $6\overline{)49}$ (h) $9\overline{)5}$ (i) $3\overline{)32}$.

4. Find the quotients and remainders.

(a) $2\overline{)135,027}$ (b) $3\overline{)522,152}$ (c) $6\overline{)513,804}$

(d) $7\overline{)917,535}$ (e) $8\overline{)700,000}$ (f) $9\overline{)777,777}$.

5. Divide 5726 by 97 using the
   (a) Egyptian doubling method.
   (b) "galley" or "scratch" method.

6. Find the quotients and remainders. Check by "multiplication."

(a) $73\overline{)52,655}$ (b) $46\overline{)40,388}$ (c) $87\overline{)94,000}$.

7. Do the divisions and check by "casting out nines."

(a) $652\overline{)8,365,305}$ (b) $1,043\overline{)1,087,892}$ (c) $3,670\overline{)30,615,155}$.

8. Find the quotients to two significant digits.

(a) $5,983\overline{)28,299,621}$ (b) $2,145\overline{)13,479,193}$

(c) $4,737\overline{)51,822,894}$ (d) $7,175\overline{)39,857,137}$.

9. Which of the following are primes? Decompose the composites into products of primes: 15, 17, 22, 25, 29, 30, 31, 32, 33, 35.

10. Find the sets of divisors of: (a) 74   (b) 196   (c) 1925.

11. Find the largest factor less than 20 in each of the following integers: (a) 735   (b) 624   (c) 4,945.

12. Find the smallest prime factor in (a) 525   (b) 899   (c) 4,199.

13. Find the LCM and GCD for each of the following pairs of numbers.
   (a) 8 and 24   (b) 6 and 15   (c) 11 and 13   (d) 15 and 12
   (e) 9 and 12   (f) 21 and 14   (g) 18 and 24   (h) 27 and 16.

14. Find the LCM and GCD for each of the following sets of numbers.
   (a) 6, 8, 9, and 12   (b) 4, 12, 32, and 60
   (c) 26, 65, and 78   (d) 306, 360, and 450.

15. Find the quotients and remainders.
   (a) $104 \div (-11)$ (b) $(-451) \div (-72)$ (c) $(-754) \div 15$

(d) $\dfrac{-523}{57}$ (e) $\dfrac{689}{-13}$ (f) $\dfrac{-395}{-24}$.

16. Find the simplest numerals for:

(a) $\dfrac{12 - 5 \times 7}{15 + 8}$ (b) $\dfrac{4 \times (7 + 4)}{13 - 2}$ (c) $\dfrac{3 \times 3 + 3}{18 - 2 \times 3}$

(d) $\dfrac{35}{5} + 5 \times 7$ (e) $\left(5 + \dfrac{45}{5}\right) \times 5$ (f) $\dfrac{\dfrac{27}{3} + 3}{3 - \dfrac{6}{3}}$.

17. Solve the following equations.

(a) $\dfrac{5N + 7}{16} = 7$ (b) $3 \times \left(\dfrac{N}{3} + 8\right) = 37$ (c) $\dfrac{9}{5 - 2N} = 3$

(d) $\dfrac{\dfrac{6}{N} + 2}{5} = 1$ (e) $\dfrac{4N - 3}{5 + 3N} = 1$ (f) $\dfrac{2N + 1}{3 + \dfrac{N}{2}} = 2.$

18. A rectangular building lot has a 54-foot frontage and is 8,856 square feet in area. How deep is the lot?

19. A utility company was required to make equal refunds to 937 customers. If the total refund was equal to $8,530 less $97 in expenses, then what was each customer's share of the refund?

20. A department store inventoried its suits and found that there were 387 suits in stock. If they decided to hang them on 24 racks for a sale, with each rack holding the same number of suits except for one odd rack of suits, find the largest number of suits that can be hung on each rack except for the odd rack.

21. Four girls sharing an apartment had the following expenses during a certain month: Rent, $100, utilities, $37, food, $108, and miscellaneous, $45. What was each girl's share of the expenses?

22. Find the smallest number containing 14, 21, and 18 as divisors.

23. If the lowest common multiple of two positive integers is 2,805 and the greatest common divisor is 15, then what are the two integers?

24. If the product of two positive integers is 54 and their quotient is 6, then what are the two numbers?

Group II.

1. Division is a "shortcut" operation for finding how many times we can _____ a fixed subtrahend from a given minuend. The given minuend is then called the _____, the subtrahend the _____, and the number of times we can do the _____ is called the _____.

2. If a dividend is not exactly divisible by a divisor, the division operation will result in a _____. The remainder is always between _____ and the _____.

3. Find the quotients and remainders.

(a) $28 \div 7$ (b) $43 \div 9$ (c) $95 \div 3$

(d) $\dfrac{51}{4}$ (e) $\dfrac{77}{8}$ (f) $\dfrac{69}{6}$

(g) $5\overline{)37}$ (h) $7\overline{)5}$ (i) $2\overline{)72}.$

4. Find the quotients and remainders.

(a) $4\overline{)324,103}$ (b) $5\overline{)901,335}$ (c) $8\overline{)177,002}$

(d) $7\overline{)757,409}$ (e) $6\overline{)425,003}$ (f) $7\overline{)999,999}$.

5. Divide 6281 by 73 using the
   (a) Egyptian doubling method.
   (b) "galley" or "scratch" method.

6. Find the quotients and remainders. Check by "multiplication."

   (a) $57\overline{)81,058}$ (b) $92\overline{)36,989}$ (c) $76\overline{)75,000}$.

7. Do the divisions and check by "casting out nines."

   (a) $527\overline{)7,030,900}$ (b) $3,710\overline{)3,900,444}$ (c) $7,514\overline{)75,040,605}$.

8. Find the quotients to two significant digits.

   (a) $3,745\overline{)22,599,408}$ (b) $6,727\overline{)15,283,744}$

   (c) $8,131\overline{)8,740,852}$ (d) $5,873\overline{)15,563,457}$.

9. Which of the following are primes? Decompose the composites into products of primes: 16, 19, 23, 25, 26, 28, 37, 38, 41, 43.

10. Find the sets of divisors of: (a) 125   (b) 315   (c) 1573.

11. Find the largest factor less than 20 in each of the following integers: (a) 882   (b) 950   (c) 5,491.

12. Find the smallest prime factor in (a) 726   (b) 529   (c) 1859.

13. Find the LCM and GCD for each of the following pairs of numbers.
   (a) 4 and 14   (b) 5 and 25   (c) 15 and 21   (d) 18 and 30
   (e) 7 and 11   (f) 12 and 28   (g) 15 and 33   (h) 26 and 14.

14. Find the LCM and GCD for each of the following sets of numbers.
   (a) 4, 10, 12, and 30   (b) 6, 15, 18, and 45
   (c) 27, 63, and 72   (d) 385, 315, and 1155.

15. Find the quotients and remainders.
   (a) $282 \div (-17)$ (b) $(-635) \div (-84)$ (c) $(-907) \div 49$
   (d) $\dfrac{-170}{32}$ (e) $\dfrac{543}{-28}$ (f) $\dfrac{-487}{-57}$.

16. Find the simplest numerals for:
   (a) $\dfrac{6 + 7 \times 4}{12 + 5}$ (b) $\dfrac{5 \times (7 - 11)}{5 - 9}$ (c) $\dfrac{7 \times 7 - 7}{(5 + 2) \times 3}$

   (d) $4 \times 9 - \dfrac{36}{4}$ (e) $4 \times \left(9 - \dfrac{36}{4}\right)$ (f) $\dfrac{12 - \dfrac{18}{6}}{\dfrac{6}{3} + 1}$.

17. Solve the following equations.

   (a) $\dfrac{3N - 11}{5} = 11$ (b) $\dfrac{4 - \dfrac{2N}{7}}{9} = 6$ (c) $\dfrac{25}{6N + 7} = 1$

   (d) $\dfrac{\dfrac{12}{N} + 15}{9} = 2$ (e) $\dfrac{5N + 2}{26 - 3N} = 1$ (f) $2 \times \left(\dfrac{2}{N} + \dfrac{3}{N}\right) = 10$.

18. The cross section of a rectangular solid is 15 by 18 inches. If the solid has a volume of 7,020 cubic inches, then how long is the solid?

19. A small assessment district had to raise $1,267 plus $31 in expenses by equally assessing 103 people. How much was each person assessed?

20. A meeting hall has a total of 714 seats. If each row except one has the same number of seats and the exception has fewer seats than the number of rows, then how many seats are in each row given that there are 19 rows of seats in all?

21. Seven people contributed to a worthy cause as follows: 2 gave $100 each, 3 gave $75 each, and the other 2 gave $64 each. If each of the seven were to have contributed the same amount, then how much would each have had to contribute in order to have given the same total amount?

22. Find the smallest number containing 20, 42, and 105 as divisors.

23. If the lowest common multiple of two positive integers is 2,548 and the greatest common divisor is 28, then what are the two integers?

24. If the product of two positive integers is 63 and their quotient is 7, then what are the two numbers?

Problem Set (5)

1. The quotient of the sum of two positive integers divided by their difference is 3, while the product less the quotient is 96. Find the integers.

2. Is the statement, "If the product of all the consecutive positive integers from 1 to $N - 1$ increased by 1 is exactly divisible by N, then N must be a prime," true? If so, can you present a good argument why? Even if the statement is true, why wouldn't it be a practical test for the primeness of a positive integer?

3. A huckster has 29 boxes of toys with the same number in each box. He sells the toys by the dozen and finally has 7 left over. What is the smallest number of toys the huckster could have had in each of the boxes?

4. If the cents in my pocket were changed to dollars and the dollars were changed to cents, then I would have 52 cents more than twice what I have now. How much do I have?

5. When we divide a positive integer B by another positive integer A, we obtain a quotient Q and remainder R: $\dfrac{B}{A} = Q + \dfrac{R}{A}$, $0 \leq R < A$.

Suppose we fix A (constant), ignore the quotient Q, and turn our attention only to the remainder R. Let $A = 3$. The possible remainders R will be 0, 1, and 2.

Consider: If $B = 7$, then $R = 1$; if $B = 11$, then $R = 2$; and so forth.

If $B = 7 + 11$, then $R = 0$; but notice that for $B = 1 + 2$, we also have $R = 0$. That is, the remainder of the sum of remainders is equal to the remainder of the sum of original numbers.

Consider: If $B = 28$, $R = 1$ and if $B = 34$, $R = 1$. Now $B = 28 + 34$ has remainder $R = 2$. Also, $B = 1 + 1$ has $R = 2$.

We can construct a simple table for the sums of remainders:

(a) Complete the table at the right for sums of remainders with $A = 3$.

+	0	1	2
0			
1		2	0
2			

Consider: For $B = 7 \times 11 = 77$, $R = 2$. But, $B = 1 \times 2 = 2$ has $R = 2$ also. For $B = 28 \times 34 = 952$ we have $R = 1$. But, here again, for $B = 1 \times 1 = 1$ we have $R = 1$.

We can construct a simple table for the products of remainders:

(b) Complete the table at the right for products of remainders with $A = 3$.

×	0	1	2
0			
1		1	2
2			

(c) Discuss the various properties (such as closure, commutativity, and so forth) of the above "operations."

Vocabulary List, Chapters 1–5

Vocabulary List, Chapters 1–5—*Continued*

Vocabulary List, Chapters 1–5 — *Continued*

Comprehensive Check-Test, Chapters 1–5

1. Write the Roman and Hindu-Arabic numerals for:
   (a) One thousand, four hundred ninety-six.
   (b) Nineteen hundred sixty-four.
2. Write out in words how the following should be read: (a) 12,129 (b) 307,050.
3. Write the following decimal numerals in expanded form: (a) 3,507 (b) 20,110.
4. List the first seven numerals used in counting by fours beginning with 13.
5. List the prime numbers between 25 and 50.
6. Find the sums: (a) $27 + 305 + 9 + 83$ (b) 7051
$$\begin{array}{r} 7051 \\ 758 \\ 2147 \\ \underline{665} \end{array}$$

7. What is the sum of the following addends?
       7,324; 2,060; 19,307; 992,430.

8. Find the differences: (a) 72,405   (b) 401,926
$$\begin{array}{r} 72{,}405 \\ -\ 2{,}595 \end{array} \qquad \begin{array}{r} 401{,}926 \\ -391{,}950 \end{array}$$

9. Subtract 375,068 from 1,000,900.

10. Find the sums: (a) $27 + (-18) + 0 + (-8)$.
    (b) $(-205) + 52 + (-10) + 477$.

11. Find the differences: (a) $409 - (-105)$ (b) $(-86) - (-68)$.

12. Order the following numerals from smallest to largest:
    $8 + 9,\ 10,\ 3 + 3,\ 15 - 2,\ 7,\ 12 + 13$.

13. Which of the following are equations? Which of the statements are true?

    (a) $3 + 4 = 34$ (b) $34 - 3 + 4$ (c) $5 > 1 + 2$
    (d) $21 - 0 = 21$ (e) $-4 < -6$ (f) $N + N = 2N$
    (g) $5 - 2 = 3$ (h) $6 > 4$.

14. Solve the following equations:

    (a) $N + 47 = 102$ (b) $M - 16 = 39$ (c) $28 = 74 + P$
    (d) $51 = 80 - Q$.

15. Use the variable N to write mathematical descriptions of:

    (a) Two more than five less than a multiple of three.

    (b) Four less than a number is between -3 and 7.

16. Find the value of N in each of the following equations so that the equations will be true.

    (a) $3 + N = 3$ (b) $7 \times N = 7$ (c) $4 \div N = 4$ (d) $6 - N = 6$
    (e) $0 \times 5 = N$ (f) $0 \div 9 = N$ (g) $1 \times N = 8$ (h) $N \div 2 = 1$.

17. Find the products:

    (a) $7 \times [5 + (3 \times 8)]$ (b) $[(7 \times 5) - 3] \times 8$.

18. Find the products: (a) 1706   (b) 374,800
$$\begin{array}{r} 1706 \\ \times\ 493 \end{array} \qquad \begin{array}{r} 374{,}800 \\ \times\ 6{,}910 \end{array}$$

19. Multiply 405,805 by 22,001.

20. What must 87 be multiplied by in order to result in a product equal to 1,479?

21. Round the following to the nearest multiple of 1,000.

    (a) 407,429   (b) 736,654   (c) 245,561   (d) 478,550.

22. Round the numerals in Problem 21 above to four significant digits.

23. Find the products to two significant digits.

    (a) 217,945   (b) 608,375
$$\begin{array}{r} 217{,}945 \\ \times\ 4{,}026 \end{array} \qquad \begin{array}{r} 608{,}375 \\ \times\ 1{,}994 \end{array}$$

24. Find the value of N in each of the following equations so that the equations will be true.

    (a) $-7 \times N = -7$ (b) $N \div 8 = -8$ (c) $N \times (-6) = 6$

(d) $N \div (-4) = -4$ (e) $N \times 9 = -9$ (f) $(-5) \div N = 5$
(g) $9 \div (-3) = N$ (h) $(-3) \times (-9) = N$.

25. Find the products: (a) $(-37) \times [61 \times (-84)]$.
(b) $69 \times [(-52) \times 77]$.

26. Find the simplest numeral for: (a) $(24 + 18) \times (57 + 21)$
(b) $(32 - 23) \times 49 - 11$ (c) $86 + 31 \times (64 - 19)$.

27. Solve the following equations:
(a) $5N + 7 = 52$ (b) $(N - 7) \times 3 = 21$ (c) $6 \times (9 - 2N) = 30$.

28. Find the quotients and remainders.

(a) $37 \overline{)54,397}$ (b) $63 \overline{)37,674}$ (c) $408 \overline{)459,007}$.

29. Find the quotients and remainders:

(a) $7293 \overline{)92,930,120}$ (b) $20,546 \overline{)17,055,000}$.

30. Find the quotients to one significant digit.

(a) $59,237 \overline{)22,517,498}$ (b) $8,395 \overline{)10,074,317}$.

31. Express as a product of primes: (a) $2,028$ (b) $4,675$.

32. Find the sets of divisors of: (a) 539 (b) 374.

33. Find the lowest common multiple and the greatest common divisor for each of the following sets of numbers.
(a) 3, 4, and 6   (b) 10, 12, and 18   (c) 36, 90, and 72.

34. Find the simplest numeral for:

(a) $\dfrac{21 - 6 \times 2}{1 + 2}$ (b) $\left(7 - \dfrac{6}{2}\right) \times \left(\dfrac{2 + 13}{3}\right)$ (c) $\dfrac{18 - 5}{5 + 8} + \dfrac{4 + 5}{5 - 4}$.

35. Solve the following equations:

(a) $\dfrac{N}{7} - 16 = 5$ (b) $9 + \dfrac{N - 4}{11} = 13$ (c) $\dfrac{75}{6N + 3} = 1$.

36. Which of the following statements are true?
(a) There is a smallest natural number.
(b) There is a largest natural number.
(c) The sum of any two natural numbers is a natural number.
(d) The difference between any two natural numbers is a natural number.
(e) There are two multiples of three in every set of five consecutive even numbers.
(f) Exactly one of any three consecutive odd numbers is divisible by three.

37. Which of the following statements are true?
(a) The sum of any two odd numbers is even.
(b) The product of any two odd numbers is even.
(c) The quotient of two consecutive multiples of any fixed number is equal to the fixed number.
(d) The difference between two consecutive multiples of any fixed number is equal to the fixed number.

(e) Every composite number can be expressed as a product of primes.

(f) Every prime number has exactly two divisors.

38. Which of the following statements are true?

(a) The sum of negative integers is always negative.

(b) The difference between any two negative integers is always negative.

(c) The product of two negative integers is always positive.

(d) The product of a positive and a negative integer is positive.

(e) The quotient of two negative integers is always negative.

(f) The quotient of a positive and a negative integer is negative.

39. Which of the following statements are true?

(a) The order of addition is immaterial.

(b) The order of subtraction is immaterial.

(c) The order of multiplication is immaterial.

(d) The order of division is immaterial.

(e) Zero, 0, plus any number is zero.

(f) Zero, 0, times any number is zero.

(g) One, 1, is the identity of addition.

(h) One, 1, is the identity of multiplication.

40. Give a justifying reason for each step in the following step-by-step solution.

(a) $\dfrac{2N+7}{3} - 2 = 3$ (given)   (i) $2N + 7 = 15$

(b) $\left(\dfrac{2N+7}{3} - 2\right) + 2 = 3 + 2$ (j) $(2N+7) - 7 = 15 - 7$

(c) $\dfrac{2N+7}{3} + (-2+2) = 5$ (k) $2N + (7-7) = 8$

(d) $\dfrac{2N+7}{3} + 0 = 5$ (l) $2N + 0 = 8$

(e) $\dfrac{2N+7}{3} = 5$ (m) $2N = 8$

(f) $\left(\dfrac{2N+7}{3}\right) \times 3 = 5 \times 3$ (n) $\dfrac{2N}{2} = \dfrac{8}{2}$

(g) $(2N+7) \times \dfrac{3}{3} = 15$ (o) $N = 4.$

(h) $(2N+7) \times 1 = 15$

41. If five withdrawals of $72 each were made on a checking account with an original balance of $937, then what was the remaining balance in the account?

42. A young couple purchased the following for their living room: rug, $149; sofa, $237; coffee table, $42; side table, $34; two lamps, $21

each; two chairs, $37 each. What was the total cost of the purchases after a tax of $23 was added?

43. A sheet of typewriter paper is 83 type spaces wide. If we wish to type a line of 54 spaces with a margin which is 5 spaces more on the left than on the right, then how many spaces should we leave for the left margin?

44. A bus goes from Smithville to Johnstown averaging 46 miles per hour. If the distance between the towns is 368 miles, how many hours does the trip take?

45. During the summer Bill had three jobs. The first job paid $64 per week for three weeks, the second $75 per week for five weeks, and the third paid $82 per week for four weeks. How much did Bill make on the three jobs?

46. A store sold 39 radios for $64 each and 11 radios for $57 each. If the store paid $2,500 for the 50 radios, then what was the gross profit on the 50 radios?

47. Bill, on his motor scooter, can average 28 miles per hour on the road. Sam, who has a motorcycle, can average 40 miles per hour. If Bill has a three hour head start on a trip, then how many miles must Sam go on the same road to catch up to Bill?

48. Find the quotient of the sum of 24 and 18 divided by their difference.

49. How much more is the product of 101 and 20 than ten times the sum of 101 and 20?

50. If 12 less than an integer is greater than 15 and 22 more than the integer is less than 51, find the integer.

RATIONAL NUMBERS AND MEASUREMENT

CHAPTER 6

The Rational Numbers

6.1 The Number Line

6.1.1 Men probably invented numbers to describe counting. As we have seen, counting leads to the ideas of cardinal and ordinal numbers. That is, to the ideas of the number of elements in a set and the order of elements in a set. It was from these beginning ideas that we developed a description of the natural numbers.

Men also had a need to describe comparative measures. That is, a need to describe the idea of the size of a subset as compared to a "whole" set. For example, a farmer in the marketplace selling wheat or corn had to describe equal measures of value. An early manuscript written by an Egyptian priest, named Ahmes, about 1700 B.C. deals largely with these questions of measuring parts of "wholes."

Examples.

(a) If a pie is cut into eight equal portions, then what part of the pie is a portion?

DISCUSSION. Can we visualize the situation? Eight portions are equal to the "whole" pie. There is a "whole" pie. There is a portion. The portion is a part of the "whole" pie. Can we compare the "part" to the "whole"? (See Figure 53.)

The whole pie 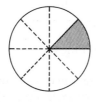 The portion of pie

FIGURE 53

257

The idea of comparing two quantities in this way is called a **ratio**. We say that a portion of the pie is to the whole pie as 1 is to 8. That is, we write

$$\frac{\text{Portion of pie}}{\text{Whole pie}} = \frac{1}{8}.$$

Let P be the number idea which describes the comparison of the portion to the whole. Then, we could write $P = \frac{1}{8}$. We call numbers such as P **rational numbers** or **fractions**. We read $P = \frac{1}{8}$ as "P equals one-eighth."

(b) What part of a dollar is a dime?

DISCUSSION. Ten dimes are equal to one dollar. There is a dollar. There is a dime. Then, there is the "part" of the dollar that the dime "is."

Let K be the part of the dollar that the dime "is." We can write that $10K = \$1$. Now, recalling division, we can also write $K = \frac{1}{10}$. We read this as "K equals one-tenth." That is, a dime is 1 of the 10 equal parts of a dollar. The number K is a rational number (Figure 54).

FIGURE 54

(c) Two cities are 20 miles apart. If we have covered 5 miles from one city to the other, what part of the total distance have we covered?

DISCUSSION. Notice that the distances are measured in miles. A mile is a standard unit of distance derived from an ancient Roman measure of 1,000 paces. In drawing a figure, such as Figure 55, it is convenient

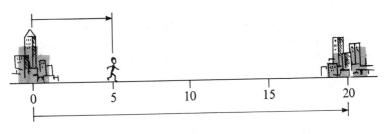

FIGURE 55

to represent the distances along a line with equal divisions marked with numerals to indicate the units of measure in the representation. Such a representation is called a **scale**.

Looking at the scale on our figure, we can read off the part of the distance covered: 5 out of 20. That is, we have covered $\frac{5}{20}$, read "five-twentieth," of the distance between the two cities.

In writing $\frac{5}{20}$ we might recall, from division, that $\frac{A \times C}{B \times C} = \frac{A}{B}$ so that since $\frac{5}{20} = \frac{1 \times 5}{4 \times 5}$ we have $\frac{5}{20} = \frac{1}{4}$. That is, five-twentieth is equal to one-fourth.

Our modern conception of rational numbers is much more general than the ideas associated with things such as portions of a pie, parts of a dollar, and so on. Just as we extended the natural numbers to the integers, we extend the integers to answer the "embarrassing" question of "what is the 'exact' quotient when a divisor is not a factor of the dividend in a division?" Recalling the problem of finding a number N such that $27 = N \times 4$, we now write $N = \frac{27}{4}$ and call $\frac{27}{4}$ a rational number. That is, a **rational number** is the quotient (or ratio) of two integers. To distinguish our "new point of view" it is useful to introduce some new descriptive vocabulary.

$$\frac{\textbf{Numerator}}{\textbf{Denominator}} \quad \frac{N}{D} \ = \ R \quad \textbf{Rational number}$$

Notice that a rational number can be represented as an ordered pair of integers. The order is essential since we cannot, in general, interchange the numerator and denominator without changing the value of the rational number. Since a rational number is a quotient, the denominator (divisor) cannot be zero. A rational number thus indicates an ordered relationship between two numbers.

$$\frac{N}{D} = R \text{ for } D \neq 0 \text{ means the same thing as } N = R \times D.$$

The rational numbers are ideas. The symbols used to name them are numerals. The **form,** $\frac{N}{D}$, in which we have introduced the rational number idea is called a **fractional form**. Thus, where it will not cause any difficulties, we refer to both the rational number and numeral as fractions. In our development our intent will be to extend and carry out the four fundamental arithmetical operations using the rational numbers. In doing this, our desire will be to have all of the properties which we have discussed "carry over" to the rational numbers. That is, we will expect that our manipulations will conform to all previously agreed upon properties and rules.

Our intuitive development of the rational numbers can be aided considerably by the use of scales. A **scale** consists of a line segment with at least two fixed points marked on it and named by numerals. For example, an ordinary ruler marked in inches or centimeters. If equal distances are made to correspond to equal numerical differences, then, once two points have been marked and named, further points can be named.

Examples.

(a)

The "end points" of the segment have been marked "0" and "1." Since the asterisked, *, point divides the segment into two equal parts,

we call it the **midpoint** and mark it "$\frac{1}{2}$."

(b)

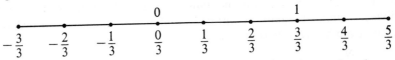

The two points marked "0" and "1" on the segment above suggest simple names for the unmarked points. The two points between 0 and 1 divide the marked segment into three equal parts so that counting from 0 to the right we have $\frac{1}{3}, \frac{2}{3}$, and so on. Each of the short equal segments is $\frac{1}{3}$ of the segment marked "0" to "1." We count positive to the right and negative to the left and obtain the following scale:

$$-\frac{3}{3} \quad -\frac{2}{3} \quad -\frac{1}{3} \quad \frac{0}{3} \quad \frac{1}{3} \quad \frac{2}{3} \quad \frac{3}{3} \quad \frac{4}{3} \quad \frac{5}{3}$$

If we begin with a line and mark a segment off on it, naming the end points "0" and "1," then we can use this basic marked segment, called the **unit segment**, to determine further division points along the line. Beginning with the unit segment, we mark off points which can be named by the integers

$$\xleftarrow{\qquad} \quad -1 \quad\quad 0 \quad\quad 1 \quad\quad 2 \quad \xrightarrow{\qquad}$$

The integers can be thought of as rational numbers by writing $-1 = -\frac{1}{1}, 0 = \frac{0}{1}, 1 = \frac{1}{1}, 2 = \frac{2}{1}$, and so on. That is, every integer can be thought of as a rational number with denominator 1 and with a numerator equal to the integer.

Now if we divide each unit segment into two equal parts, we can mark the division points beginning with $0 \frac{0}{2}, \frac{1}{2}, \frac{2}{2}, \frac{3}{2}$, and so on, to the right and $\frac{-1}{2}, \frac{-2}{2}, \frac{-3}{2}$, and so on, to the left. Starting over, if we divide each unit segment into three equal parts, we obtain division points for $\frac{0}{3}, \frac{1}{3}, \frac{2}{3}, \frac{3}{3}, \frac{4}{3}$, and so on, to the right beginning with 0. To the left we have $\frac{-1}{3}, \frac{-2}{3}, \frac{-3}{3}$, and so on, for the division points. The process can be repeated with 4, 5, 6, and so on, equal divisions of the unit segments. In this way we obtain a scale with the various rational numerals marked on it. A line which is thought of as marked off in this way is often called a **rational number line** (Figure 56).

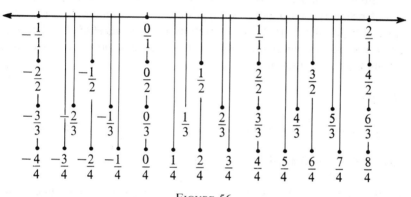

FIGURE 56

6.1.2 From our examples and discussion it should be evident that many rational numerals (fractions) name the same rational number. For example, $\frac{1}{2}, \frac{2}{4}, \frac{3}{6}, \frac{4}{8}, \frac{5}{10}, \frac{6}{12}$, and so on, all name the same rational number. We ask, "When do two fractions name the same rational number?"

Since a fraction $\frac{N}{D} = R$ means $N = R \times D$, let us consider two equal fractions $\frac{A}{B} = R$ and $\frac{P}{Q} = R$. But if $\frac{A}{B} = \frac{P}{Q}$, then $A = \frac{P}{Q} \times B = \frac{P \times B}{Q}$. Now we can write $\frac{P \times B}{Q} = A$ means $P \times B = A \times Q$. That is, if $\frac{A}{B} = \frac{P}{Q}$, then we must have $A \times Q = P \times B$. Since we can "reverse" our argument, we will say that two fractions are equal and write $\frac{A}{B} = \frac{P}{Q}$ whenever $A \times Q = P \times B$.

Examples.

(a) $\frac{1}{2} = \frac{4}{8}$ since $1 \times 8 = 4 \times 2$ (b) $\frac{42}{48} = \frac{7}{8}$ since $42 \times 8 = 7 \times 48$

(c) $\frac{72}{54} = \frac{8}{6}$ since $72 \times 6 = 8 \times 54$ (d) $\frac{8}{6} = \frac{4}{3}$ since $8 \times 3 = 4 \times 6$.

Among a set of equal fractions we will call the fraction with numerator and denominator relatively prime the **reduced**† fraction of the set. That is, when all of the common factors of the numerator and denominator have been eliminated from a fraction, the fraction will be said to be **reduced**. For example, $\frac{1}{2}$ in Example (a) above; $\frac{7}{8}$ in (b); and $\frac{4}{3}$ in (d). But neither of the fractions in Example (c) above are reduced. A fundamental property of fractions is suggested here: common factors in the numerator and denominator of a fraction may be **cancelled**. By the same token, a common factor may also be introduced to both numerator and denominator of a fraction.

Examples.

(a) Reduce $\frac{9}{6}$. We write $\frac{9}{6} = \frac{3 \times 3}{2 \times 3} = \frac{3}{2}$. Since 3 and 2 have no common factors, $\frac{3}{2}$ is the reduced fraction.

(b) Reduce $\frac{36}{60}$. We have $\frac{36}{60} = \frac{2 \times 2 \times 3 \times 3}{2 \times 2 \times 3 \times 5} = \frac{3}{5}$ is the reduced fraction equal to $\frac{36}{60}$.

(c) Write $\frac{4}{7}$ as a fraction with a denominator equal to 35. We begin by writing $\frac{4}{7} = \frac{N}{35}$. But then $N = \frac{4}{7} \times 35 = \frac{4 \times 35}{7} = \frac{4 \times 5 \times 7}{7} = 4 \times 5 = 20$. Thus, $\frac{4}{7} = \frac{20}{35}$. Notice that $\frac{4}{7} = \frac{4 \times 5}{7 \times 5} = \frac{20}{35}$.

(d) Write $\frac{3}{8}$ as a fraction with numerator equal to 18. Since $18 = 3 \times 6$ we have $\frac{3}{8} = \frac{3 \times 6}{8 \times 6} = \frac{18}{48}$.

The **fundamental property of the rational numbers** used above is of such importance that it has been called the "Golden Rule" of fractions.

For $\frac{A}{B}$ a fraction and $C \neq 0$, we have $\frac{A \times C}{B \times C} = \frac{A}{B}$.

† Corresponding to "reduced to lowest terms" or "reduced to lowest form."

Practice 1.

1. Use a fraction to describe the shaded portion of each of the following figures (Figure 57) as compared to the "whole."

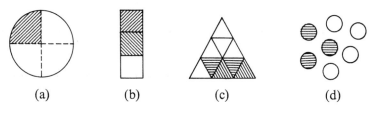

| (a) | (b) | (c) | (d) |

FIGURE 57

2. What fractional part of the set of dots shown in Figure 58 is bounded by (inside of)

(a) The circle?   (b) The rectangle?   (c) The oval (ellipse)?

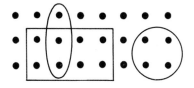

FIGURE 58

3. Figure 59 represents actual scales for inches and centimeters. What fractional part of an inch is a centimeter (approximately)?

Inches (in.)

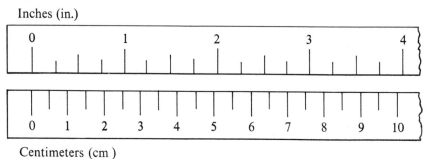

Centimeters (cm)

FIGURE 59

4. If the distance from San Francisco to New York is 2,800 miles and the distance from San Francisco to Denver is about 1,000 miles,

then what fraction of the distance from San Francisco to New York is Denver from San Francisco? From New York?

5. Copy and mark the points on the following scales with reduced fractions (numerals).

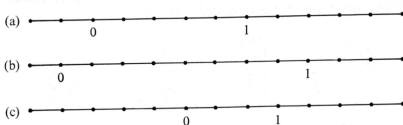

(a)

0   1

(b)

0   1

(c)

0   1

6. Supply the missing numerator or denominator N in each of the following:

(a) $\frac{3}{4} = \frac{N}{20}$ (b) $\frac{N}{5} = \frac{27}{45}$ (c) $\frac{1}{N} = \frac{8}{40}$ (d) $\frac{21}{28} = \frac{3}{N}$

(e) $\frac{5}{7} = \frac{N}{49}$ (f) $\frac{2}{3} = \frac{12}{N}$ (g) $\frac{1}{6} = \frac{N}{48}$ (h) $\frac{N}{12} = \frac{18}{36}$

(i) $\frac{7}{10} = \frac{N}{100}$ (j) $\frac{15}{N} = \frac{3}{5}$.

7. Reduce the following fractions.

(a) $\frac{2}{6}$ (b) $\frac{6}{8}$ (c) $\frac{9}{27}$ (d) $\frac{10}{15}$ (e) $\frac{8}{32}$ (f) $\frac{12}{60}$

(g) $\frac{4}{40}$ (h) $\frac{18}{48}$ (i) $\frac{42}{70}$ (j) $\frac{25}{55}$ (k) $\frac{6}{10}$ (l) $\frac{110}{440}$.

8. Write the following fractions with numerators and denominators expressed as products of primes, then reduce.

(a) $\frac{12}{18}$ (b) $\frac{30}{105}$ (c) $\frac{42}{70}$ (d) $\frac{315}{350}$ (e) $\frac{250}{525}$ (f) $\frac{700}{2205}$.

9. Express with denominators as indicated:

(a) $\frac{3}{7}$ with denominator 28   (b) $\frac{6}{9}$ with denominator 27

(c) $\frac{5}{8}$ with denominator 40   (d) $\frac{12}{16}$ with denominator 8

(e) $\frac{10}{15}$ with denominator 3   (f) $\frac{1}{4}$ with denominator 28.

10. Express the following pairs of fractions with the same common denominators as indicated:

(a) $\frac{1}{2}$ and $\frac{2}{3}$ with 6   (b) $\frac{1}{3}$ and $\frac{3}{4}$ with 12

(c) $\frac{3}{5}$ and $\frac{3}{4}$ with 20   (d) $\frac{5}{6}$ and $\frac{1}{4}$ with 12

(e) $\frac{1}{6}$ and $\frac{2}{9}$ with 18   (f) $\frac{7}{12}$ and $\frac{5}{8}$ with 24.

Answers.

1. (a) $\frac{1}{4}$ (b) $\frac{2}{3}$ (c) $\frac{4}{9}$ (d) $\frac{3}{7}$.

2. (a) $\frac{4}{24} = \frac{1}{6}$ (b) $\frac{8}{24} = \frac{1}{3}$ (c) $\frac{3}{24} = \frac{1}{8}$.

3. Approximately $\frac{2}{5}$.

4. $\frac{1000}{2800} = \frac{5}{14}$; $\frac{9}{14}$ from New York.

5. (a)

$$-\frac{2}{5} \quad -\frac{1}{5} \quad 0 \quad \frac{1}{5} \quad \frac{2}{5} \quad \frac{3}{5} \quad \frac{4}{5} \quad 1 \quad \frac{6}{5} \quad \frac{7}{5} \quad \frac{8}{5} \quad \frac{9}{5} \quad 2$$

(b)

$$-\frac{1}{8} \quad 0 \quad \frac{1}{8} \quad \frac{1}{4} \quad \frac{3}{8} \quad \frac{1}{2} \quad \frac{5}{8} \quad \frac{3}{4} \quad \frac{7}{8} \quad 1 \quad \frac{9}{8} \quad \frac{5}{4} \quad \frac{11}{8}$$

(c)

$$-\frac{5}{3} \quad -\frac{4}{3} \quad -1 \quad -\frac{2}{3} \quad -\frac{1}{3} \quad 0 \quad \frac{1}{3} \quad \frac{2}{3} \quad 1 \quad \frac{4}{3} \quad \frac{5}{3} \quad 2 \quad \frac{7}{3}$$

6. (a) 15   (b) 3   (c) 5   (d) 4   (e) 35
   (f) 18   (g) 8   (h) 6   (i) 70   (j) 25.

7. (a) $\frac{1}{3}$ (b) $\frac{3}{4}$ (c) $\frac{1}{3}$ (d) $\frac{2}{3}$ (e) $\frac{1}{4}$ (f) $\frac{1}{5}$

   (g) $\frac{1}{10}$ (h) $\frac{3}{8}$ (i) $\frac{3}{5}$ (j) $\frac{5}{11}$ (k) $\frac{3}{5}$ (l) $\frac{1}{4}$.

8. (a) $\frac{12}{18} = \frac{2 \times 2 \times 3}{2 \times 3 \times 3} = \frac{2}{3}$ (b) $\frac{30}{105} = \frac{2 \times 3 \times 5}{3 \times 5 \times 7} = \frac{2}{7}$

   (c) $\frac{42}{70} = \frac{2 \times 3 \times 7}{2 \times 5 \times 7} = \frac{3}{5}$ (d) $\frac{315}{350} = \frac{3 \times 3 \times 5 \times 7}{2 \times 5 \times 5 \times 7} = \frac{9}{10}$

   (e) $\frac{250}{525} = \frac{2 \times 5 \times 5 \times 5}{3 \times 5 \times 5 \times 7} = \frac{10}{21}$ (f) $\frac{700}{2205} = \frac{2 \times 2 \times 5 \times 5 \times 7}{3 \times 3 \times 5 \times 7 \times 7} = \frac{20}{63}$.

9. (a) $\frac{12}{28}$ (b) $\frac{18}{27}$ (c) $\frac{25}{40}$ (d) $\frac{6}{8}$ (e) $\frac{2}{3}$ (f) $\frac{7}{28}$.

10. (a) $\frac{3}{6}$ and $\frac{4}{6}$ (b) $\frac{4}{12}$ and $\frac{9}{12}$ (c) $\frac{12}{20}$ and $\frac{15}{20}$

    (d) $\frac{10}{12}$ and $\frac{3}{12}$ (e) $\frac{3}{18}$ and $\frac{4}{18}$ (f) $\frac{14}{24}$ and $\frac{15}{24}$.

6.1.3   In working with fractions it is convenient to distinguish between various types of fractions. For example, reduced fractions such as $\frac{1}{2}, \frac{1}{3}, \frac{2}{3}$, and so forth, as contrasted to fractions which can be reduced such as $\frac{2}{4}, \frac{4}{12}, \frac{12}{18}$, and so forth. Another useful distinction is that between fractions with numerators smaller than the denominators as contrasted with fractions with numerators equal to or greater than their denominators. For example; $\frac{2}{3}$ and $\frac{3}{7}$ as distinct from $\frac{3}{3}, \frac{4}{3}, \frac{7}{3}$, and so forth. For any fraction $\frac{N}{D}$, if the value of N is properly between $-D$ and D, then we say that $\frac{N}{D}$ is a **proper fraction**. If a fraction is not proper, we say that it is an **improper fraction**.

Examples.

Proper fractions: $\frac{5}{8}, -\frac{7}{9}, \frac{-4}{5}, \frac{1}{-2}, \frac{-3}{-4}, \frac{23}{32}$.

Improper fractions: $\frac{8}{5}, -\frac{6}{6}, \frac{-9}{4}, \frac{13}{-2}, \frac{-7}{-3}, \frac{54}{53}$.

Notice that we compare the **absolute values** of the numerator and denominator of a fraction to determine whether the fraction is proper or improper. That is, for any fraction, if the absolute value of the numerator is less than the absolute value of the denominator, then the fraction is proper. Otherwise it is an improper fraction. A proper fraction names a rational number between -1 and 1. Proper and improper fractions can be easily indicated on a rational number line as shown in Figure 60. Only a few fractions have been marked on the line.

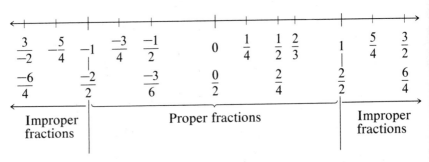

FIGURE 60

The terms proper and improper fractions refer to distinct sets of rational numbers. On the other hand, the term reduced fraction refers to the form of the numeral used to name a rational number. The segment of the rational number line shown in Figure 61 suggests the idea underlying the naming of a reduced fraction. The reduced fractions are $\frac{2}{3}, \frac{5}{4}$, and $\frac{3}{2}$ at the tops of the columns.

The proper fractions in Figure 61 are those in the left-hand column below $\frac{2}{3}$. Proper fractions express the remainder term in the division algorithm. Improper fractions, however, express indicated divisions.

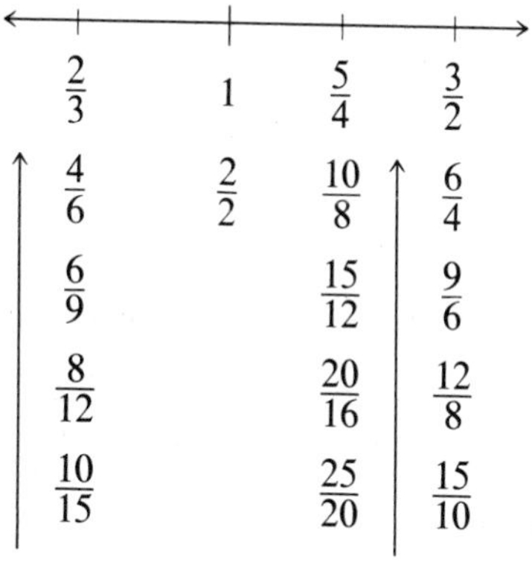

$$\frac{2}{3} \quad 1 \quad \frac{5}{4} \quad \frac{3}{2}$$

$$\frac{4}{6} \quad \frac{2}{2} \quad \frac{10}{8} \quad \frac{6}{4}$$

$$\frac{6}{9} \quad \quad \frac{15}{12} \quad \frac{9}{6}$$

$$\frac{8}{12} \quad \quad \frac{20}{16} \quad \frac{12}{8}$$

$$\frac{10}{15} \quad \quad \frac{25}{20} \quad \frac{15}{10}$$

FIGURE 61

If we "expand" an improper fraction, we obtain an integer (the quotient) plus a proper fraction. For example, $\frac{9}{4} = 2 + \frac{1}{4}$. Historically, $2 + \frac{1}{4}$ has been written $2\frac{1}{4}$. That is, $\frac{9}{4} = 2\frac{1}{4}$. When improper fractions are written as the sum of an integer and a proper fraction, for example, $2\frac{1}{4}$, we call it a **mixed fraction**. Sometimes a mixed fraction is called a **mixed number** meaning the sum of an integer and a fraction.

Examples.

   (a) Proper fractions: $\frac{-3}{4}, \frac{-2}{6}, \frac{0}{1}, \frac{1}{3}, \frac{12}{16}, \frac{8}{9}$.

   (b) Improper fractions: $\frac{-4}{2}, \frac{-15}{9}, \frac{-1}{1}, \frac{2}{2}, \frac{5}{3}, \frac{12}{4}$.

(c) Mixed fractions: $-4\frac{2}{3}, -1\frac{3}{5}, 1\frac{1}{2}, 3\frac{3}{4}, 27\frac{5}{8}, 30\frac{9}{10}$.

6.1.4   As with the natural numbers and integers, the rational numbers can be ordered. However, the **serial order** obtained with the rational numbers is quite different. Every integer has one definite immediate predecessor and one definite immediate successor. A rational number, on the other hand, has no definite immediate predecessor or definite immediate successor. That is, we can always find a distinct rational number between any two distinct rational numbers. This is easily seen by applying the fundamental property of the rational numbers to two distinct rational numbers. For example, given $\frac{7}{8}$ and $\frac{8}{9}$ we can write the

equal fractions $\frac{7}{8} = \frac{7 \times 9 \times 2}{8 \times 9 \times 2} = \frac{126}{144}$ and $\frac{8}{9} = \frac{8 \times 8 \times 2}{9 \times 8 \times 2} = \frac{128}{144}$ so that $\frac{127}{144}$

is clearly a distinct rational number between $\frac{7}{8}$ and $\frac{8}{9}$. Because of this distinctive property the rational numbers are said to be "**dense.**"

To compare or combine two or more fractions, it is helpful to write them with **common denominators**. For example, we can compare $\frac{2}{3}$ and $\frac{3}{4}$ by first finding a common denominator. The **least common denominator** is the lowest common multiple of the denominators; for 3 and 4 we have $3 \times 4 = 12$. Thus we can write $\frac{2}{3} = \frac{N}{12}$ and $\frac{3}{4} = \frac{M}{12}$ to obtain $\frac{2}{3} = \frac{8}{12}$ and $\frac{3}{4} = \frac{9}{12}$. Now it is clear that $\frac{2}{3}$ is $\frac{1}{12}$ less than $\frac{3}{4}$. Of course, any multiple of the LCM 12 would have done for a common denominator for the two fractions. For example, $\frac{24}{36}$ and $\frac{27}{36}$ would have sufficed to compare the fractions. However, to minimize computations, it is often helpful to look for the least common denominator (LCD).

Examples.

(a) To express the fractions $\frac{3}{4}, \frac{5}{6},$ and $\frac{7}{9}$ so that they have the same least common denominator.

First we look for the lowest common multiple of the three denominators: $4 = 2 \times 2$, $6 = 2 \times 3$, and $9 = 3 \times 3$. Thus, $2 \times 2 \times 3 \times 3 = 36$ is the least common denominator for the three fractions. Next, we apply the fundamental property of the rational numbers to determine the numerators for the fractions: $\frac{3}{4} = \frac{A}{36}, \frac{5}{6} = \frac{B}{36}, \frac{7}{9} = \frac{C}{36}$. Since $4 \times 9 = 36$, we have $3 \times 9 = 27 = A$. Since $6 \times 6 = 36$, we have $5 \times 6 = 30 = B$. Since $9 \times 4 = 36$, we have $7 \times 4 = 28 = C$. Now we can write

$$\frac{3}{4} = \frac{3 \times 9}{4 \times 9} = \frac{27}{36}, \frac{5}{6} = \frac{5 \times 6}{6 \times 6} = \frac{30}{36}, \frac{7}{9} = \frac{7 \times 4}{9 \times 4} = \frac{28}{36}.$$

Thus the required fractions are $\frac{27}{36}, \frac{30}{36},$ and $\frac{28}{36}$ (Figure 62).

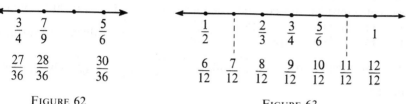

| FIGURE 62 | FIGURE 63 |

(b) To order the following set of rational numbers from smallest to largest: $\frac{5}{6}, \frac{1}{2}, \frac{2}{3}, \frac{3}{4}$.

To compare the fractions we first find the least common denominator. The LCD will be the lowest common multiple of the set of denominators. Thus, since the LCM of 6, 2, 3, and 4 is 12, we have

$$\frac{5}{6} = \frac{5 \times 2}{6 \times 2} = \frac{10}{12}, \frac{1}{2} = \frac{1 \times 6}{2 \times 6} = \frac{6}{12}, \frac{2}{3} = \frac{2 \times 4}{3 \times 4} = \frac{8}{12}, \text{ and } \frac{3}{4} = \frac{3 \times 3}{4 \times 3} = \frac{9}{12}.$$

Now the fractions are easily ordered by noting their numerators, $\frac{6}{12}$, $\frac{8}{12}, \frac{9}{12}, \frac{10}{12}$ or, in terms of the given fractions, $\frac{1}{2}, \frac{2}{3}, \frac{3}{4}, \frac{5}{6}$ (Figure 63).

(c) To order $\frac{5}{8}, \frac{11}{12}, \frac{2}{9}, \frac{7}{18}, \frac{2}{6},$ and $\frac{3}{4}$ from smallest to largest.

Since the LCM of 8, 12, 9, 18, 6, and 4 is 72, we have $\frac{5}{8} = \frac{5 \times 9}{8 \times 9} = \frac{45}{72}$,

$$\frac{11}{12} = \frac{11 \times 6}{12 \times 6} = \frac{66}{72}, \frac{2}{9} = \frac{2 \times 8}{9 \times 8} = \frac{16}{72}, \frac{7}{18} = \frac{7 \times 4}{18 \times 4} = \frac{28}{72}, \frac{2}{6} = \frac{2 \times 12}{6 \times 12} = \frac{24}{72},$$

and $\frac{3}{4} = \frac{3 \times 18}{4 \times 18} = \frac{54}{72}$ (Figure 64).

$\frac{2}{9}$	$\frac{2}{6}$	$\frac{7}{18}$	$\frac{5}{8}$	$\frac{3}{4}$	$\frac{11}{12}$
$\frac{16}{72}$	$\frac{24}{72}$	$\frac{28}{72}$	$\frac{45}{72}$	$\frac{54}{72}$	$\frac{66}{72}$

FIGURE 64

Thus, from smallest to largest we have

$$\frac{2}{9}, \frac{2}{6}, \frac{7}{18}, \frac{5}{8}, \frac{3}{4}, \frac{11}{12}.$$

(d) Find at least one distinct rational number between $\frac{11}{15}$ and $\frac{15}{18}$.

We change the form by multiplying both numerator and denominator of each fraction by a factor, which results in a multiple of the least common denominator of the two fractions. Since $15 = 3 \times 5$ and $18 = 3 \times 6$ we can consider the common denominator $3 \times 5 \times 6 = 90$ to obtain $\frac{11}{15} = \frac{11 \times 6}{15 \times 6} = \frac{66}{90}$ and $\frac{15}{18} = \frac{15 \times 5}{18 \times 5} = \frac{75}{90}$. We can now easily name 8 distinct rational numbers between $\frac{11}{15}$ and $\frac{15}{18}$: $\frac{67}{90}, \frac{68}{90}, \frac{69}{90}, \dots, \frac{73}{90}$, and $\frac{74}{90}$ (Figure 65).

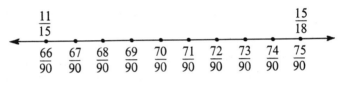

FIGURE 65

(e) Find a rational number between $\frac{14}{17}$ and $\frac{15}{17}$. Now find a distinct rational number between the pairs of resulting rational numbers.

Observe that $\frac{14}{17} = \frac{28}{34}$ and $\frac{15}{17} = \frac{30}{34}$ so that $\frac{14}{17} < \frac{29}{34} < \frac{15}{17}$.

Now, we can also write $\frac{56}{68} < \frac{57}{68} < \frac{58}{68} < \frac{59}{68} < \frac{60}{68}$.

Notice our convenient use of the inequality sign to indicate the ordering of the rational numbers (Figure 66).

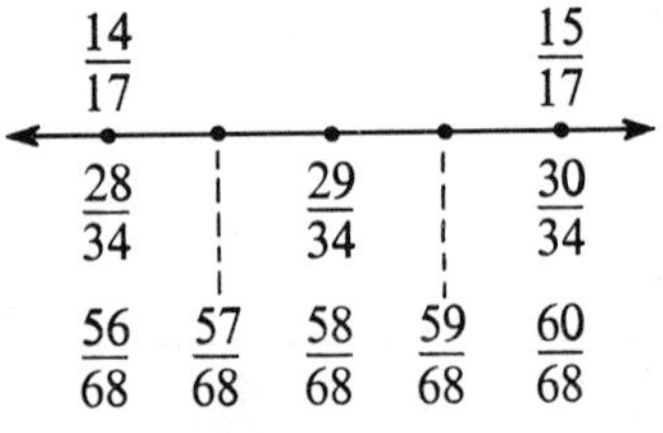

FIGURE 66

6.1.5   Only brief note has been made of the negative rational numbers and the effect of the negative sign on the fraction. To examine this situation, we refer again to the meaning of a rational number:

$$\frac{N}{D} = R \text{ means the same thing as } N = R \times D, \text{ where}$$

N and D are integers with $D \neq 0$.

It should be quite clear that if $N = 0$, then the rational number R must also equal 0. That is, $\frac{0}{D} = 0$ for all $D \neq 0$. By our construction of the rational numbers, we also have that if $N < 0$ and $D > 0$, then $R < 0$. That is, if the numerator of a fraction is negative and the denominator is positive, then the fraction must be negative. For example, $\frac{-2}{3} = R < 0$.

If we write $\frac{2}{-3} = R$, we have $2 = (-3)R$ and R must be negative from our discussion of products. Thus, if $N > 0$ and $D < 0$, we have $R < 0$. That is, if the numerator of a fraction is positive and the denominator is negative, then the fraction is negative. If both numerator and denominator of a fraction are negative, then the fraction is positive. For example, $\frac{-2}{-3} = R$ means $-2 = (-3)R$ so that $R > 0$. To indicate a negative fraction, we prefix a negative sign to it: $-\frac{2}{3}$. The following examples illustrate the possibilities.

Examples.

(a) $\dfrac{-5}{8} = \dfrac{5}{-8} = -\dfrac{5}{8} = -\dfrac{-5}{-8} < 0$ (negative).

(b) $\dfrac{3}{7} = \dfrac{-3}{-7} = -\dfrac{-3}{7} = -\dfrac{3}{-7} > 0$ (positive).

Note that if an odd number of negative signs appear, the rational number is negative and if an even number, including zero, of negative signs appear, the rational number is positive.

Practice 2.

1. Copy and complete the marking of the following scales.

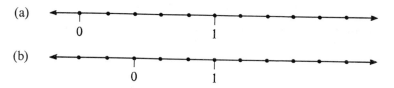

(a)   0   1

(b)   0   1

(c)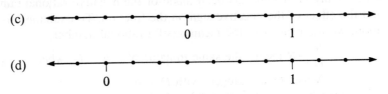

(d)

2. (a) Group the following fractions into sets of equal fractions.
   (b) Which of the fractions are reduced?

$$\frac{3}{7}, \frac{12}{15}, \frac{25}{20}, \frac{15}{9}, \frac{30}{18}, \frac{14}{8}, \frac{7}{4}, \frac{5}{3}, \frac{4}{5}, \frac{9}{21}, \frac{15}{35}, \frac{24}{30}, \frac{21}{49}, \frac{49}{28}, \frac{28}{35}, \frac{10}{6}.$$

   (c) Which of the fractions are proper, which are improper?

3. Reduce the following fractions.

   (a) $\frac{6}{9}$ (b) $\frac{4}{12}$ (c) $\frac{9}{15}$ (d) $\frac{8}{16}$ (e) $\frac{2}{8}$ (f) $\frac{6}{2}$

   (g) $\frac{30}{24}$ (h) $\frac{72}{27}$ (i) $\frac{42}{48}$ (j) $\frac{56}{77}$ (k) $\frac{24}{54}$ (l) $\frac{98}{14}.$

4. Reduce the following fractions.

   (a) $\frac{60}{84}$ (b) $\frac{96}{208}$ (c) $\frac{288}{420}$ (d) $\frac{486}{360}$ (e) $\frac{392}{84}$ (f) $\frac{182}{210}.$

5. Express the following pairs of fractions as fractions with a least common denominator (LCD).

   (a) $\frac{2}{3}, \frac{3}{5}$ (b) $\frac{1}{4}, \frac{5}{6}$ (c) $\frac{1}{2}, \frac{5}{8}$ (d) $\frac{4}{5}, \frac{7}{30}$ (e) $\frac{1}{6}, \frac{5}{9}$

   (f) $\frac{2}{7}, \frac{4}{15}$ (g) $\frac{3}{10}, \frac{7}{35}$ (h) $\frac{11}{12}, \frac{25}{42}$ (i) $\frac{7}{20}, \frac{5}{30}$ (j) $\frac{8}{21}, \frac{9}{35}.$

6. Express the following sets of fractions as fractions with a least common denominator (LCD).

   (a) $\frac{1}{2}, \frac{1}{3}, \frac{1}{4}$ (b) $\frac{2}{3}, \frac{3}{5}, \frac{5}{6}$ (c) $\frac{3}{4}, \frac{5}{7}, \frac{5}{8}$

   (d) $\frac{1}{2}, \frac{2}{3}, \frac{3}{4}, \frac{4}{5}$ (e) $\frac{4}{9}, \frac{5}{6}, \frac{7}{12}, \frac{11}{15}$ (f) $\frac{9}{14}, \frac{1}{18}, \frac{4}{21}, \frac{7}{24}.$

7. (a) Group the following fractions into proper and improper fractions.
   (b) Reduce all fractions if they are not already reduced.
   (c) Express the improper fractions as mixed fractions with reduced fractional parts.

$$\frac{6}{15}, \frac{5}{2}, \frac{7}{8}, \frac{20}{28}, \frac{45}{25}, \frac{8}{3}, \frac{9}{12}, \frac{49}{28}, \frac{24}{20}, \frac{14}{63}, \frac{5}{6}, \frac{18}{54}.$$

8. Order the following sets of fractions from smallest to largest.

   (a) $\frac{3}{4}, \frac{5}{8}, \frac{2}{3}, \frac{5}{6}, \frac{11}{16}, \frac{7}{12}$ (b) $\frac{2}{5}, \frac{1}{2}, \frac{1}{3}, \frac{3}{7}, \frac{5}{12}, \frac{7}{15}.$

9. Find at least one distinct rational number between each of the following pairs of rational numbers.

(a) $\dfrac{7}{16}, \dfrac{8}{15}$ (b) $\dfrac{10}{13}, \dfrac{11}{13}$ (c) $\dfrac{21}{25}, \dfrac{38}{45}$ (d) $\dfrac{3}{17}, \dfrac{5}{34}$.

10. (a) State whether the following fractions are positive or negative.

(b) Using only negative signs, write the three alternative forms for each of the following fractions.

$$\dfrac{7}{11}, \dfrac{-9}{15}, \dfrac{4}{-7}, \dfrac{-5}{-7}, \dfrac{6}{-5}, \dfrac{-8}{-9}, \dfrac{-9}{17}, \dfrac{3}{-4}.$$

Answers.

1. (a)

$$0 \quad \tfrac{1}{5} \quad \tfrac{2}{5} \quad \tfrac{3}{5} \quad \tfrac{4}{5} \quad 1 \quad \tfrac{6}{5} \quad \tfrac{7}{5} \quad \tfrac{8}{5} \quad \tfrac{9}{5} \quad 2$$

(b)

$$-\tfrac{2}{3} \quad -\tfrac{1}{3} \quad 0 \quad \tfrac{1}{3} \quad \tfrac{2}{3} \quad 1 \quad \tfrac{4}{3} \quad \tfrac{5}{3} \quad 2 \quad \tfrac{7}{3} \quad \tfrac{8}{3}$$

(c)

$$-1 \quad -\tfrac{3}{4} \quad -\tfrac{2}{4} \quad -\tfrac{1}{4} \quad 0 \quad \tfrac{1}{4} \quad \tfrac{2}{4} \quad \tfrac{3}{4} \quad 1 \quad \tfrac{5}{4} \quad \tfrac{6}{4}$$

(d)

$$-\tfrac{1}{7} \quad 0 \quad \tfrac{1}{7} \quad \tfrac{2}{7} \quad \tfrac{3}{7} \quad \tfrac{4}{7} \quad \tfrac{5}{7} \quad \tfrac{6}{7} \quad 1 \quad \tfrac{8}{7} \quad \tfrac{9}{7}$$

2. (a)

$\dfrac{3}{7}$	$\dfrac{4}{5}$	$\dfrac{7}{4}$	$\dfrac{5}{3}$
$\dfrac{9}{21}$	$\dfrac{12}{15}$	$\dfrac{14}{8}$	$\dfrac{15}{9}$
$\dfrac{15}{35}$	$\dfrac{24}{30}$	$\dfrac{35}{20}$	$\dfrac{30}{18}$
$\dfrac{21}{49}$	$\dfrac{28}{35}$	$\dfrac{49}{28}$	$\dfrac{10}{6}$

(The equal fractions are in columns.)

(b) $\dfrac{3}{7}, \dfrac{4}{5}, \dfrac{7}{4}, \dfrac{5}{3}$.

(c) The two left-hand columns are proper. The two right-hand columns are improper.

3. (a) $\dfrac{2}{3}$ (b) $\dfrac{1}{3}$ (c) $\dfrac{3}{5}$ (d) $\dfrac{1}{2}$ (e) $\dfrac{1}{4}$ (f) 3

(g) $\dfrac{5}{4}$　(h) $\dfrac{8}{3}$　(i) $\dfrac{7}{8}$　(j) $\dfrac{8}{11}$　(k) $\dfrac{4}{9}$　(l) 7.

4. (a) $\dfrac{5}{7}$　(b) $\dfrac{6}{13}$　(c) $\dfrac{24}{35}$　(d) $\dfrac{27}{20}$　(e) $\dfrac{14}{3}$　(f) $\dfrac{13}{15}$.

5. (a) $\dfrac{10}{15}, \dfrac{9}{15}$　(b) $\dfrac{3}{12}, \dfrac{10}{12}$　(c) $\dfrac{4}{8}, \dfrac{5}{8}$　(d) $\dfrac{24}{30}, \dfrac{7}{30}$　(e) $\dfrac{3}{18}, \dfrac{10}{18}$

　(f) $\dfrac{30}{105}, \dfrac{28}{105}$　(g) $\dfrac{21}{70}, \dfrac{14}{70}$　(h) $\dfrac{77}{84}, \dfrac{50}{84}$　(i) $\dfrac{21}{60}, \dfrac{10}{60}$

　(j) $\dfrac{40}{105}, \dfrac{27}{105}$.

6. (a) $\dfrac{6}{12}, \dfrac{4}{12}, \dfrac{3}{12}$　(b) $\dfrac{20}{30}, \dfrac{18}{30}, \dfrac{25}{30}$　(c) $\dfrac{42}{56}, \dfrac{40}{56}, \dfrac{35}{56}$

　(d) $\dfrac{30}{60}, \dfrac{40}{60}, \dfrac{45}{60}, \dfrac{48}{60}$　(e) $\dfrac{80}{180}, \dfrac{150}{180}, \dfrac{105}{180}, \dfrac{132}{180}$

　(f) $\dfrac{324}{504}, \dfrac{28}{504}, \dfrac{96}{504}, \dfrac{147}{504}$.

7. (a) Proper: $\dfrac{6}{15}, \dfrac{7}{8}, \dfrac{20}{28}, \dfrac{9}{12}, \dfrac{14}{63}, \dfrac{5}{6}, \dfrac{18}{54}$.

　(b) $\dfrac{6}{15} = \dfrac{2}{5}, \dfrac{20}{28} = \dfrac{5}{7}, \dfrac{45}{25} = \dfrac{9}{5}, \dfrac{9}{12} = \dfrac{3}{4}, \dfrac{49}{28} = \dfrac{7}{4}, \dfrac{24}{20} = \dfrac{6}{5}, \dfrac{14}{63} = \dfrac{2}{9}, \dfrac{18}{54} = \dfrac{1}{3}$.

　(c) $\dfrac{5}{2} = 2\dfrac{1}{2}, \dfrac{9}{5} = 1\dfrac{4}{5}, \dfrac{8}{3} = 2\dfrac{2}{3}, \dfrac{7}{4} = 1\dfrac{3}{4}, \dfrac{6}{5} = 1\dfrac{1}{5}$.

8. (a) $\dfrac{7}{12}, \dfrac{5}{8}, \dfrac{2}{3}, \dfrac{11}{16}, \dfrac{3}{4}, \dfrac{5}{6}$ (LCD = 48).

　(b) $\dfrac{1}{3}, \dfrac{2}{5}, \dfrac{5}{12}, \dfrac{3}{7}, \dfrac{7}{15}, \dfrac{1}{2}$ (LCD = 420).

9. (a) $\dfrac{105}{240} < \dfrac{110}{240} < \dfrac{128}{240}$　(b) $\dfrac{20}{26} < \dfrac{21}{26} < \dfrac{22}{26}$

　(c) $\dfrac{378}{450} < \dfrac{379}{450} < \dfrac{380}{450}$　(d) $\dfrac{12}{68} > \dfrac{11}{68} > \dfrac{10}{68}$. (Note: there are many

other possible answers to each part.)

10. $\dfrac{7}{11} = -\dfrac{-7}{11} = -\dfrac{7}{-11} = \dfrac{-7}{-11}$ positive.

　$\dfrac{-9}{15} = -\dfrac{9}{15} = \dfrac{9}{-15} = -\dfrac{-9}{-15}$ negative.

　$-\dfrac{4}{5} = \dfrac{-4}{5} = \dfrac{4}{-5} = -\dfrac{-4}{-5}$ negative.

　$\dfrac{-5}{-7} = \dfrac{5}{7} = -\dfrac{-5}{7} = -\dfrac{5}{-7}$ positive.

$$\frac{6}{-5} = \frac{-6}{5} = -\frac{-6}{-5} = -\frac{6}{5} \text{ negative.}$$

$$-\frac{-8}{-9} = -\frac{8}{9} = \frac{-8}{9} = \frac{8}{-9} \text{ negative.}$$

$$-\frac{-9}{17} = \frac{9}{17} = -\frac{9}{-17} = \frac{-9}{-17} \text{ positive.}$$

$$-\frac{3}{-4} = -\frac{-3}{4} = \frac{-3}{-4} = \frac{3}{4} \text{ positive.}$$

Exercises

1. If we cut a cake into 12 equal pieces, we can describe the relationship between a piece of cake and the whole cake with a _____ _____. The idea of comparing two quantities in this way is called a _____. The comparison can be written in a fractional form as _____.

2. What part of a dollar is a nickel? A quarter?

3. In using the _____ form $\frac{N}{D}$ to name a rational number, N is called the _____ and D the _____. A rational number is thus the indicated _____ (or ratio) of _____ _____.

4. Use a fraction to describe the shaded portion of each of the following figures (Figure 67).

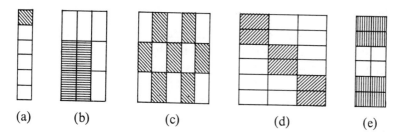

(a)   (b)   (c)   (d)   (e)

FIGURE 67

5. What fractional part of the set of dots shown in Figure 68 is bounded by (inside of)

    (a) the small circle?   (b) the large circle?
    (c) the triangle?   (d) the large circle but outside
    (e) the small circle and   the small circle?
    the triangle?

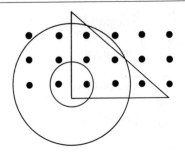

FIGURE 68

6. Use a fraction to compare the following pairs of line segments.

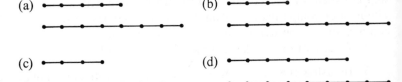

(a)

(b)

(c)

(d)

7. A twelve-foot long seesaw (teeter-totter) is supported five feet from one end. Use a fraction to compare the two parts into which the seesaw is divided by the support.

8. Carefully construct a rational number line for the rational numbers R such that $0 \le R \le 2$ and $R = \dfrac{N}{D}$ with $0 \le N \le 2D$ and $1 \le D \le 6$.

9. For the rational numbers of Exercise 8 above:
   (a) How many distinct rational numbers are named?
   (b) Which of the fractions are reduced?
   (c) Which of the rational numbers are proper?
   (d) Which of the rational numbers are improper?
   (e) Express the improper fractions as mixed fractions.

10. Reduce the following fractions:

   (a) $\dfrac{90}{819}$ (b) $\dfrac{504}{924}$ (c) $\dfrac{245}{105}$ (d) $\dfrac{1365}{1617}$ (e) $\dfrac{2475}{1785}$.

11. Express each of the following sets of fractions as fractions with a least common denominator (LCD).

   (a) $\dfrac{2}{3}, \dfrac{5}{6}$ (b) $\dfrac{3}{4}, \dfrac{1}{6}$ (c) $\dfrac{7}{12}, \dfrac{8}{15}$ (d) $\dfrac{6}{18}, \dfrac{5}{6}$ (e) $\dfrac{9}{10}, \dfrac{7}{18}$.

12. Express each of the following sets of fractions as fractions with a least common denominator.

   (a) $\dfrac{4}{5}, \dfrac{4}{9}, \dfrac{4}{15}$ (b) $\dfrac{5}{6}, \dfrac{7}{15}, \dfrac{13}{25}$ (c) $\dfrac{1}{8}, \dfrac{1}{9}, \dfrac{1}{12}, \dfrac{1}{15}$.

13. Reduce the following fractions and express the improper fractions as mixed fractions.

(a) $\dfrac{210}{357}$ (b) $\dfrac{476}{110}$ (c) $\dfrac{882}{357}$ (d) $\dfrac{363}{686}$ (e) $\dfrac{1375}{429}$.

14. Order the following sets of fractions from smallest to largest.

(a) $\dfrac{4}{9}, \dfrac{2}{3}, \dfrac{5}{12}, \dfrac{7}{18}, \dfrac{17}{36}$ (b) $\dfrac{4}{21}, \dfrac{17}{84}, \dfrac{5}{28}, \dfrac{1}{6}, \dfrac{3}{14}$.

15. Find the one rational number midway between each of the following pairs of rational numbers.

(a) $\dfrac{2}{5}, \dfrac{8}{15}$ (b) $\dfrac{1}{2}, \dfrac{3}{5}$ (c) $\dfrac{5}{9}, \dfrac{4}{7}$ (d) $\dfrac{2}{7}, \dfrac{5}{7}$ (e) $\dfrac{5}{9}, \dfrac{11}{12}$.

Answers.

1. rational number; ratio; $\dfrac{1}{12}$.

2. $\dfrac{1}{20}; \dfrac{1}{4}$.

3. fractional, numerator, denominator, quotient, two integers.

4. (a) $\dfrac{1}{6}$ (b) $\dfrac{4}{9}$ (c) $\dfrac{7}{15}$ (d) $\dfrac{6}{18} = \dfrac{1}{3}$ (e) $\dfrac{8}{12} = \dfrac{2}{3}$.

5. (a) $\dfrac{2}{18} = \dfrac{1}{9}$ (b) $\dfrac{10}{18} = \dfrac{5}{9}$ (c) $\dfrac{6}{18} = \dfrac{1}{3}$ (d) $\dfrac{8}{18} = \dfrac{4}{9}$ (e) $\dfrac{1}{18}$.

6. (a) $\dfrac{4}{7}$ (b) $\dfrac{3}{8}$ (c) $\dfrac{3}{6} = \dfrac{1}{2}$ (d) $\dfrac{6}{8} = \dfrac{3}{4}$.

7. $\dfrac{5}{7}$.

8.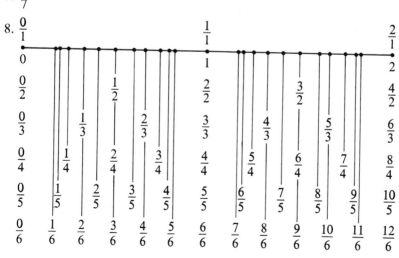

FIGURE 69

9. (a) 25.   (b) Those appearing at the tops of the columns below the line, for example, $0, \frac{1}{4}, \frac{1}{3}, \frac{2}{3}$, and so forth.   (c) Those to the left of 1, for example, $0, \frac{1}{4}, \frac{2}{3}$ $\left(\text{but not } \frac{3}{3}, \frac{4}{3}, \text{ and so forth}\right)$.   (d) Those to the right of and including 1, for example, $\frac{3}{3}, \frac{4}{3}$, and so forth. (Those which are not proper.)   (e) $1 = 1, \frac{7}{6} = 1\frac{1}{6}, \frac{6}{5} = 1\frac{1}{5}, \frac{5}{4} = 1\frac{1}{4}, \frac{4}{3} = 1\frac{1}{3}, \frac{7}{5} = 1\frac{2}{5}, \frac{3}{2} = 1\frac{1}{2}, \frac{8}{5} = 1\frac{3}{5}, \frac{5}{3} = 1\frac{2}{3}, \frac{7}{4} = 1\frac{3}{4}, \frac{9}{5} = 1\frac{4}{5}, \frac{11}{6} = 1\frac{5}{6}, 2 = 2.$

10. (a) $\frac{10}{91}$ (b) $\frac{6}{11}$ (c) $\frac{7}{3}$ (d) $\frac{65}{77}$ (e) $\frac{165}{119}$.

11. (a) $\frac{4}{6}, \frac{5}{6}$ (b) $\frac{9}{12}, \frac{2}{12}$ (c) $\frac{35}{60}, \frac{32}{60}$ (d) $\frac{2}{6}, \frac{5}{6}$ (e) $\frac{81}{90}, \frac{35}{90}$.

12. (a) $\frac{36}{45}, \frac{20}{45}, \frac{12}{45}$ (b) $\frac{125}{150}, \frac{70}{150}, \frac{78}{150}$ (c) $\frac{45}{360}, \frac{40}{360}, \frac{30}{360}, \frac{24}{360}$.

13. (a) $\frac{10}{17}$ (b) $\frac{238}{55} = 4\frac{18}{55}$ (c) $\frac{42}{17} = 2\frac{8}{17}$ (d) $\frac{363}{686}$

   (e) $\frac{125}{39} = 3\frac{8}{39}$.

14. (a) $\frac{7}{18}, \frac{5}{12}, \frac{4}{9}, \frac{17}{36}, \frac{2}{3}$ (b) $\frac{1}{6}, \frac{5}{28}, \frac{4}{21}, \frac{17}{84}, \frac{3}{14}$.

15. (a) $\frac{7}{15}$ (b) $\frac{11}{20}$ (c) $\frac{71}{126}$ (d) $\frac{7}{14}$ (e) $\frac{53}{72}$.

6.2 Products and Quotients

6.2.1 Historically, the difficulties of working with fractions were avoided in three ways: by restricting the numerators of fractions to unity; by computing with simple multiples of proper fractions only; and by restricting the denominators to certain multiples of a single positive integer. An early approach to our modern form of working with fractions dates to a Greek, Diophantus of Alexandria (about 250 to 275 A.D.), who, in a work called the *Arithmetica*, wrote fractions with the denominator over the numerator.

As we have seen, practical necessity leads us to the idea of rational numbers. However, our mathematical language offers the tools for developing and extending the usefulness of these ideas. Three properties used in our discussion of division with integers are of central importance to our understanding of the manipulations with rational numbers. Thus, we repeat them as follows:

   1. $\frac{N}{D} = R$ means the same thing as $N = R \times D, D \neq 0.$

2. For $\dfrac{A}{B}$ a rational number and $C \neq 0$, we have $\dfrac{A \times C}{B \times C} = \dfrac{A}{B}$.

3. $\dfrac{A}{B} \times C = A \times \dfrac{C}{B} = \dfrac{A \times C}{B}$ for $B \neq 0$.

The special products involving 0 and 1 are easily obtained from property three above as $0 \times \dfrac{A}{B} = 0$ and $1 \times \dfrac{A}{B} = \dfrac{A}{B}$. This is just as we would expect from our work with the integers. At this point it is also useful to note the three special types of fractions involving 0 and 1: $\dfrac{0}{D} = 0$, $\dfrac{N}{1} = N$, and $\dfrac{D}{D} = 1$ for $D \neq 0$.

Since $1 \times \dfrac{A}{B} = \dfrac{1 \times A}{B} = A \times \dfrac{1}{B}$ by property three above, we can immediately notice that every fraction can be expressed as a product of an integer and a fraction with numerator equal to one, for example, $\dfrac{3}{5} = 3 \times \dfrac{1}{5}$. Furthermore, property three enables us to multiply an integer times a fraction by simply finding the product of the integer times the numerator and using this product as the numerator of the resulting fraction with the same denominator, for example, $3 \times \dfrac{7}{4} = \dfrac{3 \times 7}{4} = \dfrac{21}{4}$.

Examples.

(a) $0 \times \dfrac{15}{23} = 0$ (b) $1 \times \dfrac{15}{23} = \dfrac{15}{23}$ (c) $\dfrac{0}{23} = 0$

(d) $\dfrac{15}{1} = 15$ (e) $\dfrac{23}{23} = 1$ (f) $\dfrac{9}{16} = 9 \times \dfrac{1}{16}$

(g) $9 \times \dfrac{3}{5} = \dfrac{9 \times 3}{5} = \dfrac{27}{5}$ (h) $\dfrac{2}{15} \times 6 = \dfrac{2 \times 6}{15} = \dfrac{4}{5}$.

As we proceed to the consideration of finding the products of rational numbers, we observe that our previous interpretation of multiplication as a repeated addition process is inadequate. In writing $\dfrac{1}{5} \times 3$ we ask "What does it mean to add 3 to itself $\dfrac{1}{5}$ times?" Since multiplication is commutative, we can always write $\dfrac{1}{5} \times 3 = 3 \times \dfrac{1}{5} = \dfrac{3}{5}$ and obtain the product. But this does not answer our question, nor does it help our intuition. Furthermore, if we consider products such as $\dfrac{1}{5} \times \dfrac{1}{3}$, it becomes evident that a "new" interpretation and clarification is desirable. Thus, we consider the following examples.

Examples.

(a) Observe that $2 \times 3 = 6$

$1 \times 3 = 3$

$\dfrac{3}{4} \times 3 = \dfrac{9}{4} = 2\dfrac{1}{4}$

$\dfrac{1}{2} \times 3 = \dfrac{3}{2} = 1\dfrac{1}{2}$

$\dfrac{1}{3} \times 3 = \dfrac{3}{3} = 1$

$\dfrac{1}{5} \times 3 = \dfrac{3}{5}$

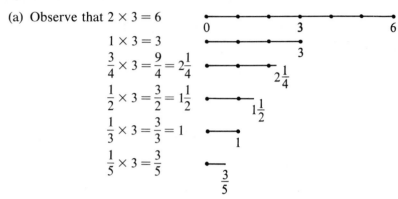

(b)

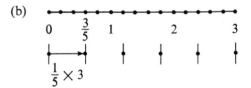

(c)

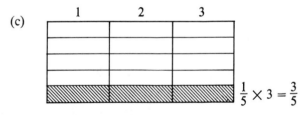

$$\frac{1}{5} \times 3 = \frac{3}{5}$$

FIGURE 70

In working with fractions, it is evident that numerators multiply and denominators divide. That is, in fractions such as $\dfrac{3}{5}$ we can think of the "3" as a multiplier and the "5" as a divisor. Observing that $\dfrac{3}{5} = 3 \times \dfrac{1}{5}$, we can think of $\dfrac{3}{5}$ as "one of the five equal parts of three" or as "three of the five equal parts of one."

Now we can interpret a product such as $\dfrac{1}{5} \times \dfrac{1}{3}$ as "one of the five equal parts of one-third." That is, as "one of the five equal parts of one of the three equal parts of one." The result is clearly one of the fifteen equal parts of one, $\frac{1}{15}$. In general, the product of two fractions can easily be obtained from our observations above. For example, $\frac{5}{7} \times \frac{3}{4}$

$$= \left(5 \times \frac{1}{7}\right) \times \left(3 \times \frac{1}{4}\right) = (5 \times 3) \times \left(\frac{1}{7} \times \frac{1}{4}\right) = 15 \times \frac{1}{28} = \frac{15}{28}.$$ Since multiplica-

tion is commutative and associative, our manipulations are justified. Briefly, we can write $\frac{5}{7} \times \frac{3}{4} = \frac{5 \times 3}{7 \times 4} = \frac{15}{28}$. In ordinary English we would say that "to multiply two fractions together, multiply the numerators to form the numerator of the product and multiply the denominators to form the denominator of the product." In mathematical symbols we would write

4. If $\frac{A}{B}$ and $\frac{C}{D}$ are rational numbers, then $\frac{A}{B} \times \frac{C}{D} = \frac{A \times C}{B \times D}.$

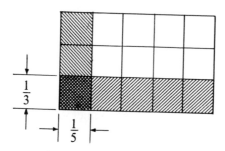

FIGURE 71

Examples.

(a) $\frac{5}{7} \times \frac{3}{4} = \frac{5 \times 3}{7 \times 4} = \frac{15}{28}.$

Observe that in Figure 72(a) we have 15 of the 28 equal parts of one whole. In Figure 72(b) we have 1 of the 28 equal parts of 15 wholes. That is, $\frac{5}{7} \times \frac{3}{4} = 15 \times \frac{1}{28} = \frac{1}{28} \times 15 = \frac{15}{28}.$

(b) $\frac{3}{8} \times \frac{6}{15} = \frac{3 \times 6}{8 \times 15} = \frac{18}{120} = \frac{3}{20}$ (when reduced)

(c) $\frac{9}{5} \times \frac{2}{9} = \frac{9 \times 2}{5 \times 9} = \frac{2}{5}$ (d) $\frac{7}{12} \times \frac{6}{21} = \frac{7 \times 6}{12 \times 21} = \frac{1 \times 1}{2 \times 3} = \frac{1}{6}.$

Notice that common factors in numerator and denominator may be cancelled to simplify the operation and obtain reduced fractions. The

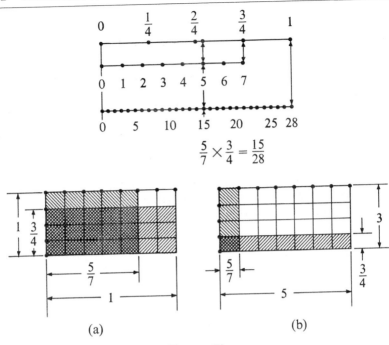

$$\frac{5}{7} \times \frac{3}{4} = \frac{15}{28}$$

(a)   (b)

FIGURE 72

reduction process can be simplified considerably by a cancellation process before multiplying out the numerators and the denominators.

Examples.

(a) $\dfrac{7}{12} \times \dfrac{9}{35} = \dfrac{\overset{1}{\cancel{7}} \times \overset{3}{\cancel{9}}}{\underset{4}{\cancel{12}} \times \underset{5}{\cancel{35}}} = \dfrac{1 \times 3}{4 \times 5} = \dfrac{3}{20}.$

Observe that the common factor 7 in 7 and 35 is cancelled, leaving the factors 1 and 5 respectively. The common factor 3 is cancelled from 12 and 9 leaving 4 and 3. Thus, in the numerator we have $1 \times 3 = 3$ and in the denominator we have $4 \times 5 = 20$.

(b) $\dfrac{7}{15} \times \dfrac{5}{7} = \dfrac{\overset{1}{\cancel{7}} \times \overset{1}{\cancel{5}}}{\underset{3}{\cancel{15}} \times \underset{1}{\cancel{7}}} = \dfrac{1}{3}$

(c) $\dfrac{18}{21} \times \dfrac{14}{27} = \dfrac{\overset{2}{\cancel{18}} \times \overset{2}{\cancel{14}}}{\underset{3}{\cancel{21}} \times \underset{3}{\cancel{27}}} = \dfrac{2 \times 2}{3 \times 3} = \dfrac{4}{9}$

(d) $\dfrac{6}{7} \times \dfrac{14}{21} = \dfrac{2 \times \overset{1}{\cancel{3}} \times 2 \times \overset{1}{\cancel{7}}}{7 \times \underset{1}{\cancel{3}} \times \underset{1}{\cancel{7}}} = \dfrac{2 \times 2}{7} = \dfrac{4}{7}$

(e) $\dfrac{\overset{3}{\cancel{15}}}{\underset{1}{\cancel{28}}} \times \dfrac{\overset{4}{\cancel{112}}}{\underset{25}{\cancel{125}}} = \dfrac{3 \times 4}{25} = \dfrac{12}{25}$ (f) $\dfrac{\overset{2}{\cancel{4}}}{\underset{3}{\cancel{9}}} \times \dfrac{5}{\underset{3}{\cancel{6}}} \times \dfrac{\overset{1}{\cancel{3}}}{\underset{7}{\cancel{14}}} = \dfrac{5}{63}$

(g) $\dfrac{\overset{2}{\underset{1}{\cancel{6}}}}{\underset{\underset{1}{\cancel{5}}}{\cancel{25}}} \times \dfrac{\overset{\overset{1}{\cancel{2}}}{\cancel{10}}}{\underset{\underset{1}{\cancel{3}}}{\cancel{33}}} \times \dfrac{\overset{\cancel{5}}{\cancel{55}}}{\underset{13}{\cancel{26}}} = \dfrac{2}{13}.$

Practice 1.

1. Find the fraction suggested in each of the following:

(a)   (b)

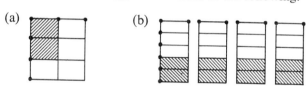

(c)

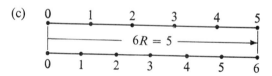

(d)

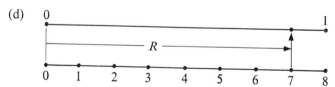

2. Find the products:

(a) $6 \times \dfrac{1}{7}$ (b) $9 \times \dfrac{1}{11}$ (c) $5 \times \dfrac{1}{8}$ (d) $1 \times \dfrac{1}{3}$ (e) $0 \times \dfrac{1}{9}$

(f) $1 \times \dfrac{3}{5}$ (g) $4 \times \dfrac{0}{8}$ (h) $12 \times \dfrac{1}{3}$ (i) $0 \times \dfrac{0}{4}$ (j) $7 \times \dfrac{1}{7}.$

3. Find the products in reduced form.

(a) $8 \times \dfrac{3}{4}$ (b) $9 \times \dfrac{5}{36}$ (c) $4 \times \dfrac{3}{16}$ (d) $12 \times \dfrac{9}{10}$

(e) $5 \times \dfrac{4}{25}$ (f) $\dfrac{5}{7} \times 21$ (g) $\dfrac{9}{11} \times 55$ (h) $\dfrac{7}{12} \times 3$

(i) $\dfrac{35}{42} \times 4$ (j) $\dfrac{15}{26} \times 10.$

4. Find the products in reduced form:

(a) $\dfrac{1}{2} \times \dfrac{1}{4}$ (b) $\dfrac{1}{3} \times \dfrac{1}{7}$ (c) $\dfrac{1}{5} \times \dfrac{1}{6}$ (d) $\dfrac{1}{8} \times \dfrac{1}{8}$ (e) $\dfrac{1}{9} \times \dfrac{1}{1}$

(f) $\dfrac{1}{4} \times \dfrac{2}{3}$ (g) $\dfrac{3}{7} \times \dfrac{1}{9}$ (h) $\dfrac{4}{7} \times \dfrac{5}{6}$ (i) $\dfrac{3}{4} \times \dfrac{8}{9}$ (j) $\dfrac{7}{8} \times \dfrac{8}{7}.$

5. Find the products in reduced form:

(a) $\dfrac{3}{7} \times \dfrac{28}{33}$ (b) $\dfrac{6}{35} \times \dfrac{21}{22}$ (c) $\dfrac{25}{28} \times \dfrac{7}{10}$ (d) $\dfrac{3}{5} \times \dfrac{10}{21}$

(e) $\dfrac{55}{81} \times \dfrac{9}{22}$ (f) $\dfrac{24}{27} \times \dfrac{1}{32}$ (g) $\dfrac{64}{81} \times \dfrac{9}{16}$ (h) $\dfrac{15}{42} \times \dfrac{77}{125}$

(i) $\dfrac{12}{13} \times \dfrac{17}{30}$ (j) $\dfrac{36}{75} \times \dfrac{25}{42}.$

6. Find the products in reduced form:

(a) $\dfrac{2}{3} \times \dfrac{5}{2} \times \dfrac{3}{5}$ (b) $\dfrac{1}{4} \times \dfrac{2}{3} \times \dfrac{3}{5}$ (c) $\dfrac{4}{7} \times \dfrac{5}{6} \times \dfrac{7}{6}$ (d) $\dfrac{8}{9} \times \dfrac{3}{4} \times \dfrac{3}{5}$

(e) $\dfrac{7}{20} \times \dfrac{10}{21} \times \dfrac{3}{4}$ (f) $\dfrac{5}{7} \times \dfrac{7}{10} \times \dfrac{2}{3}$ (g) $\dfrac{4}{9} \times \dfrac{15}{18} \times \dfrac{81}{100}$

(h) $\dfrac{42}{75} \times \dfrac{18}{21} \times \dfrac{15}{54}.$

7. Find the products:

(a) $5 \times \dfrac{1}{5}$ (b) $\dfrac{1}{7} \times 7$ (c) $\dfrac{1}{4} \times \dfrac{4}{1}$ (d) $\dfrac{15}{1} \times \dfrac{1}{15}$

(e) $\dfrac{1}{10} \times 10$ (f) $12 \times \dfrac{1}{12}$ (g) $\dfrac{3}{4} \times \dfrac{4}{3}$ (h) $\dfrac{9}{4} \times \dfrac{4}{9}$

(i) $\dfrac{3}{11} \times \dfrac{11}{3}$ (j) $\dfrac{19}{25} \times \dfrac{25}{19}.$

Answers.

1. (a) $\dfrac{2}{6} = \dfrac{1}{3}$ (b) $4 \times \dfrac{2}{5} = \dfrac{8}{5} = 1\dfrac{3}{5}$ (c) $R = \dfrac{5}{6}$ (d) $R = \dfrac{7}{8}.$

2. (a) $\dfrac{6}{7}$ (b) $\dfrac{9}{11}$ (c) $\dfrac{5}{8}$ (d) $\dfrac{1}{3}$ (e) 0

(f) $\dfrac{3}{5}$ (g) 0 (h) $\dfrac{12}{3} = 4$ (i) 0 (j) $\dfrac{7}{7} = 1.$

3. (a) 6 (b) $\dfrac{5}{4} = 1\dfrac{1}{4}$ (c) $\dfrac{3}{4}$ (d) $\dfrac{54}{5} = 10\dfrac{4}{5}$ (e) $\dfrac{4}{5}$

(f) 15   (g) 45   (h) $\frac{7}{4} = 1\frac{3}{4}$ (i) $\frac{10}{3} = 3\frac{1}{3}$

(j) $\frac{75}{13} = 5\frac{10}{13}$.

4. (a) $\frac{1}{8}$ (b) $\frac{1}{21}$ (c) $\frac{1}{30}$ (d) $\frac{1}{64}$ (e) $\frac{1}{9}$

(f) $\frac{1}{6}$ (g) $\frac{1}{21}$ (h) $\frac{10}{21}$ (i) $\frac{2}{3}$ (j) 1.

5. (a) $\frac{4}{11}$ (b) $\frac{9}{55}$ (c) $\frac{5}{8}$ (d) $\frac{2}{7}$ (e) $\frac{5}{18}$

(f) $\frac{1}{36}$ (g) $\frac{4}{9}$ (h) $\frac{11}{50}$ (i) $\frac{34}{65}$ (j) $\frac{2}{7}$.

6. (a) 1   (b) $\frac{1}{10}$ (c) $\frac{5}{9}$ (d) $\frac{2}{5}$ (e) $\frac{1}{8}$ (f) $\frac{1}{3}$ (g) $\frac{3}{10}$

(h) $\frac{2}{15}$.

7. All answers are equal to 1.

6.2.2   Exercise 7 of the practice set above suggests and illustrates a special relationship between pairs of fractions. Notice that if $\frac{A}{B}$ is a fraction with $A \neq 0$, then $\frac{A}{B} \times \frac{B}{A} = 1$. To distinguish this relationship, we say that if $\frac{A}{B}$ is a fraction with $A \neq 0$, then $\frac{B}{A}$ is its **reciprocal**. That is, the **reciprocal** of a fraction is the fraction formed by interchanging the numerator and denominator of the given fraction, providing the numerator of the given fraction is not equal to 0. A "zero" fraction, $\frac{0}{B}$, has no reciprocal.

The relationship between a pair of reciprocal fractions is that their product is equal to 1. For example, $\frac{3}{2}$ is the reciprocal of $\frac{2}{3}$ since $\frac{2}{3} \times \frac{3}{2} = 1$. The reciprocal of 18 is $\frac{1}{18}$ since $18 \times \frac{1}{18} = 1$. Notice that if a fraction is the reciprocal of a second fraction, then the second fraction is the reciprocal of the first.

Using the idea of reciprocal fractions and the fundamental property of the rational numbers, we can quite readily develop the division operation for rational numbers. Recall that if R is the dividend, S the divisor, and Q the quotient, then we write $R \div S = Q$ or $\frac{R}{S} = Q$, meaning $R = Q \times S$.

Now think of R, S, and Q as rational numbers; that is, let $R = \dfrac{A}{B}$, $S = \dfrac{C}{D}$, and $Q = \dfrac{E}{F}$. We can then write

$$\frac{A}{B} \div \frac{C}{D} = \frac{E}{F} \quad \text{or} \quad \frac{\dfrac{A}{B}}{\dfrac{C}{D}} = \frac{E}{F} \quad \text{means} \quad \frac{A}{B} = \frac{E}{F} \times \frac{C}{D}.$$

Examples.

(a) $R = \dfrac{2}{3}$, $S = \dfrac{1}{4}$, then $\dfrac{2}{3} \div \dfrac{1}{4} = \dfrac{\dfrac{2}{3}}{\dfrac{1}{4}} = \dfrac{E}{F}$ means $\dfrac{2}{3} = \dfrac{E}{F} \times \dfrac{1}{4}$.

(b) $R = 5 = \dfrac{5}{1}$, $S = \dfrac{10}{11}$, then $5 \div \dfrac{10}{11} = \dfrac{\dfrac{5}{1}}{\dfrac{10}{11}} = \dfrac{E}{F}$ means $5 = \dfrac{E}{F} \times \dfrac{10}{11}$.

(c) $R = \dfrac{3}{4}$, $S = 6 = \dfrac{6}{1}$, then $\dfrac{3}{4} \div 6 = \dfrac{\dfrac{3}{4}}{\dfrac{6}{1}} = \dfrac{E}{F}$ means $\dfrac{3}{4} = \dfrac{E}{F} \times 6$.

A close study of the examples should suggest that if we can eliminate the divisor from the product form, then we could isolate the quotient $\dfrac{E}{F}$. We should also note that the division in a fractional form suggests that we simplify the expression. Using equal multiplication or the fundamental property of the rational numbers, we can easily "follow through" with both of the above ideas. To accomplish this we use the reciprocal of the divisor.

Examples.

(a) $\dfrac{2}{3} \div \dfrac{1}{4} = \dfrac{E}{F}$ is written $\dfrac{\dfrac{2}{3} \times \dfrac{4}{1}}{\dfrac{1}{4} \times \dfrac{4}{1}} = \dfrac{\dfrac{8}{3}}{1} = \dfrac{8}{3} = \dfrac{E}{F}$ or $\dfrac{E}{F} = 2\dfrac{2}{3}$.

Notice that $\dfrac{2}{3} \times \dfrac{4}{1} = \dfrac{E}{F} \times \left(\dfrac{1}{4} \times \dfrac{4}{1}\right) = \dfrac{E}{F}$ so that $\dfrac{8}{3} = \dfrac{E}{F}$ the quotient.

(b) $5 \div \dfrac{10}{11} = \dfrac{5 \times \dfrac{11}{10}}{\dfrac{10}{11} \times \dfrac{11}{10}} = \dfrac{5 \times \dfrac{11}{10}}{1} = \dfrac{11}{2} = \dfrac{E}{F} = 5\dfrac{1}{2}.$

Notice that: $5 \times \dfrac{11}{10} = \dfrac{E}{F} \times \left(\dfrac{10}{11} \times \dfrac{11}{10}\right) = \dfrac{E}{F}$ so that $\dfrac{11}{2} = \dfrac{E}{F}.$

(c) $\dfrac{3}{4} \div 6 = \dfrac{\dfrac{3}{4} \times \dfrac{1}{6}}{6 \times \dfrac{1}{6}} = \dfrac{\dfrac{1}{8}}{1} = \dfrac{1}{8} = \dfrac{E}{F}$ the quotient.

(d) $\dfrac{5}{8} \div \dfrac{7}{10} = \left(\dfrac{5}{8} \times \dfrac{10}{7}\right) \div \left(\dfrac{7}{10} \times \dfrac{10}{7}\right) = \dfrac{25}{28} \div 1 = \dfrac{25}{28}.$

(e) $\dfrac{\dfrac{5}{8}}{\dfrac{7}{10}} = \dfrac{\dfrac{5}{8} \times \dfrac{10}{7}}{\dfrac{7}{10} \times \dfrac{10}{7}} = \dfrac{\dfrac{25}{28}}{1} = \dfrac{25}{28}.$

To find the quotient of two rational numbers we multiply both dividend and divisor by the reciprocal of the divisor. The quotient is then easily obtained as the product of the dividend times the reciprocal of the divisor. In general, we have

5. $\dfrac{A}{B} \div \dfrac{C}{D} = \dfrac{\dfrac{A}{B}}{\dfrac{C}{D}} = \dfrac{A}{B} \times \dfrac{D}{C}$, where $B \neq 0$, $C \neq 0$, and $D \neq 0$.

Observe that division of rational numbers is accomplished by converting the process to a multiplication operation. Also notice that the fractional form of division is more readily handled than the "operational" form of division. In the fractional form, the numerator and denominator of the divisor "reverse" their roles. That is, the denominator acts like a multiplier and the numerator like a divisor in the multiplication and division of integers.

The division of rational numbers can be interpreted and illustrated using scales as in the multiplication of rational numbers. For example, $\dfrac{2}{3} \div \dfrac{1}{4} = \dfrac{8}{3}$ tells us that $\dfrac{1}{4}$ can be subtracted $\dfrac{8}{3}$ times from $\dfrac{2}{3}$ to exhaust it. Alternatively, we can think $\dfrac{2}{3} \div \dfrac{1}{4} = \dfrac{2}{3} \times 4 = \dfrac{8}{3}$ or that $\dfrac{2}{3} \div \dfrac{1}{4} = \dfrac{8}{3}$ means that $\dfrac{2}{3} = \dfrac{8}{3} \times \dfrac{1}{4}$ (Figure 73).

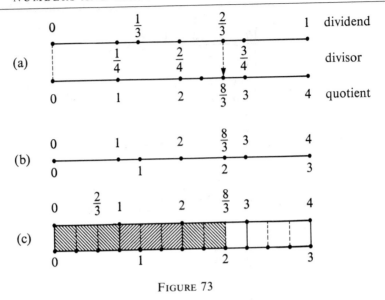

FIGURE 73

There are four possible situations involving 0 and 1. These cases are handled just as with the integers.

1. $\dfrac{A}{B} \div 1 = \dfrac{A}{B}$.

Examples.

(a) $\dfrac{2}{3} \div 1 = \dfrac{2}{3}$ (b) $\dfrac{5}{9} \div 1 = \dfrac{5}{9}$ (c) $\dfrac{\frac{3}{7}}{1} = \dfrac{3}{7}$.

2. If $\dfrac{A}{B} \neq 0$, then $1 \div \dfrac{A}{B} = \dfrac{B}{A}$.

Examples.

(a) $1 \div \dfrac{2}{3} = \dfrac{3}{2}$ (b) $1 \div \dfrac{5}{9} = \dfrac{9}{5}$ (c) $\dfrac{1}{\frac{3}{7}} = \dfrac{7}{3}$.

3. If $\dfrac{A}{B} \neq 0$, then $0 \div \dfrac{A}{B} = 0$.

Examples.

(a) $0 \div \frac{2}{3} = 0$ (b) $0 \div \frac{5}{9} = 0$ (c) $\dfrac{0}{\dfrac{3}{7}} = 0.$

4. $\dfrac{A}{B} \div 0$ is **not permitted** and has no answer.

Examples.

(a) $\dfrac{3}{5} \div \dfrac{5}{7} = \dfrac{3}{5} \times \dfrac{7}{5} = \dfrac{21}{25}$

(b) $\dfrac{4}{15} \div \dfrac{12}{25} = \dfrac{4}{15} \times \dfrac{25}{12} = \dfrac{5}{9}$

(c) $\dfrac{24}{35} \div \dfrac{3}{28} = \dfrac{24}{35} \times \dfrac{28}{3} = \dfrac{32}{5} = 6\dfrac{2}{5}$

(d) $\dfrac{10}{13} \div \dfrac{15}{26} = \dfrac{10}{13} \times \dfrac{26}{15} = \dfrac{4}{3} = 1\dfrac{1}{3}$

(e) $\dfrac{\dfrac{5}{9}}{\dfrac{2}{3}} = \dfrac{5}{\overset{3}{\cancel{9}}} \times \dfrac{\overset{1}{\cancel{3}}}{2} = \dfrac{5}{6}$

(f) $\dfrac{\dfrac{42}{77}}{\dfrac{35}{44}} = \dfrac{\overset{6}{\cancel{42}}}{\cancel{77}} \times \dfrac{\overset{4}{\cancel{44}}}{\cancel{35}} = \dfrac{24}{35}$

(g) $\dfrac{\dfrac{36}{85}}{\dfrac{78}{119}} = \dfrac{\overset{6}{\cancel{36}}}{\cancel{85}} \times \dfrac{\overset{7}{\cancel{119}}}{\cancel{78}} = \dfrac{42}{65}.$

Practice 2.

1. Find the reciprocals of:

(a) $\dfrac{1}{9}$ (b) $\dfrac{17}{3}$ (c) $\dfrac{8}{11}$ (d) $\dfrac{4}{7}$ (e) $\dfrac{18}{5}$ (f) 10

(g) $\dfrac{1}{100}$ (h) 1 (i) $\dfrac{1}{10}$ (j) 100 (k) $\dfrac{10}{27}$ (l) $\dfrac{39}{85}.$

2. Find the number R such that each of the following will be true.

(a) $\dfrac{2}{3} \times R = 1$ (b) $\dfrac{9}{4} \times R = 1$ (c) $\dfrac{1}{25} \times R = 1$

(d) $17 \times R = 1.$

3. Find the reduced rational quotients:

(a) $\dfrac{1}{4} \div \dfrac{1}{3}$ (b) $\dfrac{1}{5} \div \dfrac{1}{2}$ (c) $\dfrac{1}{3} \div \dfrac{1}{7}$ (d) $\dfrac{0}{6} \div \dfrac{1}{4}$ (e) $\dfrac{1}{9} \div \dfrac{1}{6}$

(f) $\dfrac{\dfrac{1}{7}}{\dfrac{1}{4}}$ (g) $\dfrac{\dfrac{1}{8}}{\dfrac{1}{3}}$ (h) $\dfrac{\dfrac{1}{3}}{\dfrac{1}{6}}$ (i) $\dfrac{\dfrac{1}{5}}{\dfrac{1}{5}}$ (j) $\dfrac{\dfrac{1}{2}}{\dfrac{1}{8}}.$

4. Find the reduced rational quotients:

(a) $4 \div \frac{2}{3}$ (b) $2 \div \frac{1}{2}$ (c) $12 \div \frac{3}{4}$ (d) $1 \div \frac{7}{3}$

(e) $63 \div \frac{9}{10}$ (f) $\frac{2}{3} \div 1$ (g) $\frac{1}{2} \div 3$ (h) $\frac{14}{19} \div 7$

(i) $\frac{6}{25} \div 4$ (j) $\frac{27}{32} \div 18$.

5. Find the reduced rational quotients:

(a) $\frac{3}{5} \div \frac{2}{3}$ (b) $\frac{4}{7} \div \frac{5}{7}$ (c) $\frac{9}{16} \div \frac{3}{4}$ (d) $\frac{15}{28} \div \frac{5}{14}$

(e) $\frac{36}{55} \div \frac{42}{75}$ (f) $\dfrac{\frac{4}{15}}{\frac{7}{9}}$ (g) $\dfrac{\frac{2}{7}}{\frac{5}{7}}$ (h) $\dfrac{\frac{3}{5}}{\frac{5}{6}}$

(i) $\dfrac{\frac{2}{3}}{\frac{5}{6}}$ (j) $\dfrac{\frac{28}{165}}{\frac{14}{35}}$.

6. Find the number R such that each of the following will be true.

(a) $\frac{5}{7} \times R = 0$ (b) $R \times \frac{3}{4} = 1$ (c) $\frac{4}{9} \times R = \frac{4}{9}$

(d) $R \times \frac{3}{7} = \frac{7}{3}$ (e) $R \div \frac{6}{7} = \frac{7}{6}$ (f) $\frac{2}{5} \div R = \frac{2}{5}$

(g) $R \div \frac{7}{9} = 0$ (h) $\frac{5}{6} \div R = 1$.

7. Find the value of N which will make each of the following equations true.

(a) $N = \frac{6}{13} \times \frac{65}{72}$ (b) $N = \frac{6}{25} \div \frac{8}{15}$ (c) $\frac{2}{3} = N \times \frac{4}{5}$

(d) $\frac{5}{8} = \frac{3}{8} \div N$ (e) $\frac{N}{4} \times \frac{5}{9} = \frac{5}{12}$ (f) $\frac{5}{7} \times \frac{3}{N} = \frac{15}{28}$

(g) $\frac{N}{9} \div \frac{5}{21} = \frac{14}{15}$ (h) $\frac{2}{3} \div \frac{15}{N} = \frac{14}{35}$ (i) $\frac{6}{7} \times \frac{1}{3} = \frac{2}{N}$

(j) $\frac{2}{5} \times \frac{5}{7} = \frac{N}{42}$ (k) $\frac{4}{9} \div \frac{N}{27} = 12$ (l) $\frac{25}{N} \div \frac{5}{3} = \frac{3}{1}$.

Answers.

1. (a) 9   (b) $\frac{3}{17}$ (c) $\frac{11}{8}$ (d) $\frac{7}{4}$ (e) $\frac{5}{18}$ (f) $\frac{1}{10}$

(g) 100   (h) 1   (i) 10   (j) $\frac{1}{100}$ (k) $\frac{27}{10}$ (l) $\frac{85}{39}$.

2. (a) $\frac{3}{2}$ (b) $\frac{4}{9}$ (c) 25   (d) $\frac{1}{17}$.

3. (a) $\frac{3}{4}$ (b) $\frac{2}{5}$ (c) $\frac{7}{3}$ (d) 0   (e) $\frac{2}{3}$

   (f) $\frac{4}{7}$ (g) $\frac{3}{8}$ (h) 2   (i) 1   (j) 4.

4. (a) 6   (b) 4   (c) 16   (d) $\frac{3}{7}$ (e) 70

   (f) $\frac{2}{3}$ (g) $\frac{1}{6}$ (h) $\frac{2}{19}$ (i) $\frac{3}{50}$ (j) $\frac{3}{64}$.

5. (a) $\frac{9}{10}$ (b) $\frac{4}{5}$ (c) $\frac{3}{4}$ (d) $\frac{3}{2}$ (e) $\frac{90}{77}$

   (f) $\frac{12}{35}$ (g) $\frac{2}{5}$ (h) $\frac{18}{25}$ (i) $\frac{4}{5}$ (j) $\frac{14}{33}$.

6. (a) 0   (b) $\frac{4}{3}$ (c) 1   (d) $\frac{49}{9}$ (e) 1   (f) 1

   (g) 0   (h) $\frac{5}{6}$.

7. (a) $\frac{5}{12}$ (b) $\frac{9}{20}$ (c) $\frac{5}{6}$ (d) $\frac{3}{5}$ (e) 3   (f) 4

   (g) 2   (h) 9   (i) 7   (j) 12   (k) 1   (l) 5.

Exercises

1. Express the following rational numbers as products.

   (a) $\frac{2}{3} = R$ (b) $\frac{7}{1} = R$ (c) $\frac{1}{6} = R$ (d) $\frac{5}{8} = R$

   (e) $\frac{12}{4} = R$.

2. Why is $\frac{6}{8} = \frac{3}{4}$?

3. Express the following fractions as products of an integer and a fraction with numerator 1.

   (a) $\frac{5}{7}$ (b) $\frac{7}{8}$ (c) $\frac{1}{3}$ (d) $\frac{0}{4}$ (e) $\frac{2}{2}$ (f) $\frac{6}{1}$.

4. Find the products in reduced form:

   (a) $5 \times \frac{3}{17}$ (b) $6 \times \frac{1}{32}$ (c) $12 \times \frac{3}{52}$ (d) $1 \times \frac{14}{15}$

   (e) $3 \times \frac{0}{6}$ (f) $\frac{1}{4} \times 4$ (g) $\frac{12}{25} \times 5$ (h) $\frac{1}{7} \times 0$

   (i) $\frac{16}{3} \times 6$ (j) $\frac{8}{9} \times 9$.

5. Find the products in reduced form:

(a) $\dfrac{4}{5} \times \dfrac{3}{7}$ (b) $\dfrac{6}{11} \times \dfrac{11}{12}$ (c) $\dfrac{8}{10} \times \dfrac{15}{6}$ (d) $\dfrac{2}{3} \times \dfrac{5}{20}$

(e) $\dfrac{42}{45} \times \dfrac{27}{49}$ (f) $\dfrac{18}{21} \times \dfrac{6}{54}$ (g) $\dfrac{32}{63} \times \dfrac{21}{40}$ (h) $\dfrac{19}{21} \times \dfrac{49}{51}$

(i) $\dfrac{12}{32} \times \dfrac{24}{81}$ (j) $\dfrac{35}{44} \times \dfrac{110}{147}$.

6. Find the products in reduced form:

(a) $\dfrac{1}{5} \times \dfrac{7}{8} \times \dfrac{10}{11}$ (b) $\dfrac{3}{10} \times \dfrac{5}{6} \times \dfrac{8}{13}$ (c) $\dfrac{4}{7} \times \dfrac{3}{5} \times \dfrac{14}{15}$

(d) $\dfrac{21}{32} \times \dfrac{15}{17} \times \dfrac{48}{63}$.

7. (a) Find $\dfrac{3}{4}$ of $\dfrac{8}{9}$.

(b) What is the product of $\dfrac{2}{5}$ and $\dfrac{15}{16}$?

(c) What number is 4 times as large as $\dfrac{5}{6}$?

(d) What number is $\dfrac{1}{4}$ as large as $\dfrac{2}{3}$?

8. (a) What is the reciprocal of $\dfrac{7}{9}$?

(b) What number has no reciprocal?

(c) What number is its own reciprocal?

(d) If a fraction is proper, then what can we say about its reciprocal?

(e) If a fraction is improper, then what can we say about its reciprocal?

9. Find the quotients in reduced form:

(a) $\dfrac{1}{5} \div \dfrac{1}{3}$ (b) $\dfrac{1}{4} \div \dfrac{1}{8}$ (c) $6 \div \dfrac{2}{3}$ (d) $5 \div \dfrac{15}{2}$ (e) $1 \div \dfrac{4}{7}$

(f) $\dfrac{8}{15} \div 6$ (g) $\dfrac{12}{17} \div 1$ (h) $\dfrac{5}{9} \div 5$ (i) $\dfrac{3}{4} \div \dfrac{8}{9}$ (j) $\dfrac{6}{7} \div \dfrac{6}{7}$.

10. Find the quotients in reduced form:

(a) $\dfrac{6}{19} \div \dfrac{4}{5}$ (b) $\dfrac{10}{21} \div \dfrac{2}{3}$ (c) $\dfrac{15}{32} \div \dfrac{5}{8}$ (d) $\dfrac{9}{7} \div \dfrac{3}{14}$

(e) $\dfrac{24}{25} \div \dfrac{8}{15}$ (f) $\dfrac{30}{72} \div \dfrac{20}{30}$ (g) $\dfrac{98}{105} \div \dfrac{14}{15}$ (h) $\dfrac{45}{77} \div \dfrac{27}{35}$

(i) $\dfrac{22}{91} \div \dfrac{143}{156}$ (j) $\dfrac{117}{175} \div \dfrac{99}{105}$.

11. Find the value of N which will make each of the following equations true.

(a) $\dfrac{3}{N} \times \dfrac{2}{9} = \dfrac{1}{6}$ (b) $\dfrac{4}{7} \times \dfrac{N}{8} = 0$ (c) $\dfrac{3}{7} \times \dfrac{5}{N} = \dfrac{3}{7}$

(d) $\dfrac{9}{N} \times \dfrac{2}{3} = 1$ (e) $\dfrac{N}{5} \times \dfrac{3}{4} = \dfrac{3}{10}$.

12. Find the value of N which will make each of the following equations true.

(a) $\dfrac{8}{N} \div \dfrac{4}{5} = 1$ (b) $\dfrac{N}{7} \div \dfrac{7}{9} = 0$ (c) $\dfrac{3}{5} \div \dfrac{1}{N} = 3$

(d) $\dfrac{5}{9} \div \dfrac{N}{45} = 1$ (e) $\dfrac{N}{4} \div \dfrac{5}{6} = \dfrac{3}{5}$ (f) $\dfrac{7}{9} \div \dfrac{N}{2} = \dfrac{21}{54}$

(g) $\dfrac{2}{3} \div \dfrac{5}{6} = \dfrac{4}{N}$ (h) $\dfrac{7}{9} \div \dfrac{N}{12} = \dfrac{14}{15}$.

13. (a) How many $\dfrac{2}{7}$'s are in $\dfrac{10}{21}$?   (b) What part of $\dfrac{9}{11}$ is in $\dfrac{3}{5}$?

(c) $\dfrac{2}{3}$ is $\dfrac{5}{7}$ of what number?   (d) $\dfrac{5}{8}$ is what part of $\dfrac{9}{10}$?

14. (a) If the product of two fractions is $\dfrac{15}{28}$ and one of the factors is $\dfrac{5}{7}$, then what is the other factor?

(b) If the quotient of two fractions is $\dfrac{4}{15}$ and the divisor is $\dfrac{5}{6}$, then what is the dividend?

(c) If the quotient of two fractions is $\dfrac{7}{16}$ and the dividend is $\dfrac{3}{8}$, then what is the divisor?

15. Sally said "My little brother is seven-fifths of one-third of my age." If Sally was fifteen, how old was her brother?

16. If $\dfrac{3}{4}$ of a class scored over 90 out of 100 on the objective part of an examination and $\dfrac{2}{3}$ of these students scored over 90 out of 100 on the verbal part also, then what fraction of the class scored over 90 on both parts of the examination?

17. Sam ate $\dfrac{1}{3}$ of a pie. If Bill ate $\dfrac{1}{4}$ of the remaining part of the pie, then how many times more than Bill did Sam have of the pie?

18. Mr. Anderson earns 735 dollars per month. If Mr. Olson earns $\dfrac{7}{9}$ of what Mr. Anderson does and Mr. Johnson earns $\dfrac{6}{5}$ of what Mr. Olson does, then how much does Mr. Johnson earn per month?

19. If $\dfrac{3}{5}$ of the height of the hull of a boat is below the water line and there is 8 feet of the hull above the water, then how deep in the water does the hull of the boat lie?

20. Find the smallest natural number N such that N times $\frac{5}{7}$ is an integer and N divided by $\frac{3}{4}$ is an integer.

Answers.

1. (a) $2 = 3R$ (b) $7 = R$ (c) $1 = 6R$ (d) $5 = 8R$
    (e) $12 = 4R$.
2. Because $6 \times 4 = 3 \times 8 = 24$.
3. (a) $5 \times \frac{1}{7}$ (b) $7 \times \frac{1}{8}$ (c) $1 \times \frac{1}{3}$ (d) $0 \times \frac{1}{4}$ (e) $2 \times \frac{1}{2}$
    (f) $6 \times \frac{1}{1}$.
4. (a) $\frac{15}{17}$ (b) $\frac{3}{16}$ (c) $\frac{9}{13}$ (d) $\frac{14}{15}$ (e) 0
    (f) 1   (g) $\frac{12}{5} = 2\frac{2}{5}$ (h) 0   (i) 32   (j) 8.
5. (a) $\frac{12}{35}$ (b) $\frac{1}{2}$ (c) 2   (d) $\frac{1}{6}$ (e) $\frac{18}{35}$
    (f) $\frac{2}{21}$ (g) $\frac{4}{15}$ (h) $\frac{133}{153}$ (i) $\frac{1}{9}$ (j) $\frac{25}{42}$.
6. (a) $\frac{7}{44}$ (b) $\frac{2}{13}$ (c) $\frac{8}{25}$ (d) $\frac{15}{34}$.
7. (a) $\frac{2}{3}$ (b) $\frac{3}{8}$ (c) $\frac{10}{3} = 3\frac{1}{3}$ (d) $\frac{1}{6}$.
8. (a) $\frac{9}{7}$ (b) 0   (c) 1   (d) Its reciprocal is improper
    (e) Its reciprocal is proper or equal to 1.
9. (a) $\frac{3}{5}$ (b) 2   (c) 9   (d) $\frac{2}{3}$ (e) $\frac{7}{4} = 1\frac{3}{4}$
    (f) $\frac{4}{45}$ (g) $\frac{12}{17}$ (h) $\frac{1}{9}$ (i) $\frac{27}{32}$ (j) 1.
10. (a) $\frac{15}{38}$ (b) $\frac{5}{7}$ (c) $\frac{3}{4}$ (d) 6   (e) $\frac{9}{5} = 1\frac{4}{5}$
    (f) $\frac{5}{8}$ (g) 1   (h) $\frac{25}{33}$ (i) $\frac{24}{91}$ (j) $\frac{39}{55}$.
11. (a) 4   (b) 0   (c) 5   (d) 6   (e) 2.
12. (a) 10   (b) 0   (c) 5   (d) 25   (e) 2   (f) 4   (g) 5
    (h) 10.
13. (a) $\frac{5}{3} = 1\frac{2}{3}$ (b) $\frac{11}{15}$ (c) $\frac{14}{15}$ (d) $\frac{25}{36}$.

14. (a) $\dfrac{3}{4}$ (b) $\dfrac{2}{9}$ (c) $\dfrac{6}{7}$.

15. 7 years old.

16. $\dfrac{1}{2}$.

17. 2 times more.

18. $686.

19. 12 feet.

20. $N = 21$.

6.3 Sums and Differences

6.3.1 Our discussion of **scales** and the **rational number line** suggests methods for finding the sum and difference of pairs of rational numbers. For simplicity, let us consider first a rational number line with a scale marked with fractions whose denominators are all 10. That is, each unit is divided into 10 equal parts (Figure 74).

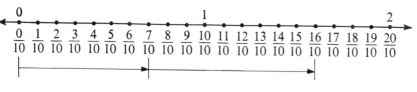

FIGURE 74

Since addition is a "putting together" or successive counting process, to add any two fractions with the same or like denominators we need only ask "How many of these equal parts are there?" to obtain the sum. For example, to add $\dfrac{7}{10}$ and $\dfrac{9}{10}$ together we ask "How many tenths are there together?" That is, $\dfrac{7}{10} + \dfrac{9}{10} = \dfrac{?}{10}$. By a simple counting or addition of the numerators we obtain $\dfrac{7}{10} + \dfrac{9}{10} = \dfrac{16}{10}$. Alternatively, we can write

$$\dfrac{7}{10} + \dfrac{9}{10} = \left(7 \times \dfrac{1}{10}\right) + \left(9 \times \dfrac{1}{10}\right) = 7 \text{ tenths} + 9 \text{ tenths} = (7 + 9) \text{ tenths}$$

$$= 16 \text{ tenths} = 16 \times \dfrac{1}{10} = \dfrac{16}{10}.$$

Examples.

(a) $\dfrac{4}{15} + \dfrac{8}{15} = \dfrac{4+8}{15} = \dfrac{12}{15} = \dfrac{4 \times 3}{5 \times 3} = \dfrac{4}{5}.$

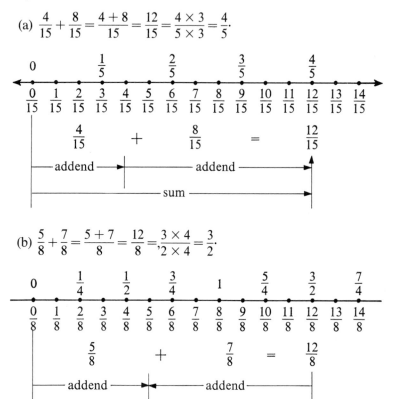

(b) $\dfrac{5}{8} + \dfrac{7}{8} = \dfrac{5+7}{8} = \dfrac{12}{8} = \dfrac{3 \times 4}{2 \times 4} = \dfrac{3}{2}.$

In ordinary English we might describe this addition of fractions by saying "To add two fractions with the same denominator, add their numerators and the sum will be the fraction with the sum of the numerators of the addends as a numerator and the same denominator as a denominator." Observe that this is an extension of our interpretation of the distributive property of division. That is, adding fractions with common denominators is consistent with our discussion of the fundamental operations with the integers. Since subtraction can be expressed in terms of addition, we might anticipate that the difference between fractions is analogous to finding the sum. That is, in mathematical symbols, we have

$$\frac{A}{B} + \frac{C}{B} = \frac{A+C}{B} \text{ and } \frac{A}{B} - \frac{C}{B} = \frac{A-C}{B}.$$

Examples.

(a) $\dfrac{11}{15} - \dfrac{7}{15} = \dfrac{11-7}{15} = \dfrac{4}{15}.$

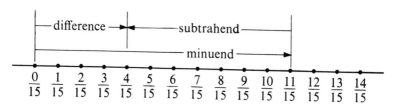

(b) $\dfrac{5}{8} - \dfrac{7}{8} = \dfrac{5-7}{8} = \dfrac{-2}{8} = -\dfrac{1}{4}.$

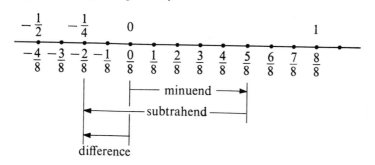

(c) $\dfrac{7}{12} - \dfrac{11}{12} = \dfrac{7}{12} + \dfrac{-11}{12} = \dfrac{7+(-11)}{.12} = \dfrac{-4}{12} = -\dfrac{1}{3}.$

Practice 1.

1. Find the sums:
    (a) $\dfrac{4}{5} + \dfrac{2}{5}$ (b) $\dfrac{9}{11} + \dfrac{5}{11}$ (c) $\dfrac{13}{19} + \dfrac{15}{19}$ (d) $\dfrac{5}{4} + \dfrac{9}{4}$
    (e) $\dfrac{4}{6} + \dfrac{3}{6}$ (f) $\dfrac{2}{3} + \dfrac{7}{3}$ (g) $\dfrac{5}{7} + \dfrac{2}{7}$ (h) $\dfrac{9}{12} + \dfrac{10}{12}$
    (i) $\dfrac{7}{6} + \dfrac{5}{6}$ (j) $\dfrac{10}{18} + \dfrac{15}{18}.$
2. Find the differences:
    (a) $\dfrac{4}{5} - \dfrac{2}{5}$ (b) $\dfrac{2}{5} - \dfrac{4}{5}$ (c) $\dfrac{15}{18} - \dfrac{10}{18}$ (d) $\dfrac{5}{8} - \dfrac{1}{8}$

(e) $\dfrac{15}{16}-\dfrac{15}{16}$ (f) $\dfrac{3}{7}-\dfrac{4}{7}$ (g) $\dfrac{1}{4}-\dfrac{5}{4}$ (h) $\dfrac{3}{6}-\dfrac{4}{6}$

(i) $\dfrac{4}{6}-\dfrac{3}{6}$ (j) $\dfrac{2}{3}-\dfrac{8}{3}.$

3. Find the sum or difference as indicated:

(a) $\dfrac{2}{5}+\dfrac{4}{5}$ (b) $\dfrac{2}{3}-\dfrac{4}{3}$ (c) $\dfrac{0}{7}+\dfrac{5}{7}$ (d) $\dfrac{5}{7}-\dfrac{0}{7}$

(e) $\dfrac{3}{10}+\dfrac{0}{10}$ (f) $\dfrac{10}{10}-\dfrac{3}{10}$ (g) $\dfrac{0}{7}-\dfrac{5}{7}$ (h) $\dfrac{2}{3}+\dfrac{2}{3}$

(i) $\dfrac{2}{9}-\dfrac{2}{9}$ (j) $\dfrac{0}{8}+\dfrac{0}{8}.$

4. Find:

(a) $\dfrac{6}{8}+\dfrac{4}{8}+\dfrac{5}{8}$ (b) $\dfrac{5}{9}+\dfrac{2}{9}-\dfrac{3}{9}$ (c) $\dfrac{3}{6}-\dfrac{5}{6}+\dfrac{2}{6}$

(d) $\dfrac{9}{12}-\dfrac{8}{12}-\dfrac{6}{12}$ (e) $\dfrac{12}{28}+\dfrac{6}{28}+\dfrac{21}{28}$ (f) $\dfrac{21}{15}-\dfrac{10}{15}+\dfrac{9}{15}$

(g) $\dfrac{15}{18}+\dfrac{12}{18}-\dfrac{14}{18}$ (h) $\dfrac{15}{30}-\dfrac{10}{30}-\dfrac{6}{30}.$

Answers.

1. (a) $\dfrac{6}{5}=1\dfrac{1}{5}$ (b) $\dfrac{14}{11}=1\dfrac{3}{11}$ (c) $\dfrac{28}{19}=1\dfrac{9}{19}$ (d) $\dfrac{14}{4}=3\dfrac{1}{2}$

(e) $\dfrac{7}{6}=1\dfrac{1}{6}$ (f) $\dfrac{9}{3}=3$ (g) $\dfrac{7}{7}=1$ (h) $\dfrac{19}{12}=1\dfrac{7}{12}$

(i) $\dfrac{12}{6}=2$ (j) $\dfrac{25}{18}=1\dfrac{7}{18}.$

2. (a) $\dfrac{2}{5}$ (b) $-\dfrac{2}{5}$ (c) $\dfrac{5}{18}$ (d) $\dfrac{4}{8}=\dfrac{1}{2}$ (e) 0   (f) $-\dfrac{1}{7}$

(g) $-\dfrac{4}{4}=-1$ (h) $-\dfrac{1}{6}$ (i) $\dfrac{1}{6}$ (j) $-\dfrac{6}{3}=-2.$

3. (a) $\dfrac{6}{5}=1\dfrac{1}{5}$ (b) $-\dfrac{2}{3}$ (c) $\dfrac{5}{7}$ (d) $\dfrac{5}{7}$ (e) $\dfrac{3}{10}$

(f) $\dfrac{7}{10}$ (g) $-\dfrac{5}{7}$ (h) $\dfrac{4}{3}=1\dfrac{1}{3}$ (i) 0   (j) 0.

4. (a) $\dfrac{15}{8}=1\dfrac{7}{8}$ (b) $\dfrac{4}{9}$ (c) 0   (d) $-\dfrac{5}{12}$

(e) $\dfrac{39}{28}=1\dfrac{11}{28}$ (f) $\dfrac{20}{15}=1\dfrac{1}{3}$ (g) $\dfrac{13}{18}$ (h) $-\dfrac{1}{30}.$

6.3.2   From the above examples and exercises it should be clear that finding the sums and differences of pairs of rational numbers requires no more than an adequate knowledge of the operations with the integers providing the fractions involved have the same denominators. But we have already noted how any two fractions may be expressed with a common denominator; thus, we can find the sum or difference of any two fractions.

In any addition or subtraction of fractions our plan of "attack" will be to express the fractions involved in terms of a least common denominator (LCD), then to add or subtract the numerators as required. For example, $\frac{2}{3} + \frac{3}{5} = \frac{10}{15} + \frac{9}{15} = \frac{10 + 9}{15} = \frac{19}{15} = 1\frac{4}{15}$.

Examples.

(a) $\frac{5}{6} + \frac{7}{8} = \frac{5 \times 4}{6 \times 4} + \frac{7 \times 3}{8 \times 3} = \frac{20}{24} + \frac{21}{24} = \frac{20 + 21}{24} = \frac{41}{24} = 1\frac{17}{24}$.

(b) $\frac{3}{4} - \frac{1}{6} = \frac{3 \times 3}{4 \times 3} - \frac{1 \times 2}{6 \times 2} = \frac{9}{12} - \frac{2}{12} = \frac{9 - 2}{12} = \frac{7}{12}$.

(c) $\frac{4}{9} + \frac{3}{5} - \frac{11}{15} = \frac{4 \times 5}{9 \times 5} + \frac{3 \times 9}{5 \times 9} - \frac{11 \times 3}{15 \times 3} = \frac{20}{45} + \frac{27}{45} - \frac{33}{45}$

$= \frac{20 + 27 - 33}{45} = \frac{14}{45}$.

Of course, the common denominator need not be the least common denominator in order for us to add or subtract fractions. However, if a multiple of the LCD is used, then the sum or difference will require reduction. For example, a simple procedure to add $\frac{5}{6}$ and $\frac{7}{8}$ would be to use the denominator $6 \times 8 = 48$:

$\frac{5}{6} + \frac{7}{8} = \frac{5 \times 8}{6 \times 8} + \frac{7 \times 6}{8 \times 6} = \frac{40}{48} + \frac{42}{48} = \frac{40 + 42}{48} = \frac{82}{48} = \frac{41 \times 2}{24 \times 2} = \frac{41}{24} = 1\frac{17}{24}$.

Using the above idea we can describe a general "pattern" for adding or subtracting fractions. The universally true equations

$$\frac{A}{B} + \frac{C}{D} = \frac{A \times D + B \times C}{B \times D} \text{ and } \frac{A}{B} - \frac{C}{D} = \frac{A \times D - B \times C}{B \times D}$$

describe a direct approach for finding the sums and differences of fractions.

Practice 2.

1. Find the sums:

(a) $\frac{1}{2} + \frac{1}{3}$ (b) $\frac{1}{3} + \frac{2}{5}$ (c) $\frac{2}{3} + \frac{1}{4}$ (d) $\frac{3}{4} + \frac{1}{5}$ (e) $\frac{5}{9} + \frac{2}{7}$

(f) $\frac{3}{5} + \frac{1}{6}$ (g) $\frac{4}{5} + \frac{4}{9}$ (h) $\frac{2}{3} + \frac{1}{7}$ (i) $\frac{1}{9} + \frac{3}{4}$ (j) $\frac{3}{8} + \frac{4}{9}$.

2. Find the sums:

(a) $\dfrac{2}{3}+\dfrac{1}{2}$ (b) $\dfrac{7}{8}+\dfrac{5}{7}$ (c) $\dfrac{2}{3}+\dfrac{4}{5}$ (d) $\dfrac{4}{5}+\dfrac{1}{2}$ (e) $\dfrac{2}{3}+\dfrac{3}{8}$

(f) $\dfrac{2}{3}+\dfrac{3}{4}$ (g) $\dfrac{4}{5}+\dfrac{5}{6}$ (h) $\dfrac{3}{7}+\dfrac{4}{5}$ (i) $\dfrac{4}{5}+\dfrac{5}{8}$ (j) $\dfrac{7}{9}+\dfrac{1}{2}$.

3. Find the sums:

(a) $\dfrac{1}{2}+\dfrac{5}{6}$ (b) $\dfrac{2}{3}+\dfrac{5}{9}$ (c) $\dfrac{3}{4}+\dfrac{1}{6}$ (d) $\dfrac{1}{2}+\dfrac{1}{4}$ (e) $\dfrac{1}{6}+\dfrac{8}{9}$

(f) $\dfrac{3}{8}+\dfrac{3}{4}$ (g) $\dfrac{2}{3}+\dfrac{5}{6}$ (h) $\dfrac{1}{2}+\dfrac{7}{8}$ (i) $\dfrac{5}{8}+\dfrac{1}{6}$ (j) $\dfrac{1}{3}+\dfrac{1}{6}$.

4. Find:

(a) $\dfrac{4}{9}+\dfrac{5}{12}$ (b) $\dfrac{6}{15}+\dfrac{7}{18}$ (c) $\dfrac{5}{12}+\dfrac{8}{15}$ (d) $\dfrac{2}{13}+\dfrac{7}{9}$

(e) $\dfrac{3}{22}+\dfrac{2}{33}$ (f) $\dfrac{1}{18}+\dfrac{1}{12}$ (g) $\dfrac{9}{20}+\dfrac{5}{8}$ (h) $\dfrac{15}{16}+\dfrac{11}{12}$

(i) $\dfrac{9}{14}+\dfrac{13}{24}$ (j) $\dfrac{5}{18}+\dfrac{9}{10}$.

5. Find the differences:

(a) $\dfrac{1}{2}-\dfrac{1}{3}$ (b) $\dfrac{1}{3}-\dfrac{1}{4}$ (c) $\dfrac{3}{5}-\dfrac{1}{3}$ (d) $\dfrac{1}{6}-\dfrac{1}{5}$ (e) $\dfrac{3}{4}-\dfrac{2}{3}$

(f) $\dfrac{2}{9}-\dfrac{5}{7}$ (g) $\dfrac{5}{8}-\dfrac{4}{9}$ (h) $\dfrac{6}{7}-\dfrac{4}{5}$ (i) $\dfrac{3}{5}-\dfrac{5}{8}$ (j) $\dfrac{7}{8}-\dfrac{4}{7}$.

6. Find:

(a) $\dfrac{5}{6}-\dfrac{3}{4}$ (b) $\dfrac{5}{8}-\dfrac{1}{6}$ (c) $\dfrac{1}{2}-\dfrac{1}{8}$ (d) $\dfrac{7}{9}-\dfrac{2}{3}$ (e) $\dfrac{3}{4}-\dfrac{3}{8}$

(f) $\dfrac{1}{6}-\dfrac{1}{2}$ (g) $\dfrac{5}{6}-\dfrac{5}{9}$ (h) $\dfrac{7}{12}-\dfrac{7}{8}$ (i) $\dfrac{2}{3}-\dfrac{5}{12}$ (j) $\dfrac{5}{12}-\dfrac{7}{10}$.

7. Find:

(a) $\dfrac{7}{12}-\dfrac{5}{9}$ (b) $\dfrac{3}{10}-\dfrac{5}{18}$ (c) $\dfrac{7}{20}-\dfrac{5}{16}$ (d) $\dfrac{3}{10}-\dfrac{1}{12}$

(e) $\dfrac{9}{15}-\dfrac{11}{18}$ (f) $\dfrac{4}{21}-\dfrac{3}{14}$ (g) $\dfrac{7}{9}-\dfrac{9}{21}$ (h) $\dfrac{3}{14}-\dfrac{5}{16}$

(i) $\dfrac{11}{40}-\dfrac{11}{30}$ (j) $\dfrac{5}{12}-\dfrac{7}{22}$.

8. (a) $\dfrac{1}{2}+\dfrac{1}{3}+\dfrac{1}{4}$ (b) $\dfrac{2}{3}+\dfrac{3}{4}+\dfrac{4}{5}$ (c) $\dfrac{5}{6}+\dfrac{2}{9}+\dfrac{3}{4}$ (d) $\dfrac{3}{8}+\dfrac{1}{6}+\dfrac{2}{3}$

(e) $\dfrac{3}{5}+\dfrac{5}{7}+\dfrac{2}{3}$ (f) $\dfrac{7}{8}+\dfrac{8}{9}+\dfrac{6}{7}$ (g) $\dfrac{3}{8}+\dfrac{1}{2}+\dfrac{1}{6}$ (h) $\dfrac{3}{4}+\dfrac{4}{9}+\dfrac{2}{3}$.

9. (a) $\dfrac{2}{3}+\dfrac{1}{4}-\dfrac{3}{5}$ (b) $\dfrac{5}{6}+\dfrac{1}{3}-\dfrac{3}{4}$ (c) $\dfrac{1}{5}+\dfrac{1}{8}-\dfrac{1}{2}$ (d) $\dfrac{4}{9}-\dfrac{5}{6}+\dfrac{7}{8}$

(e) $\dfrac{2}{3}-\dfrac{4}{7}+\dfrac{4}{9}$ (f) $\dfrac{1}{6}-\dfrac{4}{5}+\dfrac{1}{3}$ (g) $\dfrac{8}{9}-\dfrac{1}{4}-\dfrac{1}{3}$ (h) $\dfrac{6}{7}-\dfrac{5}{8}-\dfrac{4}{9}$.

10. (a) $\dfrac{1}{2}+\dfrac{1}{4}+\dfrac{1}{6}+\dfrac{1}{8}$ (b) $\dfrac{2}{3}+\dfrac{4}{5}+\dfrac{6}{7}+\dfrac{8}{9}$ (c) $\dfrac{1}{2}-\dfrac{1}{3}+\dfrac{1}{4}-\dfrac{1}{5}+\dfrac{1}{6}$

  (d) $\dfrac{3}{4}+\dfrac{1}{8}-\dfrac{1}{16}-\dfrac{1}{32}$ (e) $\dfrac{5}{6}-\dfrac{4}{5}-\dfrac{3}{4}-\dfrac{2}{3}$ (f) $\dfrac{5}{8}-\dfrac{3}{4}+\dfrac{2}{3}-\dfrac{3}{5}+\dfrac{5}{6}.$

Answers.

1. (a) $\dfrac{5}{6}$ (b) $\dfrac{11}{15}$ (c) $\dfrac{11}{12}$ (d) $\dfrac{19}{20}$ (e) $\dfrac{53}{63}$ (f) $\dfrac{23}{30}$

  (g) $\dfrac{56}{45}=1\dfrac{11}{45}$ (h) $\dfrac{17}{21}$ (i) $\dfrac{31}{36}$ (j) $\dfrac{59}{72}.$

2. (a) $\dfrac{7}{6}=1\dfrac{1}{6}$ (b) $\dfrac{89}{56}=1\dfrac{33}{56}$ (c) $\dfrac{22}{15}=1\dfrac{7}{15}$ (d) $\dfrac{13}{10}=1\dfrac{3}{10}$

  (e) $\dfrac{25}{24}=1\dfrac{1}{24}$ (f) $\dfrac{17}{12}=1\dfrac{5}{12}$ (g) $\dfrac{49}{30}=1\dfrac{19}{30}$ (h) $\dfrac{43}{35}=1\dfrac{8}{35}$

  (i) $\dfrac{57}{40}=1\dfrac{17}{40}$ (j) $\dfrac{23}{18}=1\dfrac{5}{18}.$

3. (a) $\dfrac{8}{6}=1\dfrac{1}{3}$ (b) $\dfrac{11}{9}=1\dfrac{2}{9}$ (c) $\dfrac{11}{12}$ (d) $\dfrac{3}{4}$ (e) $\dfrac{19}{18}=1\dfrac{1}{18}$

  (f) $\dfrac{9}{8}=1\dfrac{1}{8}$ (g) $\dfrac{9}{6}=1\dfrac{1}{2}$ (h) $\dfrac{11}{8}=1\dfrac{3}{8}$ (i) $\dfrac{19}{24}$ (j) $\dfrac{3}{6}=\dfrac{1}{2}.$

4. (a) $\dfrac{31}{36}$ (b) $\dfrac{71}{90}$ (c) $\dfrac{57}{60}$ (d) $\dfrac{109}{117}$ (e) $\dfrac{13}{66}$ (f) $\dfrac{5}{36}$

  (g) $\dfrac{43}{40}=1\dfrac{3}{40}$ (h) $\dfrac{89}{48}=1\dfrac{41}{48}$ (i) $\dfrac{199}{168}=1\dfrac{31}{168}$ (j) $\dfrac{106}{90}=1\dfrac{8}{45}.$

5. (a) $\dfrac{1}{6}$ (b) $\dfrac{1}{12}$ (c) $\dfrac{4}{15}$ (d) $-\dfrac{1}{30}$ (e) $\dfrac{1}{12}$

  (f) $-\dfrac{31}{63}$ (g) $\dfrac{13}{72}$ (h) $\dfrac{2}{35}$ (i) $-\dfrac{1}{40}$ (j) $\dfrac{17}{56}.$

6. (a) $\dfrac{1}{12}$ (b) $\dfrac{11}{24}$ (c) $\dfrac{3}{8}$ (d) $\dfrac{1}{9}$ (e) $\dfrac{3}{8}$

  (f) $-\dfrac{1}{3}$ (g) $\dfrac{5}{18}$ (h) $-\dfrac{7}{24}$ (i) $\dfrac{1}{4}$ (j) $-\dfrac{17}{60}.$

7. (a) $\dfrac{1}{36}$ (b) $\dfrac{1}{45}$ (c) $\dfrac{3}{80}$ (d) $\dfrac{13}{60}$ (e) $-\dfrac{1}{90}$

  (f) $-\dfrac{1}{42}$ (g) $\dfrac{22}{63}$ (h) $-\dfrac{11}{112}$ (i) $-\dfrac{11}{120}$ (j) $\dfrac{13}{132}.$

8. (a) $\dfrac{13}{12}=1\dfrac{1}{12}$ (b) $\dfrac{133}{60}=2\dfrac{13}{60}$ (c) $\dfrac{65}{36}=1\dfrac{29}{36}$ (d) $\dfrac{29}{24}=1\dfrac{5}{24}$

  (e) $\dfrac{208}{105}=1\dfrac{103}{105}$ (f) $\dfrac{1321}{504}=2\dfrac{313}{504}$ (g) $\dfrac{25}{24}=1\dfrac{1}{24}$ (h) $\dfrac{67}{36}=1\dfrac{31}{36}.$

9. (a) $\dfrac{19}{60}$ (b) $\dfrac{5}{12}$ (c) $-\dfrac{7}{40}$ (d) $\dfrac{35}{72}$ (e) $\dfrac{34}{63}$ (f) $-\dfrac{3}{10}$

   (g) $\dfrac{11}{36}$ (h) $-\dfrac{107}{504}$.

10. (a) $\dfrac{25}{24} = 1\dfrac{1}{24}$ (b) $\dfrac{1012}{315} = 3\dfrac{67}{315}$ (c) $\dfrac{23}{60}$ (d) $\dfrac{25}{32}$

   (e) $-\dfrac{83}{60} = -1\dfrac{23}{60}$ (f) $\dfrac{31}{40}$.

6.3.3   In concluding this chapter we observe that we have attained our goal of carrying out the four fundamental arithmetical operations with the rational numbers. In summary, the set of rational numbers with the two basic operations of addition and multiplication form a mathematical structure called a **field**. Since the set of rational numbers are **ordered**, we say that it forms an **ordered field**. Furthermore, the fundamental property of the rational numbers leads to the distinctive property called **denseness**.

More formally, any mathematical structure consisting of a set with two operations which satisfy the following requirements is called a **field**:

1. Both operations are **closed**.
2. Both operations are **commutative**.
3. Both operations are **associative**.
4. One of the operations is **distributive** over the other.
5. There are two **identities** in the set. One for each of the operations.
6. If we delete the identity for the operation which is not distributive, then every other element in the set has two **inverses** associated with it. One for each of the operations.

Exercises

1. Construct and label scales which illustrate:

   (a) $\dfrac{4}{9} + \dfrac{7}{9}$ (b) $\dfrac{7}{9} - \dfrac{4}{9}$ (c) $\dfrac{6}{11} + \dfrac{5}{11}$ (d) $\dfrac{6}{11} - \dfrac{5}{11}$.

2. Construct and label scales which illustrate:

   (a) $-\dfrac{4}{7} + \dfrac{6}{7}$ (b) $\dfrac{6}{7} - \dfrac{4}{7}$ (c) $\dfrac{5}{12} - \dfrac{11}{12}$ (d) $\dfrac{11}{12} - \dfrac{5}{12}$.

3. Find the sum or difference as indicated:

   (a) $\dfrac{5}{2} - \dfrac{3}{2}$ (b) $\dfrac{1}{8} + \dfrac{4}{8}$ (c) $\dfrac{8}{12} - \dfrac{3}{12}$ (d) $\dfrac{3}{12} - \dfrac{8}{12}$

   (e) $\dfrac{7}{16} + \dfrac{0}{16}$.

4. Find the least common denominator (LCD) for the following sets of fractions.

(a) $\dfrac{1}{12}, \dfrac{7}{30}, \dfrac{5}{36}$ (b) $\dfrac{2}{3}, \dfrac{3}{4}, \dfrac{5}{12}$ (c) $\dfrac{2}{7}, \dfrac{1}{8}, \dfrac{3}{14}$.

5. Find the sum of each set of fractions in Exercise 4 above.

6. Find the sums:

(a) $\dfrac{6}{7} + \dfrac{3}{8} + \dfrac{5}{14}$ (b) $\dfrac{1}{4} + \dfrac{1}{8} + \dfrac{1}{12}$ (c) $\dfrac{9}{11} + \dfrac{2}{33} + \dfrac{1}{44}$

(d) $\dfrac{2}{3} + \dfrac{3}{5} + \dfrac{1}{9}$ (e) $\dfrac{5}{6} + \dfrac{1}{3} + \dfrac{5}{12}$ (f) $\dfrac{17}{18} + \dfrac{11}{24} + \dfrac{9}{16}$.

7. Find the differences:

(a) $\dfrac{13}{15} - \dfrac{18}{75}$ (b) $\dfrac{11}{30} - \dfrac{4}{15}$ (c) $\dfrac{3}{5} - \dfrac{3}{8}$ (d) $\dfrac{2}{7} - \dfrac{3}{14}$

(e) $\dfrac{11}{16} - \dfrac{5}{12}$ (f) $\dfrac{19}{20} - \dfrac{3}{5}$ (g) $\dfrac{5}{8} - \dfrac{1}{3}$ (h) $\dfrac{13}{21} - \dfrac{5}{14}$

(i) $\dfrac{1}{4} - \dfrac{1}{5}$ (j) $\dfrac{9}{20} - \dfrac{5}{12}$.

8. Find the value of

(a) $\dfrac{1}{3} + \dfrac{3}{2} - \dfrac{2}{3}$ (b) $\dfrac{2}{7} - \dfrac{1}{6} + \dfrac{5}{21}$ (c) $\dfrac{11}{24} + \dfrac{7}{9} - \dfrac{3}{4}$

(d) $\dfrac{3}{4} - \dfrac{1}{12} - \dfrac{4}{15}$ (e) $\dfrac{1}{8} + \dfrac{1}{9} + \dfrac{2}{5}$ (f) $\dfrac{11}{15} - \dfrac{7}{10} + \dfrac{5}{6}$.

9. (a) How many tenths are equal to 1?
(b) How many hundredths are equal to 1?
(c) How many hundredths are equal to one-tenth?
(d) What part of 2 is one-tenth?
(e) What part of 2 is one-hundredth?

10. Find two distinct positive integers such that the sum of their reciprocals is equal to one-half.

11. Find a fraction such that if you subtract 4 from both the numerator and the denominator, the new fraction will be one-half the original fraction.

12. The sum of $\dfrac{5}{6}$ and $\dfrac{7}{16}$ times the difference, $\dfrac{5}{6}$ less $\dfrac{7}{16}$, is divided by $\dfrac{19}{36}$. Find the resulting reduced fraction.

13. An inheritance was divided among two sons and a daughter so that the younger son received half again as much as the daughter and the older son received half again as much as the younger son. If the inheritance amounted to $38,000, then how much did the daughter receive?

14. Bill had $360 in a savings account at the bank. If he withdrew three-eighth of his savings and then a week later withdrew one-third

of what was left in his account, then how much did he have left in his savings account at the bank?

15. Figure 75 represents the Centigrade and Fahrenheit scales for measuring temperatures in degrees. Using the scale references and fractions, determine the

(a) Centigrade temperature if the temperature is given as 86° Fahrenheit.

(b) Fahrenheit temperature given that it is 45° Centigrade.

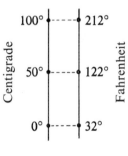

FIGURE 75

Answers.

1. (a)

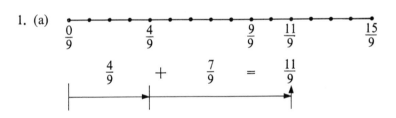

(b)

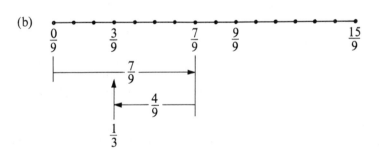

(c)

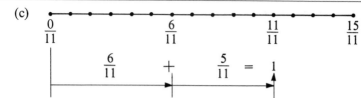

(d)

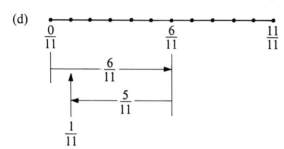

2. (a)

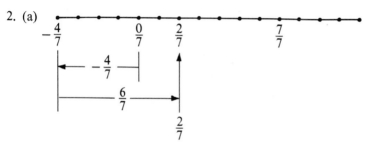

(b)

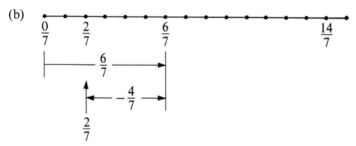

(c)

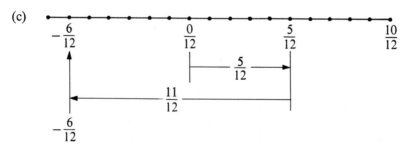

(d)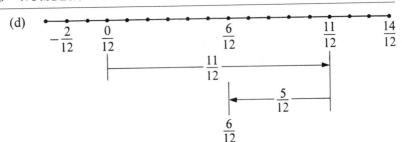

3. (a) 1   (b) $\frac{5}{8}$ (c) $\frac{5}{12}$ (d) $-\frac{5}{12}$ (e) $\frac{7}{16}$.

4. (a) 180   (b) 12   (c) 56.

5. (a) $\frac{41}{90}$ (b) $\frac{11}{6} = 1\frac{5}{6}$ (c) $\frac{5}{8}$.

6. (a) $\frac{89}{56} = 1\frac{33}{56}$ (b) $\frac{11}{24}$ (c) $\frac{119}{132}$ (d) $\frac{62}{45} = 1\frac{17}{45}$

   (e) $\frac{19}{12} = 1\frac{7}{12}$ (f) $\frac{283}{144} = 1\frac{139}{144}$.

7. (a) $\frac{47}{75}$ (b) $\frac{1}{10}$ (c) $\frac{9}{40}$ (d) $\frac{1}{14}$ (e) $\frac{13}{48}$ (f) $\frac{7}{20}$

   (g) $\frac{7}{24}$ (h) $\frac{11}{42}$ (i) $\frac{1}{20}$ (j) $\frac{1}{30}$.

8. (a) $1\frac{1}{6}$ (b) $\frac{5}{14}$ (c) $\frac{35}{72}$ (d) $\frac{2}{5}$ (e) $\frac{229}{360}$ (f) $\frac{13}{15}$.

9. (a) 10   (b) 100   (c) 10   (d) $\frac{1}{20}$ (e) $\frac{1}{200}$.

10. 3 and 6.

11. $\frac{6}{12}$.

12. $\frac{61}{64}$.

13. $8,000.

14. $150.

15. (a) 30°C   (b) 113°F.

Review Summary

In this chapter we noted that men had a need to describe the idea of a part of a set as compared to a "whole" set. More formally, we faced the "embarrassing" question of "What is the 'exact' quotient when a divisor is not a factor of the dividend in a division?"

Our answer was to extend the integers to the idea of _____ numbers.

rational

In developing our ideas concerning the rational numbers we compared "parts" to "wholes." When a "part" is compared to a "whole," we say that we have formed a _____. For example, comparing a nickel to a dollar we write $\frac{5}{100}$ or, more simply, $\frac{1}{20}$. When we repre-

ratio

sent quantities along a line segment and indicate measurements in this way, we say that we have constructed a _____. Both ratios and scales are convenient methods for examining and illustrating our ideas.

scale

In writing, to distinguish our "new point of view," we introduced some new vocabulary. In $\frac{N}{D} = R$ we call N the _____, D the _____, and R a _____ number for N and D integers with $D \neq 0$. By $\frac{N}{D} = R$ we mean that $N = $ _____. The form, $\frac{N}{D}$, in which the rational numbers

numerator,
denominator,
rational

$R \times D$

have been introduced is called a _____ form. Thus, for simplicity, we often refer to both the number idea and the numeral as fractions.

fractional

As we developed our ideas concerning the rational numbers we kept in mind all of the properties of the arithmetical operations. Our desire was to have these properties "carry over" to the manipulations of rational numbers. To build our intuition concerning the rational numbers we practiced interpreting various types of situations. For example, in Figure 76 we can compare the shaded portion to the whole and describe this comparison with the fraction _____. Since two pints make a quart and four quarts make a gallon, we can say that one pint is to a gallon as _____ is to _____ or use the fraction _____ to describe the part of a gallon that a pint is. If the scale on a drawing states that "$\frac{1}{4}$ inch is

$\frac{5}{12}$

1, 8

$\frac{1}{8}$

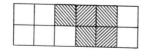

FIGURE 76

equal to 1 foot," then a 3-inch line segment on the map must represent a length of _____ feet. To further   *12*

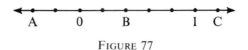

FIGURE 77

strengthen our intuition we discussed the construction of scales. From our discussion we might naturally name the points marked *A, B,* and *C* in Figure 77 as *A* = _____, $-\frac{2}{5}, \frac{2}{5}, \frac{6}{5}$
B = _____, and *C* = _____. When a line is marked off in unit segments and by equal divisions of the unit segment, we often refer to it as a _____ _____ _____.   *rational number line*

In writing names for rational numbers it became evident that a given fraction has many names. Keeping in mind our previously agreed upon properties for manipulating with numbers, we said that two fractions $\frac{A}{B}$ and $\frac{C}{D}$ are equal whenever _____. If the numerator   *A × D = C × B*
and denominator of a fraction are relatively prime, that is, have no common factors other than 1, then we said that the fraction was _____. The property of   *reduced*
fractions which enabled us to reduce and change the numerator or denominator of a fraction is called the fundamental property of the rational numbers. It is expressed by:

For $\frac{A}{B}$ a rational number and $C \neq 0$,

we have $\frac{A \times C}{B \times C} =$ _____. $\frac{A}{B}$

For example, $\frac{3}{7} = \frac{}{105}, \frac{5}{8} = \frac{40}{}$ *45, 64*

In contrast to distinguishing the various forms of fractions, we classified the rational numbers into proper and improper fractions. A proper fraction names a rational number between _____ and _____. If a fraction   *−1, 1*
is not proper, we say that it is _____. For example, $\frac{9}{8}$ *improper*
is an _____ fraction, whereas $\frac{8}{9}$ is a _____ fraction.   *improper, proper*
Improper fractions are often expressed in mixed form.

For example, the _____ fraction $1\frac{2}{5}$ expresses the _____   *mixed, sum*

of the integer 1 and the fraction $\frac{2}{5}$.

As with the natural numbers and integers, the rational numbers can be ordered. However, the order obtained is quite different. We cannot name consecutive rational numbers for between any two distinct rational numbers we can find another distinct rational number. Because of this distinctive property, the rational numbers are said to be dense. For example, between $\frac{6}{7}$ and $\frac{19}{20}$ we

have $\frac{25}{28}$. To "see" this we write the fractions with a

_____ _____ of 140. That is, $\frac{6}{7}$ = _____ and $\frac{19}{20}$ =

_____. Also, since $\frac{25}{28} = \frac{125}{140}$ we "see" that $\frac{25}{28}$ is indeed

between the two given fractions. The least common denominator is the lowest common multiple of the set of denominators under consideration. A set of fractions can be ordered by first expressing the fractions with a

_____ _____.

common denomina-

$\frac{120}{140}$

$\frac{133}{140}$

common denominator

As with the integers, the rational numbers can be separated into positive, zero, and negative rationals. Using the negative sign, both positive and negative rational numbers may be represented in four ways.

For example, $\frac{5}{6} = \frac{-5}{-6} = -\frac{-5}{6} = -\frac{5}{-6}$ and $-\frac{4}{5} =$ _____ =

_____ = _____.

$\frac{-4}{5}$

$\frac{4}{-5}, -\frac{-4}{-5}$

In our development of multiplication of fractions we first noted that every fraction can be expressed as a product of an integer and a fraction with _____   *numerator*
equal to 1. Next we observed that the product of an integer times a fraction was the fraction formed with the product of the integer and the numerator of the fraction as a _____ and the denominator of the fraction as a   *numerator*
_____. At this point we noted that the special products   *denominator*
involving 0 and 1 were $0 \times \frac{N}{D} =$ _____ and $1 \times \frac{N}{D}$ *0*

= _____. The special fractions involving 0 and 1 were $\frac{N}{D}$

$\frac{0}{D} =$ _____, $\frac{N}{1} =$ _____, and $\frac{D}{D} =$ _____ for $D \neq 0$.   *0, N, 1*

In multiplying with fractions, it became evident
that _____ multiply while _____ divide. That is, in $\frac{5}{7} \times 4$ *numerators,*
denominators
the 5 acts as a multiplier while the 7 acts as a divisor. By
applying the commutative and associative properties of
multiplication we obtained a general procedure for
finding the product of two fractions. In ordinary English:
"Multiply the numerators to form the numerator of the
product and multiply the denominators to form the
denominator of the product." In mathematical symbols
we can express this by

$$\frac{A}{B} \times \frac{C}{D} = \underline{\hspace{1cm}}$$

$\frac{A \times C}{B \times D}$

The work involved in multiplying fractions can
often be simplified if there are common factors in
the numerators and the denominators of the fractions
involved. For example, to do $\frac{66}{70} \times \frac{35}{78}$ we can find the
products 66×35 and 70×78 to form the product fraction $\frac{2310}{5460}$ and then reduce the fraction to _____. However, if we notice that $66 = 6 \times 11$, $70 = 2 \times 35$, and
$78 = 6 \times 13$, then we can think:

$\frac{11}{26}$

$$\frac{66}{70} \times \frac{35}{78} = \frac{6 \times 11 \times 35}{2 \times 35 \times 6 \times 13} = \frac{11}{26}$$

by cancelling the common factors _____ and _____   *6, 35*
from both the numerator and denominator. Briefly,
we might write

$$\frac{\overset{11}{\cancel{66}}}{\underset{2}{\cancel{70}}} \times \frac{\overset{1}{\cancel{35}}}{\underset{13}{\cancel{78}}} = \frac{11}{26}.$$

In $\frac{6}{7} \times \frac{14}{27}$ there is a common factor of _____ in 6 and   *3*
27 and a common factor of _____ in 7 and 14 so that   *7*
we can _____ the common factors to obtain $\frac{2}{1} \times \frac{2}{9} = \frac{4}{9}$ *cancel*
as the product of $\frac{6}{7}$ and $\frac{14}{27}$.

When the product of two fractions equaled 1 we said
that the fractions were _____ of each other. For ex-   *reciprocals*

ample, the reciprocal of $\frac{3}{7}$ is _____ since $\frac{3}{7} \times \frac{7}{3} = 1$. The $\frac{7}{3}$

reciprocal of a fraction not equal to zero is obtained by interchanging the numerator and denominator of the given fraction. The number _____ has no reciprocal. 0

Using the idea of reciprocal fractions, we easily developed procedures for the division of a fraction by another fraction not equal to zero. To obtain the quotient of two fractions, we multiplied both the dividend and divisor by the reciprocal of the _____. This resulted in a product of   *divisor*
the _____ times the reciprocal of the divisor. For   *dividend*
example, $\frac{3}{4} \div \frac{5}{8} = \frac{3}{4} \times$ _____ $= \frac{6}{5}$. In general, we have $\frac{8}{5}$

$$\frac{A}{B} \div \frac{C}{D} = \frac{A}{B} \times \frac{D}{C}, \text{ where } B \neq 0, C \neq 0, \text{ and } D \neq 0.$$

The four situations involving 0 and 1 were treated

just as with the integers. That is, $\frac{N}{D} \div 1 =$ _____, $1 \div \frac{N}{D}$ $\frac{N}{D}$

$=$ _____ for $\frac{N}{D} \neq 0$, $0 \div \frac{N}{D} =$ _____ for $\frac{N}{D} \neq 0$, and $\frac{N}{D} \div 0$ $\frac{D}{N}, 0$
is not permitted.

We used scales and the rational number line to study the operations of addition and subtraction with fractions. The sum or difference of fractions with the same or like denominators was quite easy to find. We simply found the sum or difference of the _____. For example,   *numerators*
$\frac{2}{9} + \frac{5}{9} = \frac{7}{9}$ and $\frac{8}{9} - \frac{2}{9} = \frac{6}{9} = \frac{2}{3}$.

Since we can find the sum or difference of fractions with common denominators, we proceeded to express fractions involved in additions or subtractions in terms of a _____ _____ _____. Once expressed in terms of   *least com-*
common denominators, fractions are easily summed and   *mon denom-*
differences easily determined. For example, $\frac{4}{15} + \frac{5}{18}$ *inator*

$= \frac{}{90} + \frac{}{90} = \frac{}{90}$ and $\frac{7}{12} - \frac{3}{8} = \frac{14}{-} - \frac{9}{-} = \frac{5}{24}$. A direct and   *24, 25, 49,*
general approach for finding the sums and differences of   *24, 24*
fractions is described by

$$\frac{A}{B} + \frac{C}{D} = \frac{A \times D + B \times C}{B \times D} \text{ and } \frac{A}{B} - \frac{C}{D} = \frac{A \times D - B \times C}{B \times D}.$$

With the rational numbers we attained the goal of carrying out the four fundamental arithmetical operations. The structure attained by the set of rational numbers is called an ordered field.

Of course, knowing HOW to add, subtract, multiply, and divide with fractions is only one step toward an understanding of the rational numbers. Learning WHEN to do the operations and interpreting the results of operations are other important steps in understanding and using the rational numbers.

Chapter Exercises (6)

Group I.

1. The idea of comparing a part to a whole is called a _____. When we think of this idea as a number, we call it a _____ _____.

2. In writing $\frac{3}{5} = R$ we call 3 the _____, 5 the _____, and R the _____ _____. The form $\frac{3}{5}$ is called a _____ form.

3. Since 2 pints make 1 quart, what fraction of 3 quarts is 1 pint? How many pints make $5\frac{1}{3}$ quarts? What fraction of 4 quarts is 3 pints?

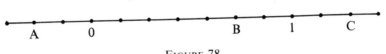

A   0   B   1   C

FIGURE 78

4. Given the scale in Figure 78, we might naturally name the points marked A, B, and C with the reduced fractions _____, _____, and _____.

5. Find N in each of the following so that the equations will be true:

(a) $\frac{5}{8} = \frac{N}{56}$ (b) $\frac{N}{7} = \frac{33}{77}$ (c) $\frac{8}{N} = \frac{48}{54}$ (d) $\frac{1}{6} = \frac{12}{N}$

(e) $\frac{36}{60} = \frac{N}{15}$.

6. Reduce the following fractions:

(a) $\frac{36}{66}$ (b) $\frac{98}{105}$ (c) $\frac{150}{45}$ (d) $\frac{325}{1365}$ (e) $\frac{1674}{1728}$.

7. Given $\frac{-6}{5}$; $\frac{4}{12}$; $-\frac{3}{7}$; $\frac{-8}{-6}$:

(a) Which are proper fractions?
(b) Which are positive fractions?
(c) Which are reduced fractions?

8. Order the following set of rational numbers from smallest to largest: $\dfrac{4}{7}, \dfrac{7}{10}, \dfrac{3}{5}, \dfrac{9}{14}, \dfrac{22}{35}$.

9. Given the rational "points" $\dfrac{1}{3}$ and $\dfrac{3}{8}$ on a rational number line, find the reduced rational numbers for the two points dividing the given segment into three equal parts.

10. Writing $\dfrac{4}{7} = 4 \times \dfrac{1}{7}$ suggests two interpretations of fractions. $\dfrac{4}{7}$ suggests "_____ of the _____ equal parts of _____." $4 \times \dfrac{1}{7}$ suggests "_____ of the _____ equal parts of _____."

11. The statement "To multiply two fractions together, we multiply the numerators to form the numerator of the product and multiply the denominators to form the denominator of the product" can be translated into mathematical symbols as _____.

12. Find the products in reduced form:

(a) $2 \times \dfrac{4}{9}$ (b) $6 \times \dfrac{3}{20}$ (c) $\dfrac{7}{11} \times \dfrac{33}{35}$ (d) $\dfrac{11}{12} \times \dfrac{18}{25}$

(e) $\dfrac{39}{49} \times \dfrac{35}{78}$.

13. Find the products in reduced form:

(a) $\dfrac{4}{21} \times \dfrac{5}{6} \times \dfrac{9}{10}$ (b) $\dfrac{2}{7} \times \dfrac{9}{11} \times \dfrac{7}{2}$ (c) $\dfrac{14}{18} \times \dfrac{45}{49} \times \dfrac{21}{28}$.

14. The reciprocal of $\dfrac{7}{9}$ is _____, since $\dfrac{7}{9} \times$ _____ = _____.

15. Find the reduced rational quotients:

(a) $4 \div \dfrac{6}{7}$ (b) $\dfrac{6}{7} \div 4$ (c) $\dfrac{5}{8} \div \dfrac{15}{16}$ (d) $\dfrac{26}{75} \div \dfrac{143}{105}$

(e) $\dfrac{25}{40} \div \dfrac{35}{84}$.

16. Find the value of K in each of the following equations so that the equation will be true.

(a) $\dfrac{4}{11} \times K = 1$ (b) $K \times \dfrac{5}{7} = 0$ (c) $\dfrac{6}{13} \times K = \dfrac{6}{13}$

(d) $K \times \dfrac{3}{5} = \dfrac{5}{3}$ (e) $K \div \dfrac{2}{9} = \dfrac{2}{9}$ (f) $\dfrac{3}{7} \div K = \dfrac{7}{3}$

(g) $K \div \dfrac{7}{9} = 0$ (h) $\dfrac{8}{11} \div K = 1$.

17. The mathematical statement: $\dfrac{A}{B} \div \dfrac{C}{D} = \dfrac{A}{B} \times \dfrac{D}{C}$ can be translated into ordinary English as "_____."

18. (a) Express $\frac{5}{6}$ as a fraction with denominator 54.

(b) What is the product of $\frac{12}{25}$ and $\frac{15}{16}$ in reduced form?

(c) Find the quotient when $\frac{4}{7}$ is divided by $\frac{20}{21}$.

(d) How many times larger than $\frac{2}{3}$ is $\frac{14}{15}$?

19. Construct and label scales which illustrate:

(a) $\frac{4}{15} + \frac{8}{15}$ (b) $\frac{9}{16} - \frac{13}{16}$ (c) $-\frac{6}{7} + \frac{2}{7}$ (d) $-\frac{7}{10} - \frac{3}{10}$.

20. Find the least common denominator (LCD) for each of the following sets of fractions.

(a) $\frac{1}{6}, \frac{4}{9}, \frac{3}{4}$ (b) $\frac{4}{5}, \frac{2}{3}, \frac{1}{2}$ (c) $\frac{5}{8}, \frac{5}{9}, \frac{5}{12}$ (d) $\frac{2}{3}, \frac{5}{6}, \frac{7}{9}$.

21. Find the sum of each set of fractions in Exercise 20 above.

22. Find the differences:

(a) $\frac{13}{24} - \frac{7}{16}$ (b) $\frac{4}{15} - \frac{5}{18}$ (c) $\frac{27}{32} - \frac{27}{40}$ (d) $\frac{25}{54} - \frac{5}{36}$.

23. Recall the conventions for the order of operations and apply them to find the simplest reduced fractions for:

(a) $\frac{8}{9} - \left(\frac{7}{8} + \left[\frac{6}{7} - \frac{5}{6}\right]\right)$ (b) $\frac{3}{4} - \dfrac{\frac{2}{3} + \left(\frac{3}{5} \times \frac{1}{2}\right)}{\frac{19}{20} + \frac{1}{2}}$

(c) $\dfrac{\frac{3}{5} \times \left(\frac{5}{6} + \frac{3}{5}\right)}{\frac{29}{25} - \frac{1}{5}} - \frac{2}{3}$.

24. Match the lettered examples with the numbered descriptions so that they best illustrate the property described.

(a) $\frac{5}{9} \times \frac{9}{5} = 1$ 1. associative

(b) $\frac{5}{9} \times \frac{4}{4} = \frac{20}{36}$ 2. additive inverse

(c) $\frac{3}{4} \times \frac{5}{6} = \frac{5}{8}$ 3. closure

(d) $-\frac{3}{4} + \frac{3}{4} = 0$ 4. commutative

(e) $\frac{2}{3} \times \left(\frac{6}{7} + \frac{3}{4}\right) = \frac{4}{7} + \frac{1}{2}$ 5. distributive

(f) $\frac{1}{2} \times \left(\frac{2}{5} \times \frac{3}{7}\right) = \left(\frac{1}{2} \times \frac{2}{5}\right) \times \frac{3}{7}$ 6. reciprocal

(g) $\frac{4}{7} + \frac{0}{4} = \frac{4}{7}$ 7. one

(h) $\frac{1}{2} + \frac{2}{3} = \frac{2}{3} + \frac{1}{2}$ 8. zero

25. If Mr. Jones spends $\frac{4}{15}$ of his income for housing and $\frac{3}{10}$ for food, then what fraction of his income remains for all other expenses?

26. Two pumps can be used to fill a tank. One pump used by itself can fill the tank in 6 hours and 15 minutes. The second pump can fill the tank in $\frac{2}{3}$ the time it takes the first pump. How long would it take if both pumps were used together?

27. A zoning ordinance specifies that the maximum number of above ground floors in a building must not exceed $\frac{2}{5}$ of the sum of $\frac{1}{10}$ the width in feet and $\frac{1}{8}$ the depth in feet of a building lot. What is the maximum number of above ground floors possible in a building on a 50 feet wide and 100 feet deep lot?

28. Five-ninths of a positive number is equal to the number less its reciprocal. Find the number.

Group II.

1. When lengths along a line are marked with equal divisions and the division points are named with numerals, we call the representation a _____. Such representations help our intuitive understanding of the _____ _____.

2. When we write $\frac{9}{7} = K$ we call 7 the _____, 9 the _____, and K the _____ _____. $\frac{9}{7} = K$ means the same thing as $9 = $ _____.

3. Since there are 3 feet in 1 yard, what fraction of 2 yards is 1 foot? How many feet make $4\frac{1}{2}$ yards? What fraction of 5 yards is 6 feet?

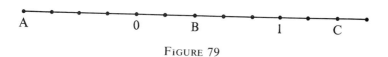

FIGURE 79

4. Given the scale in Figure 79, we might naturally name the points marked *A, B,* and *C* with the reduced fractions _____, _____, and _____.

5. Find *M* in each of the following so that the equations will be true:

(a) $\frac{4}{7} = \frac{M}{28}$ (b) $\frac{M}{6} = \frac{6}{36}$ (c) $\frac{9}{M} = \frac{63}{77}$ (d) $\frac{1}{5} = \frac{10}{M}$

(e) $\frac{18}{24} = \frac{M}{8}$.

6. Reduce the following fractions:

(a) $\frac{35}{42}$ (b) $\frac{91}{143}$ (c) $\frac{108}{63}$ (d) $\frac{264}{825}$ (e) $\frac{1734}{7956}$.

7. Given $\frac{4}{-7}; \frac{9}{5}; \frac{-2}{6}; \frac{-15}{12}$:

(a) Which are proper fractions?

(b) Which are positive fractions?

(c) Which are reduced fractions?

8. Order the following set of rational numbers from smallest to largest: $\frac{5}{21}, \frac{3}{14}, \frac{1}{4}, \frac{9}{35}, \frac{1}{5}$.

9. Given the rational "points" $\frac{2}{5}$ and $\frac{3}{7}$ on a rational number line, find the reduced rational numbers for the two points dividing the given segment into three equal parts.

10. The multiplication $\frac{5}{6} \times 12 = 10$ suggests that the numerator _____ of the fraction acts like a _____ while the denominator _____ of the fraction acts like a _____.

11. The mathematical statement, $\frac{A}{B} \times \frac{C}{D} = \frac{A \times C}{B \times D}$ can be translated into ordinary English as "_____."

12. Find the products in reduced form:

(a) $3 \times \frac{6}{11}$ (b) $\frac{8}{9} \times 12$ (c) $\frac{5}{14} \times \frac{42}{55}$ (d) $\frac{16}{27} \times \frac{18}{25}$

(e) $\frac{34}{63} \times \frac{49}{85}$.

13. Find the products in reduced form:

(a) $\frac{6}{7} \times \frac{7}{12} \times \frac{8}{9}$ (b) $\frac{10}{21} \times \frac{9}{14} \times \frac{49}{55}$ (c) $\frac{30}{77} \times \frac{28}{39} \times \frac{26}{25}$.

14. The rational number *K* such that $\frac{5}{9} \times K = 1$ is called the _____ of _____; $K = $ _____.

15. Find the reduced rational quotients:

(a) $9 \div \dfrac{3}{4}$ (b) $\dfrac{3}{4} \div 9$ (c) $\dfrac{3}{7} \div \dfrac{9}{14}$ (d) $\dfrac{16}{25} \div \dfrac{108}{175}$

(e) $\dfrac{24}{35} \div \dfrac{39}{56}$.

16. Find the value of S in each of the following equations so that the equation will be true.

(a) $S \times \dfrac{3}{2} = 1$ (b) $\dfrac{4}{9} \times S = \dfrac{4}{9}$ (c) $S \times \dfrac{5}{8} = 0$ (d) $\dfrac{2}{3} \times S = \dfrac{3}{2}$

(e) $\dfrac{6}{7} \div S = \dfrac{6}{7}$ (f) $S \div \dfrac{3}{5} = 1$ (g) $\dfrac{7}{8} \div S = \dfrac{1}{7}$ (h) $S \div \dfrac{4}{5} = \dfrac{4}{5}$.

17. The statement "The quotient of two rational numbers is obtained by finding the product of the dividend times the reciprocal of the divisor" can be translated into mathematical symbols as _____.

18. (a) Express $\dfrac{3}{8}$ as a fraction with numerator 27.

(b) What is the product of $\dfrac{16}{27}$ and $\dfrac{45}{56}$ in reduced form?

(c) Find $\dfrac{16}{17}$ of $\dfrac{119}{120}$. Express the result as a reduced fraction.

(d) How many times can $\dfrac{2}{5}$ be subtracted from $\dfrac{34}{35}$?

19. Construct and label scales which illustrate:

(a) $\dfrac{3}{4} + \dfrac{7}{4}$ (b) $\dfrac{2}{7} - \dfrac{5}{7}$ (c) $-\dfrac{8}{13} + \dfrac{11}{13}$ (d) $-\dfrac{5}{12} - \dfrac{5}{12}$.

20. Find the least common denominator (LCD) for each of the following sets of fractions.

(a) $\dfrac{2}{3}, \dfrac{1}{4}, \dfrac{5}{6}$ (b) $\dfrac{5}{12}, \dfrac{1}{2}, \dfrac{3}{8}$ (c) $\dfrac{7}{9}, \dfrac{3}{5}, \dfrac{2}{15}$ (d) $\dfrac{5}{6}, \dfrac{7}{8}, \dfrac{7}{10}$.

21. Find the sum of each set of fractions in Exercise 20 above.

22. Find the differences:

(a) $\dfrac{7}{18} - \dfrac{4}{15}$ (b) $\dfrac{8}{21} - \dfrac{7}{24}$ (c) $\dfrac{25}{36} - \dfrac{25}{63}$ (d) $\dfrac{11}{42} - \dfrac{8}{35}$.

23. Recall the conventions for the order of operations and apply them to find the simplest reduced fractions for:

(a) $\left[\left(\dfrac{3}{4} - \dfrac{2}{3} \right) + \dfrac{5}{6} \right] \times \dfrac{6}{7}$ (b) $\dfrac{\dfrac{4}{9} - \left(\dfrac{4}{5} - \dfrac{3}{4} \right)}{\dfrac{5}{18} + \dfrac{23}{45}}$ (c) $\dfrac{6}{7} - \dfrac{\dfrac{5}{6} \times \left(\dfrac{4}{5} + \dfrac{2}{3} \right)}{\dfrac{16}{27} + \dfrac{5}{6}}$.

24. Match the lettered examples with the numbered descriptions so that they best illustrate the property described.

(a) $\frac{1}{5} \times 5 = 1$ 1. closure

(b) $\frac{4}{7} \times \frac{5}{5} = \frac{4}{7}$ 2. associative

(c) $\frac{1}{3} + \frac{1}{2} = \frac{5}{6}$ 3. reciprocal

(d) $\frac{3}{4} - \frac{3}{4} = 0$ 4. distributive

(e) $\frac{5}{6} \times \left(\frac{3}{4} + \frac{2}{3}\right) = \frac{5}{8} + \frac{5}{9}$ 5. additive inverse

(f) $\frac{2}{5} \times \left(\frac{5}{7} \times \frac{8}{9}\right) = \left(\frac{2}{5} \times \frac{5}{7}\right) \times \frac{8}{9}$ 6. commutative

(g) $\frac{8}{9} + \frac{0}{4} = \frac{8}{9}$ 7. zero

(h) $\frac{5}{9} \times \frac{4}{7} = \frac{4}{7} \times \frac{5}{9}$ 8. one

25. Mr. Jones earned $7,400 during the year. If his housing cost was $\frac{1}{5}$ of his earnings and he spent $\frac{1}{5}$ of what remained for food, then how much did he have left for all of his other expenses for the year? To what fraction of his year's earnings did this amount?

26. Two pumps used together take 3 hours and 18 minutes to fill a tank. If the smaller of the pumps can pump only $\frac{1}{3}$ of what the larger pump does, then how long would it take for the larger pump to fill the tank by itself?

27. If $\frac{5}{8}$ of a group of people are over 40 years old, $\frac{3}{10}$ of the group earn over $10,000 per year, and $\frac{1}{5}$ of the group are under 40 years old and make less than $10,000 per year, then what fraction of the group are over 40 and making in excess of $10,000 per year?

28. The product of a fraction and $\frac{3}{4}$ more than its reciprocal is equal to the reciprocal of $\frac{3}{4}$. Find the fraction.

Problem Set (6)

1. The following is a typical problem from the sixteenth century. A merchant bought saffron in Siena for 18 lira a pound and took it

to Venice where he found that a pound of Siena weight was equal to $\frac{6}{5}$ pound in Venetian weight and that 10 Siena lira only brought 8 Venetian lira. He sold the saffron for 14 lira a pound in Venice. What was his profit per pound in Siena weight and money?

2. Arrange the positive rational numbers written in fractional form in a serial order with a first fraction, and so forth, so that all the rational numbers will be included.

3. Which of the properties of a field are true for the set of elements a, b, and c with the operations of "addition" and "multiplication" described by the tables in Figure 80 below?

$\oplus$	a	b	c
a	a	b	c
b	b	c	a
c	c	a	b

$\otimes$	a	b	c
a	a	a	a
b	a	b	c
c	a	c	b

FIGURE 80

4. Notice that $\dfrac{7}{12} = \dfrac{1}{1+\frac{5}{7}} = \dfrac{1}{1+\dfrac{1}{1+\frac{2}{5}}} = \dfrac{1}{1+\dfrac{1}{1+\dfrac{1}{2+\frac{1}{1+1}}}}$

(a) Find the simplest reduced fraction for:

$$\cfrac{1}{1+\cfrac{1}{1+\cfrac{1}{1+\cfrac{1}{1+\frac{1}{1+2}}}}}$$

(b) Express $\dfrac{8}{13}$ as a "complex" fraction similar to the examples above.

5. (a) Can the sum $\dfrac{1}{1} + \dfrac{1}{2} + \dfrac{1}{3} + \cdots + \dfrac{1}{n}$, for n a natural number, be made "as large as you please"? If so, how large must n be in order that the sum exceeds 5?

(b) Is there a number such that the sum $\dfrac{1}{1} + \dfrac{1}{2} + \dfrac{1}{4} + \dfrac{1}{8} + \dfrac{1}{16} + \dfrac{1}{32} + \cdots$ will never exceed it no matter how many addends we have? If so, find the smallest such number.

CHAPTER 7

Notation

7.1 Mixed Fractions

7.1.1   As we have named, developed, and described our number ideas we have used a variety of symbols and forms. The symbolic patterns and forms we use in describing our ideas concerning numbers and operations with them are called **notation**. Historically, many of the difficulties encountered in the development of number concepts were due to lack of adequate notation.

In our extension of the integers to the rational numbers, recall that we noted that proper fractions can be used to express the remainder term in division. For example, in $181 \div 16$ we obtain the quotient 11 and remainder 5. In fractional form we might write this: $\frac{181}{16} = 11 + \frac{5}{16}$. That is, we can interpret $11 + \frac{5}{16}$ to be the **exact quotient** of $181 \div 16$. Rather than writing the sum of an integer and a proper fraction, it is customary to omit the plus sign and write $11\frac{5}{16}$ for $11 + \frac{5}{16}$. When we write the sum of an integer and a fraction in this form, we call the resulting numeral a **mixed fraction**. The exact quotient of two integers can thus be expressed as the sum of an integer and a proper fraction in the form of a mixed fraction.

Examples.

(a)
$$11\frac{5}{16}$$
$$16\overline{)181}$$
$$\underline{16}$$
$$21$$
$$\underline{16}$$
$$5 \qquad 5 \div 16 = \frac{5}{16}$$

(b)
$$44\frac{3}{28}$$
$$84\overline{)3705}$$
$$\underline{336}$$
$$345$$
$$\underline{336}$$
$$9 \qquad 9 \div 84 = \frac{9}{84} = \frac{3}{28}.$$

The introduction of mixed fractions into computations can, however, cause difficulties. First, we must always remember that a mixed fraction expresses the sum of an integer and a fraction. Second, a mixed fraction can be imagined as having parentheses "around" it so that in computations we apply operations to the mixed fraction as a single quantity.

Examples.

(a) $5\frac{2}{3} = 5 + \frac{2}{3}$.

(b) $-5\frac{2}{3} = -\left(5 + \frac{2}{3}\right) = -5 + \left(-\frac{2}{3}\right) = -5 - \frac{2}{3}$.

(c) $3\frac{1}{2} + 5\frac{3}{4} = \left(3 + \frac{1}{2}\right) + \left(5 + \frac{3}{4}\right) = (3 + 5) + \left(\frac{1}{2} + \frac{3}{4}\right) = 8 + \frac{5}{4}$

$= 8 + 1 + \frac{1}{4} = 9\frac{1}{4}$.

(d) $5\frac{3}{4} - 3\frac{1}{2} = \left(5 + \frac{3}{4}\right) - \left(3 + \frac{1}{2}\right) = (5 - 3) + \left(\frac{3}{4} - \frac{1}{2}\right) = 2 + \frac{1}{4} = 2\frac{1}{4}$.

(e) $5\frac{3}{4} \times 3\frac{1}{2} = \left(5 + \frac{3}{4}\right) \times \left(3 + \frac{1}{2}\right) = (5 \times 3) + \left(5 \times \frac{1}{2}\right) + \left(\frac{3}{4} \times 3\right)$

$+ \left(\frac{3}{4} \times \frac{1}{2}\right) = 15 + \frac{5}{2} + \frac{9}{4} + \frac{3}{8} = 20 + \frac{1}{8} = 20\frac{1}{8}$.

(f) $5\frac{3}{4} \times 3\frac{1}{2} = \frac{23}{4} \times \frac{7}{2} = \frac{161}{8} = 20 + \frac{1}{8} = 20\frac{1}{8}$. Notice that we have con-

verted the mixed fractions into improper fraction forms. Since $5 = \frac{5 \times 4}{1 \times 4}$

$= \frac{20}{4}$ we have $5\frac{3}{4} = 5 + \frac{3}{4} = \frac{20}{4} + \frac{3}{4} = \frac{23}{4}$. Also, $3\frac{1}{2} = \frac{6}{2} + \frac{1}{2} = \frac{7}{2}$.

(g) $5\frac{3}{4} \div 3\frac{1}{2} = \frac{23}{4} \div \frac{7}{2} = \frac{23}{4} \times \frac{2}{7} = \frac{23}{14} = 1\frac{9}{14}$. In division it is usually

most convenient to convert mixed fractions into improper fraction forms and then to proceed with the division.

7.1.2   In computing with mixed fractions we must often convert them into improper fraction forms and also convert improper fractions into mixed fraction forms.

Examples.

(a) $3\frac{7}{8} = 3 + \frac{7}{8} = \frac{3 \times 8}{1 \times 8} + \frac{7}{8} = \frac{31}{8}$

(b) $17\frac{2}{5} = \frac{17 \times 5}{5} + \frac{2}{5} = \frac{87}{5}$

(c) $\frac{37}{3} = 12 + \frac{1}{3} = 12\frac{1}{3}$

(d) $\frac{57}{6} = 9 + \frac{3}{6} = 9\frac{1}{2}$.

The two processes of conversion can be described briefly by
$A\frac{N}{D} = \frac{A \times D + N}{D}$, where A is the integral part and $\frac{N}{D}$ is the fractional part of the mixed fraction $A\frac{N}{D}$.

$\frac{N}{D} = Q + \frac{R}{D}$, where $N \geq D$ and Q is the quotient in the division of N by D and R is the remainder, then we have $Q\frac{R}{D}$.

Practice 1.

1. Convert to mixed fraction form:

   (a) $\frac{8}{5}$ (b) $\frac{17}{7}$ (c) $\frac{29}{3}$ (d) $\frac{51}{4}$ (e) $\frac{85}{22}$

   (f) $\frac{113}{13}$ (g) $\frac{206}{18}$ (h) $\frac{369}{10}$ (i) $\frac{390}{56}$ (j) $\frac{497}{142}$.

2. Convert to improper fraction form:

   (a) $1\frac{5}{8}$ (b) $7\frac{7}{9}$ (c) $8\frac{3}{8}$ (d) $10\frac{1}{5}$ (e) $25\frac{2}{5}$

   (f) $14\frac{10}{11}$ (g) $27\frac{2}{7}$ (h) $6\frac{15}{16}$ (i) $42\frac{12}{19}$ (j) $37\frac{7}{10}$.

3. Find the exact quotients:

   (a) $53\overline{)2387}$ (b) $64\overline{)1040}$ (c) $324\overline{)7182}$.

Answers.

1. (a) $1\frac{3}{5}$ (b) $2\frac{3}{7}$ (c) $9\frac{2}{3}$ (d) $12\frac{3}{4}$ (e) $3\frac{21}{22}$

   (f) $8\frac{9}{13}$ (g) $11\frac{4}{9}$ (h) $36\frac{9}{10}$ (i) $6\frac{27}{28}$ (j) $3\frac{1}{2}$.

2. (a) $\frac{13}{8}$ (b) $\frac{70}{9}$ (c) $\frac{67}{8}$ (d) $\frac{51}{5}$ (e) $\frac{127}{5}$

   (f) $\frac{164}{11}$ (g) $\frac{191}{7}$ (h) $\frac{111}{16}$ (i) $\frac{810}{19}$ (j) $\frac{377}{10}$.

3. (a) $45\frac{2}{53}$ (b) $16\frac{1}{4}$ (c) $22\frac{1}{6}$.

7.1.3 To add mixed fractions we can add the integral and fractional parts separately, after which we reduce and combine the "partial" sums thus obtained.

Examples.

(a) $15\frac{1}{6} + 9\frac{2}{3} = \left(15 + \frac{1}{6}\right) + \left(9 + \frac{2}{3}\right) = (15 + 9) + \left(\frac{1}{6} + \frac{2}{3}\right) = 24 + \frac{5}{6}$

$$= 24\frac{5}{6}.$$

(b) $7\frac{3}{8} + 5\frac{3}{4} + 28\frac{5}{6} = (7 + 5 + 28) + \left(\frac{3}{8} + \frac{3}{4} + \frac{5}{6}\right) = 40 + \frac{47}{24}$

$$= 40 + \left(1 + \frac{23}{24}\right) = 41\frac{23}{24}.$$

(c)

$16\frac{2}{3} = 16 + \dfrac{12}{18}$ We convert the fractional parts to fractions with a common denominator to add.

$54\frac{5}{9} = 54 + \dfrac{10}{18}$

$+73\frac{1}{2} = 73 + \dfrac{9}{18}$

$143 + \dfrac{31}{18} = 143 + \left(1 + \dfrac{13}{18}\right) = 144\dfrac{13}{18}.$

(d)

$35\frac{2}{7}$ $\dfrac{2}{7} = \dfrac{144}{504}$

$49\frac{5}{9}$ $\dfrac{5}{9} = \dfrac{280}{504}$

$+ 26\frac{7}{8}$ $\dfrac{7}{8} = \dfrac{441}{504}$

$\overline{110}$ $\dfrac{865}{504} = 1 + \dfrac{361}{504}$

$1\frac{361}{504}$

$\overline{111\frac{361}{504}}$

Practice 2. Add and express the sum in reduced mixed fraction form (called the **simplest form**).

	(a)	(b)	(c)	(d)	(e)
1.	$3\frac{2}{5} + 2\frac{1}{5}$	$4\frac{3}{8} + 5\frac{3}{8}$	$6\frac{2}{9} + 3\frac{4}{9}$	$7\frac{3}{4} + 1\frac{1}{4}$	$8\frac{6}{7} + 5\frac{4}{7}$
2.	$9\frac{3}{16} + 14\frac{7}{16}$	$8\frac{5}{12} + 3\frac{7}{12}$	$16\frac{5}{8} + 27\frac{7}{8}$	$4\frac{5}{7} + 6\frac{3}{7}$	$21\frac{4}{15} + 12\frac{13}{15}$
3.	$6\frac{2}{3} + 1\frac{1}{4}$	$3\frac{5}{9} + 5\frac{1}{2}$	$7\frac{5}{6} + 9\frac{3}{4}$	$4\frac{4}{7} + 3\frac{3}{5}$	$9\frac{8}{9} + 6\frac{5}{6}$

4. $\quad 7\frac{1}{8}$ $\qquad 4\frac{6}{7}$ $\qquad 9\frac{7}{11}$ $\qquad 2\frac{5}{8}$ $\qquad 1\frac{5}{12}$

$\quad \dfrac{12\frac{3}{8}}{}$ $\qquad \dfrac{3\frac{5}{7}}{}$ $\qquad \dfrac{8\frac{9}{11}}{}$ $\qquad \dfrac{5\frac{1}{4}}{}$ $\qquad \dfrac{1\frac{5}{8}}{}$

5. $\quad 5\frac{5}{21}$ $\qquad 10\frac{2}{3}$ $\qquad 7\frac{8}{15}$ $\qquad 2\frac{3}{8}$ $\qquad 16\frac{17}{18}$

$\quad \dfrac{2\frac{9}{14}}{}$ $\qquad \dfrac{30\frac{5}{6}}{}$ $\qquad \dfrac{8\frac{7}{12}}{}$ $\qquad \dfrac{19\frac{11}{14}}{}$ $\qquad \dfrac{97\frac{7}{30}}{}$

6. $\quad 5\frac{2}{3}$ $\qquad 7\frac{5}{6}$ $\qquad 15\frac{7}{16}$ $\qquad 1\frac{3}{10}$ $\qquad 3\frac{4}{5}$

$\quad 1\frac{1}{2}$ $\qquad \frac{7}{8}$ $\qquad 9\frac{11}{12}$ $\qquad 10\frac{1}{3}$ $\qquad 17\frac{7}{10}$

$\quad \dfrac{1\frac{3}{4}}{}$ $\qquad \dfrac{2\frac{8}{9}}{}$ $\qquad \dfrac{\frac{3}{8}}{}$ $\qquad \dfrac{100\frac{5}{6}}{}$ $\qquad \dfrac{1\frac{13}{15}}{}$

7. (a) $5\frac{1}{3} + 1\frac{3}{4} + \frac{5}{6} + 7$ $\qquad$ (b) $10\frac{7}{12} + \frac{3}{8} + 1 + 4\frac{5}{9}$

$\quad$ (c) $2\frac{4}{5} + 15\frac{2}{3} + \frac{8}{9} + 36\frac{8}{15}$ $\qquad$ (d) $8\frac{1}{5} + 3\frac{7}{10} + 6\frac{12}{25} + 2\frac{17}{20}$.

8. (a) $\frac{7}{9} + 2\frac{1}{6} + 27\frac{5}{8} + 80$ $\qquad$ (b) $18\frac{4}{7} + 3\frac{9}{11} + 8\frac{6}{7} + 1\frac{4}{11}$

$\quad$ (c) $1 + \frac{9}{10} + 7\frac{16}{25} + 1\frac{3}{4}$ $\qquad$ (d) $6\frac{1}{4} + 5\frac{7}{8} + 9\frac{17}{32} + 4\frac{5}{16}$.

Answers.

	(a)	(b)	(c)	(d)	(e)
1.	$5\frac{3}{5}$	$9\frac{3}{4}$	$9\frac{2}{3}$	9	$14\frac{3}{7}$
2.	$23\frac{5}{8}$	12	$44\frac{1}{2}$	$11\frac{1}{7}$	$34\frac{2}{15}$
3.	$7\frac{11}{12}$	$9\frac{1}{18}$	$17\frac{7}{12}$	$8\frac{6}{35}$	$16\frac{13}{18}$
4.	$19\frac{1}{2}$	$8\frac{4}{7}$	$18\frac{5}{11}$	$7\frac{7}{8}$	$3\frac{1}{24}$
5.	$7\frac{37}{42}$	$41\frac{1}{2}$	$16\frac{7}{60}$	$22\frac{9}{56}$	$114\frac{8}{45}$
6.	$8\frac{11}{12}$	$11\frac{43}{72}$	$25\frac{35}{48}$	$112\frac{7}{15}$	$23\frac{11}{30}$

7. (a) $14\frac{11}{12}$ $\quad$ (b) $16\frac{37}{72}$ $\quad$ (c) $55\frac{8}{9}$ $\quad$ (d) $21\frac{23}{100}$.

8. (a) $110\frac{41}{72}$ $\quad$ (b) $32\frac{47}{77}$ $\quad$ (c) $11\frac{29}{100}$ $\quad$ (d) $25\frac{31}{32}$.

7.1.4   To find the difference between two mixed fractions we can proceed as with addition in working with the integral and fractional parts separately. If "borrowing" is necessary, it is convenient to convert 1 into an improper fraction with the appropriate denominator.

Examples.

(a) $7\frac{5}{8} - 4\frac{1}{6} = \left(7 + \frac{5}{8}\right) - \left(4 + \frac{1}{6}\right) = (7 - 4) + \left(\frac{5}{8} - \frac{1}{6}\right) = 3 + \frac{11}{24} = 3\frac{11}{24}.$

(b) $6\frac{2}{9} - 1\frac{2}{3} = (6 - 1) + \left(\frac{2}{9} - \frac{2}{3}\right) = 5 + \left(-\frac{4}{9}\right) = 4 + \frac{9}{9} - \frac{4}{9} = 4 + \frac{5}{9} = 4\frac{5}{9}.$

(c) $3\frac{2}{7} - 1\frac{5}{7} = (2 - 1) + \left(\frac{7}{7} + \frac{2}{7} - \frac{5}{7}\right) = 1 + \frac{4}{7} = 1\frac{4}{7}.$

(d) $8 - \frac{7}{8} = 7 + 1 - \frac{7}{8} = 7 + \frac{8}{8} - \frac{7}{8} = 7 + \frac{1}{8} = 7\frac{1}{8}.$

(e)
$$\begin{array}{rl}
4\frac{3}{4} & \frac{3}{4} = \frac{15}{20} \\
-1\frac{2}{5} & \frac{2}{5} = \frac{8}{20} \\
\hline
3\frac{7}{20} & \frac{7}{20}
\end{array}$$

(f)
$$\begin{array}{rl}
13\frac{3}{8} & 12\frac{33}{24} \\
-7\frac{5}{6} & 7\frac{20}{24} \\
\hline
& 5\frac{13}{24}
\end{array}$$

(g)
$$\begin{array}{rl}
6\frac{2}{3} & \frac{4}{6} \\
-8\frac{5}{6} & \frac{5}{6} \\
\hline
-2\frac{1}{6} &
\end{array}$$

(h) $3\frac{7}{8} - 9\frac{1}{2} = (3 - 9) + \left(\frac{7}{8} - \frac{1}{2}\right) = -6 + \frac{3}{8} = -5 - \frac{8}{8} + \frac{3}{8} = -5 - \frac{5}{8}$

$= -\left(5 + \frac{5}{8}\right) = -5\frac{5}{8}.$

Practice 3. Find the indicated differences in reduced mixed fraction form.

	(a)	(b)	(c)	(d)	(e)
1.	$5\frac{7}{9} - 1\frac{2}{9}$	$7\frac{3}{8} - 6\frac{5}{8}$	$13\frac{1}{4} - 7\frac{3}{4}$	$9\frac{2}{3} - 4\frac{5}{6}$	$11\frac{9}{10} - 3\frac{14}{15}$
2.	$12\frac{2}{7} - 8\frac{3}{4}$	$1 - \frac{9}{16}$	$21\frac{1}{2} - 18\frac{2}{3}$	$10\frac{4}{9} - 9\frac{3}{4}$	$35\frac{7}{16} - 14\frac{13}{24}$
3.	$3\frac{1}{3} - 2\frac{3}{4}$	$1\frac{5}{8} - \frac{8}{9}$	$4\frac{3}{5} - 9\frac{6}{7}$	$2\frac{4}{5} - 6\frac{3}{10}$	$\frac{7}{8} - 3\frac{1}{4}$

4.
$$\begin{array}{l}
17\frac{5}{6} \\
-12\frac{1}{6} \\
\hline
\end{array}
\qquad
\begin{array}{l}
25\frac{5}{8} \\
-18\frac{3}{8} \\
\hline
\end{array}
\qquad
\begin{array}{l}
11\frac{7}{9} \\
-5\frac{2}{3} \\
\hline
\end{array}
\qquad
\begin{array}{l}
9\frac{1}{3} \\
-2\frac{5}{6} \\
\hline
\end{array}
\qquad
\begin{array}{l}
27\frac{6}{7} \\
-8\frac{3}{5} \\
\hline
\end{array}$$

5.
$$\begin{array}{l}
32\frac{1}{4} \\
-16\frac{2}{3} \\
\hline
\end{array}
\qquad
\begin{array}{l}
3\frac{5}{9} \\
-\frac{5}{6} \\
\hline
\end{array}
\qquad
\begin{array}{l}
30 \\
-\frac{7}{10} \\
\hline
\end{array}
\qquad
\begin{array}{l}
15\frac{7}{12} \\
-8\frac{8}{9} \\
\hline
\end{array}
\qquad
\begin{array}{l}
41\frac{11}{15} \\
-40\frac{23}{25} \\
\hline
\end{array}$$

6. $106\frac{1}{2}$ $5\frac{3}{4}$ $8\frac{1}{3}$ $26\frac{17}{20}$ $\frac{11}{16}$

  $-16\frac{9}{11}$ $-7\frac{1}{2}$ $-10\frac{4}{5}$ $-125\frac{9}{10}$ $-2\frac{5}{32}$

Answers.

	(a)	(b)	(c)	(d)	(e)
1.	$4\frac{5}{9}$	$\frac{3}{4}$	$5\frac{1}{2}$	$4\frac{5}{6}$	$7\frac{29}{30}$
2.	$3\frac{15}{28}$	$\frac{7}{16}$	$2\frac{5}{6}$	$\frac{25}{36}$	$20\frac{43}{48}$
3.	$\frac{7}{12}$	$\frac{53}{72}$	$-5\frac{9}{35}$	$-3\frac{1}{2}$	$-2\frac{3}{8}$
4.	$5\frac{2}{3}$	$7\frac{1}{4}$	$6\frac{1}{9}$	$6\frac{1}{2}$	$19\frac{9}{35}$
5.	$15\frac{7}{12}$	$2\frac{13}{18}$	$29\frac{3}{10}$	$6\frac{25}{36}$	$\frac{61}{75}$
6.	$89\frac{15}{22}$	$-1\frac{3}{4}$	$-2\frac{7}{15}$	$-99\frac{1}{20}$	$-1\frac{15}{32}$

Notice how important and useful the associative and commutative properties of addition are in working with mixed fractions. In subtraction careful attention must be paid to the minus sign as applied to both the integral and fractional parts of the difference.

7.1.5   Two general procedures can be used to find the product of mixed fractions. The mixed fractions may be converted to an improper fraction form and the multiplication can be carried out as with ordinary fractions or the mixed fractions can be written as indicated sums and the distributive property applied to obtain the sum of partial products.

Examples.

(a) $6\frac{3}{5} \times 5\frac{2}{3} = \frac{33}{5} \times \frac{17}{3} = \frac{187}{5} = 37\frac{2}{5}.$

(b) $6\frac{3}{5} \times 5\frac{2}{3} = \left(6 + \frac{3}{5}\right) \times \left(5 + \frac{2}{3}\right) = \left(6 + \frac{3}{5}\right) \times 5 + \left(6 + \frac{3}{5}\right) \times \frac{2}{3}$

$= 6 \times 5 + \frac{3}{5} \times 5 + 6 \times \frac{2}{3} + \frac{3}{5} \times \frac{2}{3} = 30 + 3 + 4 + \frac{2}{5} = 37\frac{2}{5}.$

(c) $4\frac{2}{3} \times 7\frac{5}{8} = \frac{14}{3} \times \frac{61}{8} = \frac{427}{12} = 35\frac{7}{12}.$

(d) $4\frac{2}{3} \times 7\frac{5}{8} = \left(4 + \frac{2}{3}\right) \times \left(7 + \frac{5}{8}\right) = 4 \times 7 + \frac{2}{3} \times 7 + 4 \times \frac{5}{8} + \frac{2}{3} \times \frac{5}{8}$

$$= 28 + \frac{14}{3} + \frac{5}{2} + \frac{5}{12} = 28 + \frac{91}{12} = 28 + 7 + \frac{7}{12} = 35\frac{7}{12}.$$

Practice 4. Find the products in reduced mixed fraction form.

A. Convert to improper fractions and multiply.

      (a)   (b)   (c)   (d)   (e)

1. $5\frac{5}{8} \times 2\frac{4}{9}$ $3\frac{5}{7} \times 6\frac{6}{13}$ $4\frac{1}{6} \times 9\frac{3}{10}$ $\left(-7\frac{1}{2}\right) \times 2\frac{1}{3}$ $\left(-11\frac{2}{5}\right) \times \left(-3\frac{11}{18}\right)$

2. $9\frac{6}{7} \times 1\frac{1}{6}$ $5\frac{3}{4} \times 3\frac{1}{5}$ $2\frac{8}{9} \times 27$ $6\frac{2}{3} \times \frac{9}{16}$ $16\frac{9}{10} \times \left(-3\frac{6}{13}\right)$

B. Write as indicated sums and apply the distributive property to obtain the products.

      (a)   (b)   (c)   (d)   (e)

3. $6\frac{1}{3} \times 9\frac{1}{2}$ $4\frac{5}{6} \times 8\frac{1}{4}$ $3\frac{7}{10} \times 5\frac{4}{9}$ $14\frac{2}{3} \times 9\frac{4}{7}$ $4\frac{5}{13} \times 13\frac{15}{16}$

4. $8\frac{7}{9} \times 9\frac{3}{4}$ $12\frac{4}{5} \times 15\frac{3}{4}$ $21 \times 4\frac{3}{7}$ $\frac{19}{20} \times 8\frac{15}{38}$ $\left(-16\frac{2}{3}\right) \times 6\frac{5}{8}$

C. Examine each problem and use the "easier" method.

      (a)   (b)   (c)   (d)   (e)

5. $10\frac{2}{3} \times 9\frac{4}{5}$ $5\frac{7}{8} \times 4\frac{4}{15}$ $2\frac{11}{12} \times 5\frac{1}{7}$ $6\frac{7}{8} \times 3\frac{5}{11}$ $\left(-8\frac{13}{18}\right) \times \left(-9\frac{3}{4}\right)$

6. $6\frac{3}{10} \times 6\frac{3}{7}$ $14\frac{2}{3} \times 9\frac{1}{2}$ $7\frac{5}{9} \times 5\frac{1}{4}$ $8\frac{7}{12} \times 18\frac{1}{4}$ $10\frac{2}{3} \times \left(-3\frac{1}{8}\right)$

Answers.

	(a)	(b)	(c)	(d)	(e)
1.	$13\frac{3}{4}$	24	$38\frac{3}{4}$	$-17\frac{1}{2}$	$41\frac{1}{6}$
2.	$11\frac{1}{2}$	$18\frac{2}{5}$	78	$3\frac{3}{4}$	$-58\frac{1}{2}$
3.	$60\frac{1}{6}$	$39\frac{7}{8}$	$20\frac{13}{90}$	$140\frac{8}{21}$	$61\frac{23}{208}$
4.	$85\frac{7}{12}$	$201\frac{3}{5}$	93	$7\frac{39}{40}$	$-110\frac{5}{12}$
5.	$104\frac{8}{15}$	$25\frac{1}{15}$	15	$23\frac{3}{4}$	$85\frac{1}{24}$
6.	$40\frac{1}{2}$	$139\frac{1}{3}$	$39\frac{2}{3}$	$156\frac{31}{48}$	$-33\frac{1}{3}$

7.1.6   As we have already noted, division with mixed fractions can be accomplished by converting the mixed fractions into improper fraction forms and proceeding as with ordinary division of fractions. A second procedure is to multiply both dividend and divisor by the least common denominator of the fractions involved and then to proceed with the resulting division of integers.

Examples.

(a) $7\frac{5}{8} \div 2\frac{3}{4} = \frac{61}{8} \div \frac{11}{4} = \frac{61}{8} \times \frac{4}{11} = \frac{61}{22} = 2\frac{17}{22}.$

(b) $7\frac{5}{8} \div 2\frac{3}{4} = \left(8 \times 7\frac{5}{8}\right) \div \left(8 \times 2\frac{3}{4}\right) = 61 \div 22 = 2\frac{17}{22}.$

(c) $\dfrac{19\frac{2}{3}}{13\frac{5}{7}} = \dfrac{\frac{59}{3}}{\frac{96}{7}} = \frac{59}{3} \times \frac{7}{96} = \frac{413}{288} = 1\frac{125}{288}.$

(d) $\dfrac{19\frac{2}{3}}{13\frac{5}{7}} = \dfrac{21 \times 19\frac{2}{3}}{21 \times 13\frac{5}{7}} = \frac{413}{288} = 1\frac{125}{288}.$

Practice 5. Find the exact quotients in reduced mixed fraction form.

	(a)	(b)	(c)	(d)	(e)
1.	$8\frac{3}{5} \div 6\frac{1}{7}$	$3\frac{1}{3} \div 2\frac{1}{2}$	$12\frac{5}{6} \div 5\frac{3}{4}$	$9\frac{5}{7} \div 2\frac{3}{7}$	$3\frac{7}{8} \div 4\frac{55}{56}$
2.	$13\frac{4}{9} \div 1\frac{5}{6}$	$5\frac{3}{4} \div 2\frac{3}{10}$	$7\frac{11}{12} \div 7\frac{3}{5}$	$\frac{34}{35} \div 3\frac{3}{7}$	$11\frac{7}{10} \div \frac{27}{50}$
3.	$\dfrac{4\frac{2}{3}}{1\frac{3}{7}}$	$\dfrac{16\frac{5}{8}}{3\frac{7}{16}}$	$\dfrac{21\frac{1}{9}}{17\frac{2}{9}}$	$\dfrac{7\frac{3}{4}}{11\frac{5}{8}}$	$\dfrac{27\frac{1}{2}}{4\frac{1}{6}}$
4.	$\dfrac{11\frac{1}{2}}{1\frac{11}{12}}$	$\dfrac{9\frac{6}{7}}{8\frac{1}{4}}$	$\dfrac{5\frac{1}{3}}{4\frac{8}{11}}$	$\dfrac{1\frac{1}{9}}{3\frac{3}{4}}$	$\dfrac{24\frac{3}{7}}{5\frac{1}{7}}$

Answers.

	(a)	(b)	(c)	(d)	(e)
1.	$1\frac{2}{5}$	$1\frac{1}{3}$	$2\frac{16}{69}$	4	$\frac{7}{9}$
2.	$7\frac{1}{3}$	$2\frac{1}{2}$	$1\frac{1}{24}$	$\frac{17}{60}$	$21\frac{2}{3}$
3.	$3\frac{4}{15}$	$4\frac{46}{55}$	$1\frac{7}{31}$	$\frac{2}{3}$	$6\frac{3}{5}$
4.	6	$1\frac{15}{77}$	$1\frac{5}{39}$	$\frac{8}{27}$	$4\frac{3}{4}$

7.1.7 Although working with fractions with small numerals is considered rather routine today, it was not always easy. For example, the Egyptians wrote all fractions except $\frac{2}{3}$ with the numerator 1. Such fractions are called **unit fractions**. The fraction $\frac{3}{4}$ was written as $\frac{1}{2}+\frac{1}{4}$ and $\frac{2}{5}$ as $\frac{1}{4}+\frac{1}{10}+\frac{1}{20}$. The Greeks used two sets of fractions: common fractions somewhat as we have developed them and "astronomical" or "physical" fractions. These latter were fractions whose denominators were limited to products of 60. Today these are known as *sexagesimal* fractions and persist in our measurements of time and angles. For example, 1 second of time is $\frac{1}{60}$ of 1 minute and 1 minute is $\frac{1}{60}$ of an hour. Thus, 1 second is $\frac{1}{60} \times \frac{1}{60} = \frac{1}{3600}$ of an hour. The seconds and minutes of an angle of 1 degree are measured similarly.

It is surprising that the idea of expanding a numeral using a fixed number base was not extended to fractions earlier in mathematics. Consider how we expand $420 = 4(100) + 2(10) + 0(1)$. Can we expand a fraction, say $\frac{1}{8}$, in a similar manner? The answer is yes. We write $\frac{1}{8} = \frac{N}{1000}$ and solve

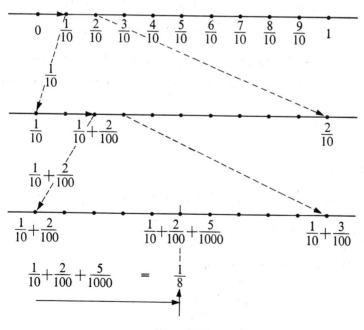

FIGURE 81

for N. $N = \dfrac{1000}{8} = 125$ so that $\dfrac{1}{8} = \dfrac{125}{1000} = \dfrac{100 + 20 + 5}{1000} = \dfrac{100}{1000} + \dfrac{20}{1000} +$

$\dfrac{5}{1000} = \dfrac{1}{10} + \dfrac{2}{100} + \dfrac{5}{1000}$. Of course, difficulties may arise if we are not care-

ful. For example, $\dfrac{4}{9} = \dfrac{N}{1000}$ results in $N = \dfrac{4000}{9} = 444\dfrac{4}{9}$, a mixed fraction, so

that we have $\dfrac{4}{9} = \dfrac{444\frac{4}{9}}{1000} = \dfrac{400 + 40 + 4 + \frac{4}{9}}{1000} = \dfrac{400}{1000} + \dfrac{40}{1000} + \dfrac{4}{1000} + \dfrac{\frac{4}{9}}{1000} =$

$\dfrac{4}{10} + \dfrac{4}{100} + \dfrac{4}{1000} + \left(\dfrac{4}{9} \times \dfrac{1}{1000}\right)$. A fraction which has a fraction as a numera-

tor or a denominator or both is called a **complex fraction**. Notice also that in a mixed fraction the proper fraction refers to the place position of the digit to its immediate left.

Examples.

(a) $2\dfrac{3}{4} = 2 + \dfrac{3}{4} = 2 + \dfrac{7}{10} + \dfrac{5}{100}$ since for $\dfrac{3}{4} = \dfrac{N}{100}$ we have $N = 75$ and

$\dfrac{3}{4} = \dfrac{75}{100} = \dfrac{70 + 5}{100} = \dfrac{70}{100} + \dfrac{5}{100} = \dfrac{7}{10} + \dfrac{5}{100}$.

(b) Since $\dfrac{5}{12} = \dfrac{4166\frac{2}{3}}{10000}$ we have $\dfrac{5}{12} = \dfrac{4}{10} + \dfrac{1}{100} + \dfrac{6}{1000} + \dfrac{6\frac{2}{3}}{10000}$.

(c) $\dfrac{2}{7} = \dfrac{2\frac{6}{7}}{10} = \dfrac{28\frac{4}{7}}{100} = \dfrac{285\frac{5}{7}}{1000} = \dfrac{2857\frac{1}{7}}{10000} = \dfrac{28571\frac{3}{7}}{100000} = \dfrac{285714\frac{2}{7}}{1000000} = \cdots$

$\dfrac{2}{7} = \dfrac{2}{10} + \dfrac{8}{100} + \dfrac{5}{1000} + \dfrac{7}{10000} + \dfrac{1}{100000} + \dfrac{4\frac{2}{7}}{1000000}$.

Just as with the integers, we can "round off" expanded fractions to a given denominator size. For example, $\dfrac{5}{12}$ rounded to the nearest $\dfrac{1}{100}$ would be $\dfrac{42}{100}$.

Examples.

(a) Since $\dfrac{1}{6} = \dfrac{166\frac{2}{3}}{1000}$ we find that $\dfrac{1}{6}$ to the nearest $\dfrac{1}{10}$ is $\dfrac{2}{10}$, to the nearest

$\dfrac{1}{100}$ is $\dfrac{17}{100}$, and to the nearest $\dfrac{1}{1000}$ is $\dfrac{167}{1000}$.

(b) $\dfrac{2}{7}$ to the nearest $\dfrac{1}{10}$ is $\dfrac{3}{10}$

$\dfrac{1}{100}$ is $\dfrac{29}{100}$

$\dfrac{1}{1000}$ is $\dfrac{286}{1000}$.

Practice 6.

1. Find N in each of the following:

(a) $\dfrac{1}{2}=\dfrac{N}{10}$ (b) $\dfrac{1}{5}=\dfrac{N}{10}$ (c) $\dfrac{1}{4}=\dfrac{N}{100}$ (d) $\dfrac{1}{3}=\dfrac{N}{100}$ (e) $\dfrac{1}{9}=\dfrac{N}{100}$

(f) $\dfrac{1}{6}=\dfrac{N}{100}$ (g) $\dfrac{1}{7}=\dfrac{N}{100}$ (h) $\dfrac{1}{8}=\dfrac{N}{100}$ (i) $\dfrac{3}{5}=\dfrac{N}{100}$ (j) $\dfrac{2}{3}=\dfrac{N}{100}$.

2. Find N in each of the following:

(a) $\dfrac{7}{13}=\dfrac{N}{10}$ (b) $\dfrac{7}{13}=\dfrac{N}{100}$ (c) $\dfrac{7}{13}=\dfrac{N}{1000}$ (d) $\dfrac{7}{13}=\dfrac{N}{10000}$

(e) $\dfrac{5}{8}=\dfrac{N}{10}$ (f) $\dfrac{5}{8}=\dfrac{N}{100}$ (g) $\dfrac{5}{8}=\dfrac{N}{1000}$ (h) $\dfrac{5}{8}=\dfrac{N}{10000}$.

3. Find N in each of the following and expand the fraction into a sum of fractions with 10, 100, 1000, and 10000 as denominators:

(a) $\dfrac{5}{6}=\dfrac{N}{10000}$ (b) $\dfrac{7}{9}=\dfrac{N}{10000}$ (c) $\dfrac{4}{7}=\dfrac{N}{10000}$

(d) $\dfrac{3}{8}=\dfrac{N}{10000}$ (e) $\dfrac{7}{12}=\dfrac{N}{10000}$ (f) $\dfrac{5}{16}=\dfrac{N}{10000}$

(g) $\dfrac{9}{11}=\dfrac{N}{10000}$ (h) $\dfrac{12}{13}=\dfrac{N}{10000}$ (i) $\dfrac{15}{17}=\dfrac{N}{10000}$.

4. Round each of the fractions in Problem 3 above to the nearest $\dfrac{1}{1000}$.

Answers.

1. (a) 5   (b) 2   (c) 25   (d) $33\frac{1}{3}$ (e) $11\frac{1}{9}$

(f) $16\frac{2}{3}$ (g) $14\frac{2}{7}$ (h) $12\frac{1}{2}$ (i) 60   (j) $66\frac{2}{3}$.

2. (a) $5\frac{5}{13}$ (b) $53\frac{11}{13}$ (c) $538\frac{6}{13}$ (d) $5384\frac{8}{13}$

(e) $6\frac{1}{4}$ (f) $62\frac{1}{2}$ (g) 625   (h) 6250.

3. (a) $\dfrac{8333\frac{1}{3}}{10000}=\dfrac{8}{10}+\dfrac{3}{100}+\dfrac{3}{1000}+\dfrac{3\frac{1}{3}}{10000}$.

(b) $\dfrac{7777\frac{7}{9}}{10000}=\dfrac{7}{10}+\dfrac{7}{100}+\dfrac{7}{1000}+\dfrac{7\frac{7}{9}}{10000}$.

(c) $\dfrac{5714\frac{2}{7}}{10000}=\dfrac{5}{10}+\dfrac{7}{100}+\dfrac{1}{1000}+\dfrac{4\frac{2}{7}}{10000}$.

(d) $\dfrac{3750}{10000}=\dfrac{3}{10}+\dfrac{7}{100}+\dfrac{5}{1000}+\dfrac{0}{10000}$.

(e) $\dfrac{5833\frac{1}{3}}{10000}=\dfrac{5}{10}+\dfrac{8}{100}+\dfrac{3}{1000}+\dfrac{3\frac{1}{3}}{10000}$.

(f) $\dfrac{3125}{10000} = \dfrac{3}{10} + \dfrac{1}{100} + \dfrac{2}{1000} + \dfrac{5}{10000}.$

(g) $\dfrac{8181\frac{9}{11}}{10000} = \dfrac{8}{10} + \dfrac{1}{100} + \dfrac{8}{1000} + \dfrac{1\frac{9}{11}}{10000}.$

(h) $\dfrac{9230\frac{10}{13}}{10000} = \dfrac{9}{10} + \dfrac{2}{100} + \dfrac{3}{1000} + \dfrac{\frac{10}{13}}{10000}.$

(i) $\dfrac{8823\frac{9}{17}}{10000} = \dfrac{8}{10} + \dfrac{8}{100} + \dfrac{2}{1000} + \dfrac{3\frac{9}{17}}{10000}.$

4. (a) $\dfrac{833}{1000}$ (b) $\dfrac{778}{1000}$ (c) $\dfrac{571}{1000}$ (d) $\dfrac{375}{1000}$ (e) $\dfrac{583}{1000}$

(f) $\dfrac{312}{1000}$ (g) $\dfrac{818}{1000}$ (h) $\dfrac{923}{1000}$ (i) $\dfrac{882}{1000}.$

Exercises

1. The symbolic patterns and forms we use to describe our ideas concerning numbers and operations with them are called _____.

2. The form of $5\frac{7}{8}$ is called a _____ _____. In using such a form we must remember that it expresses the _____ of an integer and a fraction.

3. Convert to mixed fraction form:

   (a) $\dfrac{19}{5}$ (b) $\dfrac{72}{17}$ (c) $\dfrac{150}{16}$ (d) $\dfrac{132}{72}$ (e) $\dfrac{462}{165}.$

4. Convert to improper fraction form:

   (a) $3\frac{5}{6}$ (b) $7\frac{9}{14}$ (c) $10\frac{3}{5}$ (d) $12\frac{11}{15}$ (e) $25\frac{7}{10}.$

5. Find the exact quotients:

   (a) $21\overline{)2550}$ (b) $85\overline{)6732}$ (c) $108\overline{)22000}.$

6. Find the sums in simplest form:

   (a) $73\frac{5}{7} + 16\frac{2}{3}$ (b) $105\frac{1}{6} + 94\frac{14}{15}$ (c) $4\frac{5}{12}$ (d) $16\frac{3}{5}$

   $+7\frac{1}{2}$ $9\frac{7}{8}$

   $+30\frac{9}{10}$

   (e) $57\frac{3}{4} + 102\frac{7}{15} + 1\frac{5}{6}.$

7. Find the differences:

   (a) $7\frac{5}{8} - 3\frac{1}{3}$ (b) $4\frac{5}{12} - 1\frac{7}{9}$ (c) $10\frac{3}{10}$ (d) $5\frac{3}{4}$

   $- 3\frac{9}{25}$ $-9\frac{5}{6}$

(e) $6\frac{4}{5} - 7\frac{3}{7}$.

8. Find the products:

(a) $6\frac{1}{4} \times 9\frac{3}{5}$ (b) $5\frac{5}{21} \times 7\frac{14}{15}$ (c) $\left(-3\frac{7}{21}\right) \times 2\frac{17}{30}$

(d) $\left(-17\frac{1}{12}\right) \times \left(-34\frac{2}{15}\right)$ (e) $7\frac{5}{6} \times 8\frac{3}{14}$.

9. Find the quotients:

(a) $13\frac{3}{4} \div 5\frac{5}{9}$ (b) $4\frac{2}{3} \div 1\frac{1}{6}$ (c) $\frac{16\frac{7}{8}}{2\frac{1}{12}}$ (d) $\frac{29\frac{2}{5}}{17\frac{1}{2}}$

(e) $3\frac{4}{7} \div 7\frac{1}{2}$.

10. Verify that $\left(\frac{1}{2} + \frac{1}{4}\right) \times \left(\frac{1}{4} + \frac{1}{10} + \frac{1}{20}\right) = \frac{1}{5} + \frac{1}{10}$ by repeatedly applying the distributive property and combining fractions while always working with fractions with numerator 1.

11. Find the simplest numeral for:

(a) $\frac{2\frac{1}{3} + 1\frac{2}{5}}{5\frac{1}{3} - 1\frac{1}{4}}$ (b) $\frac{75\frac{3}{4} - 9\frac{1}{12}}{5\frac{2}{15} + 28\frac{1}{5}}$ (c) $\left(3\frac{5}{8} - 7\frac{5}{7}\right) \times \left(3\frac{4}{15} + 2\frac{1}{3}\right)$.

12. Find N in each of the following:

(a) $\frac{2}{5} = \frac{N}{1000}$ (b) $\frac{6}{7} = \frac{N}{1000}$ (c) $\frac{4}{9} = \frac{N}{1000}$

(d) $\frac{3}{11} = \frac{N}{1000}$ (e) $\frac{1}{12} = \frac{N}{1000}$ (f) $\frac{7}{12} = \frac{N}{1000}$.

13. Round the fractions in Exercise 12 above to the nearest $\frac{1}{100}$.

14. Add $3\frac{5}{8}$ to $5\frac{2}{3}$ and multiply the sum by $4\frac{4}{5}$. Subtract $16\frac{1}{4}$ from the product and then divide the difference by $6\frac{3}{4}$. What is the resulting quotient?

15. A rectangle is $6\frac{3}{4}$ inches wide and $11\frac{2}{3}$ inches long. If we cut $2\frac{1}{2}$ inches from its length, then how much must be added to its width to form a new rectangle with the same area as the original rectangle?

Answers.

1. notation.
2. mixed fraction; sum.
3. (a) $3\frac{4}{5}$ (b) $4\frac{4}{17}$ (c) $9\frac{3}{8}$ (d) $1\frac{5}{6}$ (e) $2\frac{4}{5}$.
4. (a) $\frac{23}{6}$ (b) $\frac{107}{14}$ (c) $\frac{53}{5}$ (d) $\frac{191}{15}$ (e) $\frac{257}{10}$.

5. (a) $121\frac{3}{7}$ (b) $79\frac{1}{5}$ (c) $203\frac{19}{27}$.

6. (a) $90\frac{8}{21}$ (b) $200\frac{1}{10}$ (c) $11\frac{11}{12}$ (d) $57\frac{3}{8}$ (e) $162\frac{1}{20}$.

7. (a) $4\frac{7}{24}$ (b) $2\frac{23}{36}$ (c) $6\frac{47}{50}$ (d) $-4\frac{1}{12}$ (e) $-\frac{22}{35}$.

8. (a) 60 (b) $41\frac{5}{9}$ (c) $-8\frac{5}{9}$ (d) $583\frac{1}{9}$ (e) $64\frac{29}{84}$.

9. (a) $2\frac{19}{40}$ (b) 4 (c) $8\frac{1}{10}$ (d) $1\frac{17}{25}$ (e) $\frac{10}{21}$.

10. $-$.

11. (a) $\frac{32}{35}$ (b) 2 (c) $-22\frac{9}{10}$.

12. (a) 400 (b) $857\frac{1}{7}$ (c) $444\frac{4}{9}$ (d) $272\frac{8}{11}$ (e) $83\frac{1}{3}$

   (f) $583\frac{1}{3}$.

13. (a) $\frac{40}{100}$ (b) $\frac{86}{100}$ (c) $\frac{44}{100}$ (d) $\frac{27}{100}$ (e) $\frac{8}{100}$ (f) $\frac{58}{100}$

14. $4\frac{1}{5}$.

15. $1\frac{37}{44}$ inches must be added.

7.2 Decimal Notation

7.2.1   The uniform **decimal form** of notation was not extended to include the nonintegral rational numbers until the sixteenth century. By this period the use of fractions with large numerators and denominators had led to a great deal of difficulty in computations. A practical mathematician, Simon Stevin (1548–1620), is usually credited as the first writer to discuss the decimal system of notation as applied to the rational numbers. He described it as an arithmetic based on the idea of successive place positions by tens, making use of the ordinary Arabic numerals, in which any number might be written and by which all computations might be met by integer operations alone without the aid of fractions.

To develop the idea, we observe that $420 = 4(100) + 2(10) + 0(1)$. Each place position has a value ten times the place to its right. We can also think of each place position as having a value one-tenth of that to its left. The essential idea is simply to extend to the right of the ones' place the decimal place position system. In extending our notation to the right, it becomes necessary to identify the value of at least one place position in a numeral. Consider

$$420\frac{1}{8} = 4(100) + 2(10) + 0(1) + 1\left(\frac{1}{10}\right) + 2\left(\frac{1}{100}\right) + 5\left(\frac{1}{1000}\right)$$

might be written 420125, providing we knew which digit referred to the ones' place. This is accomplished by placing a point, called the **decimal point**, at the right "foot" of the ones' digit in a decimal. For example, 420.125 to indicate that there are 0 ones and that the digits to the right refer to place positions whose values are less than 1. As in writing the names of integers, the place positions of the digits in a decimal have been given names as shown in Table 15.

Examples.

(a) $2\frac{3}{4} = 2 + \frac{7}{10} + \frac{5}{100} = 2.75.$

(b) $305\frac{1}{40} = 3(100) + 0(10) + 5(1) + 0\left(\frac{1}{10}\right) + 2\left(\frac{1}{100}\right) + 5\left(\frac{1}{1000}\right)$

$= 305.025.$

(c) $7.4 = 7(1) + 4\left(\frac{1}{10}\right) = 7\frac{4}{10} = 7\frac{2}{5}.$

(d) $12.375 = 1(10) + 2(1) + 3\left(\frac{1}{10}\right) + 7\left(\frac{1}{100}\right) + 5\left(\frac{1}{1000}\right) = 12\frac{375}{1000}$

$= 12\frac{3}{8}.$

TABLE 15

									.								
100,000,000	10,000,000	1,000,000	100,000	10,000	1,000	100	10	1		$\frac{1}{10}$	$\frac{1}{100}$	$\frac{1}{1,000}$	$\frac{1}{10,000}$	$\frac{1}{100,000}$	$\frac{1}{1,000,000}$	$\frac{1}{10,000,000}$	$\frac{1}{100,000,000}$
hundred-millions	ten-millions	millions	hundred-thousands	ten-thousands	thousands	hundreds	tens	ones	decimal point →	tenths	hundredths	thousandths	ten-thousandths	hundred-thousandths	millionths	ten-millionths	hundred-millionths

The center of the decimal notation is the ones' place and not th
position of the decimal point. For example, in 420.125 we have tens t
the left of the ones' place and tenths to the right of the ones' place. T
the left of the tens' place we have hundreds and to the right of the tenths
place we have hundredths. Notice the expanded form

$$420.125 = 4(100) + 2(10) + 0(1) + 1\left(\frac{1}{10}\right) + 2\left(\frac{1}{100}\right) + 5\left(\frac{1}{1000}\right).$$

Although it is becoming common practice to read numerals such a
"420.125" as "four, twenty, point, one, two, five," it is preferable, in th
beginning, to be explicit and read them in a more traditional manner
That is, 420.125 would be read "four hundred twenty and one hundre
twenty-five thousandths."

Three simple conventions are usually followed in reading and writing
decimals:

1. The integral part to the left of the decimal is read or written a
previously discussed.

2. We read or write the decimal point as "and."

3. We read or write the part to the right of the decimal point as th
integral numerator followed by the place value of the last digit on the righ
which names the denominator.

Examples.

(a) $2.75 = 2\frac{75}{100}$ is read "two and seventy-five hundredths."

(b) $1{,}304.135 = 1{,}304\frac{135}{1000}$ is read "one thousand, three hundre
four and one hundred thirty-five thousandths."

(c) $0.00007 = \frac{7}{100000}$ is read "seven hundred-thousandths."

(d) $0.700 = \frac{700}{1000}$ is read "seven-hundred thousandths."

(e) $27.15\frac{1}{2} = 27\frac{15\frac{1}{2}}{100}$ is read "twenty-seven and fifteen and one-half
hundredths."

When a decimal names a number between -1 and 1 (a proper fraction)
we often call it a **pure decimal**. Notice that we have written a zero in the
ones' place to avoid "losing" the decimal point placement. Notice the
change in meaning with and without the hyphen in "hundred-thousandths." Although the practice is not common, when a mixed fractional
form is written to the right of the decimal point, the numeral is called a
complex decimal fraction. Observe also that the number of digits to the
right of the decimal point indicate the number of zeroes in the denom-

inator of the fractional equivalent. That is, $0.1 = \dfrac{1}{10}$, $0.01 = \dfrac{1}{100}$, 0.123 $= \dfrac{123}{1000}$, and so forth.

7.2.2   Just as with fractions, a scale or rational number line can be helpful in ordering and rounding decimals. For example, $0.639 = 6(0.1) + 3(0.01) + 9(0.001)$ is illustrated in Figure 82.

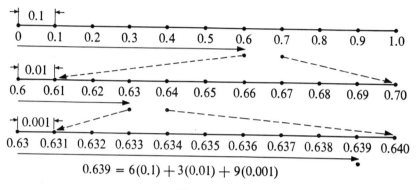

$$0.639 = 6(0.1) + 3(0.01) + 9(0.001)$$

FIGURE 82

Ordering a set of decimals is easy, providing we remember the place position idea and note the decimal point carefully. For example, to order 3.27, 23.7, 2.73, 3.72, and 32.7 we note the decimal point placement in each numeral and place the leftmost digit. That is, 3.27, 2.73, and 3.72 are all between 1 and 10, while 23.7 and 32.7 are between 10 and 100. The succeeding digits to the right in each numeral are then noted. Thus, from smallest to largest, we have 2.73, 3.27, 3.72, 23.7, 32.7. An alternative method is to introduce zeroes to the right as necessary to obtain numerals all of which have the same number of decimal place positions. In the above example, we would write 3.27, 23.70, 2.73, 3.72, and 32.70. That is, $\dfrac{327}{100}$, $\dfrac{2370}{100}$, $\dfrac{273}{100}$, $\dfrac{372}{100}$, and $\dfrac{3270}{100}$ so that the decimal point is eliminated.

Examples.

(a) Order from smallest to largest:
0.123, 2.103, 1.032, 1.230, 0.312.
ANSWER. 0.123, 0.312, 1.032, 1.230, 2.103.
(b) Order 3.105, 15.2, 0.73, 1.075, 3.52 from smallest to largest. We first write 3.105, 15.200, 0.730, 1.075, 3.520.
ANSWER. 0.73, 1.075, 3.105, 3.52, 15.2.

Decimals may be rounded off to name the nearest multiple of a given place position just as was done with the integers. In rounding to a specified place position the digits to the right of that position are dropped if the place position is to the right of the decimal point and replaced by zeroes if the place position is to the left of the decimal point.

Examples.

(a) 307.148 rounded to the nearest ones is 307; nearest tens is 310; nearest tenths is 307.1; nearest hundreds is 300; nearest hundredths is 307.15.

(b) 7.560099 rounded to one place position is 8; two place positions is 7.6; three place positions is 7.56; four place positions is 7.560; five places is 7.5601; six places is 7.56010.

Practice 1.

1. Write the following in ordinary words:

    (a) 20.51   (b) 0.306   (c) 120.021   (d) 0.004

    (e) 876.9   (f) 8.00001   (g) 14.1002   (h) 300.0003

    (i) 729.575   (j) $1.8\frac{3}{4}$ (k) $64.02\frac{6}{7}$ (l) $0.0\frac{2}{3}$.

2. Write the following in decimal form:

    (a) Twenty-six and three tenths.

    (b) Ten and three hundredths.

    (c) Ten thousandths.

    (d) One ten-thousandths.

    (e) Four hundred twenty ten-thousandths.

    (f) Four hundred and twenty ten-thousandths.

    (g) Two and twenty-one thousandths.

    (h) Five ten-millionths.

    (i) Twelve and twenty and one-third hundredths.

    (j) One hundred sixty-six and two and three-fourth tenths.

    (k) Nine and nine hundred-thousandths.

    (l) Six and six-seventh tenths.

3. Order from smallest to largest:

    (a) 6.042, 20.46, 0.624, 4.602, 24.60.

    (b) 1.011, 1.101, 11.10, 10.11, 0.111, 110.1, 1.110.

4. Round each of the decimals in Problem 1 above to the nearest tenths.

5. Round each of the decimals in Problem 1 above to three place positions, where meaningful.

Answers.

1. (a) Twenty and fifty-one hundredths.
   (b) Three hundred six thousandths.
   (c) One hundred twenty and twenty-one thousandths.
   (d) Four thousandths.
   (e) Eight hundred seventy-six and nine tenths.
   (f) Eight and one hundred-thousandths.
   (g) Fourteen and one thousand two ten-thousandths.
   (h) Three hundred and three ten-thousandths.
   (i) Seven hundred twenty-nine and five hundred seventy-five thousandths.
   (j) One and eight and three-fourth tenths.
   (k) Sixty-four and two and six-seventh hundredths.
   (l) Two-thirds tenths.

2. (a) 26.3 (b) 10.03 (c) 0.010 (d) 0.0001
   (e) 0.0420 (f) 400.0020 (g) 2.021 (h) 0.0000005
   (i) $12.20\frac{1}{3}$ (j) $166.2\frac{3}{4}$ (k) 9.00009 (l) $6.0\frac{6}{7}$.

3. (a) 0.624, 4.602, 6.042, 20.46, 24.60.
   (b) 0.111, 1.011, 1.101, 1.110, 10.11, 11.10, 110.1.

4. (a) 20.5 (b) 0.3 (c) 120.0 (d) 0.0 (e) 876.9
   (f) 8.0 (g) 14.1 (h) 300.0 (i) 729.6 (j) 1.9
   (k) 64.0 (l) 0.1.

5. (a) 20.5 (b) 0.306 (c) 120 (d) 0.004 (e) 877
   (f) 8.00 (g) 14.1 (h) 300 (i) 730 (j) 1.88
   (k) 64.0 (l) 0.0667.

7.2.3 In order to make adequate use of decimal notation, it is important to be able to convert from fractional form to decimal form and vice versa rapidly and accurately. Remembering that decimal notation is based on products of 10, we can often approximate the decimal expansion of a fraction. For example, since $\frac{5}{11}$ is equivalent to $\frac{5 \times 9}{11 \times 9} = \frac{45}{99}$ and 99 is almost 100, we might approximate $\frac{5}{11}$ with 0.45. Of course, 0.45 means $\frac{45}{100} = \frac{9}{20}$ so that our approximation differs from $\frac{5}{11}$ by $\frac{5}{11} - \frac{9}{20} = \frac{1}{220}$. Since $91 \times 11 = 1,001$, we might write $\frac{5}{11} = \frac{5 \times 91}{11 \times 91} = \frac{455}{1,001}$ and estimate $\frac{5}{11}$ by 0.455. Now $\frac{455}{1,001}$ and $\frac{455}{1,000}$ differ by only $\frac{1}{2,200}$.

More routinely, we can obtain the decimal form for a fraction by a division process. For example, $\frac{5}{11} = \frac{5.000}{11}$ so that by division we have

$$
\begin{array}{r}
454\frac{6}{11} \\
11\overline{)5.000} \\
\underline{4\,4} \\
60 \\
\underline{55} \\
50 \\
\underline{44} \\
6
\end{array}
$$

where the decimal point may be placed by noting that $\frac{5}{11}$ is between $\frac{1}{10}$ and $\frac{5}{10}$. Thus, $\frac{5}{11} = 0.454\frac{6}{11}$. In equation form we can write $\frac{5}{11} = \frac{N}{1,000}$ to obtain $N = 454\frac{6}{11}$, so that $\frac{5}{11} = \frac{454\frac{6}{11}}{1,000} = 0.454\frac{6}{11}$. Of course, we might have used denominators of 100 or 10,000 to obtain fewer or more places in the decimal form of $\frac{5}{11}$.

Examples.

(a) $\frac{3}{8} = \frac{3 \times 125}{8 \times 125} = \frac{375}{1000} = 0.375.$

(b) $\frac{3}{8} = \frac{N}{1000}$ leads us to

$$
\begin{array}{r}
375 = N \\
8\overline{)3,000} \\
\underline{2\,4} \\
60 \\
\underline{56} \\
40 \\
\underline{40} \\
0
\end{array}
$$

so that $\frac{3}{8} = 0.375.$

(c) $\frac{23}{7} = \frac{N}{10,000}$ leads to

$$
\begin{array}{r}
3\ 2857\frac{1}{7} = N \\
7\overline{)23\ 0000} \\
\underline{21} \\
2\ 0 \\
\underline{1\ 4} \\
60 \\
\underline{56} \\
40 \\
\underline{35} \\
50 \\
\underline{49} \\
1
\end{array}
$$

so that $\frac{23}{7} = 3.2857\frac{1}{7}.$

Notice that in the division used in converting a fractional form to a decimal, the number of zeroes introduced into the dividend tells us where to place the decimal point in N, the numerator of the "decimal" fraction. The number of decimal places obtained can be made as few or as many as we please by merely terminating or continuing the division process appropriately.

Examples.

(a) $\dfrac{15}{4} = \dfrac{15.00}{4} = 3.75$ (b) $\dfrac{13}{11} = \dfrac{13.0000}{11} = 1.1818\dfrac{2}{11}$.

Decimals can easily be converted to fractional form by using the meaning of decimals to introduce the appropriate denominator and then reducing the resulting fraction.

Examples.

(a) $3.725 = 3\dfrac{725}{1000} = 3\dfrac{29}{40}$ (b) $0.916\dfrac{2}{3} = \dfrac{916\frac{2}{3}}{1000} = \dfrac{2750}{3000} = \dfrac{11}{12}$.

Practice 2.

1. Find two or three decimal place approximations for each of the following fractions.

(a) $\dfrac{2}{5}$ (b) $\dfrac{1}{3}$ (c) $\dfrac{1}{6}$ (d) $\dfrac{4}{9}$ (e) $\dfrac{5}{12}$ (f) $\dfrac{8}{15}$ (g) $\dfrac{11}{32}$

(h) $\dfrac{204}{499}$.

2. Find exact three decimal place forms for each of the fractions in Problem 1 above.

3. Convert the following fractions to decimal forms:

(a) $\dfrac{1}{2}$ (b) $\dfrac{1}{4}$ (c) $\dfrac{1}{5}$ (d) $\dfrac{1}{8}$ (e) $\dfrac{3}{4}$ (f) $\dfrac{3}{5}$ (g) $\dfrac{5}{8}$

(h) $\dfrac{7}{8}$.

4. Convert the following fractions to decimal forms as indicated:

(a) $\dfrac{7}{16}$ to 4 places   (b) $\dfrac{19}{6}$ to 3 places   (c) $\dfrac{17}{18}$ to 5 places

(d) $\dfrac{13}{30}$ to 2 places   (e) $\dfrac{27}{12}$ to 2 places   (f) $\dfrac{11}{64}$ to 4 places.

5. Convert the following to fractional forms:
   (a) 0.15   (b) 3.364   (c) 0.025   (d) 6.125   (e) 0.008
   (f) $1.33\dfrac{1}{3}$ (g) 0.0032   (h) $7.583\dfrac{1}{3}$ (i) 3.275   (j) $2.42\dfrac{6}{7}$.

Answers.

1. (a) 0.40   (b) 0.33   (c) 0.17   (d) 0.44
   (e) 0.415   (f) 0.533   (g) 0.344   (h) 0.408.

2. (a) 0.400   (b) $0.333\frac{1}{3}$ (c) $0.166\frac{2}{3}$ (d) $0.444\frac{4}{9}$

   (e) $0.416\frac{2}{3}$ (f) $0.533\frac{1}{3}$ (g) $0.343\frac{3}{4}$ (h) $0.408\frac{408}{499}$.

3. (a) 0.5   (b) 0.25   (c) 0.2   (d) 0.125
   (e) 0.75   (f) 0.6   (g) 0.625   (h) 0.875.

4. (a) 0.4375   (b) $3.166\frac{2}{3}$ (c) $0.94444\frac{4}{9}$

   (d) $0.43\frac{1}{3}$ (e) 2.25   (f) $0.1718\frac{3}{4}$.

5. (a) $\frac{3}{20}$ (b) $3\frac{91}{250}$ (c) $\frac{1}{40}$ (d) $6\frac{1}{8}$ (e) $\frac{1}{125}$

   (f) $1\frac{1}{3}$ (g) $\frac{2}{625}$ (h) $7\frac{7}{12}$ (i) $3\frac{11}{40}$ (j) $2\frac{3}{7}$.

7.2.4   Addition and subtraction with decimals should offer little difficulty providing that we remember the principle of place position and base. That is, in adding or subtracting with decimals, we "operate" by place positions and "carry" just as with the integers.

Examples.

(a) To add 1.68, 0.037, 14, and 19.395 we can arrange the computation vertically, aligning the digits with the decimal point as a reference:

```
T  O  T  H  T
e  n  e  u  h
n  e  n  n  o
s  s  t  d  u
      h  r  s
      s  e  a
         d  n
         t  d
         h  t
         s  h
            s

   1.6 8
   0.0 3 7
 1 4.              Remember, the decimal point is at the
+1 9.3 9 5         right "foot" of the ones' digit.
 3 5.1 1 2
```

(b) Of course, we could add 1.68, 0.037, 14, and 19.395 by adding

the integral and pure decimal parts separately: $1.68 = 1 + \dfrac{680}{1000}$, 0.037
$= \dfrac{37}{1000}$, $14 = 14$, $19.395 = 19 + \dfrac{395}{1000}$. Thus, we have $1 + 14 + 19 = 34$ and

$680 + 37 + 395 = 1{,}112$, so that the sum is $34 + \dfrac{1112}{1000} = 34 + 1 + \dfrac{112}{1000}$
$= 35.112$.

    (c)   2.15   (d)   8.0034
          16.   2041.706
         0.307   370.8515
         1.0409   +   12.9407
    +20.503   2433.5016
     40.0009

Notice the importance of aligning the decimal point vertically.

    (e) To subtract 635.1358 from 8043.0527 we align the decimal points and proceed as in ordinary subtraction with the integers

          8043.0527
      − 635.1358
       7407.9169

    (f) The difference between 14.053 and 6.45092 is computed as

          14.05300
      − 6.45092
        7.60208

Notice that we have written zeroes to the right of 14.053. Why is this permissible?

    (g) To compute $201.40072 - 321.50406$ we note the equivalence of $-(321.50406 - 201.40072)$ and write

         -321.50406
          201.40072
        -120.10334

    (h)   21.00000   (i) 10.2003004
       − 0.00981   − 1.0123045
       20.99019   9.1879959

Practice 3.

    1. Find the sums:

      (a) 27.075   (b) 4.1008   (c) 705.23
           0.325   0.06   70.523
        71.006   0.007   7.0523
         4.602   16.7305   0.70523

(d) 3009.4	(e) 28.0	(f) 726.5
20.006	0.375	79.086
800.57	174.009	989.997
0.024	8.5	4.349
110	7.42	486.04

2. Find the sums:
   (a) 6.3 + 0.084 + 20.01 + 3.8577.
   (b) 48 + 13.076 + 0.55 + 0.0040.
   (c) 159 + 0.632 + 13.8 + 30.08.
   (d) 4562.52 + 307.06 + 5000.02 + 40.55.
   (e) 0.007 + 8.5 + 30.08 + 7.956.
   (f) 715 + 0.075 + 10.425 + 2.50.

3. Round the sums of Problem 1 above as indicated below:
   (a) To thousandths   (b) To hundredths   (c) To hundredths
   (d) To ones   (e) To tenths   (f) To tenths.

4. Round the sums of Problem 2 above as indicated below:
   (a) Two place positions   (b) Two place positions
   (c) Three place positions   (d) Four place positions
   (e) One place position   (f) Two place positions.

5. Find the differences:

(a) 327.5729	(b) 105.6207	(c) 62.054
− 23.1075	− 12.543	− 1.8475

(d) 400.3006	(e) 25.625	(f) 4.0072
− 1.3007	−50.015	−0.10756

6. Do as indicated:
   (a) Subtract 0.0607 from 2   (b) What is 1.32 less 0.407?
   (c) Add −7.504 to 8.49   (d) Take 23.006 away from 32.06
   (e) Find the difference between 41.06 and 31.161.

7. Do as indicated:
   (a) 0.531 + 0.606 − 0.0094   (b) 3.150 + 10.07 − 7.616
   (c) 1.3704 − 0.4065 + 0.9809   (d) 0.50011 − 3.009 + 7.6109
   (e) 0.0001098 + 0.0099076 − 0.0000727 − 0.0098457.

Answers.

1. (a) 103.008   (b) 20.8983   (c) 783.51053
   (d) 3,940.000   (e) 218.304   (f) 2,285.972.
2. (a) 30.2517   (b) 61.63   (c) 203.512
   (d) 9,910.15   (e) 46.543   (f) 728.
3. (a) 103.008   (b) 20.90   (c) 783.51   (d) 3,940
   (e) 218.3   (f) 2,286.0.
4. (a) 30   (b) 62   (c) 204   (d) 9.910   (e) 50   (f) 730.

5. (a) 304.4654   (b) 93.0777   (c) 60.2065
   (d) 398.9999   (e) −24.390   (f) 3.89964.
6. (a) 1.9393   (b) 0.913   (c) 0.986   (d) 8.954   (e) 9.899.
7. (a) 0.6497   (b) 5.604   (c) 1.9448   (d) 5.10201
   (e) 0.000099.

7.2.5   Before proceeding to the general consideration of how to find the products and quotients of decimals, let us pause to examine further the notion of place position with respect to the decimal point. When we write 2.75 we mean 2 ones plus 7 tenths plus 5 hundredths. The decimal point is a reference to the left of which we have the ones' place position. If we write 27.5 we mean 2 tens plus 7 ones plus 5 tenths. Also, 275 means 2 hundreds plus 7 tens plus 5 ones. That is,

$$2.75 = 2(1) + 7\left(\frac{1}{10}\right) + 5\left(\frac{1}{100}\right) = 2(1) + 7(0.1) + 5(0.01)$$
$$10 \times 2.75 = 10 \times [2(1) + 7(0.1) + 5(0.01)]$$
$$= 2(10) + 7(1) + 5(0.1) = 27.5$$
$$100 \times 2.75 = 100 \times [2(1) + 7(0.1) + 5(0.01)]$$
$$= 2(100) + 7(10) + 5(1) = 275.$$

From the above, we note that in multiplying a decimal by 10 the digits "move" one place to the left with respect to the decimal point. In multiplying by 100, the digits are "shifted" two place positions to the left. Alternatively, the same results are achieved by placing the decimal point one or two place positions to the right.

Now, since division is the inverse operation to multiplication, we would expect (and correctly) that

$$2.75 \div 10 = \frac{2.75}{10} = 0.275 \quad \text{and} \quad 2.75 \div 100 = \frac{2.75}{100} = 0.0275.$$

That is, in dividing a decimal by 10 the digits "move" one place to the right with respect to the decimal point. In dividing by 100, the digits are "shifted" two place positions to the right. Alternatively, we can move the decimal point one or two places to the left.

Examples.

(a) $100 \times 0.034 = 3.4$ (b) $0.034 \div 100 = 0.00034$
(c) $1000 \times 47.625 = 47625$ (d) $47.625 \div 1000 = 0.047625$
(e) $100,000 \times 0.601 = 60,100$ (f) $0.601 \div 100,000 = 0.00000601.$

7.2.6   To find the product of two numbers expressed in decimal form we can begin by converting the decimals into fractions. For example, $1.35 \times 0.79 = \frac{135}{100} \times \frac{79}{100} = \frac{135 \times 79}{100 \times 100} = \frac{10665}{10000} = 1.0665$. Notice that the decimal places in the product equal the sum of the decimal places of the multiplier and multiplicand. In direct computational form:

$$
\begin{array}{r}
1.3\ 5 \quad \text{(has 2 decimal places)}\\
\times 0.7\ 9 \quad \text{(has 2 decimal places)}\\
\hline
1\ 2\ 1\ 5\\
9\ 4\ 5\\
\hline
1.0\ 6\ 6\ 5 \quad \text{(must have 4 decimal places)}
\end{array}
$$

Examples.

(a) $13.1 \times 7.006 = \dfrac{131}{10} \times \dfrac{7006}{1000} \times \dfrac{131 \times 7006}{10000} = \dfrac{917786}{10000} = 91.7786.$

(b) $62.04 \times 1,078.5 = 66,910.140$ since

$$
\begin{array}{r}
1\ 0\ 7\ 8.5\\
\times 6\ 2.0\ 4\\
\hline
4\ 3\ 1\ 4\ 0\\
2\ 1\ 5\ 7\ 0\\
6\ 4\ 7\ 1\ 0\\
\hline
6\ 6,9\ 1\ 0.1\ 4\ 0
\end{array}
$$

Notice that we do not align the decimal points in the factors, but rather the right hand digits. Also, decimal places are counted from the right of the numeral.

(c) $0.018 \times 5.0725 = 0.0913050$ since

$$
\begin{array}{r}
5.0\ 7\ 2\ 5\\
\times\ \ \ 0.0\ 1\ 8\\
\hline
4\ 0\ 5\ 8\ 0\ 0\\
5\ 0\ 7\ 2\ 5\\
\hline
0.0\ 9\ 1\ 3\ 0\ 5\ 0
\end{array}
$$

Observe that the process of multiplication is just the same as with the integers. The zero digits to the right must be retained and counted in placing the decimal point correctly in the product.

(d) $672 \times 0.00009 = 0.06048$ since

$$
\begin{array}{r}
6\ 7\ 2 \quad \text{(0 decimal places)}\\
\times 0.0\ 0\ 0\ 0\ 9 \quad \text{(5 decimal places)}\\
\hline
0.0\ 6\ 0\ 4\ 8 \quad \text{(5 decimal places)}
\end{array}
$$

In many applications decimal products are rounded to a specified number of place positions. For example, $1.35 \times 0.79 = 1.0665$ might be rounded to 1.1 since 0.79 has only 2 place positions. The product $13.1 \times 7.006 = 91.7786$ might be estimated by 91.8 while 62.04×1078.5 might be estimated by $66,910$.

Practice 4.

1. Find:
   - (a) 100×63.4
   - (b) 3.76×10
   - (c) 0.74×1000
   - (d) 10×0.071
   - (e) 4.05×1000
   - (f) 100×0.506
   - (g) 35.8×100
   - (h) 1000×0.1
   - (i) $\begin{array}{r} 436.09 \\ \times\ 1000 \\ \hline \end{array}$
   - (j) $\begin{array}{r} 2.071 \\ \times\ 100 \\ \hline \end{array}$
   - (k) $\begin{array}{r} 30.708 \\ \times\ 1000 \\ \hline \end{array}$
   - (l) $\begin{array}{r} 0.00521 \\ \times\ 10000 \\ \hline \end{array}$

2. Find:
   - (a) $63.4 \div 100$
   - (b) $3.76 \div 10$
   - (c) $0.74 \div 1000$
   - (d) $0.071 \div 10$
   - (e) $4.05 \div 1000$
   - (f) $0.506 \div 100$
   - (g) $35.8 \div 100$
   - (h) $0.1 \div 1000$
   - (i) $100\overline{)38.65}$
   - (j) $1000\overline{)0.735}$
   - (k) $10\overline{)0.009}$
   - (l) $100\overline{)5.673.}$

3. Find the products:
   - (a) 1.05×3.2
   - (b) 0.62×7.43
   - (c) 5.30×0.06
   - (d) 0.502×0.09
   - (e) 24.1×1.772
   - (f) 0.0041×0.037
   - (g) 801.3×75.6
   - (h) 0.505×60.8
   - (i) 0.742×36.05
   - (j) 0.0097×47.3
   - (k) 4.09×0.094
   - (l) $27.07 \times 0.064.$

4. Round the products in Problem 3 above to three place positions.

5. Find the products:
   - (a) $\begin{array}{r} 40.7 \\ \times 6.03 \\ \hline \end{array}$
   - (b) $\begin{array}{r} 2.31 \\ \times 0.46 \\ \hline \end{array}$
   - (c) $\begin{array}{r} 0.815 \\ \times\ 0.27 \\ \hline \end{array}$
   - (d) $\begin{array}{r} 0.6501 \\ \times\ 0.92 \\ \hline \end{array}$
   - (e) $\begin{array}{r} 3.659 \\ \times 0.085 \\ \hline \end{array}$
   - (f) $\begin{array}{r} 0.1602 \\ \times\ 0.304 \\ \hline \end{array}$
   - (g) $\begin{array}{r} 0.0058 \\ \times 0.0307 \\ \hline \end{array}$
   - (h) $\begin{array}{r} 64.509 \\ \times\ 0.908 \\ \hline \end{array}$
   - (i) $\begin{array}{r} 705.3 \\ \times\ 1.21 \\ \hline \end{array}$
   - (j) $\begin{array}{r} 62.315 \\ \times\ 0.053 \\ \hline \end{array}$
   - (k) $\begin{array}{r} 200.07 \\ \times\ 1.009 \\ \hline \end{array}$
   - (l) $\begin{array}{r} 0.06075 \\ \times 0.01008 \\ \hline \end{array}$

6. Round the products in Problem 5 above to four place positions.

7. (a) Find 0.475 of 16.08   (b) What is 3.62 times 45.8?
   (c) Multiply 84.001 by 0.007   (d) Find 9.2 times 0.92
   (e) What is the product of 2.35 and 1.005?

8. Find the products:
   - (a) $0.7 \times 1.2 \times 0.98$
   - (b) $3.5 \times 0.87 \times 2.06$
   - (c) $0.09 \times 0.701 \times 0.005$
   - (d) $3.405 \times 0.6 \times 0.705$
   - (e) $0.2 \times 0.04 \times 0.006$
   - (f) $1.9 \times 0.27 \times 0.308 \times 0.026.$

Answers.

1. (a) 6,340   (b) 37.6   (c) 740   (d) 0.71   (e) 4,050
   (f) 50.6   (g) 3,580   (h) 100   (i) 436,090   (j) 207.1
   (k) 30,708   (l) 52.1.

2. (a) 0.634   (b) 0.376   (c) 0.00074   (d) 0.0071
   (e) 0.00405   (f) 0.00506   (g) 0.358   (h) 0.0001
   (i) 0.3865   (j) 0.000735   (k) 0.0009   (l) 0.05673.

3. (a) 3.360   (b) 4.6066   (c) 0.3180   (d) 0.04518
    (e) 42.7052   (f) 0.0001517   (g) 60,578.28   (h) 30.7040
    (i) 26.74910   (j) 0.45881   (k) 0.38446   (l) 1.73248.

4. (a) 3.36   (b) 4.61   (c) 0.318   (d) 0.0452
    (e) 42.7   (f) 0.000152   (g) 60,600   (h) 30.7
    (i) 26.7   (j) 0.459   (k) 0.384   (l) 1.73.

5. (a) 245.421   (b) 1.0626   (c) 0.22005   (d) 0.598092
    (e) 0.311015   (f) 0.0487008   (g) 0.00017806   (h) 58.574172
    (i) 853.413   (j) 3.302695   (k) 201.87063   (l) 0.0006123600.

6. (a) 245.4   (b) 1.063   (c) 0.2200   (d) 0.5981
    (e) 0.3110   (f) 0.04870   (g) 0.0001781   (h) 58.57
    (i) 853.4   (j) 3.303   (k) 201.9   (l) 0.0006124.

7. (a) 7.638   (b) 165.796   (c) 0.588007   (d) 8.464
    (e) 2.36175.

8. (a) .8232   (b) 6.2727   (c) 0.00031545
    (d) 1.440315   (e) 0.000048   (f) 0.004108104.

7.2.7 The quotient of two numbers expressed in a decimal form can be denoted in a variety of ways. For example, to indicate the quotient of 1.35 divided by 0.79 we might write

     (a) $1.35 \div 0.79$ (b) $\dfrac{1.35}{0.79}$ (c) $0.79\overline{)1.35.}$

To describe how we compute the quotient it is convenient to consider the fractional form $\dfrac{1.35}{0.79}$ and convert this form to the more familiar form,

$$\frac{\frac{135}{100}}{\frac{79}{100}} = \frac{135}{100} \times \frac{100}{79} = \frac{135}{79} = 1.7\frac{7}{79}.$$

Alternatively, we can multiply both dividend and divisor by 100 to obtain

$$\frac{1.35}{0.79} = \frac{1.35 \times 100}{0.79 \times 100} = \frac{135}{79} = 1.7\frac{7}{79}.$$

Examples.

   (a) $\dfrac{81.34}{1.4} = \dfrac{\frac{8134}{100}}{\frac{14}{10}} = \dfrac{8134}{100} \times \dfrac{10}{14} = \dfrac{8134}{140} = 58.1.$

   (b) $\dfrac{81.34}{1.4} = \dfrac{81.34 \times 100}{1.4 \times 100} = \dfrac{8134}{140} = 58.1.$

   (c) $\dfrac{0.1202}{3.005} = \dfrac{0.1202 \times 1000}{3.005 \times 1000} = \dfrac{120.2}{3005} = 0.04.$

A careful study of the examples should lead to the following observations:

    1. The digits of the quotient can be obtained by proceeding as in ordinary division of integers.

    2. The decimal point in the quotient is obtained by "moving" the

decimal points in the dividend and the divisor to the right as many decimal places as are in the divisor. That is, multiplying both the dividend and divisor by factors of ten to convert the divisor to an integer.

The division $1.35 \div 0.79$ in computational form would then appear as

$$
\begin{array}{r}
1.7\frac{7}{79} \\
0.79\overline{)1.35{}_\wedge 0} \\
\underline{79} \\
56\ 0 \\
\underline{55\ 3} \\
7
\end{array}
$$

Examples.

(a)
$$
\begin{array}{r}
4.7 \\
23\overline{)108.1} \\
\underline{92} \\
16\ 1 \\
\underline{16\ 1} \\
0
\end{array}
$$

(b)
$$
\begin{array}{r}
58.1 \\
1.4\overline{)81.3{}_\wedge 4} \\
\underline{70} \\
11\ 3 \\
\underline{11\ 2} \\
1\ 4 \\
\underline{1\ 4} \\
0
\end{array}
$$

(c)
$$
\begin{array}{r}
73.6 \\
0.057\overline{)4.200{}_\wedge 0} \\
\underline{3\ 99} \\
210 \\
\underline{171} \\
39\ 0 \\
\underline{34\ 2} \\
4\ 8
\end{array}
$$

(d)
$$
\begin{array}{r}
0.04 \\
3.005\overline{)0.120{}_\wedge 20} \\
\underline{120\ 20} \\
0
\end{array}
$$

In the examples the symbol "$\wedge$," called a *caret*, has been used to indicate the placement of the decimal point. Notice that the digits in the quotient are aligned vertically with the digits of the dividend. Zeroes may be introduced to the right in the dividend when necessary for the placement of the decimal point.

Many division problems involving decimals do not end with a remainder of zero. Thus, a complex decimal quotient or a rounded estimate of the quotient may be appropriate as an answer. Finally, in placing the decimal point in a quotient we should always use a "common sense" estimate as a check.

Practice 5.

1. Find the quotients:

(a) $\dfrac{8.064}{5.04}$ (b) $\dfrac{44.5}{0.625}$ (c) $\dfrac{0.182}{0.175}$

(d) $\dfrac{0.2349}{2.7}$ (e) $\dfrac{0.234}{0.65}$ (f) $\dfrac{45.05}{0.7208}$.

2. Find the quotients:
   (a) $6.14\overline{)7.982}$ (b) $5.308\overline{)92.89}$ (c) $0.304\overline{)0.38}$
   (d) $3.26\overline{)2.9666}$ (e) $0.094\overline{)0.014758}$ (f) $3.43\overline{)0.002058}$.

3. Find the quotients:
   (a) $2.247 \div 1.07$ (b) $0.756 \div 3.6$ (c) $340.3 \div 0.82$
   (d) $77.9 \div 2.05$ (e) $0.2286 \div 0.036$ (f) $0.03675 \div 0.75$.

4. (a) Find $0.369 \div 1.87$ to the nearest thousandths.

   (b) Divide 13.06 by 0.0052 to the nearest ones.

   (c) What is the quotient of 70.4 divided by 8.09 to the nearest hundredths?

   (d) Find $\dfrac{13.5}{0.56}$ to the nearest tenths.

   (e) Divide 2.56 into 38.6 to obtain a quotient to the nearest tenths.

   (f) What is the quotient of 6.54 divided by 93.8 to the nearest ten-thousandths?

5. Find to three significant digits:
   (a) $14.6\overline{)731.8}$ (b) $5.02\overline{)29.6}$ (c) $1.37\overline{)0.527}$
   (d) $0.098\overline{)12.2}$ (e) $0.605\overline{)0.00628}$ (f) $468.7\overline{)3.19}$
   (g) $32.04\overline{)8.006}$ (h) $84.5\overline{)0.03605}$ (i) $0.292\overline{)51.7}$
   (j) $6.001\overline{)24.1}$ (k) $0.11\overline{)3.06}$ (l) $0.00308\overline{)0.0271}$.

6. Find to three significant digits:
   (a) $\dfrac{14.5 \times 8.07}{32.4}$ (b) $\dfrac{5.62}{0.715 \times 20.9}$ (c) $\dfrac{1.64 \times 38.2}{8.01 \times 0.305}$

   (d) $\dfrac{4.07 \times 6.82}{29.2 \times 0.631}$ (e) $\dfrac{0.940 \times 0.0761}{0.0515 \times 0.402}$ (f) $\dfrac{0.215 \times 2.41}{5.42 \times 80.3}$.

Answers.

1. (a) 1.6   (b) 71.2   (c) 1.04   (d) 0.087   (e) 0.36
   (f) 62.5.
2. (a) 1.3   (b) 17.5   (c) 1.25   (d) 0.91   (e) 0.157
   (f) 0.0006.
3. (a) 2.1   (b) 0.21   (c) 415   (d) 38   (e) 6.35
   (f) 0.049.
4. (a) 0.197   (b) 2512   (c) 8.70   (d) 24.1   (e) 15.1
   (f) 0.0697.
5. (a) 50.1   (b) 5.90   (c) 0.385   (d) 124   (e) 0.0104
   (f) 0.00681   (g) 0.250   (h) 0.000427   (i) 177
   (j) 4.02   (k) 27.8   (l) 8.80.
6. (a) 3.61   (b) 0.376   (c) 25.6   (d) 1.51   (e) 3.46
   (f) 0.00119.

Exercises

1. In the decimal form of notation, each place position has a value _____ times the place position to its right and _____ the place position to its left. The digit to the _____ of the decimal point marks the ones' place position.
_(right or left)

2. Write the following in ordinary words:

   (a) 507.507   (b) 0.0603   (c) $2.30\frac{3}{5}$ (d) 41.009.

3. Write in decimal form:
   (a) Three hundred one ten-thousandths.
   (b) Three hundred and one thousandths.
   (c) Three and fifty-four and one-half hundredths.
   (d) Seventy-two and eighteen hundred-thousandths.

4. Round the following as indicated:
   (a) 405.07815 to thousandths   (b) 24.3607 to tenths
   (c) 50.0091 to hundredths   (d) 728.501 to ones
   (e) 405.07815 to four place positions
   (f) 24.3607 to five place positions
   (g) 50.0091 to three place positions
   (h) 728.501 to four place positions.

5. Estimate the following fractions to three decimal places (to thousandths).

   (a) $\frac{3}{7}$ (b) $\frac{7}{9}$ (c) $\frac{15}{11}$ (d) $\frac{14}{3}$ (e) $\frac{13}{16}$ (f) $\frac{28}{15}$

   (g) $\frac{18}{23}$ (h) $\frac{99}{32}$ (i) $\frac{43}{64}$ (j) $\frac{31}{30}$ (k) $\frac{1}{18}$ (l) $\frac{51}{28}$.

6. Convert the following decimals to reduced fractional forms:
   (a) 0.40   (b) 0.25   (c) 0.05   (d) 0.55   (e) 0.28
   (f) 0.34   (g) 0.125   (h) 0.075   (i) 0.008   (j) 0.875
   (k) 0.9375   (l) 0.0625.

7. Arrange the following sets of numbers in order of size, from smallest to largest.

   (a) $\frac{3}{4}, \frac{2}{3}, \frac{5}{6}, \frac{3}{8}, \frac{5}{9}$ (b) $\frac{97}{100}, \frac{7}{10}, \frac{79}{100}, \frac{9}{10}, \frac{879}{1000}$

   (c) $\frac{546}{1000}, \frac{465}{1000}, \frac{645}{1000}, \frac{456}{1000}, \frac{564}{1000}$

   (d) 0.07, 0.25, 0.068, 1.01, 0.61
   (e) 8.57, 0.875, 58.7, 0.758, 5.78
   (f) 0.321, 0.231, 0.123, 2.13, 0.0321.

8. Find the sums:

(a) 321.056	(b) 12.507	(c) 39.005	(d) 7.005
67.98	9.038	2.037	10.614
101.502	0.704	421.8	0.073
475.6	7.751	0.1987	15.9
			30.04
			7.208

(e) 4.007 + 40.81 + 1.050 + 37.009
(f) 204.6 + 8.9007 + 36.05 + 0.0758.

9. Find the differences:

(a) 560.804	(b) 321.059	(c) 600.06	(d) 0.51073
−51.705	−22.76	−12.475	−0.09765

(e) 13.604 − 8.72   (f) 207.537 − 750.573.

10. (a) Subtract 14.09 from the sum of 8.43 and 5.97.

(b) Add 0.065 to the difference between 1.307 and 0.958.

(c) Find the difference between the sum of 0.138 and 0.762 and the quantity 0.091.

(d) Find the sum of 3.57 and 1.49 less the difference between 3.57 and 1.49.

11. Find:

(a) 100×3.617 (b) $10,000 \times 0.48$ (c) 68.07×10
(d) 0.00091×1000 (e) $3.617 \div 100$ (f) $0.48 \div 10,000$
(g) $68.07 \div 10$ (h) $0.91 \div 1000$.

12. Find the products to four place positions:

(a) 42.06×1.903 (b) 6.318×7.192
(c) 0.5204×8.051 (d) 16.30×0.07562

(e) 180.1	(f) 0.7113	(g) 32.50	(h) 980.7
×0.905	×0.0460	×12.01	×0.00319

13. Find the quotients to four place positions:

(a) $\dfrac{1.568}{0.07162}$ (b) $\dfrac{0.02903}{12.04}$ (c) $\dfrac{57.12}{59.08}$

(d) $5.004\overline{)957.6}$ (e) $0.07233\overline{)0.2181}$ (f) $1.072\overline{)0.006436}$
(g) $0.1117 \div 10.69$ (h) $2407 \div 31.49$ (i) $17.78 \div 2.301$.

14. (a) Find the product of 3.65 and 0.904 divided by 2.285.

(b) Find the quotient of 9.207 divided by the product of 4.65 and 13.2.

(c) What is the product of the sum of 3.005 and 0.785 times the difference between 8.31 and 7.76?

(d) What is the quotient of the difference between 9.669 and 3.531 divided by their sum?

15. If Bill made $76.80 during a 40-hour work week, then what was his

hourly rate of pay? What would his gross earnings be for a 48-week working year at 40 hours per week?

16. The perimeter of a triangle is the sum of the lengths of its sides. If a triangle has sides 24.05 inches, 18.63 inches, and 9.54 inches long, then what is its perimeter?

17. If an auto travels 259.2 miles on 14.3 gallons of gasoline, then how far will it go on 1 gallon of gasoline? (To tenths of a mile.)

18. A store purchased certain yard goods for $0.37 per yard and sold it at $0.43 per yard. What was the total profit on $138\frac{1}{2}$ yards of goods sold?

19. Find the dimensions marked A and B on Figure 83.

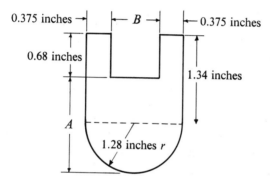

FIGURE 83

20. If gasoline costs 32.9 cents per gallon and Bill paid $4.38 for a tank of gas, then how many gallons of gasoline (to 0.1 gallon) did Bill purchase?

Answers.

1. 10; $\frac{1}{10}$; left.

2. (a) Five hundred seven and five hundred seven thousandths.
   (b) Six hundred three ten-thousandths.
   (c) Two and thirty and three-fifths hundredths.
   (d) Forty-one and nine thousandths.

3. (a) 0.0301   (b) 300.001   (c) $3.54\frac{1}{2}$ (d) 72.00018

4. (a) 405.078   (b) 24.4   (c) 50.01   (d) 728
   (e) 405.1   (f) 24.361   (g) 50.0   (h) 728.5.

5. (a) 0.429   (b) 0.778   (c) 1.364   (d) 4.667   (e) 0.812
   (f) 1.867   (g) 0.783   (h) 3.094   (i) 0.672   (j) 1.033
   (k) 0.056   (l) 1.821.

6. (a) $\frac{2}{5}$ (b) $\frac{1}{4}$ (c) $\frac{1}{20}$ (d) $\frac{11}{20}$ (e) $\frac{7}{25}$ (f) $\frac{17}{50}$
   (g) $\frac{1}{8}$ (h) $\frac{3}{40}$ (i) $\frac{1}{125}$ (j) $\frac{7}{8}$ (k) $\frac{15}{16}$ (l) $\frac{1}{16}$.

7. (a) $\frac{3}{8}, \frac{5}{9}, \frac{2}{3}, \frac{3}{4}, \frac{5}{6}$ (b) $\frac{7}{10}, \frac{79}{100}, \frac{879}{1000}, \frac{9}{10}, \frac{97}{100}$
   (c) $\frac{456}{1000}, \frac{465}{1000}, \frac{546}{1000}, \frac{564}{1000}, \frac{645}{1000}$ (d) 0.068, 0.07, 0.25, 0.61, 1.01
   (e) 0.758, 0.875, 5.78, 8.57, 58.7
   (f) 0.0321, 0.123, 0.231, 0.321, 2.13.

8. (a) 966.138   (b) 30.000   (c) 463.0407
   (d) 70.840   (e) 82.876   (f) 249.6265.

9. (a) 509.099   (b) 298.299   (c) 587.585
   (d) 0.41308   (e) 4.884   (f) −543.036.

10. (a) 0.31   (b) 0.414   (c) 0.809   (d) 2.98.

11. (a) 361.7   (b) 4800   (c) 680.7   (d) 0.91
   (e) 0.03617   (f) 0.000048   (g) 6.807   (h) 0.00091.

12. (a) 80.04   (b) 45.44   (c) 4.190   (d) 0.1233
   (e) 163.0   (f) 0.03272   (g) 390.3   (h) 3.128.

13. (a) 21.89   (b) 0.002411   (c) 0.9668   (d) 191.4
   (e) 3.015   (f) 0.006004   (g) 0.01045   (h) 76.43
   (i) 7.725.

14. (a) 1.46   (b) 0.15   (c) 2.0845   (d) 0.465.

15. $1.92 per hour; $3,686.40 for one year.

16. 52.22 inches long.

17. 18.1 miles.

18. $8.31.

19. $A = 1.94$ inches and $B = 1.81$ inches.

20. 13.3 gallons.

7.3 Percent

7.3.1 The importance of arithmetic in business and commerce from earliest times to the present has had profound effects on the development of arithmetic. Although utilitarian applications of arithmetic did not generally appear in texts on arithmetic until the end of the fourteenth century, undoubtedly the problems of profit, loss, and taxation led to the development of special tools in arithmetic. For example, Roman taxes which were based on $\frac{1}{25}, \frac{1}{20}$, and $\frac{1}{100}$ of a total quantity may have led to the development of the **percent** basis for description. The word **"percent"** comes from the Latin **per centum**, meaning **by the hundred**. The symbol, "%," used to indicate percent probably originated during the fifteenth century. It is interesting to note that "%" contains two zeros as a part of the symbol.

Although the idea of percent originated as a business device, the percent notation has a much broader scope of usage in our modern world. We can think of percent as a specialized form of decimal; it is formed by multiplying an ordinary decimal by 100 and indicated by the symbol "%" to the right of the numeral. For example, the fraction $\frac{1}{8}$ can be written in the ordinary decimal form 0.125 which in turn can be specialized to the percent form 12.5%. Notice that we have $0.125 = \frac{125}{1000} = \frac{125}{10} \times \frac{1}{100} = 12.5 \times \frac{1}{100} = 12.5\%$.

A percent is another form in which we write numerals. However, its most common usage is to indicate comparisons. For example, the percent interest we pay on a loan compares the cost of the loan with the total amount of the loan. We do not use percent notation ordinarily to express measures of properties directly; for example, weight, distance. Rather, percents are used to express relative comparisons between two quantities in the sense of a **ratio**. For example, to compare 23 correct answers on a test with a total of 25 possible answers, we can write $\frac{23}{25} = \frac{92}{100}$ so that we can say that the test was done 92% correctly.

7.3.2   Our ability to convert between fractions, decimals, and percents determines to a good extent the utility which we gain with the notation. In this connection, recall that a fraction can be thought of as an indicated division with any nonzero divisor, a decimal can be thought of as the quotient obtained as a result of a division by factors of 10, and now with percents we can think of a division by 100. That is,

Fractions: $\frac{1}{2}, \frac{1}{3}, \frac{5}{8}, \frac{11}{7}, \frac{23}{12}$, and so forth.

Decimals: 0.5, 0.33, 0.625, 1.5714, and so forth.

Percents: 50%, 33%, 62.5%, $157\frac{3}{7}\%$, and so forth.

To convert from a decimal form to a percent we ask "How many hundredths is the decimal?" That is, if D is a decimal, then $D = \frac{P}{100}$, where P indicates the percent value which will result in the percent form. For example, $0.157 = \frac{P}{100}$ leads to $P = 0.157 \times 100 = 15.7$ so that $0.157 = 15.7\%$.

Examples.

(a) $0.07 = \dfrac{7}{100} = 7\%$ (b) $0.12 = \dfrac{12}{100} = 12\%$

(c) $0.3 = \dfrac{30}{100} = 30\%$ (d) $0.27\frac{1}{2} = \dfrac{27\frac{1}{2}}{100} = 27\frac{1}{2}\%$

(e) $0.045 = (0.045 \times 100)\% = 4.5\%$

(f) $0.003 = (0.003 \times 100)\% = 0.3\%$

(g) $1.25 = (1.25 \times 100)\% = 125\%$ (h) $0.015 = 1.5\%$.

To convert from a percent form to a decimal we simply reverse the above process. For example, $15.7\% = \dfrac{15.7}{100} = 0.157$.

Examples.

(a) $6\% = \dfrac{6}{100} = 0.06$ (b) $7.5\% = \dfrac{7.5}{100} = 0.075$

(c) $36\% = \dfrac{36}{100} = 0.36$ (d) $0.25\% = \dfrac{0.25}{100} = 0.0025$

(e) $12\frac{1}{2}\% = \dfrac{12\frac{1}{2}}{100} = 0.12\frac{1}{2}$ (f) $365\% = \dfrac{365}{100} = 3.65$.

From the above we can easily obtain the conversion from a percent to a fraction form. For example, $15.7\% = \dfrac{15.7}{100} = \dfrac{157}{1000}$.

Examples.

(a) $6\% = \dfrac{3}{50}$ (b) $7.5\% = \dfrac{75}{1000} = \dfrac{3}{40}$ (c) $36\% = \dfrac{9}{25}$

(d) $0.25\% = \dfrac{1}{400}$ (e) $12\frac{1}{2}\% = \dfrac{25}{200} = \dfrac{1}{8}$ (f) $365\% = \dfrac{73}{20} = 3\frac{13}{20}$.

To convert from a fraction form to a percent we can proceed as in converting to a decimal; however, here we use the fixed divisor 100. That is, if $\dfrac{A}{B}$ represents a fraction we write $\dfrac{A}{B} = \dfrac{P}{100}$ and obtain $\dfrac{A}{B} = P\%$. For example, $\dfrac{3}{4} = \dfrac{P}{100}$ leads to $\dfrac{3}{4} = 75\%$.

Examples.

(a) $\dfrac{3}{20} = \dfrac{P}{100}$ results in $P = 15$ so that $\dfrac{3}{20} = 15\%$.

(b) $\dfrac{11}{16} = \dfrac{P}{100}$ leads to $P = 68\dfrac{3}{4}$ so that $\dfrac{11}{16} = 68\dfrac{3}{4}\%$.

(c) $\dfrac{17}{15} = \left(\dfrac{17}{15} \times 100\right)\% = 113\dfrac{1}{3}\%$.   (d) $\dfrac{2}{25} = \left(\dfrac{2}{25} \times 100\right)\% = 8\%$.

(e) $\dfrac{1}{125} = \dfrac{1 \times 8}{125 \times 8} = \dfrac{8}{1000} = \dfrac{8}{10} \times \dfrac{1}{100} = \dfrac{8}{10}\% = \dfrac{4}{5}\% = 0.8\%$.

(f) $3\dfrac{1}{2} = 3 + \dfrac{1}{2} = \dfrac{300}{100} + \dfrac{50}{100} = 350\%$.

Practice 1.

1. Convert the following decimals to percent forms.
   (a) 0.01   (b) 0.1   (c) 1.0   (d) 1.01
   (e) 0.39   (f) 3.2   (g) 0.025   (h) 0.705
   (i) $1.65\dfrac{1}{3}$ (j) 0.004   (k) 5.3005   (l) 0.0725.

2. Convert the following percents to decimal forms.
   (a) 4%   (b) 18%   (c) $22\dfrac{1}{4}\%$ (d) 80%

   (e) 6.8%   (f) 175%   (g) $\dfrac{3}{8}\%$ (h) 0.125%

   (i) 1200%   (j) 0.075%   (k) 1%   (l) $105\dfrac{2}{5}\%$.

3. Convert the following percents to fractional forms.
   (a) 5%   (b) $6\dfrac{1}{4}\%$ (c) 28%   (d) 30%

   (e) 45%   (f) 14.5%   (g) 115%   (h) $83\dfrac{1}{3}\%$

   (i) 37.5%   (j) 1225%   (k) $\dfrac{1}{2}\%$ (l) $16\dfrac{2}{3}\%$.

4. Convert the following fractions to percents.
   (a) $\dfrac{3}{4}$ (b) $\dfrac{2}{3}$ (c) $1\dfrac{17}{25}$ (d) $\dfrac{7}{15}$

   (e) $10\dfrac{1}{5}$ (f) $\dfrac{19}{50}$ (g) $\dfrac{7}{6}$ (h) $\dfrac{4}{125}$

   (i) $\dfrac{11}{1000}$ (j) $\dfrac{7}{200}$ (k) $3\dfrac{7}{10}$ (l) $23\dfrac{17}{30}$.

5. Complete the following table.

	Fraction	Decimal	Percent
(a)	$\dfrac{1}{10}$	0.1	10%
(b)	$\dfrac{1}{25}$	–	–
(c)	–	0.05	–
(d)	–	–	12%
(e)	$\dfrac{2}{9}$	–	–
(f)	–	0.44	–
(g)	–	–	1.5%
(h)	$\dfrac{19}{300}$	–	–
(i)	–	0.705	–
(j)	–	–	$37\frac{1}{2}\%$
(k)	$\dfrac{54}{23}$	–	–
(l)	–	6.875	–
(m)	–	–	728%

Answers.

1. (a) 1%   (b) 10%   (c) 100%   (d) 101%   (e) 39%
   (f) 320%   (g) 2.5%   (h) 70.5%   (i) $165\frac{1}{3}\%$ (j) 0.4%
   (k) 530.05%   (l) 7.25%.

2. (a) 0.04   (b) 0.18   (c) $0.22\frac{1}{4}$ (d) 0.8   (e) 0.068
   (f) 1.75   (g) $0.00\frac{3}{8}$ (h) 0.00125   (i) 12   (j) 0.00075
   (k) 0.01   (l) $1.05\frac{2}{5}$.

3. (a) $\dfrac{1}{20}$ (b) $\dfrac{1}{16}$ (c) $\dfrac{7}{25}$ (d) $\dfrac{3}{10}$ (e) $\dfrac{9}{20}$ (f) $\dfrac{29}{200}$
   (g) $1\dfrac{3}{20}$ (h) $\dfrac{5}{6}$ (i) $\dfrac{3}{8}$ (j) $12\frac{1}{4}$ (k) $\dfrac{1}{200}$ (l) $\dfrac{1}{6}$.

4. (a) 75%   (b) $66\frac{2}{3}\%$ (c) 168%   (d) $46\frac{2}{3}\%$ (e) 1020%
   (f) 38%   (g) $116\frac{2}{3}\%$ (h) 3.2%   (i) 1.1%   (j) 3.5%
   (k) 370%   (l) $2356\frac{2}{3}\%$.

5. (b) 0.04, 4%   (c) $\frac{1}{20}$, 5%   (d) $\frac{3}{25}$, 0.12   (e) 0.22$\frac{2}{9}$, 22$\frac{2}{9}$%

(f) $\frac{11}{25}$, 44%   (g) $\frac{3}{200}$, 0.015   (h) 0.063$\frac{1}{3}$, 6.3$\frac{1}{3}$%

(i) $\frac{141}{200}$, 70.5%   (j) $\frac{3}{8}$, 0.375   (k) 2.3478$\frac{6}{23}$, 237$\frac{19}{23}$%

(l) 6$\frac{7}{8}$, 687.5%   (m) 7$\frac{7}{25}$, 7.28.

7.3.3   Of course knowing HOW to write percents does not tell us WHEN or WHERE to use percents. As we have noted, however, percents are used to compare two quantities in the sense of a ratio. If a number A, called the **percentage**, is to be compared to a number B, called the **base**, we write $A = C\% \times B$, where C is a percent comparison of A to B. We read $A = C\% \times B$ as "A is C percent of B."

$$A \quad = \quad C\% \quad \times \quad B$$

percentage   rate   base

The **base** B is the standard of comparison, the "whole" of some unit. The **rate** C is the percent or ratio in terms of the number of hundred parts of the "whole." The **percentage** (an unfortunate historical choice of term) A is the amount being compared to the "whole."

Percent notation is commonly used in business and statistics and wherever paired comparisons need to be made. For example, "The sales tax is 4%" means that for each sale, 0.04 of the price is charged as a tax. For a $5.25 sale the tax would be 5.25 × 0.04 = 0.21 or 21 cents.

Examples.

(a) "The bank loan requires a 6$\frac{1}{2}$% interest rate" means that for each $100 borrowed an interest of $6.50 per year must be paid.

(b) "10% discount on cash sales" means that 10% of the sales price of an item may be deducted from the price when the item is paid for in cash.

(c) "85% of the class passed the test" means that about $\frac{85}{100}$ or $\frac{17}{20}$ of the class passed the test. If there are 40 students in the class, about 34 of them passed the test.

(d) "The efficiency of an ordinary auto engine is about 22%" means that only about $\frac{22}{100}$ of the available energy of the fuel is realized as usable power.

(e) "Unemployment is at a 5.6% level" means that approximately 56 people out of 1000 willing and available for work on the labor market are out of jobs.

(f) "On two successive tests Bill scored 35% and 70%, thus Bill improved his score by 100%" means that his score was doubled.

Although the above examples illustrate the highly useful nature of percent notation, we should mention a word of caution. A survey which asserts that "80% of the survey group agreed that product 'X' was the best" might only mean that 4 people out of a group of 5 agreed. Comparing the statement, "Sam only improved his score by 25%" with Example (f) above might lead us to assume that Bill was doing better than Sam. However, Sam's scores might have been 80% and 100%. Unfortunately, as in any language, mathematics can be used to conceal and mislead as well as reveal.

Problems in terms of percent are no different from problems stated in terms of fractions or decimals. We can always convert the percent notation as convenient. However, three types of problems are commonly stated in terms of percent notation. These are based on the relation,

$$A \quad = \quad C\% \times \quad B$$

percentage   **rate**   **base**

Type 1. Given the base and the percentage we may be required to find the rate.

Examples.

(a) What percent of 85 is 71?

SOLUTION. $71 = C\% \times 85$ leads to $C\% = 83\frac{9}{17}\%$.

(b) There were 1,200 registered voters in a certain precinct and only 585 of them voted in a recent election. What percent of the voters voted?

SOLUTION. $C\% = \frac{585}{1,200} = 48\frac{3}{4}\%$.

Type 2. Given the base and the rate we may be required to find the percentage amount.

Examples.

(a) If 32% of a high school graduating class of 225 went on to college, then how many of the students in the class went to college?

SOLUTION. $A = 32\% \times 225 = 72$ students.

(b) How much will a $5,000 savings account earn at $4\frac{1}{2}\%$ interest in one year?

SOLUTION. $A = 4\frac{1}{2}\% \times 5,000 = 225$ so that \$225 will be earned.

Type 3. Given the percentage amount and the rate we may be required to find the base.

Examples.

(a) If 357 is 150% of a number, then what is the number?

SOLUTION. $357 = 150\% \times N$ so that $N = \dfrac{357}{1.5} = 238$.

(b) Bill puts aside 22% of his income for the rent. If his rent is \$105.00 per month, then what is Bill's annual income?

SOLUTION. $105 = 22\% \times M$ so that $M = 477.27\frac{1}{11}$. $12 \times 477.27\frac{1}{11} = $ 5,727.25 and his annual income is thus \$5,727.25.

Of course, problems in terms of percent are not limited to the above simple types.

Examples.

(a) What percent of 192 is equal to 72% of 145?

SOLUTION. $P\% \times 192 = 72\% \times 145$ so that $P\% = 54\frac{3}{8}\%$.

(b) If 18% of a number is equal to 9 and 35% of a second number is equal to 14, then what is 25% of the sum of the two numbers?

SOLUTION. We first solve for each number, $N = \dfrac{9}{0.18} = 50$ and $M = \dfrac{14}{0.35}$ $= 40$. Now we have $25\% \times (50 + 40) = A$ so that $0.25 \times 90 = 22.5 = A$.

Practice 2.

1. (a) What percent of 36 is 12?
   (b) 24 is what percent of 98?
   (c) Find what percent 58 is of 160.
   (d) What percent of 18 is 44?
   (e) 6 is what percent of 834?
   (f) Find what percent 47 is of 325.
2. (a) Find 16% of 192.
   (b) What is 3% of 45?
   (c) 120% of 98 is equal to what number?
   (d) Find 0.8% of 1,365.
   (e) What is 78% of 16?
   (f) $\frac{1}{2}\%$ of 25 is equal to what number?

3. (a) 7 is 21% of what number?

(b) If 92 is $133\frac{1}{3}$% of a number, then what is the number?

(c) 0.85% of a number is 2. Find the number.

(d) 54 is 95% of what number?

(e) If $\frac{4}{5}$ is 4% of a number, then what is the number?

(f) $62\frac{1}{2}$% of a number is 365. Find the number.

4. A mixture consists of 9 parts clay, 2 parts sand, and 3 parts feldspar.

(a) What percent of the mixture is sand?

(b) How much feldspar is there in 35 pounds of the mixture?

(c) How much mixture can be made with 18 pounds of clay?

5. If 28 out of 35 students in a class pass a test, then what percent of the class passed?

6. How much alcohol is there in 8 quarts of a 36% alcohol antifreeze solution?

7. Eighteen points made in a basketball game by a team came as a result of making 72% of its free-throw attempts. How many free-throw attempts did the team have? How many did they miss?

8. An auto payment amounted to $85.50. Bill earned $450.00 per month. What percent of Bill's monthly earnings would the auto payment be?

9. An office supervisor estimates that there is an 18% loss of working time in an office. Approximately how many hours are lost during a week in the office if there are 12 office workers each working $37\frac{1}{2}$ hours per week and the estimate of lost time is correct?

10. Bill's pay check amounted to $385.75. If $2\frac{3}{4}$% had been deducted for social security and $11\frac{1}{2}$% for withholding on income tax, then how much was the original amount of Bill's pay check?

Answers.

1. (a) $33\frac{1}{3}$%   (b) $24\frac{24}{49}$%   (c) $36\frac{1}{4}$%   (d) $244\frac{4}{9}$%
   (e) 0.64%   (f) 14.46%.
2. (a) 30.72   (b) 1.35   (c) 117.6   (d) 10.92   (e) 12.48
   (f) 0.125.

3. (a) $33\frac{1}{3}$ (b) 69   (c) $235\frac{5}{17}$ (d) $56\frac{16}{19}$ (e) 20
   (f) 584.

4. (a) $14\frac{2}{7}\%$ (b) $7\frac{1}{2}$ pounds   (c) 28 pounds.

5. 80%.
6. 2.88 quarts.
7. 25 attempts, 7 misses.
8. 19%.
9. 81 hours.
10. $423.76.

Exercises

1. If we write $\frac{2}{5} = \frac{K}{25}$, the K will indicate the number of _____ repre-

sented by $\frac{2}{5}$. When we write $\frac{2}{5} = P\%$ we mean the number of _____ repre-

sented by $\frac{2}{5}$. Percent notation is commonly used to indicate _____ as in

the use of ratios.

2. Find the fractional and decimal equivalents for each of the following percents.

   (a) 1%   (b) $\frac{1}{10}\%$ (c) 5%   (d) 0.25%   (e) $7\frac{1}{2}\%$

   (f) 27.5%   (g) $166\frac{2}{3}\%$ (h) 100%   (i) 45%   (j) $66.6\frac{2}{3}\%$

   (k) 1000%   (l) 0.05%.

3. Express each of the following as a percent.

   (a) $\frac{1}{50}$ (b) $\frac{5}{6}$ (c) $\frac{1}{200}$ (d) $\frac{7}{30}$ (e) $\frac{1}{40}$ (f) $\frac{2}{35}$

   (g) $\frac{1}{75}$ (h) $\frac{43}{23}$ (i) $\frac{1}{10}$ (j) $\frac{9}{1000}$ (k) $\frac{19}{15}$ (l) $\frac{19}{150}$.

4. Express each of the following as a percent.

   (a) 0.04   (b) 0.17   (c) 0.005   (d) 0.359   (e) $0.06\frac{1}{3}$

   (f) 0.0005   (g) $0.90\frac{2}{9}$ (h) 1.305   (i) 25.075

   (j) 0.9875   (k) 3.001   (l) 0.3001.

5. When we write $5 = 20\% \times 25$ we call _____ the percentage, _____
the base, and the rate is _____.

6. Solve the following:

   (a) $N = 3\% \times 83$ (b) $7 = P\% \times 175$ (c) $18 = 5\% \times B$

(d) $6.3 = 4.5\% \times B$ (e) $N = 18\frac{1}{3}\% \times 230$ (f) $38 = P\% \times 24$.

7. Fill in the missing values:

(a) _____% of 250 is $1\frac{1}{4}$ (b) 36.9 is _____% of 205

(c) _____ is 19% of 8   (d) 345% of 18 is _____

(e) 17.5 is 7% of _____   (f) 16% of _____ is $\frac{4}{5}$.

8. (a) What percent of 325 is 78?

(b) 8 is what percent of 60?

(c) What percent of $\frac{5}{7}$ is $\frac{9}{14}$?

(d) Find what percent 0.75 is of 75.

9. (a) Find 65% of 98.

(b) What is 0.75% of 125?

(c) 1,525% of 6 is equal to what number?

(d) Find $\frac{3}{4}\%$ of 6400.

10. (a) 31 is $27\frac{1}{2}\%$ of what number?

(b) If 128 is 135% of a number, then what is the number?

(c) $3\frac{3}{4}$ is 15% of a number. Find the number.

(d) $112\frac{1}{2}\%$ of a number is 486. Find the number.

11. If Mr. Williams paid a 24% tax on $6,384.50, then how much was the tax?

12. A theater had 1,855 seats. If 1,285 seats were occupied, then what percent of the theater was filled (to the nearest 1%)?

13. A $5\frac{3}{4}\%$ dividend amounting to $37.75 was received by Mr. Jay. What is the amount of the investment represented by the dividend?

14. What percent of Figure 84 is shaded?

15. A "pie" chart is shown in Figure 85. Find the approximate percent of the total represented by each of the shaded areas.

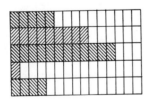

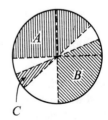

FIGURE 84   FIGURE 85

16. Find what percent each of the bars in Figure 86 represent compared to the total of the bars. (To the nearest 1%.)

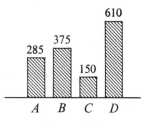

FIGURE 86

17. A man earns $542.25 per month. If he receives a $4\frac{1}{2}\%$ raise, then what are his new monthly earnings (to the nearest cent)?

18. The population of a certain city increased by 35% between 1950 and 1960. If the population was 28,500 in 1960, then what was it to the nearest one hundred in 1950?

19. During a sale a merchant offers an 18% discount on that part of a single purchase exceeding $100. An additional 4% discount is given for a cash sale. What would be the cash cost of an item marked at $185.00 if a sales tax of $2\frac{1}{2}\%$ is added to the cash price?

20. The sum of two numbers is equal to 32. If 9% of one number is 15% of the other, then what are the two numbers?

Answers.

1. twenty-fifths; hundredths; comparisons.

2. (a) $\frac{1}{100} = 0.01$ (b) $\frac{1}{1000} = 0.001$ (c) $\frac{1}{20} = 0.05$

   (d) $\frac{1}{400} = 0.0025$ (e) $\frac{3}{40} = 0.075$ (f) $\frac{11}{40} = 0.275$

   (g) $\frac{5}{3} = 1.66\frac{2}{3}$ (h) 1.   (i) $\frac{9}{20} = 0.45$

   (j) $\frac{2}{3} = 0.666\frac{2}{3}$ (k) 10   (l) $\frac{1}{2000} = 0.005$.

3. (a) 2%   (b) $83\frac{1}{3}\%$ (c) $\frac{1}{2}\%$ (d) $23\frac{1}{3}\%$

   (e) 2.5%   (f) $5\frac{5}{7}\%$ (g) $1\frac{1}{3}\%$ (h) $186\frac{22}{23}\%$

   (i) 10%   (j) 0.9%   (k) $126\frac{2}{3}\%$ (l) $12\frac{2}{3}\%$.

4. (a) 4%   (b) 17%   (c) 0.5%   (d) 35.9%
(e) $6\frac{1}{3}$%   (f) 0.05%   (g) $90\frac{2}{9}$%   (h) 130.5%
(i) 2507.5%   (j) 98.75%   (k) 300.1%   (l) 30.01%.
5. 5; 25; 20%.

6. (a) 2.49   (b) 4%   (c) 360   (d) 140   (e) $42\frac{1}{6}$ (f) $158\frac{1}{3}$%.

7. (a) $\frac{1}{2}$%   (b) 18%   (c) 1.52   (d) 62.1   (e) 250   (f) 5.

8. (a) 24%   (b) $13\frac{1}{3}$%   (c) 90%   (d) 1%.

9. (a) 63.7   (b) 0.9375   (c) 91.5   (d) 48.

10. (a) $112\frac{8}{11}$ (b) $94\frac{22}{27}$ (c) 25   (d) 432.

11. $1,532.28.
12. 69%.
13. $656.52.

14. $41\frac{1}{3}$%.

15. $A = 37.5\%$; $B = 31\frac{1}{4}\%$; $C = 6\frac{1}{4}\%$.

16. A:20%, B:26%, C:11%, D:43%.
17. $566.65.
18. 21,100.
19. $166.98.
20. 20 and 12.

Review Summary

The symbolic patterns and forms we use in denoting our ideas concerning numbers and operations with them are called _____. Historically, many of the difficulties encountered in the development of mathematics were due to lack of adequate notation.   *notation*

In order to bring together our work with the integers and fractions we introduced the idea of a sum of an integer and a fraction. That is, we wrote $3 + \frac{5}{6}$ and abbreviated this as _____. When written in this latter form, we call the resulting numeral a _____ _____. The introduction of mixed fractions led us to a discussion of computations using this notation. A mixed fraction expresses the _____ of an integer and a fraction and can be imagined as $3\frac{5}{6}$

mixed
fraction

sum

having parentheses "around" it so that it is operated on as a _____ quantity.

In computing with mixed fractions we often convert them into improper fractions and vice versa. For example, $6\frac{2}{3} =$ _____ and $\frac{15}{6} =$ _____. To find the sum or difference of mixed fractions we can treat the integral and fractional parts separately. "Borrowing" in subtraction is accomplished by converting 1 into an improper fraction with the appropriate denominator. Examples are:

(a) $2\frac{3}{4} + 7\frac{5}{6} = (2 + \underline{\hspace{1cm}}) + \left(\frac{3}{4} + \underline{\hspace{1cm}}\right)$

$= 9 + \frac{19}{12} = \underline{\hspace{1cm}}.$

(b) $7\frac{1}{3} - 4\frac{5}{6} = (6 - 4) + \left(\underline{\hspace{1cm}} - \frac{5}{6}\right)$

$= 2 + \frac{3}{6} = \underline{\hspace{1cm}}.$

Of course, we can always convert mixed fractions to improper fractions and thus avoid direct computations with mixed fractions. To find the product of mixed fractions this is often the simplest procedure. For example, $5\frac{1}{4} \times 9\frac{2}{3} = \frac{21}{4} \times \underline{\hspace{1cm}} = \frac{203}{4} = \underline{\hspace{1cm}}.$ Alternatively, we can write the mixed fractions as sums and apply the _____ property to obtain a sum of partial products. For example, $3\frac{1}{4} \times 8\frac{1}{3} = \left(3 + \frac{1}{4}\right) \times \left(8 + \frac{1}{3}\right) = (3 \times 8) + (3 \times$ _____ $) + ($ _____ $\times 8) + \left(\frac{1}{4} \times \frac{1}{3}\right) = 24 + 1 + 2 + \frac{1}{12} =$ _____.

Division with mixed fractions can be accomplished by converting to improper fractions or by multiplying both the dividend and divisor by the least common denominator of the fractions involved and proceeding as with the integers. Examples are:

(a) $9\frac{2}{7} \div 2\frac{3}{5} = \frac{65}{7} \div \frac{13}{5} = \frac{65}{7} \times \underline{\hspace{1cm}} = \frac{25}{7} = \underline{\hspace{1cm}}.$

(b) $8\frac{2}{3} \div 6\frac{1}{2} = \left(6 \times 8\frac{2}{3}\right) \div \left(\underline{\hspace{1cm}} \times 6\frac{1}{2}\right)$

$= 52 \div 39 = \underline{\hspace{1cm}}.$

single

$\frac{20}{3}, 2\frac{1}{2}$

$7, \frac{5}{6}$

$10\frac{7}{12}$

$\frac{8}{6}$

$2\frac{1}{2}$

$\frac{29}{3}, 50\frac{3}{4}$

distributive

$\frac{1}{3}, \frac{1}{4}$

$27\frac{1}{12}$

$\frac{5}{13}, 3\frac{4}{7}$

6

$1\frac{1}{3}$

It is surprising that the uniform *decimal* form of nota-tion was not extended to include the rational numbers until the sixteenth century. The decimal system is based on the idea of successive place positions with the base _____. The idea is simply to extend to the right of the ones' place the place position system derived from the Hindus and Arabs. Since each place position has a value ten times the place position to its _____, we can also think of each place position as having a value _____ of that to its left. The value of each place position is identi-fied by placing a reference point, called the _____ _____, at the right "foot" of the ones' digit in a decimal. For example, $12.59 = 1(10) + 2(1) + 5(\underline{\quad}) + 9(\underline{\quad})$. As in reading and writing integers, the place positions of the digits in a decimal have been given names. 12.59, for example, would be read as "_____ _____ _____ _____."

ten

right

one-tenth

decimal point

$\dfrac{1}{10}$, $\dfrac{1}{100}$

twelve and fifty-nine hundredths

When a decimal names a proper fraction we often call it a _____ decimal. When a fractional form appears at the right of a decimal we refer to it as a complex decimal fraction. For example, $3.12\frac{1}{3}$ is a _____ decimal fraction and 0.34 is a _____ decimal.

pure

complex

pure

Decimals may be rounded off just as was done with the integers. For example, 12.638 rounded to the nearest hundredths is _____ and to the nearest tenths is _____. 30.2984 rounded to five place positions is _____ and to three places is _____.

12.64, 12.6
30.298
30.3

A fraction can be converted to a decimal by a simple process of division. That is, to convert $\frac{5}{7}$ to a decimal to thousandths we solve $\frac{5}{7} = \frac{N}{1000}$ to obtain $\frac{5}{7} = $ _____ in decimal form. Conversely, decimals can easily be con-verted into fractions by applying the meaning of decimals and reducing the resulting fraction. For example, $1.275 = \frac{1275}{1000} = $ _____.

$0.714\frac{2}{7}$

$1\frac{11}{40}$

Ordering a set of decimals is easily accomplished by first noting the relative place positioning of the decimal points in the numerals and then by ordering them as with the integers. For example, the decimals 0.012, 0.102,

0.021, and 0.120 ordered from smallest to largest would be

0.012, _____, _____, 0.120.   *0.021, 0.102*

Addition and subtraction with decimals can be done just as with the integers. However, we must be careful to align by _____ _____. For example,   *place*
position

(a) 36.075   (b) 37.2071
      8.753   −6.2537
    +5.297
    _____   _____   *(b) 30.9534*
    _____   *(a) 50.125*

In multiplying or dividing by a product of factors of 10 such as 10, 100, 1000, and so forth, we observed that a simple "shifting" of the digits or decimal point in the numeral would result in the proper product or quotient. That is, in multiplying by 1000, the digits in a decimal are "shifted" _____ places to the _____. In dividing a decimal by 100 the digits are "shifted" _____ places to the _____. For example,   *three, left*
two
right

(a) $3.56 \times 1000 =$ _____   (b) $3.56 \div 100 =$ _____.   *3560, 0.0356*

The product of numbers expressed in decimal form can be obtained by converting to a fractional form. That is, to find $36.05 \times 8.42 = \dfrac{3605}{100} \times$ _____ $= \dfrac{3035410}{10000} =$ _____. $\dfrac{842}{100}$, *303.541*

From our observations, we have the computational form:

3 6.0 5   (has _____ decimal places)   *2*
×8.4 2   (has _____ decimal places)   *2*
7 2 1 0
1 4 4 2 0
2 8 8 4 0
_____
3 0 3.5 4 1 0   (must have _____ decimal places)   *4*

In practice we might round the above product to three place positions, _____.   *304*

The quotient of two numbers expressed in decimal form can be obtained by proceeding as in ordinary long division of integers. The decimal point in the quotient is obtained by "moving" the decimal points in the dividend and divisor to the right as many places as are in the

_____. The digits in the quotient are aligned above the *divisor*
digits in the _____. For example, since $157.5 \div 16.08 =$ *dividend*
$\dfrac{157.5}{16.08} = \dfrac{157.5 \times 100}{16.08 \times 100} = \dfrac{15750}{1608}$ we have

$$
\begin{array}{r}
9.7\;9\;4\;7 \\
1\;6.0\;8)\overline{1\;5\;7.5\;0_{\wedge}0\;0\;0\;0} \\
1\;4\;4\;7\;2 \\
\hline
1\;2\;7\;8\;0 \\
1\;1\;2\;5\;6 \\
\hline
1\;5\;2\;4\;0 \\
1\;4\;4\;7\;2 \\
\hline
7\;6\;8\;0 \\
6\;4\;3\;2 \\
\hline
1\;2\;4\;8\;0 \\
1\;1\;2\;5\;6 \\
\hline
1\;2\;2\;4
\end{array}
$$

The quotient of $157.5 \div 16.08$ would then be _____ *9.795*
rounded to four place positions. We can quickly check
by noting that the quotient is approximately 10 and the
divisor 16 so that $10 \times 16 = 160$, which is approximately
equal to the _____ so that the quotient "makes sense." *dividend*

In many applications we use the specialized idea of
percent. A percent is a form of decimal; it is used to indicate _____ "by the hundred." That is, if A and B are *comparisons*
two numbers to be compared, we can write $\dfrac{A}{B} = \dfrac{C}{100} = C\%$.
For example, to compare 18 to 72 using percent notation
we write $\dfrac{18}{72} = $ _____$\%$. *25*

For percent notation to be useful we must be able to
convert from fractions to decimals to percents. For ex-
ample, $\dfrac{3}{8} = 0.375 = $ _____$\%$, $1.625 = $ _____$\%$, $16\% = $ *37.5, 162.5*
_____ in decimal form, and $16\% = $ _____ in fractional *$0.16, \dfrac{4}{25}$*
form.

We often write $A = C\% \times B$ to describe the percent
comparison of A to B. In this form A is called the _____, *percentage*
C the _____, and B the _____. In the example $4 = 8\%$ *rate, base*
$\times 50$ we call _____ the base, _____ the percentage, *50, 4*
and _____ the rate. We read $4 = 8\% \times 50$ as "_____ *8, four is*
_____ _____ _____ _____." *eight per-*
cent of fifty

Although very useful, we noted that there are dangers
as well as advantages in the use of percent notation.

The three most common types of problems occurring in work with percent are illustrated by the following examples:

    (a) What percent of 54 is 3?

SOLUTION. $C\% \times 54 = 3$, $C\% = $ _____.   *$5\frac{5}{9}\%$*

    (b) What is $12\frac{1}{2}\%$ of 108?

SOLUTION. $A = 12\frac{1}{2}\% \times 108$, $A = $ _____.   *13.5*

    (c) 18 is 45% of what number?

SOLUTION. $18 = 45\% \times B$, $B = $ _____.   *40*

Of course, problems using percent notation are not limited to the above types alone. For example:

    If 14 is 6% of one number and 9% of a second number is 12, then what percent of the first number is the second? Answer: _____.   *$57\frac{1}{7}\%$*

Chapter Exercises (7)

Group I.

1. Although ideas are important, we must have adequate _____ to describe our ideas. Thus, our discussion of mixed fractions, decimal notation, and percentage help us to develop and describe our ideas concerning _____ numbers.

2. When we write $2\frac{3}{4}$ we call the numeral a _____ _____ and mean the _____ of the integer _____ and fraction _____.

3. Convert to improper fraction forms:

    (a) $8\frac{2}{3}$ (b) $4\frac{5}{12}$ (c) $10\frac{2}{5}$ (d) $1\frac{1}{10}$ (e) $36\frac{1}{4}$.

4. Convert to mixed fraction form:

    (a) $\frac{5}{2}$ (b) $\frac{15}{6}$ (c) $\frac{152}{12}$ (d) $\frac{222}{21}$ (e) $\frac{376}{128}$.

5. Find the sums and express in reduced mixed fraction form:

    (a) $3\frac{5}{8} + 10\frac{1}{6}$ (b) $7\frac{3}{4} + 2\frac{7}{8}$ (c) $17\frac{7}{9}$ (d) $50\frac{2}{7}$

$$5\frac{2}{3}$$
$$+91\frac{5}{27}$$

$$9\frac{4}{5}$$
$$+\frac{16}{35}$$

    (e) $39\frac{5}{16} + 20\frac{7}{12} + 8\frac{23}{24}$.

6. Find the differences and express in reduced mixed fraction form:

(a) $9\frac{5}{6} - 7\frac{2}{3}$ (b) $10\frac{5}{8} - \frac{19}{24}$ (c) $14\frac{8}{27}$ (d) $24\frac{2}{7}$

$\phantom{(c) 14\frac{8}{27}}\quad -5\frac{5}{6} -35\frac{3}{5}$

7. Convert to improper fractions and find the products in reduced mixed fraction form:

(a) $10\frac{5}{9} \times 2\frac{2}{5}$ (b) $1\frac{3}{7} \times 8\frac{3}{4}$ (c) $23\frac{7}{16} \times \left(-3\frac{9}{25}\right)$

(d) $\left(-11\frac{17}{38}\right) \times \left(-17\frac{5}{12}\right)$.

8. Apply the distributive property to find the products:

(a) $3\frac{7}{8} \times 4\frac{2}{3}$ (b) $\left(-9\frac{5}{6}\right) \times 6\frac{4}{9}$ (c) $20\frac{5}{7} \times 7\frac{4}{5}$

(d) $15\frac{7}{12} \times 16\frac{9}{10}$.

9. Find the exact quotients in reduced mixed fraction form:

(a) $12\frac{1}{3} \div 8\frac{2}{9}$ (b) $5\frac{5}{7} \div 6\frac{4}{21}$ (c) $\frac{-24\frac{3}{4}}{1\frac{3}{8}}$ (d) $\frac{31\frac{1}{2}}{4\frac{3}{8}}$.

10. Solve for N:

(a) $\frac{4}{15} = \frac{N}{100}$ (b) $\frac{11}{24} = \frac{N}{1000}$ (c) $\frac{43}{32} = \frac{N}{10000}$

(d) $\frac{1}{64} = \frac{N}{1000}$.

11. Express each of the following as a fraction with denominator 1000 to the nearest thousandths.

(a) $\frac{7}{18}$ (b) $\frac{16}{21}$ (c) $\frac{5}{32}$ (d) $\frac{7}{64}$.

12. Write the following in words:

(a) 407.06 (b) 20.305 (c) 17.615 (d) 5.0029

(e) 0.041273 (f) $300.53\frac{1}{3}$.

13. Round each of the decimals in Exercise 12 above to four place positions.

14. Write the following in decimal form.

(a) Sixty-two and fifty-one thousandths.

(b) One hundred one and eleven ten-thousandths.

(c) Seventy thousand five hundred five hundred-thousandths.

(d) Seven thousand five hundred and sixty-four and two-thirds hundredths.

15. Convert to decimals to the nearest thousandths:

(a) $\frac{13}{36}$ (b) $\frac{17}{12}$ (c) $\frac{3}{64}$ (d) $\frac{195}{19}$ (e) $\frac{2}{1001}$ (f) $\frac{451}{125}$.

16. Convert to reduced mixed fractions:
   (a) 0.064   (b) 1.375   (c) 0.28   (d) 0.075   (e) $10.714\frac{2}{7}$
   (f) 0.0056.

17. Find the sums:
   (a)   15.375   (b)   1.0706
          9.062   0.009
          0.974   10.7605
        $\underline{+30.189}$ $\underline{+\ 8.27}$

   (c) $3.014 + 0.0008 + 0.9804 + 1.076$
   (d) $300.8 + 69.09 + 570.3 + 7.016.$

18. Find the differences:
   (a)   13.062   (b)   9.40021
        $\underline{-\ 5.3817}$ $\underline{-2.4105}$

   (c) $501.395 - 40.397$ (d) $0.00759 - 0.07585.$

19. Find:
   (a) 78.5×1000 (b) 100×0.0032
   (c) $403.6 \div 100$ (d) $5.75 \div 1000$
   (e)   0.07059   (f) $10000\overline{)853.06}.$
        $\underline{\times\ \ 10000}$

20. Find the products as indicated:
To five place positions
   (a) 72.015×1.0091 (b) 7.5406×0.4025
   (c)   300.67   (d)   21.705
        $\underline{\times 50.391}$ $\underline{\times 80.414}$

To three place positions
   (e) $8.07 \times 14.5 \times 0.309$ (f) $68.3 \times 70.7 \times 2.89$
   (g) $1.32 \times 6.08 \times 7.59$ (h) $0.0821 \times 0.105 \times 0.00483.$

21. Find the quotients to four place positions:
   (a) $\frac{23.07}{8.82}$ (b) $0.705\overline{)3.64}$ (c) $6.28 \div 0.215$

   (d) $\frac{14.35}{38.7}$ (e) $41.2\overline{)0.0937}$ (f) $0.0604 \div 0.00825.$

22. (a) Find the sum of $3\frac{5}{16}$ and 8.704.

   (b) What is 1.09 less $1\frac{3}{20}$?   (c) Find $6\frac{3}{8}$ of 0.324.

   (d) What is the quotient of $9\frac{7}{12}$ divided by 2.025 to the nearest
thousandths?

23. Find to three place positions:
   (a) $\frac{50.392 + 9.8706}{16.51}$ (b) $(26.07 - 9.705) \times 1.308$

(c) $\dfrac{6.098 + 28.75}{18.62 - 4.82}$ (d) $(1.064 + 7.601) \times (3.563 - 8.577)$.

24. Complete the following table.

	Fraction	Decimal	Percent
(a)	$\dfrac{7}{20}$	_____	_____
(b)	_____	1.575	_____
(c)	_____	_____	$18\dfrac{3}{4}\%$
(d)	$\dfrac{8}{15}$	_____	_____
(e)	_____	0.025	_____
(f)	_____	_____	$\dfrac{5}{8}\%$

25. Solve the following:

   (a) $N = 7\dfrac{1}{2}\% \times 350$ (b) $4.2 = P\% \times 3.08$

   (c) $0.05 = \dfrac{3}{4}\% \times B$ (d) $N = 98\% \times 17.35$

   (e) $22.638 = P\% \times 205.8$ (f) $9.729 = 1035\% \times B$.

26. (a) What percent of 68 is 57?   (b) Find $4\dfrac{3}{4}\%$ of 10.98.

   (c) If 18.6 is 24% of a number, then find the number.

27. The area of any triangle is equal to one-half an altitude times its base. If the altitude of a triangle is $1\dfrac{5}{8}$ times its base and the base is 6.36 inches, then find the area of the triangle to the nearest tenth of a square inch.

28. Find the dimensions marked K, R, and r on Figure 87.

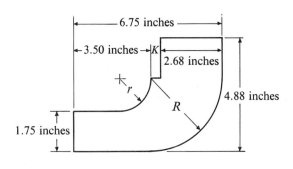

FIGURE 87

29. Bill's auto payment was $83.65. His auto maintenance cost was $18.25 per month, and gas and oil amounted to $32.80 per month. Approximately what percent of Bill's auto costs went for gas and oil?

30. Mr. Ainslee was to receive a $6\frac{1}{2}\%$ commission on $\frac{3}{4}$ of an estate after taxes. If the taxes, amounting to $1,200.00, were 16% of the value of the estate, then what should Mr. Ainslee receive as a commission?

Group II.

1. By notation we mean the symbolic patterns and _____ we use to describe our ideas. For example, $5\frac{1}{2}$, 5.5, and 550% are all different forms of _____ used to name the same number.

2. The sum of an integer and fraction is often abbreviated and written as a _____ _____. For example, $3 + \frac{5}{8}$ would be written as _____.

3. Convert to improper fraction forms:

   (a) $3\frac{2}{3}$ (b) $9\frac{6}{7}$ (c) $50\frac{9}{10}$ (d) $1\frac{1}{20}$ (e) $6\frac{4}{9}$.

4. Convert to mixed fraction forms:

   (a) $\frac{14}{4}$ (b) $\frac{18}{15}$ (c) $\frac{160}{48}$ (d) $\frac{232}{32}$ (e) $\frac{1498}{112}$.

5. Find the sums and express in reduced mixed fraction form:

   (a) $6\frac{2}{3} + 1\frac{3}{4}$ (b) $11\frac{4}{9} + 8\frac{5}{6}$ (c) $20\frac{7}{8}$ (d) $4\frac{2}{5}$

   $$6\frac{1}{4} \qquad\qquad \frac{8}{15}$$

   $$+74\frac{1}{24} \qquad\qquad +15\frac{4}{9}$$

   (e) $81\frac{7}{18} + 1\frac{5}{8} + 17\frac{23}{30}$.

6. Find the differences and express in reduced mixed fraction form:

   (a) $4\frac{7}{12} - 3\frac{5}{6}$ (b) $30\frac{7}{10} - \frac{13}{15}$ (c) $47\frac{7}{18}$ (d) $18\frac{5}{7}$

   $$- 6\frac{5}{8} \qquad\qquad -19\frac{3}{4}$$

7. Convert to improper fractions and find the products in reduced mixed fraction form:

   (a) $3\frac{6}{13} \times 8\frac{2}{3}$ (b) $2\frac{7}{9} \times 1\frac{1}{8}$ (c) $\left(-16\frac{5}{7}\right) \times 2\frac{2}{27}$

   (d) $\left(-21\frac{7}{15}\right) \times \left(-30\frac{5}{6}\right)$.

8. Apply the distributive property to find the products:

(a) $6\frac{4}{9} \times 9\frac{3}{4}$ (b) $12\frac{4}{5} \times \left(-5\frac{7}{8}\right)$ (c) $3\frac{2}{3} \times 45\frac{5}{6}$

(d) $18\frac{1}{2} \times 14\frac{8}{9}$.

9. Find the exact quotients in reduced mixed fraction form:

(a) $18\frac{3}{5} \div 7\frac{3}{4}$ (b) $1\frac{11}{12} \div 5\frac{1}{9}$ (c) $\dfrac{27\frac{1}{2}}{-5\frac{5}{6}}$ (d) $\dfrac{64\frac{17}{18}}{2\frac{11}{12}}$.

10. Solve for N:

(a) $\dfrac{5}{16} = \dfrac{N}{100}$ (b) $\dfrac{10}{21} = \dfrac{N}{1000}$ (c) $\dfrac{25}{36} = \dfrac{N}{10,000}$

(d) $\dfrac{1}{72} = \dfrac{N}{1000}$.

11. Express each of the following as a fraction with denominator 1000 to the nearest thousandths.

(a) $\dfrac{9}{14}$ (b) $\dfrac{3}{22}$ (c) $\dfrac{11}{36}$ (d) $\dfrac{5}{72}$.

12. Write the following in ordinary words.

(a) 320.705   (b) 18.075   (c) 109.32   (d) 7.0007

(e) $80.05\frac{3}{7}$ (f) 0.012025.

13. Round each of the decimals in Exercise 12 above to four place positions.

14. Write the following in decimal form.

(a) Six and two hundred thousandths.
(b) Two hundred and eleven hundredths.
(c) Five and five and two-fifths tenths.
(d) Nine thousand four hundred sixty-one and two hundred eight ten-thousandths.

15. Convert to decimals to the nearest thousandths:

(a) $\dfrac{4}{35}$ (b) $\dfrac{27}{13}$ (c) $\dfrac{2}{81}$ (d) $\dfrac{452}{45}$ (e) $\dfrac{5}{1807}$ (f) $\dfrac{369}{152}$.

16. Convert to reduced mixed fractions:

(a) 0.024   (b) 2.15   (c) 0.32   (d) 0.3125   (e) $30.77\frac{7}{9}$

(f) 0.0005.

17. Find the sums:

(a)   31.607   (b)   6.471
       17.49   327.5
        0.7028   90.36
     + 1.0002   +   0.888

(c) $7.402 + 0.9601 + 0.0079 + 5.098$
(d) $32.25 + 100.4 + 9.609 + 884.57$.

18. Find the differences:
   (a)   61.205   (b)   2.64008
        − 4.1745   −2.5517

   (c) 360.471 − 70.869   (d) 1.00307 − 1.0251.
19. Find:
   (a) 3.07 × 10,000   (b) 10 × 0.008
   (c) 560.2 ÷ 100   (d) 3.45 ÷ 1000
   (e)   0.50023   (f) 10,000)2057.41.
        ×   1000

20. Find the products as indicated:
To five place positions
   (a) 35.208 × 2.1407   (b) 2.0851 × 0.0734
   (c)   620.91   (d)   47.205
        ×85.073   ×61.058

To three place positions
   (e) 0.608 × 4.65 × 20.9   (f) 30.3 × 51.6 × 4.97
   (g) 8.51 × 2.23 × 5.18   (h) 0.2607 × 0.0515 × 0.00494.
21. Find the quotients to four place positions:
   (a) $\frac{57.14}{11.6}$ (b) 0.097)5.18   (c) 4.08 ÷ 0.176

   (d) $\frac{31.05}{42.6}$ (e) 18.7)1.0065   (f) 0.0136 ÷ 0.00271.

22. (a) Find the sum of 3.075 and $6\frac{7}{15}$.

   (b) What is $4\frac{2}{3}$ less 4.55?

   (c) Find 8.07 of $\frac{9}{11}$.

   (d) What is the quotient of 4.618 divided by $1\frac{5}{8}$ to the nearest

thousandths?
23. Find to three place positions:
   (a) $\frac{8.0472 - 21.605}{22.95}$ (b) (64.51 + 17.09) × 3.008

   (c) $\frac{12.44 - 4.505}{7.66 + 38.04}$ (d) (5.308 − 8.629) × (2.015 + 0.776).
24. Complete the following table:

	Fraction	Decimal	Percent
(a)	$\frac{7}{12}$	———	———
(b)	———	2.128	———
(c)	———	———	0.2%

(d) $\dfrac{5}{32}$ _____ _____

(e) _____ $0.208\dfrac{1}{3}$ _____

(f) _____ _____ $7\dfrac{1}{2}\%$

25. Solve the following:

(a) $N = 2\dfrac{2}{3}\% \times 96.6$ (b) $14.17 = P\% \times 218$

(c) $5.51 = 38\% \times B$ (d) $N = 0.7\% \times 14.7$

(e) $343.2 = P\% \times 32.5$ (f) $6.09 = 72.5\% \times B.$

26. (a) What percent of 136 is 8?   (b) Find $1\dfrac{5}{8}\% \times 750.5.$

(c) If 9.75 is 18% of a number, then find the number.

27. The area of a rhombus is equal to one-half the product of its two diagonals. If one diagonal is equal to 8.76 inches and the other diagonal is $\dfrac{2}{3}$ the length of the first, then find the area of the rhombus to the nearest tenth of a square inch.

28. Find the dimensions marked A and B on Figure 88.

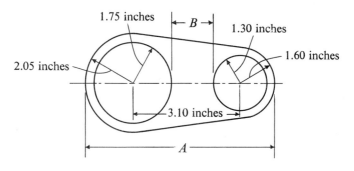

FIGURE 88

29. Sally purchased $6.95 worth of meats, $4.28 worth of vegetables, and $9.72 worth of other foods at a shopping center. Approximately what percent of her purchases went for meats?

30. Mr. Jones received a base salary of $428.50 per month and an $8\dfrac{1}{2}\%$ commission on all sales exceeding $2,500.00 per month. If sales during a certain month amounted to $4,862.75, then what were Mr. Jones' earnings for the month?

Problem Set (7)

1. If we used ordered pairs, (N,D), to name rational numbers $\left(\text{for} \right.$ example $(5,8)$ for $\left. \frac{5}{8} \right)$, then how would we describe the requirements (or conditions) for:

   (a) $(N,D) = 0$ (b) $(N,D) = 1$ (c) $(A,B) = (C,D)$
   (d) $(A,B) + (C,D) = (E,F)$ (e) $(A,B) \times (C,D) = (E,F)$.

2. Note that some fractions when converted to decimal form terminate in zeroes while others always result in a remainder. For example, $\frac{1}{8} = 0.125000 \ldots$ while $\frac{1}{7} = 0.142857 \ldots$.

   (a) Give an argument to show that every fraction when converted to decimal form either terminates in zeroes or repeats a certain fixed set of digits in its decimal form.

   (b) If a decimal form repeats a set of digits, then show how this decimal form can be converted to a fractional form.

3. We might ask whether there is a number S such that $S \times S = 3$. Using decimal notation, show how we can successively approximate S to within 0.1, 0.01, 0.001, and so forth. HINT. $1.7 < S < 1.8$. Why?

4. Mr. Smith in computing his income taxes found that he had to determine his federal tax as $1,680 plus 26% of his excess over $8,000. His state tax had to be $120 plus 4% of his excess over $6,000. Mr. Smith's adjusted gross income was $9,725 before state and federal taxes. If his federal tax was based on his adjusted gross income less the state tax and his state tax was based on his adjusted gross income less the federal tax, then what were Mr. Smith's state and federal income taxes?

5. The elements in the set of fractions $\left\{ \frac{1}{7}, \frac{2}{7}, \frac{3}{7}, \frac{4}{7}, \frac{5}{7}, \frac{6}{7} \right\}$ all have decimal forms which repeat the same cycle of digits whereas the fractions in $\left\{ \frac{1}{11}, \frac{2}{11}, \frac{3}{11}, \frac{4}{11}, \frac{5}{11}, \frac{6}{11}, \frac{7}{11}, \frac{8}{11}, \frac{9}{11}, \frac{10}{11} \right\}$ all have decimal forms with repeating digits but not the same cycle and the fractions in $\left\{ \frac{1}{9}, \frac{2}{9}, \frac{3}{9}, \frac{4}{9}, \frac{5}{9}, \frac{6}{9}, \frac{7}{9}, \frac{8}{9} \right\}$ all have decimal forms with repeating digits which are not the same. *Why?*

CHAPTER 8

Measurement

8.1 Length and Area

8.1.1 We have already encountered numbers that refer to object measurements in a few problems. Such numbers are called **concrete numbers**. In contrast to the **abstract number** ideas which we have been emphasizing, the study of concrete numbers suggests many of the possible uses of numbers.

When we talk of measurements, we think of numbers as referring to the properties or characteristics of things. For example, when we drive 2 miles to the store to buy 5 pounds of flour for $1.98 we are using the numbers 2, 5, and 1.98 to refer to a distance, a weight, and a monetary value, respectively. The quantities 2 miles, 5 pounds, and $1.98 are concrete whereas 2, 5, and 1.98 are abstract. As another example, when we say that Sam is 185 pounds, we are not measuring Sam, we are measuring his weight. A **measurement** is the association of a number to a property or characteristic of an object or thing.

How is this association made? We must have a **unit of measure**, then we can ask "How many times is the unit contained in the characteristic being measured?" For example, in measuring Sam's weight we can compare Sam's weight in pounds to the unit weight called a pound:

$$\frac{\text{Sam's weight}}{\text{Unit weight}} = \text{Numerical value.}$$

That is, Sam's weight = (Numerical value) × (Unit weight). Thus, the act of **measurement** always requires three things: a property of something to be measured, a unit by which to measure, and a means to associate the unit of measure to the property to result in a numerical value.

From early historical times certain properties have been recognized as important for measurement. The most common of these are lengths, areas, volumes, weights, and time. Other important properties are force, work, energy, and power. Units of measure did not arise "over-night," nor were they developed logically or consistently. For example, early measures of length were based on parts of the human body. A story goes that the "Black Cubit" of Arabia was the arm-length of al-Mamun's favorite slave. However, with the passage of time and the growing demands of society certain desirable characteristics of units of measure were recognized. A **unit of measure** in order to be useful and serve its purpose should be convenient to use and obtain, it should have wide acceptance, it should be uniform wherever used, standardized and independently reproducible, and finally it should be related to other units to form a system of measures. In the United States, the Bureau of Standards in Washington governs and regulates the use of units of measure. When a concrete number is expressed in terms of a standardized unit of measurement we say that it is a **denominate number**.

Two common systems of measurement are used in the United States for measuring lengths. These are called the **metric system** and the **English system**. The metric system originated in France at about the time of the French Revolution and was based upon a unit of measure called the **meter**. The **meter** was intended to be one ten-millionth of the distance from the North Pole to the equator along a meridian. In actuality, a platinum bar engraved with fine lines is used as a standard meter. This bar, known as the *International Meter*, is kept at the International Bureau of Weights and Measures in Paris. The English system is said to owe its

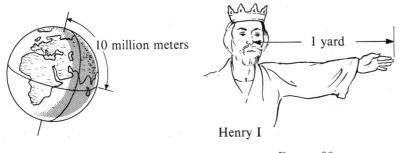

10 million meters

1 yard

Henry I

FIGURE 89   FIGURE 90

origin to an English king. The English **yard** as standardized during the reign of Henry I is supposed to have been the length of the monarch's arm. In the United States the **yard** is related to the meter by an act of Congress passed in 1866. The yard is very nearly 0.9144 meter in length.†

† See: U.S. Department of Commerce, National Bureau of Standards Miscellaneous Publication 247(U.S. Government Printing Office).

For convenience in measuring short as well as long distances we have related units of measure such as the inch and centimeter, the mile and kilometer. These related units of measure, shown in Table 16, furnish us with **standard units** of measure of distances or lengths. These measures are often referred to as **linear measures**.

A comparison of the English and metric systems of measure should immediately suggest a difference in their origins. The English system developed historically through the needs of trade and commerce whereas the metric system was devised as a system and established by the French by decree. The metric system is easy to remember and use because of the systematic use of prefixes and the regularity of the relationship between different units of measure within the system.

TABLE 16

English system	Metric system
12 inches(in.) = 1 foot	10 millimeters(mm) = 1 centimeter
3 feet(ft) = 1 yard	10 centimeters(cm) = 1 decimeter
$5\frac{1}{2}$ yards(yd) = 1 rod	10 decimeters(dm) = 1 meter
320 rods(rd) = 1 mile	10 meters(m) = 1 decameter
5280 feet = 1 mile	10 decameters(dkm) = 1 hectometer
	10 hectometers(hm) = 1 kilometer(km)
	1000 meters = 1 kilometer

1 inch = 2.54 centimeters (approximately)
1 yard = 0.9144 meter   (approximately)
39.37 inches = 1 meter   (approximately)

8.1.2   Measurement of properties in the real world around us is an approximate and often complicated process. However, from our observations we can abstract and draw simplified figures which have definite shapes and forms. When physical shapes and forms are organized and their relationships studied we call the resulting subject **geometry**. Geometric figures can help us to better understand the processes and problems of measurement.

Geometric figures consist of **points, lines,** and **planes**. What is a point?

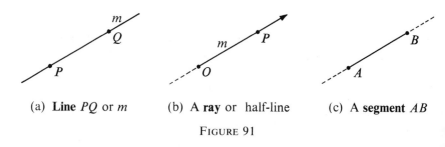

(a) **Line** *PQ* or *m*   (b) **A ray** or half-line   (c) **A segment** *AB*

FIGURE 91

It is an idea, the idea of location. We often indicate a point on a figure with a dot and name points using capital letters. What is a line? It is an idea, the idea of a direction through a point. We often name lines using two points or a lower case (smaller) letter. What is a plane? It is an idea, the idea which contains points and lines. The surface of a flat sheet of paper suggests a plane.

A **segment** is a part of a line determined by two points. Segments have two properties, length and direction. When two segments are the same in length, we say that they are **congruent**. Given proper instruments we can compare the lengths of segments as shown in Figure 92. If a segment

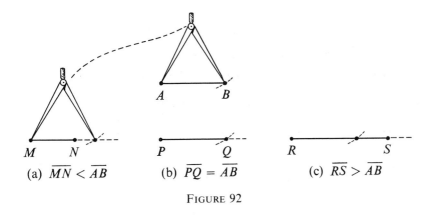

(a) $\overline{MN} < \overline{AB}$ (b) $\overline{PQ} = \overline{AB}$ (c) $\overline{RS} > \overline{AB}$

FIGURE 92

AB is chosen as a unit segment in length, we can measure the length of any other segment as illustrated in Figure 93. A bar over the name of

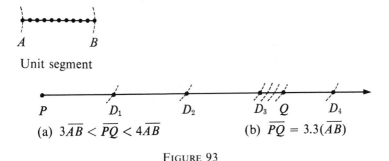

Unit segment

(a) $3\overline{AB} < \overline{PQ} < 4\overline{AB}$ (b) $\overline{PQ} = 3.3(\overline{AB})$

FIGURE 93

the segment is used to indicate its length. By dividing the unit segment into shorter equal segments, we can obtain a more accurate and refined measurement of the segment to be measured.

When three or more segments are connected "end-to-end" to form a closed figure, the resulting figure is, in general, called a **polygon**. The segments are called **sides** of the polygon. Polygons with three sides are called **triangles** while polygons formed with four segments (sides) are called **quadrilaterals**. The form and shape of polygons are very common in the world around us. What are their properties? The sides have length. The sum of the lengths of the sides of a polygon is called its **perimeter**. If the lengths of the sides of a polygon are given or can be measured, then we can find the perimeter of the polygon.

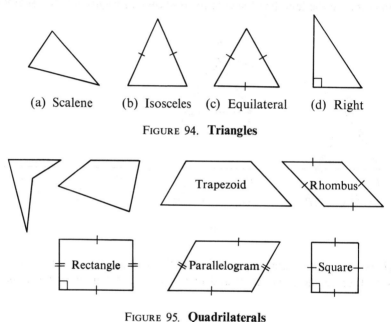

(a) Scalene   (b) Isosceles   (c) Equilateral   (d) Right

FIGURE 94. **Triangles**

Trapezoid   Rhombus

Rectangle   Parallelogram   Square

FIGURE 95. **Quadrilaterals**

Examples.

(a) Figure 96 represents the shape of a patio with the lengths of its sides as indicated. Find the perimeter of the patio shape.

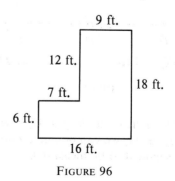

9 ft.

12 ft.

7 ft.

18 ft.

6 ft.

16 ft.

FIGURE 96

SOLUTION. The sum of the lengths of the sides is 68 ft, the perimeter of the patio shape.

(b) Find the perimeter of the "real" triangle marked ABC in Figure 97 in inches.

SOLUTION. Obtain an accurate ruler marked in inches and fractions of an inch. Measure the length of each side of the triangle with the ruler to obtain $\overline{AB} = 2\frac{1}{4}$ inches, $\overline{BC} = 3\frac{5}{8}$ inches, $\overline{AC} = 4\frac{9}{16}$ inches approximately. Thus, summing we have the perimeter of the triangle equal to approximately $10\frac{7}{16}$ inches.

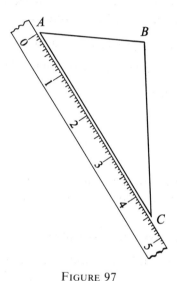

FIGURE 97

An important shape is the **circle**. It is the shape of a wheel, possibly one of the most important inventions of all time. A **circle** is located by a single point called its **center** and determined by a fixed distance measured from its center. The distance is called the **radius** of the circle.

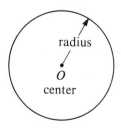

FIGURE 98

Measuring the length around a circle is different from finding the perimeter of a polygon. We measure lengths along straight-line segments and we cannot "fit" or "bend" segments around the curve of a circle. Of course, in the real world around us, we can approximate the distance around a wheel by either wrapping a measuring tape around the wheel or by marking the wheel and rolling it through one complete turn and measuring the distance it has moved. The exact length around a circle is called its **circumference**. When we compute the circumference of a circle we find that it can be expressed as twice the radius times a constant. Twice the radius, the distance across the circle through its center, is called the **diameter** of the circle. If we let C stand for the circumference and r for the radius, then $C = 2r(\pi)$ describes the relationship between the radius and circumference of the circle. The Greek symbol, "π," called "*pi*," is a constant approximately equal to $\frac{22}{7}$ or 3.1416. For example, if the radius of a circle is given as 4 units, then the circumference $C = 2 \times 4 \times \frac{22}{7} = 25\frac{1}{7}$ units.

Examples.

(a) Approximately how far will a 28-inch diameter tire travel in turning 100 times without slipping? How many times will it turn in going 100 yards?

SOLUTION. In turning once the tire will travel $C = 28 \times \frac{22}{7} = 88$ inches. Thus, in 100 turns (revolutions) it will travel $100 \times 88 = 8,800$ inches $= 733\frac{1}{3}$ ft. Since 88 inches $= \frac{22}{9}$ yd, we have $100 \div \frac{22}{9} = 40.9$ times approximately.

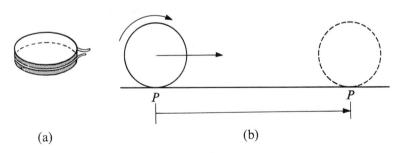

(a)   (b)

FIGURE 99

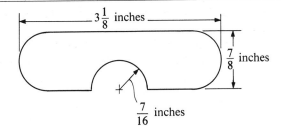

FIGURE 100

(b) Find the distance around Figure 100.

SOLUTION. Notice that the boundary includes three half-circles (**semicircles**) of the same radius. Thus we have $\frac{3}{2} \times \frac{7}{8} \times \frac{22}{7} = \frac{33}{8}$ inches for the circular portions of the figure. The straight portions are equal to $2 \times \frac{9}{4} = \frac{9}{2}$ inches less the diameter of the semicircular notch. Finally, we have $\frac{33}{8} + \frac{9}{2} - \frac{7}{8} = \frac{31}{4}$ or $7\frac{3}{4}$ inches as the distance around the figure.

Practice 1.

1. Describe commonly measured properties of the following along with the standard units used to measure them:
   (a) This textbook   (b) An auto
   (c) A person   (d) The weather.

2. If the number of centimeters in an inch is multiplied by the number of inches in a meter, then what would we expect as a product? Why?

3. (a) How many inches are there in 1 rod?
   (b) How many yards must we walk along a road to go a mile?
   (c) How many centimeters are there in 1 kilometer?
   (d) How many kilometers is it from the North Pole to the equator along the surface of the earth on a meridian line?

4. Let the segment u below be a unit segment. Measure the following segments AB to the nearest one-fourth unit:

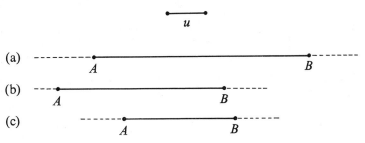

5. Use a ruler with an inch scale to measure the segments of Problem 4 to the nearest

    (a) inch   (b) quarter-inch   (c) sixteenth-inch.

6. Find the perimeters of the figures shown in Figure 101.

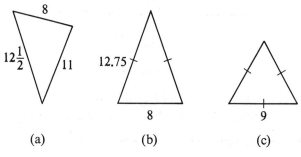

    (a)   (b)   (c)

FIGURE 101

7. Find the perimeters of the figures shown in Figure 102.

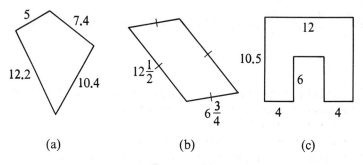

    (a)   (b)   (c)

FIGURE 102

8. Find the distances around the figures shown in Figure 103.

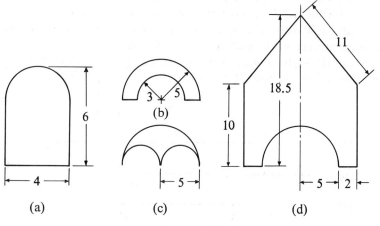

    (a)   (c)   (d)

FIGURE 103

9. Two equilateral triangles, 3 inches on a side, are used to draw a six-pointed star. What is the perimeter of the star?

10. If a segment AB is used as a unit to measure a segment CD, then $\overline{CD} = \frac{8}{3}$. What will be the measure of AB if CD is used as a unit of measure?

Answers.

1. (a) Height, width, and thickness in inches; weight in ounces; cost in dollars and cents; and so forth.

(b) Length, width, and height in feet and inches; weight in pounds; power of its engine in horsepower; cost in dollars and cents; and so forth.

(c) Height and weight in feet and inches and in pounds; age in years and months; intelligence in IQ points; and so forth.

(d) Temperature in degrees fahrenheit or centigrade; air pressure (barometric pressure) in inches of mercury or pounds per square inch; humidity as a percentage; wind velocity in miles per hour; and so forth.

2. 100; there are 100 centimeters in 1 meter.

3. (a) 198 inches   (b) 1,760 yards   (c) 100,000 centimeters   (d) 10,000 kilometers.

4. (a) $5\frac{1}{2}u$ (b) $4\frac{1}{4}u$ (c) $2\frac{3}{4}u$.

5. (a) inch: (a) 2 inches   (b) 2 inches   (c) 1 inch.

(b) quarter-inch: (a) $\frac{9}{4}$ inches   (b) $\frac{7}{4}$ inches   (c) $\frac{5}{4}$ inches.

(c) sixteenth-inch: (a) $\frac{38}{16}$ inches   (b) $\frac{29}{16}$ inches   (c) $\frac{19}{16}$ inches.

6. (a) $31\frac{1}{2}$ units   (b) $33\frac{1}{2}$ units   (c) 27 units.

7. (a) 35 units   (b) $38\frac{1}{2}$ units   (c) 57 units.

8. (a) $18\frac{2}{7}$ units   (b) $29\frac{1}{7}$ units   (c) $31\frac{3}{7}$ units   (d) $61\frac{5}{7}$ units.

9. 12 inches.

10. $\frac{3}{8}$.

8.1.3   The sides of a polygon form a boundary which encloses a part of a plane. Can we measure the part of the plane enclosed by the sides of a polygon? This property of a bounded part of a plane is called **area**. To measure this property we must have a unit of measure. We could consider a variety of shapes for use as a standard unit of area. For example, triangular, rectangular, or circular. However, the most common and

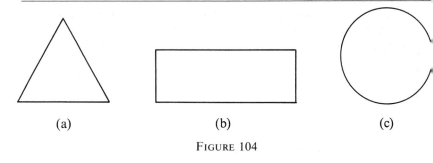

(a)   (b)   (c)

FIGURE 104

conventional unit of area is taken in the shape of a square with sides 1 unit in length. A square 1 centimeter on each side is called a **square centimeter** and a square 1 inch on each side is called a **square inch**. From the English and metric units of length we can immediately obtain further square units of area such as the **square foot** and **square meter** (Figure 105).

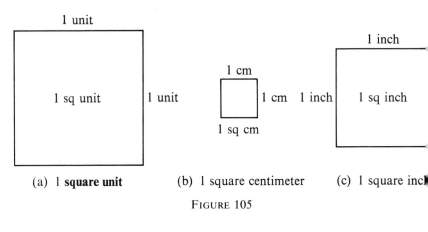

(a) 1 **square unit**   (b) 1 square centimeter   (c) 1 square inch

FIGURE 105

Now we can ask "How many square units are in a given area?" For example, how many square centimeters are there in a square inch? Since there are 2.54 cm in 1 inch there must be $2.54 \times 2.54 = 6.45$ sq cm in each square inch (see Figure 106). To find the number of square units in a given area, we only need a standard unit of length and some ingenuity in counting the unit squares in the area. If we know the lengths of the sides of a rectangle, the area will be the product of two of the adjacent sides.

Observing that our square units have perpendicular sides, we note that our linear measurements must be taken perpendicular to each other in order to measure standard areas. In Figures 108 and 109 the horizontal segments are called **bases** while the vertical measurements taken perpendicular to the bases are called **altitudes**. Squares, rectangles, and parallelograms have areas equal to the product of their base and altitude: $A = b \times h$.

Triangles, on the other hand, have areas equal to one-half the product of their base and altitude: $A = \frac{1}{2} \times b \times h$.

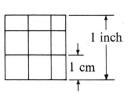

FIGURE 106

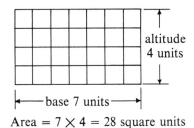

base 7 units

Area = 7 × 4 = 28 square units

FIGURE 107

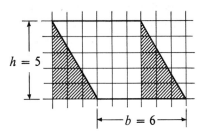

$h = 5$

$b = 6$

$A = 5 \times 6 = 30$ square units

FIGURE 108

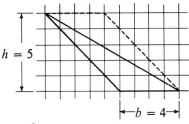

$h = 5$

$b = 4$

$A = \frac{1}{2} \times 4 \times 5 = 10$ square units

FIGURE 109

Examples.

(a) If the base of a parallelogram measures 18 ft and the altitude is 12.6 ft, then what is its area?

SOLUTION. $A = 18 \times 12.6 = 226.8$ sq ft.

(b) If the base of a triangle is 6.5 inches and the altitude is 9.8 inches, then what is the area of the triangle?

SOLUTION. $A = \frac{1}{2} \times 6.5 \times 9.8 = 31.85$ sq inches.

(c) Find the area of the patio represented in Figure 96.

SOLUTION. We think of the area as being made up of two rectangles: 9 × 12 and 6 × 16. Thus, $A = 108 + 96 = 204$ sq ft.

Just as in finding the circumference of a circle, to find the area of a circle poses a situation quite different from that of a polygon. We might approximate the area of a circle by considering a grid of small squares "covering" the circle. Another approach is to draw polygons interior to

and exterior to the circle and notice that the areas of the successive polygons approach closer and closer to the actual area of the circle as the

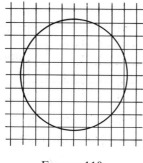

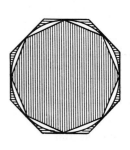

FIGURE 110   FIGURE 111

number of sides of the polygons are increased. If we carefully study one
of these polygons, we notice that we can sum the areas of triangles to
find the area of the polygon (see Figure 112). Now, as the number of

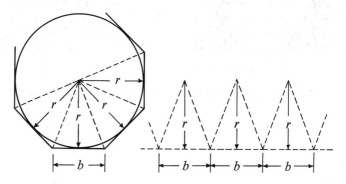

FIGURE 112.   Area $A = \pi r^2$

sides in the polygon is increased, the perimeter of the polygon approaches
the circumference of the circle closer and closer. Thus, the sum of the
areas of the triangles approaches closer and closer to $\frac{1}{2} \times r \times C$. But

$C = 2r(\pi)$ so that the area of the circle $A = \frac{1}{2} \times r \times (2r) \times \pi = \pi \times r \times r$.

That is, the area of a circle is the product of the constant π times r times
r, where r is the radius of the circle.

At this point it is convenient to introduce a simplifying notation.
Where it causes no confusion, it is conventional to omit the multiplication
symbol between two literal quantities. For example, rather than writing

$A = b \times h$ we will often write $A = bh$. The equation $A = \frac{1}{2} \times b \times h$ will be written $A = \frac{1}{2}bh$. The area of a circle is thus $A = \pi rr$. A word of caution, in computing we must be careful not to juxtapose numerals in this way. For example, if the base of a parallelogram $b = 2$ units and the altitude $h = 5$ units, then the area of the parallelogram is *not* equal to $A = 25$. We should write $A = 2 \times 5 = 10$ sq units.

A second convenient abbreviation which can lead to many refinements and new ideas is to indicate the product of a given factor taken n times by a small numeral n written at the upper right of the factor. For example, rather than $A = \pi rr$ we write $A = \pi r^2$, where the "2" at the upper right of the "r" indicates r is to be used twice as a factor: $r^2 = r \times r$.

Examples.

(a) Find the area of a circle whose radius is $5\frac{1}{4}$ inches.

SOLUTION. $A = \frac{22}{7} \times \frac{21}{4} \times \frac{21}{4} = \frac{693}{8} = 86\frac{5}{8}$ sq inches.

(b) Find the area enclosed by Figure 100.

SOLUTION. We can think of the area as consisting of three parts: the rectangle $2\frac{1}{4} \times \frac{7}{8}$, the circular ends $\frac{7}{16}$ in radius, and the notch. Thus, we have the rectangular area equal to $\frac{63}{32}$ sq inches and the two ends less the notch equal to $\frac{77}{256}$ sq inch. The area enclosed is thus $\frac{63}{32} + \frac{77}{256} = \frac{581}{256} = 2\frac{69}{256}$ sq inches or approximately 2.27 sq inches.

Since square units of measure have been developed in terms of linear units, both the English and metric systems of measurements can easily be extended to **standard square units** of measure. In the English system the **acre** developed as the area of a long rectangular field about equal to a morning's plowing. A farmer would plow about 4 furrows 40 rods long in one morning's work so that an acre originated as about equal to 160 square rods. Table 17 summarizes the commonly used relationships between standard units of square measure.

TABLE 17

	1 sq inch	= 6.452 sq cm
144 sq inches	= 1 sq ft	= 929 sq cm
9 sq ft	= 1 sq yd	= 0.836 sq m
4,840 sq yd	= 1 acre	= 4,047 sq m
640 acres	= 1 sq mile	= 2.59 sq km

Practice 2.

1. Describe four common situations in which area measurements are used along with their standard units of measurement.

2. What is the numerical relationship between successive square units in the metric system?

3. (a) How many square inches are there in 1 sq yd?

(b) How many square feet are there in 1 acre?

(c) What part of a square mile is 1 sq km?

(d) How many square meters are there in 1 sq km?

4. Approximate the area of Figure 113 using as successive units of area the areas given in Figure 104.

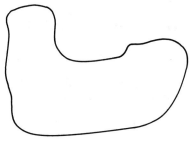

FIGURE 113

5. Estimate the area of Figure 113 in square inches and in square centimeters.

6. Find the areas of the figures shown in Figure 114.

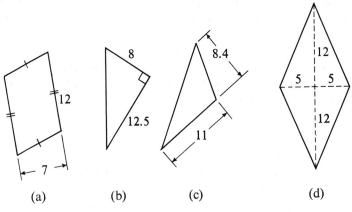

(a)   (b)   (c)   (d)

FIGURE 114

7. Find the areas of the figures shown in Figure 103.

8. (a) What is the area of a rectangle whose width is 4.6 inches and whose length is 9.5 inches?

(b) If a triangle has a base which measures $3\frac{1}{2}$ ft and an altitude measuring $2\frac{3}{4}$ ft, then what is its area?

(c) How many square feet are enclosed by a circle with diameter 25 ft?

(d) If a circle 2 inches in diameter is cut out of a square piece of paper 2 inches on a side, then what is the area of the "corner" pieces of paper left over?

9. If the circumference of a circle is 22 inches, then what is the area of the circle?

10. A rancher purchased 120 ft of fencing for a corral.

(a) If he wanted to build a rectangular corral with an area of 675 sq ft, then what should be the length and width of the corral using all 120 ft of fencing?

(b) If he builds a square shaped corral using all 120 ft of fencing, then what would be the area of the corral?

(c) In what shape should the rancher build his corral to obtain the largest possible area using the 120 ft of fencing? What would be the approximate area of this corral?

Answers.

1. (a) Rugs by the square yard   (b) Plywood by square feet
   (c) Office space by square feet   (d) Farms in acres.

2. 1 to 100.

3. (a) 1,296 sq inches   (b) 43,560 sq feet   (c) 0.386 sq mile
   (d) 1,000,000 sq meters.

4. (a) 3.9 triangular units   (b) 2 rectangular units
   (c) 2.2 circular units.

5. (a) 1.7 sq inches   (b) 11 sq cm.

6. (a) 84 sq units   (b) 50 sq units   (c) 46.2 sq units
   (d) 120 sq units.

7. (a) 22.3 sq units   (b) 25.1 sq units   (c) 58.9 sq units
   (d) 160.2 sq units.

8. (a) 43.7 sq inches   (b) $4\frac{13}{16}$ sq ft   (c) 491 sq ft

   (d) $\frac{6}{7}$ sq inch.

9. $38\frac{1}{2}$ sq inches.

10. (a) 45 ft × 15 ft   (b) 900 sq ft
    (c) A circle; 1,145 sq ft approximately.

8.1.4   In solving problems involving **denominate** numbers we may wish to change the units in which the number is expressed. For example, we may change 15 inches to 1 ft 3 inches or into 38.1 cm. Notice that there are two kinds of changes suggested in the example. First, we may change units within a given system of measurement. When units are changed in this way we call it a **reduction**. Second, we may change from one system of units to another. When changes are made in this way we call it a **conversion**. When a denominate number is expressed in terms of the largest multiples of the largest units possible we say that it is in its **simplest form**. For example, 6 yd 1 ft 3 inches or 1 rd 2 ft 9 inches would be the simplest forms for $19\frac{1}{4}$ ft.

Examples.

(a) Express $58\frac{2}{3}$ sq yd in simplest form.

SOLUTION.   Since $5\frac{1}{2}$ yd = 1 rd we have $30\frac{1}{4}$ sq yd = 1 sq rd and $58\frac{2}{3}$ sq yd = 1 sq rd + $28\frac{5}{12}$ sq yd. Now, since 9 sq ft = 1 sq yd we have $\frac{5}{12}$ sq yd = $\left(\frac{5}{12} \times 9\right)$ sq ft = $3\frac{3}{4}$ sq ft. Continuing, $\frac{3}{4}$ sq ft = $\left(\frac{3}{4} \times 144\right)$ sq inches = 108 sq inches. Finally, we have $58\frac{2}{3}$ sq yd = 1 sq rd 28 sq yd 3 sq ft 108 sq inches.

(b) Convert 1 mile into kilometers and meters.

SOLUTION.   Since 1 yd = 0.9144 m and 1 mile = 1760 yd we have 1 mile = (1760 × 0.9144) m = 1609 m = 1 km 609 m (approximately).

When denominate numbers involve two or more units of measurement, arithmetical operations may cause difficulties. To find sums and differences we add or subtract like units first, then we can reduce as necessary.

Examples.

(a) Find the sum of 2 yd 1 ft 7 inches; 1 yd 9 inches; 4 yd 2 ft 4 inches; and 2 ft 11 inches.

SOLUTION.　　 2 yd 1 ft 7 inches Notice the alignment
　　　　　　　 1 yd　　　 9 inches of "like" units
　　　　　　　 4 yd 2 ft 4 inches
　　　 +　　　　　 2 ft 11 inches
　　　　　　　 7 yd 5 ft 31 inches 31 in. = 2 ft 7 inches
　　　　　　　 7 yd 7 ft 7 inches　 7 ft = 2 yd 1 ft

　　　　　　　 9 yd 1 ft 7 inches　 9 yd = 1 rd $3\frac{1}{2}$ yd

　　　 1 rd 3 yd 2 ft 13 inches 13 in. = 1 ft 1 inch
　　　 1 rd 4 yd 0 ft 1 inch　　 in simplest form.

(b) If a rectangular plot 48 ft by 120 ft is taken from a 1-acre lot, then how many square yards are left in the lot?

SOLUTION. 48 × 120 = 5,760 sq ft; 5,760 ÷ 9 = 640 sq yd.

Now since there are 4,840 sq yd in 1 acre, we have 4,840 − 640 = 4,200 sq yd left in the lot.

(c) How far will a person go if he takes 87 steps, each step being 2 ft 4 inches?

SOLUTION. 2 ft 4 inches times 87 = (2 × 87) ft (4 × 87) inches.

　　 That is,　　 2 ft　 4 inches
　　　　　　 ×　　 87
　　　　　　 174 ft 348 inches and since 348 inches = 29 ft
　　　　　　 203 ft　　　　　 but 203 ft = 67 yd 2 ft
　　　　　　 67 yd 2 ft　　　 that he goes.

Practice 3.

1. Reduce to the units indicated:
   (a) 2 yd 1 ft 7 inches to inches.
   (b) 1 rd 2 yd 1 ft to feet.
   (c) 16.24 m to centimeters.
   (d) $5\frac{2}{3}$ sq yd to square feet.
   (e) 1,000 inches to yards.
2. Reduce to simplest form:
   (a) 15 yd 7 ft 27 inches　　 (b) 2,114 ft
   (c) 12 sq ft 544 sq inches　 (d) 1,000 inches.
3. Convert as indicated:
   (a) 1 ft 7 inches to centimeters.
   (b) 1.47 m to feet and inches.
   (c) 2.4 sq m to square feet and square inches.
   (d) 1 acre to square meters.
   (e) 100 yd to meters.

4. Find the sums in simplest form:
    (a) 3 yd 2 ft 7 inches; 5 ft 9 inches; 2 yd 5 inches; 1 yd 1 ft 3 inches
    (b) 16 yd 7 ft 45 inches; 3 rd 5 yd 6 inches; 17 rd 24 ft 9 inches
    (c) 29 sq yd 8 sq ft; 37 sq yd 5 sq ft 28 sq inches;
2 sq yd 2 sq ft 125 sq inches; 10 sq yd 4 sq ft 135 sq inches.
    (d) 5.43 km; 136 m; 2 km 809 m; 2 km 78 decameters.
    (e) 1.09 m; 7.2 decimeters; 36.8 cm; 154 mm.

5. Find the differences in simplest form:
    (a) 1.72 km less 824 m   (b) 15 yd less 7 yd 2 ft 8 inches
    (c) (2 rd 4 yd 2 ft 5 inches) − (5 yd 2 ft 9 inches)
    (d) 2.4 acres − 5,000 sq ft   (e) 1 mile less 1 kilometer.

6. Find the products:
    (a) 42 times 3 yd 2 ft 7 inches
    (b) 4 ft 5 inches times 7 ft 9 inches
    (c) 37 × (6 sq yd 7 sq ft 39 sq inches)
    (d) 15.432 m by 3.07 cm   (e) 562 × (17 sq m 42 sq cm).

7. Find the quotients:
    (a) 4 yd 1 ft 5 inches divided by 7.
    (b) 14 sq yd 5 sq ft 96 sq inches divided by 15.
    (c) 11 yd 2 ft 5 inches divided by 2 ft 1 inch.
    (d) 4 sq ft 13 sq inches divided by 1 ft 7 inches.
    (e) 15.42 km divided by 20.

8. A board is 6 ft 4 inches long. It is cut into 3 pieces so that one piece is $\frac{2}{3}$ as long as another and the third piece is $\frac{2}{3}$ as long as the shorter of the other two. What is the length of the longest piece?

Answers.

1. (a) 91 inches   (b) $23\frac{1}{2}$ ft   (c) 1,624 cm   (d) 51 sq ft
    (e) $27\frac{7}{9}$ yd.

2. (a) 3 rd 1 yd 1 ft 9 inches   (b) 128 rd 2 ft
    (c) 1 sq yd 6 sq ft 112 sq inches   (d) 4 rd 5 yd 2 ft 4 inches.

3. (a) 48.3 cm   (b) 4 ft 10 inches   (c) 25 sq ft 120 sq inches
    (d) 4,047 sq m   (e) 91.44 m.

4. (a) 1 rd 3 yd 2 ft 6 inches.   (b) 26 rd.
    (c) 2 sq rd 19 sq yd 6 sq ft 72 sq inches.
    (d) 11 kilometers 1 hectometer 5 decameters 5 meters.
    (e) 2 meters 3 decimeters 3 centimeters 2 millimeters.

5. (a) 896 m   (b) 1 rd 1 yd 1 ft 10 inches   (c) 1 rd 4 yd 1 ft 2 inches
    (d) 2 acres 45 sq rd 75 sq yd 4 sq ft   (e) 609 m.

6. (a) 29 rd 2 yd 2 ft   (b) 3 sq yd 7 sq ft 33 sq inches
   (c) 8 sq rd 9 sq yd 8 sq ft 3 sq inches   (d) 4,737.624 sq cm
   (e) 95 square decameters 56 square meters 36 square decimeters
   4 square centimeters.
7. (a) 1 ft 11 inches   (b) 8 sq ft 112 sq inches   (c) 17
   (d) 2 ft 7 inches   (e) 771 m.
8. 1 yd.

Exercises

1. What is a measurement?
2. Three things are necessary for proper measurement. What are
they?
3. The two systems of measurement used in the United States are
called the _____ system and the _____ system.
4. The yard is the basic unit of measure in the _____ system. Convenient related units are 3 _____ equaling 1 yard and 36 _____ equaling
1 yard.
5. The meter is the basic unit of measure in the _____ system. The
prefix milli- attached to this basic unit means a unit _____ of a meter
while the prefix centi- denotes a unit _____ of this unit.
6. Find the perimeters and areas of the figures shown in Figure 115.

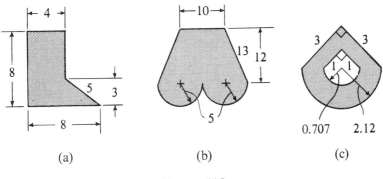

(a)   (b)   (c)

FIGURE 115

7. If a segment AB is used as a unit to measure a segment CD, then
$\overline{CD} = \frac{8}{3}$; and if CD is used as a unit to measure a segment EF, then $\overline{EF} =$
6. What will be the measure of EF if AB is used as a unit of measure?
8. What is the perimeter and area of a sheet of typewriter paper measuring $8\frac{1}{2}$ inches by 11 inches?

9. What is the circumference and area of a circular target with a radius of $2\dfrac{6}{11}$ inches?

10. A 21-inch diameter wheel is turned by a rope wrapped around its rim. If 11 ft of rope is pulled from the wheel, then how many times will the wheel turn?

11. How many yards of fringe are needed for a border on a bedspread 72 inches by 105 inches?

12. Find the value of a lot 75 ft by 194 ft if the property is worth $12,365 per acre.

13. Find the perimeters and areas of the figures shown in Figure 116.

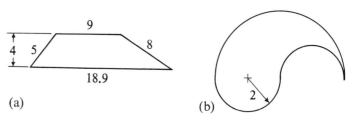

(a)　　　　　　　　　　　　　　　　　　(b)

FIGURE 116

14. Do as indicated:
   (a) Reduce 18 yd 8 ft 92 inches to simplest form.
   (b) Convert 88 sq inches to square centimeters.
   (c) Convert 15.24 m to simplest form in the English system.
15. Do as indicated:
   (a) Find the sum of 6 yd 1 ft 5 inches; 3 yd 2 ft 8 inches; 1 yd 7 inches; 2 ft 4 inches.
   (b) Subtract 2 sq ft 128 sq inches from 1 sq yd 99 sq inches.
   (c) What is the product of 7 ft 4 inches times 2 ft 9 inches?
   (d) Find one twenty-eighth of the length 17 rd 4 yd 1 ft 6 inches.

Answers.

1. A measurement is the association of a number to a property or characteristic of an object or thing.

2. A property of something to be measured; a unit by which to measure; and an instrument which relates the unit to the property.

3. English; metric.

4. English; feet; inches.

5. Metric; one-thousandths; one hundredths.

6. (a) $P = 30$ units, $A = 38$ sq units.

(b) $P = 67\frac{3}{7}$ units, $A = 258\frac{4}{7}$ sq units.

(c) $P = 16.9$ units, $A = 16.5$ sq units.

7. 16.

8. $P = 39$ inches; $A = 93\frac{1}{2}$ sq inches.

9. $C = 16$ inches; $A = 20.4$ sq inches.

10. 2 turns.

11. $9.8\frac{1}{3}$ yd.

12. $4,130.18.

13. (a) $P = 40.9$ units, $A = 55.8$ sq units.

(b) $P = 25\frac{1}{7}$ units, $A = 25\frac{1}{7}$ sq units.

14. (a) 4 rd 1 yd 8 inches   (b) 567.776 sq cm

(c) 2 rd 2 yd 2 ft $9\frac{2}{3}$ inches.

15. (a) 2 rd 1 ft   (b) 6 sq ft 115 sq inches.

(c) 20 sq ft 24 sq inches   (d) 3 yd 1 ft 6 inches.

8.2 Volume and Weight

8.2.1 A further extension of figures can easily be visualized if we think of the real world in which we live. There is depth and we can imagine points and lines in space which do not all lie in one plane. Beginning with a point, we can imagine the point "moving" to form a line segment. The line segment can then be imagined as "moving" perpendicular to itself to form an area. Now the area can be imagined as "moving" perpendicular to itself to form an object in space. The distinctive property associated with such objects is called **volume**. The following figures illustrate typical objects containing volume drawn in perspective.

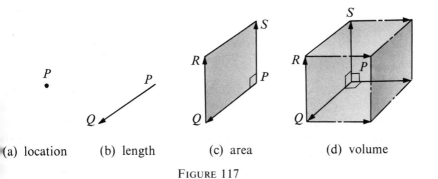

(a) location   (b) length   (c) area   (d) volume

FIGURE 117

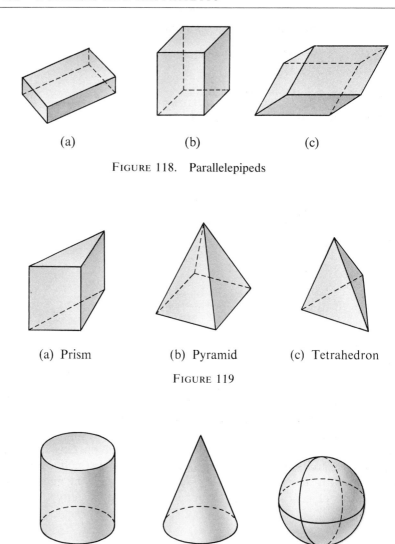

FIGURE 118.   Parallelepipeds

(a) Prism   (b) Pyramid   (c) Tetrahedron

FIGURE 119

(a) Cylinder   (b) Cone   (c) Sphere

FIGURE 120

A measure of volume can be obtained by considering three mutually perpendicular linear measurements combined. A conventional unit of volume is the **unit cube**. A cube 1 cm on each edge is called a **cubic centimeter** (cc) while a cube 1 inch on each edge is called a **cubic inch** (cu inch). The English and metric systems of linear measurements immediately lead us to further cubic units such as the **cubic foot** and

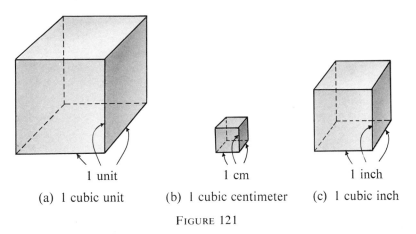

(a) 1 cubic unit　　　(b) 1 cubic centimeter　　　(c) 1 cubic inch

FIGURE 121

cubic meter. To measure the volume of an object in space we can ask "How many cubic units are contained in the object?" or "How many square units of area have moved how many perpendicular linear units in 'generating' the object in space?"

Examples.

(a) If the blocks shown in Figure 122 represent unit cubes, then Figure 122(a) shows a volume of 6 unit cubes. Figure 122(b) shows a volume of 13 unit cubes; however, there could be "hidden" unit cubes. Figure 122(c) appears to have two layers of 18 cubic units each or 36 unit cubes.

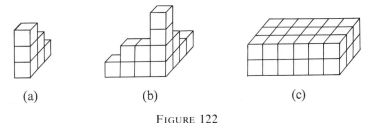

(a)　　　　　(b)　　　　　(c)

FIGURE 122

(b) If the area of B in Figure 123(a) or 123(b) is, say, 16 square units, and $h = 4\frac{1}{2}$ linear units measured perpendicular to B, then the volume "generated" would be $16 \times 4\frac{1}{2} = 72$ cubic units.

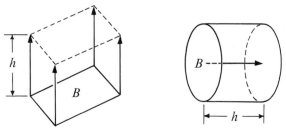

FIGURE 123

The above ideas can be readily applied to find the volumes of paral-lelepipeds, prisms, and cylinders. To find the volume of a pyramid, tetra-hedron, or cone is somewhat more difficult. It can be shown, however, that the volume will be $\frac{1}{3}$ the area of the base B times the altitude h: $V =$ $\frac{1}{3}Bh$. The volume of a sphere is given by $V = \frac{4}{3} \times \pi \times (r \times r \times r)$, where r is the radius of a "great circle" of the sphere. That is, $V = \frac{4}{3}\pi r^3$.

Examples.

(a) A room is 12 ft long, $9\frac{1}{3}$ ft wide, and has a $9\frac{1}{2}$ ft high ceiling. How many cubic feet of space are enclosed by the room?

SOLUTION. The floor has an area of $12 \times 9\frac{1}{3} = 112$ square feet. Each square foot of floor area has $9\frac{1}{2}$ feet of space above it so that we have $112 \times 9\frac{1}{2} = 1{,}064$ cubic feet of space in the room.

(b) An orange crate measuring 14 inches by 16 inches by 28 inches is twisted as shown in Figure 124 until its height is only 24 inches. How much of its volume will it have lost?

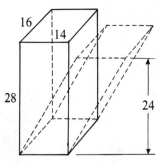

FIGURE 124

SOLUTION. Notice that the top area of the crate will have moved 4 inches down so that we have $14 \times 16 \times 4 = 896$ cu inches less volume in the crate.

(c) If the triangular base of the prism shown in Figure 119(a) has a base of 2 inches and altitude of $\frac{3}{4}$ inches and the height of the prism is 3 inches, then what is the volume of the prism?

SOLUTION. $V = B \times h$ where $B = \frac{1}{2}\left(2 \times \frac{3}{4}\right) = \frac{3}{4}$ and $h = 3$ so that $V = \frac{9}{4}$ cu inches or $V = 2\frac{1}{4}$ cu inches.

(d) If the radius of the base of the cone shown in Figure 120(b) is $1\frac{3}{4}$ inches and the height is 6 inches, then find the volume of the cone.

SOLUTION. The area of the circular base is $B = \frac{22}{7} \times \frac{7}{4} \times \frac{7}{4}$ so that the volume of the cone will be $V = \frac{1}{3} \times \frac{22}{7} \times \frac{7}{4} \times \frac{7}{4} \times 6 = \frac{77}{4}$ or $V = 19\frac{1}{4}$ cu inches.

(e) What is the volume of a spherical ball whose diameter is 12 inches?

SOLUTION. The volume is given by $V = \frac{4}{3} \times \pi \times (r \times r \times r)$, where π is approximately $\frac{22}{7}$ and $2r = 12$ inches. Thus, we have $V = \frac{4}{3} \times \frac{22}{7} \times 6 \times 6 \times 6$ $= \frac{6336}{7} = 905$ cu inches approximately.

Just as with square units of measure, standard cubic units of volume are obtained from the linear units in the English and metric systems. Table 18 gives a few useful relationships between the cubic units commonly used.

TABLE 18

	1 cu inch = 16.387 cc	
1,728 cu inches = 1 cu ft	= 0.0283 cu m	
27 cu ft	= 1 cu yd	= 0.7646 cu m

8.2.2   When we consider volumes it seems quite natural to think of substances with the property of **weight**. The property of **weight** is due to the pull of gravity, the force of attraction which the earth exerts on objects in the real world. Since the earth is not perfectly uniform in shape or substance, the pull of gravity varies in different locations and under different conditions. For example, a given object would weigh less at the top of a mountain than at the foot. It would weigh more at the earth's poles than at the equator. Thus, the standardization of a unit of weight

TABLE 19

English system	Metric system
1 grain(gr)	Weight of
437.5 grains = 1 ounce(oz)	1 cc water = 1 gram(g)
16 ounces = 1 pound(lb)	1,000 grams = 1 kilogram(kg)
2,000 pounds = 1 ton(T)	1,000 kilograms = 1 metric ton
	1 grain = 0.065 grams
	1 ounce = 28.35 grams
	1 pound = 0.45 kilograms

poses very serious problems. Early man probably used a handy sized stone as a "stones-weight" for measuring the weight of a fish or bird. For very small or light objects seeds were used. For example, a barley seed or other grain. With the introduction and use of metals, stamped metal pieces were used for both units of weight and money. Among the ancient Hebrews the *shekel* was both a coin and a unit of weight. Through the course of history a variety of standards of weights have been developed and used. In the English system, the basic unit of weight is the **pound**. The **pound** probably originated as the weight of one-sixtieth the weight of one cubic foot of water. In the metric system, the basic unit of weight is the **gram**. The **gram** is the weight of 1 cubic centimeter of water under very carefully controlled conditions. Table 19 describes the relationships between the most commonly used units of weights.

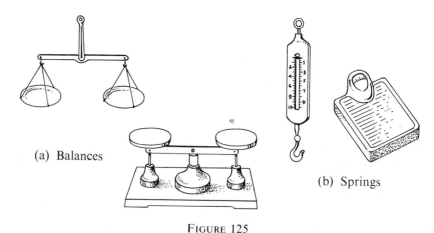

(a) Balances

(b) Springs

FIGURE 125

As in any other type of measurement, the act of measuring weight requires a measuring instrument. Weighing instruments are, in general, called **scales**. Scales are usually based on either the principle of the balance or that of a spring.

Practice 1.

1. Two systems of measurement, called dry and liquid **capacity measures**, are commonly used to measure amounts of grains and liquids. For example, we may buy fruit by the **bushel** and milk by the **quart**. Use a dictionary or other convenient source and construct tables of standard units of dry and of liquid measures.

2. What is the numerical relationship between successive cubic units in the metric system?

3. Find the volumes of the figures shown in Figure 126.

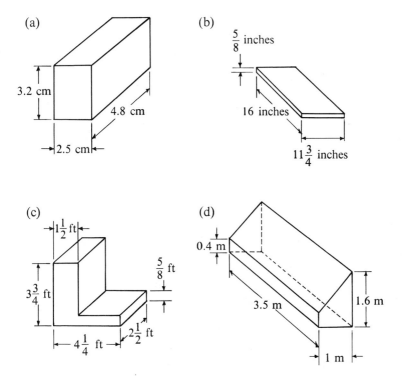

FIGURE 126

4. Find the volumes of the figures shown in Figure 127.

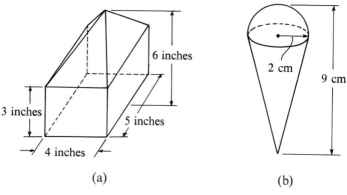

(a)   (b)

FIGURE 127

5. The blocks shown in Figure 128 represent unit cubes. How many unit cubes are in each set of blocks?

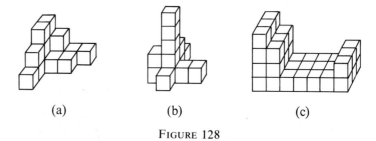

(a)   (b)   (c)

FIGURE 128

6. A cylindrical water tank is 6 feet in diameter and 7 feet in depth. What is the capacity of the tank in **gallons** if 1 gallon is equal to 231 cubic inches?

7. We know that 1 gram is the weight of 1 cubic centimeter of water. How many ounces does 1 cubic inch of water weigh? How many pounds does 1 gallon of water weigh?

8. A certain mixture of concrete weighs 1.6 Tons per cubic yard. What is the weight of a 6-inch thick rectangular floor slab of this concrete measuring $8\frac{1}{2}$ feet by 12 feet?

9. Gold is about 19.3 times as heavy as an equal volume of water. What is the approximate weight of a gold bar in the shape of a rectangular parallelepiped measuring 6.4 centimeters by 25 centimeters by 8.8 centimeters?

10. At sea level air weighs about 0.081 lb per cubic foot. If a balloon 21 ft in diameter is filled with nitrogen which weighs 0.078 lb per cubic foot, then how much weight will the balloon lift? (Assume the balloon is perfectly spherical.)

11. Mrs. Smith, while shopping, noted that there were three sizes of canned tomatoes of the same grade marketed by a certain firm. They were an 11.2 oz size for 28 cents per can, a 16 oz size for 35 cents per can, and a 21 oz size for 50 cents per can. Which size can would be the best buy for Mrs. Smith?

12. If watermelon is advertised at 3 cents per pound, then how much will a melon weighing 8 lb 12 oz cost?

Answers.

1. Dry measure: 1 pint   = 33.6 cubic inches
                2 pints = 1 quart
                8 quarts = 1 peck
                4 pecks = 1 bushel

    Liquid measure:
    (Kitchen use)   (Market use)
    3 teaspoons   = 1 tablespoon   4 gills   = 1 pint
    4 tablespoons = 1 wineglass   2 pints   = 1 quart
    4 wineglasses = 1 cup   4 quarts = 1 gallon
    2 cups   = 1 pint   1 gallon = 231 cu inches.

2. 1 to 1,000; for example, 1,000 cubic millimeters equal 1 cubic centimeter.

3. (a) 38.4 cc   (b) $117\frac{1}{2}$ cu inches   (c) $18\frac{13}{64}$ cu ft   (d) 3.5 cu m.

4. (a) 80 cu inches   (b) 46.1 cc.

5. (a) 15   (b) 13   (c) 39.

6. Approximately 5,925 gallons.

7. 1 cu inch of water weighs approximately 0.578 oz.
   1 gallon of water weighs approximately 8.345 lb.

8. Approximately 6,044 lb.

9. Approximately 27.17 kg.

10. Approximately 14.55 lb.

11. The 16 oz size.

12. $26\frac{1}{4}$ cents.

8.2.3   Just as in working with units of length and area, units of volume and weight often require reduction and conversion. The careful use of tables of standard units of measure along with some practice should result in the avoidance of unnecessary mistakes.

In finding products and quotients of denominate numbers we must be careful to observe the relationship between different kinds of units of measurement. For example, when we find the product of two lengths the result is an area. A volume measurement divided by a length results in an area unit. When we multiply or divide a denominate number by an abstract number, the product or quotient retains the unit of measure. The relationship between length, area, and volume can be illustrated as follows:

$$\text{Volume} = \text{Area} \times \text{Length} = (\text{Length} \times \text{Length}) \times \text{Length}$$
$$\frac{\text{Volume}}{\text{Area}} = \text{Length and } \frac{\text{Area}}{\text{Length}} = \text{Length}.$$

Examples.

(a) Reduce 35 cu ft 2,000 cu inches to simplest form.

SOLUTION. Since 27 cu ft = 1 cu yd we have 35 cu ft = 1 cu yd 8 cu ft. Also, 1,728 cu inches = 1 cu ft so that 2,000 cu inches = 1 cu ft 272 cu inches. Thus, 35 cu ft 2,000 cu inches = 1 cu yd 9 cu ft 272 cu inches.

(b) Convert 7.45 kg into pounds and ounces.

SOLUTION. Since 0.45 kg = 1 lb we have $7.45 \div 0.45 = 16\frac{5}{9}$ and 7.45 kg $= 16\frac{5}{9}$ lb. Since 16 oz = 1 lb we have $\frac{5}{9}$ lb $= \left(\frac{5}{9} \times 16\right)$ oz = 9 oz approximately. Thus, 7.45 kg = 16 lb 9 oz.

(c) Find the height of a box whose volume is 22 cu ft 364 cu inches with a base whose area is 7 sq ft 121 sq inches.

SOLUTION. We first reduce the volume and area to single units: 22 cu ft 364 cu inches = 38,380 cu inches and 7 sq ft 121 sq inches = 1,129 sq inches. Now dividing the volume by the area, we have $\frac{38,380}{1,129} = 34$ approximately. Thus, the height is approximately 34 inches = 2 ft 10 inches.

Practice 2.

1. Reduce as indicated:
   (a) 2.375 cu yd to simplest form   (b) 83 oz to simplest form
   (c) 16 lb 5 oz to ounces
   (d) 17 cu ft 56 cu inches to cubic inches.

2. Using the tables constructed for Problem 1 of Practice 1, reduce the following as indicated:
   (a) 2 pints 1 cup 3 wineglasses to tablespoons of liquid measure.

(b) 3 bushels 2 pecks 3 quarts to pints in dry measure.

(c) 23 pints liquid to gallons, quarts, and pints.

(d) $1\frac{1}{2}$ wineglasses to teaspoons in liquid measure.

3. Convert as indicated:

(a) 1 cu ft 365 cu inches to cubic centimeters.

(b) 1,053 g to pounds and ounces.

(c) 6 oz 5 gr to grams.

(d) 1 cu m to cubic yards, cubic feet, and cubic inches.

4. Eighteen 2 lb 12 oz packages are combined and then divided into 33 equal amounts by weight. How much should each of the new amounts weigh?

5. Do as indicated:

(a) Find the sum of 5 lb 7 oz 85 gr; 1 lb 9 oz 135 gr; and 12 oz 372 gr.

(b) Subtract 1 cu yd 7 cu ft 942 cu inches from 3 cu yd 250 cu inches.

(c) If 20 cu ft of a certain substance weighs 247 lb 8 oz, then how much does 1 cu ft of the substance weigh? That is, what is the weight of the substance per cubic foot?

(d) Find the total weight of 98 boxes each of which weighs 27 lb 6 oz.

6. A package with rectangular sides measures 14 inches by 18 inches by 10 inches.

(a) What would be the volume of a stack of packages with 4 rows, 8 columns, and 6 deep, if there is no wasted space?

(b) If each package weighs 5 lb 12 oz, what would be the total weight of the stack of packages in (a)?

Answers.

1. (a) 2 cu yd 10 cu ft 216 cu inches   (b) 5 lb 3 oz
   (c) 261 oz   (d) 29,432 cu inches.
2. (a) 92 tablespoons   (b) 230 pints
   (c) 2 gallons 3 quarts 1 pint   (d) 18 teaspoons.
3. (a) 34,298 cc   (b) 2 lb 5 oz (approximately)
   (c) 178.8 g   (d) 1 cu yd 8 cu ft 543 cu inches (approximately).
4. 1 lb 8 oz.
5. (a) 7 lb 13 oz 54.5 gr   (b) 1 cu yd 19 cu ft 1036 cu inches.
   (c) 12 lb 6 oz   (d) 1 T 682 lb 12 oz.
6. (a) 10 cu yd 10 cu ft   (b) 1,104 lb.

Exercises

1. What is the difference between volume and weight?

2. The blocks shown in Figure 129 represent unit cubes. How many unit cubes are in each set of blocks?

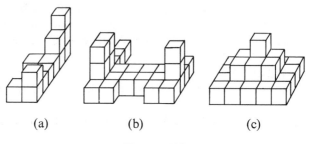

(a)   (b)   (c)

FIGURE 129

3. If a box with rectangular sides is 36 inches long and 18 inches wide, then how high must it be to contain 12 cu ft?

4. Find the volumes of the figures shown in Figure 130.

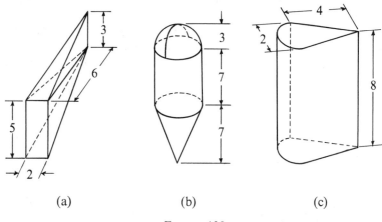

(a)   (b)   (c)

FIGURE 130

5. A rectangular shaped box measures 14 inches long, 9 inches wide, and 4 inches in height. If the length of the box were shortened to 7 inches while keeping the 9-inch width, then how high would the shortened box have to be in order to have the same volume as the original box?

6. Water weighs approximately 62.5 lb per cubic foot. The inside dimensions of an aquarium are 14 inches by 18 inches by 26 inches. If

the aquarium is filled with water, what is the weight of water in the aquarium?

7. A circular tunnel 6 ft in diameter is cut 20 ft into the side of a hill. Approximately how many cubic yards of earth were removed from the tunnel?

8. A reservoir in the shape of a cone with the point down measures 140 yd in diameter and is 27 ft deep at the center. What is the approximate capacity of the reservoir in gallons?

9. Do as indicated:

(a) Find the sum of 2 cu yd 17 cu ft 964 cu inches, 12 cu ft 898 cu inches, and 1 cu yd 9 cu ft 226 cu inches in simplest form.

(b) Subtract 110 oz from 11 lb.

(c) If a certain sand weighs 140 lb per cubic foot, then how much does a cubic yard of the sand weigh?

(d) If the volume of a rectangular box 1 ft 4 inches in height is 3 cu ft, then what is the area of the base of the box?

10. A spherical ball is made of a $\frac{1}{8}$-inch thick shell of rubber which weighs 0.72 oz per cubic inch. If the outer diameter of the ball is 2 inches, then what is the weight of the rubber used in the ball?

11. An irregular shaped object is immersed in a container first filled to the brim with water. If three gallons of water overflow the container (is displaced), then what is the volume of the immersed object?

12. An irregular shaped object floats in a container first filled to the brim with water. If three gallons of water overflow the container (are displaced), then what is the weight of the floating object?

Answers.

1. Volume is the property of objects which occupy physical space whereas weight is the property of objects resulting from the pull of gravity.

2. (a) 12   (b) 26   (c) 27.

3. 32 inches.

4. (a) 26 cu units   (b) $320\frac{4}{7}$ cu units   (c) $44\frac{4}{7}$ cu units.

5. 8 inches.

6. 236 lb 9 oz.

7. 21 cu yd approximately.

8. Approximately 9,331,200 gallons.

9. (a) 4 cu yd 12 cu ft 360 cu inches   (b) 4 lb 2 oz

    (c) 2,780 lb   (d) 2 sq ft 36 sq inches.

10. 0.996 oz or approximately 1 oz.

11. 693 cu inches.

12. 25.0 lb.

8.3 Time

8.3.1   Unlike measurements of length, area, volume, and weight which can be visualized and "felt" in a concrete way, the idea of **time** is intangible and less amenable to simple measurements. We are conscious of the passage of time with the apparent motion of the sun across the heavens and the changing of the seasons of the year. We speak of particular moments in time such as the moment of birth, and so on. We refer time to the occurrences of special events. Time is determined by the nature of the solar system in which we live. We refer to it in terms of the instruments we use to tell the time, and, by the nature of our consciousness, we are aware of the passage of time.

Primitive man probably rose at sunrise and went to sleep with the setting sun. He might have moved south in the winter and noted the harvest season in the fall. The origin of units of time are universal, they can be traced to the study of the motion of the heavenly bodies in the sky. The motion of the earth in our solar system has determined, throughout history, a natural measure of time. There are three natural major units of time: the **day**, the **month**, and the **year**. The **day** is the period of one complete rotation of the earth on its axis; the **month** is the period of one complete revolution of the moon around the earth; the **year** is the period of one complete revolution of the earth around the sun (Figure 131).

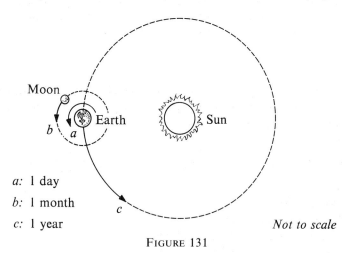

a: 1 day
b: 1 month
c: 1 year

Not to scale

FIGURE 131

Since the moon does not complete a revolution around the earth in an exact multiple of days, nor does the earth complete a revolution around the sun in a multiple of months or days, men have spent a great deal of effort in devising an adequate system for relating days, months, and years.

Such a system is called a **calendar**. An early calendar set up by the Egyptians some 6,000 years ago had a year consisting of twelve months of thirty days each with five extra "feast" days. In devising a calendar there were many confusing problems: When should the year begin? How should the year be identified? How many days and months should a year have? When should a day begin?

Early calendars were based on the month, usually twelve months of 29 to 30 days constituting a year. However, due to the resulting "shifting" of the solar year and "loss of days" in the year, these calendars had to be adjusted periodically and were never very effective. The first "modern" calendar was established by Julius Caesar (46 B.C.) when he abolished the year based on months and decreed that the solar year should regulate the calendar. This Julian calendar fixed the year at 365 days with every fourth year to have 366 days. In accomplishing this change Caesar ordered 80 days added to the initial year. Thus, the year 46 B.C. had 445 days and came to be known as the Year of Confusion! The Julian calendar continued in use until Pope Gregory XIII (1582) introduced a needed adjustment of 1 day in every 400 years. The adjusted calendar then came to be known as the Gregorian calendar and is now the calendar commonly used throughout the world.

In establishing the Julian calendar, Caesar had decreed that the first of January should begin a new year. However, a variety of different dates were used in various parts of Europe to start a new year until the middle of the eighteenth century. The passing of years were, in general, counted from a year with a date of great historical importance. For example, the Romans counted their years from the year of the founding of Rome, the Eternal City. The Mohammedans counted their years from the year of their leader's pilgrimage to Mecca. It was not until the sixth century (A.D.) that an abbot, Dionysius Exigus, proposed the numbering of years from the birth of Christ. That is, with the suffixes B.C. and A.D. Subsequent historical research has suggested that our present numbering of years places the birth of Christ in the year 8 B.C.

The names of the months of the year date back to the early Roman calendar which consisted of ten months beginning in March. March, the first month, was named in honor of the god Mars. The second month, April, in honor of Aphrodite or Venus. With the introduction of the twelve-month Julian calendar, the fifth month became the seventh month and was named Julius (July) in honor of Julius Caesar. The month following was named Augustus (August) in honor of his successor, Augustus Caesar. In much the same way the division of the month into weeks and the names of the days in a week owe their origins to historical developments. From astrology and the then known "planets" we have the names Saturday after the planet Saturn, Sunday after the Sun, Monday after the Moon.

One of the earliest instruments for measuring time was called a *gnomon*, a rod or stone pillar placed on a level area. The gnomon cast a moving shadow whose length and position could be measured. It was the forerunner of the *sundial* still to be seen occasionally in our parks and

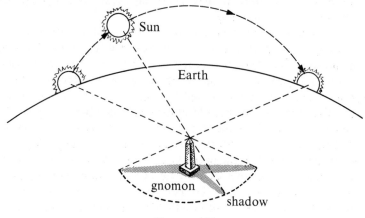

FIGURE 132

gardens. The day, from sunrise to sunset, was divided into twelve equal parts called **hours**. Since the period from sunrise to sunset varied with the seasons, the hours also varied. It was only with the invention of clocks that periods of equal time came into use; these "**clock hours**" were called so many *o'clock*. The importance of reliable and accurate instruments to measure time was so great that prizes were offered for their invention. In 1714 the British government, for example, offered 20,000 pounds sterling (about $56,000) for the invention of a reliable clock. The prize was finally awarded to a John Harrison in 1761.

The development of a system for measuring time is thus the result of natural phenomena combined with human needs, observations, and habits of thought. The most commonly used system of units for measuring time is summarized in Table 20.

TABLE 20

100 years = 1 century	30 days^a = 1 business month (mo)
366 days = 1 leap year	7 days = 1 week (wk)
$\left.\begin{array}{l} 365 \text{ days} \\ 52 \text{ weeks 1 day} \end{array}\right\} = 1$ common year	24 hours = 1 day (da)
	60 minutes = 1 hour (h)
12 calendar months = 1 year (yr)	60 seconds (sec) = 1 minute (min)

^{a}30 days in April, June, September, and November; 31 days in January, March, May, July, August, October, and December; 28 days in February except leap year in which February has 29 days.

8.3.2 Reductions and the arithmetical operations can be accomplished with measures of elapsed time just as with measures of length, area, and so forth. However, we might question the interpretation to be given to the product of two measures of time. That is, the relationship between units of measure should make "sense" in computations with denominate quantities.

Examples.

(a) Reduce 12 da 135 h 162 min 145 sec to simplest form.

SOLUTION. We begin with the smallest units and work to the larger units successively: 145 sec = 2 min 25 sec; 164 min = 2 h 44 min; 137 h = 5 da 17 h; 17 da = 2 wk 3 da. Thus, we have 12 da 135 h 162 min 145 sec = 2 wk 3 da 17 h 44 min 25 sec.

(b) Find the sum:

$$\begin{array}{r} 7 \text{ h } 22 \text{ min } 15 \text{ sec} \\ 4 \text{ h } 15 \text{ min } 38 \text{ sec} \\ 19 \text{ h } 34 \text{ min } 41 \text{ sec} \\ + \ 6 \text{ h } \ \ 9 \text{ min } 26 \text{ sec} \\ \hline 36 \text{ h } 80 \text{ min } 120 \text{ sec} = 1 \text{ da } 13 \text{ h } 22 \text{ min.} \end{array}$$

(c) If 3 h 17 min 25 sec is divided into 5 equal periods of time, how long will each period be?

SOLUTION. We first reduce the given time into convenient units. 3 h = 180 min; 180 + 17 = 197 min = 195 min 120 sec; thus, 3 h 17 min 25 sec = 195 min 145 sec and we have (195 min + 145 sec) ÷ 5 = 39 min 29 sec.

Practice 1.

1. Do as indicated:
   (a) Reduce 3 h 7 min to seconds.
   (b) Reduce 15,393 sec to simplest form.
   (c) Reduce 10,000 h to simplest form.
   (d) Reduce 6 da 14 h 36 min to hours.

2. Do as indicated:
   (a) Find the sum of 3 h 18 min 21 sec; 8 h 32 min 45 sec; 16 h 14 sec; and 47 min 38 sec.
   (b) What is 16 h 37 min 9 sec less 9 h 42 min 15 sec?
   (c) What is the total elapsed time in 17 periods of 37 min 52 sec each?
   (d) If 14 h 40 min is divided into 22 equal periods, then how long is one period?

3. Sound travels 1,090 ft in 1 sec. If a jet airplane flies at the speed of sound, then what is its speed in miles per hour?

4. The sun is approximately 93,000,000 miles from the earth. If light travels at a speed of 186,000 miles per second, then how many minutes does it take sunlight to reach the earth?

5. A leaky faucet drips water at the rate of one-half cup each minute. How many gallons of water are lost each day? If water costs $2.45 per 1,000 gallons, then how much does the lost water cost each month?

Answers.

1. (a) 11,220 sec   (b) 4 h 16 min 33 sec
   (c) 1 yr 1 mo 3 wk 16 h (common year and business month)
   (d) 158.6 h.
2. (a) 1 da 4 h 38 min 58 sec   (b) 6 h 54 min 54 sec
   (c) 10 h 43 min 44 sec   (d) 40 min.
3. 743 miles per hour approximately.
4. $8\frac{1}{3}$ min.
5. 45 gal; $3.31.

8.3.3   We measure the passage of time indirectly by using instruments of various kinds: clocks, watches, hourglasses, and so on. Marking a particular moment in time is, however, quite different from measuring

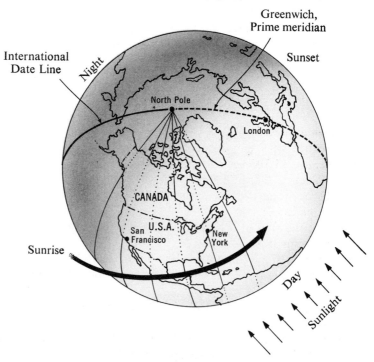

FIGURE 133

the passage of time. When we refer to 2:30 P.M. we are describing a particular moment at a particular location on the surface of the earth. For example, 2:30 P.M. in San Francisco would be 5:30 P.M. in New York City. That is, the local clock-time is different for different locations around the world at a given moment in time. When it is 12:00 noon in London, England, dawn is just coming to the Rocky Mountains in the United States. In Tokyo, Japan, it is already 9:00 P.M. and people are going to bed.

By an international agreement the world has been divided into "time zones." There are twenty-four zones, one for each hour of the day. The boundaries vary somewhat due to political and geographical boundaries but are, in general, north-south zones numbered as shown in Figure 134.

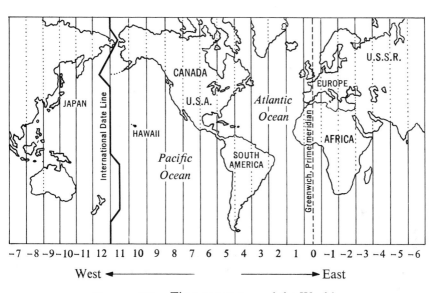

FIGURE 134. Time zones around the World

The time zones are counted from the zone containing *Greenwich, England.* The clock-time in zones to the west of Greenwich is earlier while the clock-time to the east is later. On the opposite side of the world from Greenwich the zones meet at the *International Date Line,* an imaginary boundary where the calendar date is shifted 1 day earlier going eastward and 1 day later going to the west.

In the United States there are four time zones as shown in Figure 135. They are named the Eastern, Central, Mountain, and Pacific time zones. Within each time zone the clock-time is the same at a given moment. As we move eastward across the boundary of a time zone the clock-time is shifted one hour forward. That is, the clock-time is one hour later. Moving westward across a boundary, we "gain" an hour and it is one hour

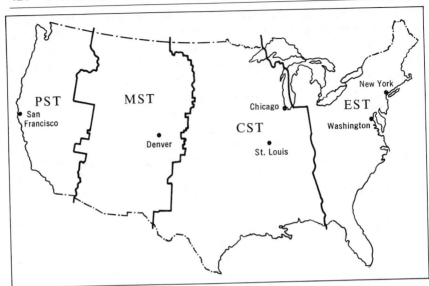

FIGURE 135. Time zones in the United States

earlier. For example, if it is 9:00 A.M. in San Francisco then the clock-time in Denver would be 10:00 A.M. while in Chicago it would be 11:00 A.M. and in New York it would be 12:00 noon.

Examples.

(a) If a jet plane leaves New York at 9:00 A.M. Eastern Standard Time and has an elapsed time of 7 hours in flight nonstop to San Francisco, then it will land at 1:00 P.M. Pacific Standard Time in San Francisco.

(b) At the moment people are celebrating midnight, December 31st, in San Francisco, we have the people in Hawaii just starting the evening at 9:30 P.M.† while in Tokyo, Japan, it is 5:00 P.M., January 1st. In London people are beginning to rise at 8:00 A.M. on New Year's Day.

(c) An astronaut is sent into a 94-minute orbit at 7:42 A.M. on May 1st from Cape Kennedy in Florida. After 22 orbits he lands in the Pacific Ocean just off the California coast. What is his local time and date of landing?

SOLUTION. His elapsed time is 22 × 94 = 2,068 min = 1 da 10 h 28 min approximately. Thus, the time and date of landing at Cape Kennedy is 7 h 42 min + 1 da 10 h 28 min = 1 da 17 h 70 min or approximately

---

† The Hawaiian Islands are in a special time zone of 10.5.

6:10 P.M. on May 2nd. His local Pacific Standard Time is then about 3:10 P.M. on May 2nd.

Practice 2.

1. (a) If the sun is almost directly overhead, about what time is it locally?

(b) Is the day any longer or shorter at the North Pole than at the equator?

(c) What causes the daylight hours to vary from season to season?

2. What is the difference in determining the day as a unit of time and the hour as a unit of time?

3. If it is 4:00 P.M. in New York, then what time is it in:

(a) San Francisco?   (b) Hawaii?   (c) London?

4. If it is 10:00 A.M. in Denver, then what time is it in:

(a) San Francisco?   (b) Chicago?   (c) New York?

5. If it is 4:00 P.M. in Washington, D.C., then what time is it in:

(a) London?   (b) Tokyo?   (c) Rome?   (d) Los Angeles?

6. A westbound boat and an eastbound boat each cross the International Date Line. How do their local times change?

7. A businessman flew from Honolulu to New York. If he did not reset (change) his watch, was it ahead or behind on his arrival in New York? By how much did it differ from the local time in New York?

8. A telegram was filed in New York at 6:00 P.M. and delivered in San Francisco at 7:30 P.M. How long was it from the time of filing to the time of delivery?

Answers.

1. (a) About 12:00 noon   (b) No

(c) The tilting of the earth's axis of rotation.

2. The day is determined by the rotation of the earth while an hour is rather arbitrarily determined by the passage of a certain fixed amount of time.

3. (a) 1:00 P.M.   (b) 10:30 A.M.   (c) 9:00 P.M.

4. (a) 9:00 A.M.   (b) 11:00 A.M.   (c) 12:00 noon.

5. (a) 9:00 P.M.   (b) 6:00 A.M. the next day.

(c) 10:00 P.M.   (d) 1:00 P.M.

6. The westbound boat "loses" 1 day while the eastbound boat "gains" 1 day.

7. Behind by $5\frac{1}{2}$ h.

8. 4 h 30 min.

Exercises

1. The three natural units of time are the _____, the _____, and the _____. The two common ways in which we refer to time are the _____ of time and a _____ in time.

2. Give two reasons why it is important to have a calendar based on the solar year rather than based on lunar months.

3. Why is it that different months have varying numbers of days? Why do we have a leap year of 366 days every four years?

4. (a) How many seconds are there in an hour?
   (b) How many minutes are there in 1 day?
   (c) How many hours are there in 1 week?

5. Construct a historical "time line" similar to a number line and mark on it a scale of years with the following historical events:
   (a) The Battle of Marathon   (b) The Birth of Christ
   (c) The Norman Conquest   (d) The Discovery of America
   (e) The organization of the United Nations.

6. Reduce:
   (a) 1 yr 1 mo 1 wk 1 day to hours   (b) 5,000 min to simplest form
   (c) 19 days 64 h 585 min 900 sec to simplest form.

7. Do as indicated:
   (a) Find the sum of 42 min 58 sec; 19 h 28 min; 7 h 22 sec; and 57 min 35 sec.
   (b) What is one-fourth of the difference between 6 h 10 min and 3 h 26 min.
   (c) Find the amount earned in 16 h 35 min at $1.47 per hour.

8. The diameter of the earth is approximately 7,920 miles. In which direction, east or west, and at what speed should an airplane fly around the equator to "keep up with the sun"? That is, to have the clock-time "stand still"?

9. Which is the better wage: $87.50 per week or $390.00 per month?

10. Sally, who attends college in Arizona, plans to call her mother in Philadelphia. If it is 10:00 A.M. in Arizona, then how long should Sally wait so that her mother will receive the call at 6:15 P.M. in Philadelphia? What time will it be in Arizona when Sally makes the call?

11. A jet plane leaves New York at 8:05 A.M. and flies at the speed of sound to an airbase in Hawaii 4,350 air miles away. If the speed of sound is 743 miles per hour, at what local time does the plane land? What time is it in New York?

12. If it takes $2\frac{1}{2}$ sec for the sound of thunder to be heard from a flash of lightning, then how far away was the flash of lightning?

Answers.

1. day; month; year; passage or elapse; fixed moment.
2. (i) So that planting and harvest dates occur on the same dates each year.

(ii) Because of convenience, wide acceptance, and uniformity.

3. Since 365 is not a multiple of 12, historical development of the calendar has resulted in months ranging from 28 to 31 days. Since the solar year is actually 365 days 5 h 48 min 46 sec approximately rather than exactly 365 days a periodic adjustment is necessary.

4. (a) 3,600 sec   (b) 1,440 min   (c) 168 h.

5.

−490	0	1066	1492	1945
(a)	(b)	(c)	(d)	(e)

6. (a) 9,672 h   (b) 3 days 11 h 20 min   (c) 3 wk 1 day 2 h.
7. (a) 1 day 4 h 8 min 55 sec   (b) 41 min   (c) $24.38.
8. West at 1,037 miles per hour.
9. $390.00 per month.
10. 6 h 15 min; 4:15 P.M.
11. 8:26 A.M. in Hawaii; 1:56 P.M.
12. 5.16 miles approximately.

Review Summary

We often refer to measurements in solving problems. In contrast to **abstract** number ideas, numbers which refer to measurements are called **concrete** numbers and have a **unit of measure** associated with them. That is, we think of 5 as an _____ number while 5 lb would be called *abstract* a _____ number. To obtain a measurement we associate *concrete* a number to a property or characteristic of an object or thing. This association is made by comparing a _____ *unit* _____ _____ to the property or characteristic. Thus, the *of measure* act of measurement always requires three things: a _____ of something to be measured, a _____ by which *property (or* to measure, and a means to _____ the unit of measure to *character-* the property to result in a numerical value. *istic), unit*

A unit of measure in order to be useful and serve its *associate (or* purpose should be convenient to use and obtain, it should *compare)* have wide acceptance, it should be uniform wherever used, standardized and independently reproducible, and finally it should be related to other units to form a system of measures. When a concrete number is expressed in terms of a standard unit of measurement we say that it is a _____ number. In the United States two standard systems are used. These are called the _____ system and the _____ system. The basic unit of measure in the metric system is called the _____ while in the English system it is the _____. These units have been related by an Act of Congress; the yard being nearly 0.9144 m in length. These measures of length are often referred to as _____ measures.

denominate
metric
English
meter
yard

linear

The measurement of properties in the real world around us is an approximate and often complicated process. Thus, to study the process of measurement, we turn to simplified figures which have definite shapes and form. When formalized, this study is called *geometry*. Geometric figures consist of points, lines, and planes. Our first observation is of parts of lines determined by two points; we call these geometric objects _____. Segments have two properties, _____ and direction. If a fixed segment AB is chosen as a unit segment in length, we can measure the length of any other segment with respect to this unit segment. For example, given the unit segment u in Figure 136, we would say that the measure of PQ is $\overline{PQ} =$ _____(u).

segments
length

5.4

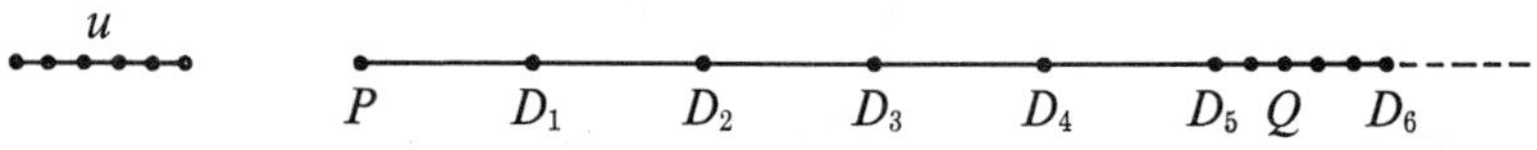

FIGURE 136

Geometric figures formed by connecting three or more segments "end-to-end" are called _____. Polygons consisting of three segments are called _____ while polygons formed with four segments are called _____. Two common properties of polygons which we can measure are called the **perimeter** and **area**. The perimeter of a polygon is the _____ of the lengths of the segments, called _____, of the polygon. The area of a polygon is the part of the plane enclosed by the sides of the polygon.

polygons
triangles
quadri-
laterals

sum
sides

If the lengths of the sides of a polygon are given or can be measured, then we can find a measure of the perimeter of the polygon. For example, the perimeter of the polygon shown in Figure 137 is $P =$ _____. If we take for a

24 units

unit of area a square with sides 1 unit in length, then we can measure the area of the polygon shown in Figure 137 by noticing that it consists of two triangles whose areas are easy to find. Thus, the area of the polygon is $A =$ _____.

30 sq units

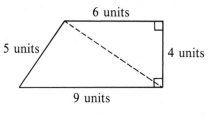

6 units

5 units

4 units

9 units

FIGURE 137

An important geometric shape is called a **circle**. A circle is located by a single point called its _____ and determined by a fixed distance measured from its center, the distance being called its _____. The length around a circle is called its _____ rather than a perimeter. If we let C stand for the circumference and r for the radius of a circle, then the circumference is given by $C =$ _____. The Greek symbol "π," called "pi," is a constant approximately equal to _____ in fractional form and _____ in decimal form. For convenience we often refer to twice the radius, $2r$, as the _____ of the circle. For example, if the diameter of a circle is $5\frac{1}{4}$ inches, then its circumference $C = 16\frac{1}{2}$ inches. The area of a circle can also be expressed in terms of π and its radius. That is, if A is the area and r the radius, we have $A = \pi r^2$. If the diameter of a circle is $5\frac{1}{4}$ inches, then its area $A =$ _____.

center

radius
circumfer-
ence
$2r(\pi)$

$\frac{22}{7}, 3.1416$

diameter

$21\frac{21}{32}$ *sq*
inches

The areas of triangles and many quadrilaterals can be expressed in terms of a side, called the base, and a measurement taken perpendicular to the base, called the _____. Squares, rectangles, and parallelograms have areas equal to the _____ of their base and altitude: $A = bh$. Triangles, on the other hand, have areas $A =$ _____.

In solving problems involving denominate numbers we may change the units in which the number is expressed. When we change units within a given system of

altitude
product
$\frac{1}{2}bh$

measurement we call it a reduction while changing from one system to another is called a conversion. For example, changing 78 cm to 30.7 inches (approximately) would be called a _____. Changing 30.7 inches to 2 ft 6.7 inches would be called a _____ to simplest form. In doing arithmetical operations with denominate numbers we must be careful to add and subtract only like quantities. For example, to subtract 2 ft 9 inches from 1 yd 7 inches, we might first reduce 1 yd 7 inches to 3 ft 7 inches and then to 2 ft _____ inches. Thus, the difference would be _____. In finding products and quotients we must be careful to observe the relationships between different kinds of units of measurement. If we divide a volume measurement by a measurement of length, the quotient will be a measure of _____. The product of an area measure and a measure of length will be a measure of _____.

conversion

reduction

19

10 inches

area

volume

Beginning with a point, we can imagine the point "moving" to form a line segment. The line segment can then be imagined as "moving" perpendicular to itself to form an _____. The area can then be imagined as "moving" perpendicular to itself to form a _____. The conventional unit of volume is a _____ _____. A cubic inch is thus a cube _____ on each edge. The volumes of certain regular shapes can be expressed in terms of measurements of their edges. For example, a rectangular parallelepiped has a volume equal to the _____ of the lengths of three mutually adjacent edges. The volume of a pyramid, tetrahedron, or cone is _____ the area of its _____ times its _____. The volume of a sphere is given by $V =$ _____.

area

volume

unit cube

1 inch

product

$\frac{1}{3}$, *base*

altitude

$\frac{4}{3} \times \pi \times r \times r \times r$

$\left(or\ \frac{4}{3}\pi r^3 \right)$

When we consider volumes it seems quite natural to think of weight. Weight is the property of objects due to the pull of gravity. Since the force of attraction which the earth exerts varies in different locations and under varying conditions, determining a standard unit of weight poses difficulties. In the English system the basic unit of weight is the _____ which probably originated as the weight of one-sixtieth the weight of one cubic foot of water. In the metric system the basic unit of weight is called the _____ which is the weight of 1 cc of water under very carefully controlled conditions. Objects are usually weighed on instruments called scales.

pound

gram

Unlike measurements of length, area, volume, and weight, time is intangible and less amenable to simple measurements. Time is determined by the nature of the solar system in which we live. There are three major units of time: the _____ which is the period of one complete revolution of the earth on its axis, the _____ which is the period of one complete revolution of the moon around the earth, and the _____ which is the period of one complete revolution of the earth around the sun. A system relating days, months, and years is called a _____. The first modern calendar was established by Julius Caesar from which we get the name Julian calendar. This Julian calendar fixed the year at _____ days with every fourth year to have _____ days. Our present numbering of years from the birth of Christ was first proposed during the sixth century while the months of the year date back to an early Roman calendar. The months of July and August were named in honor of Julius Caesar and his successor Augustus Caesar.

day

month

year

calendar

365
366

The invention of clocks brought about the introduction of shorter periods of equal time. From the division of the period from sunrise to sunset into twelve equal parts we have the unit of time called an _____. The hour was then divided into _____ equal parts called minutes which in turn are divided into 60 equal parts called _____. In computations we always work with measures of elapsed time.

hour
60

seconds

In contrast to the passage of time we often speak of a particular moment in time. When we say that it is 3:00 P.M. March 10, 1963, in San Francisco, we are referring to a particular moment in time. The local clock-time is different for different locations around the world at a given moment in time. By an international agreement the world has been divided into "time zones." There are twenty-four zones, one for each hour of the day. The time zones are numbered from the zone containing _____, England. The zones to the _____ of Greenwich having earlier clock-times while those to the _____ have later clock-times. On the opposite side of the world from Greenwich, across the Pacific Ocean there is an imaginary line where the zones meet. This line, called the *International Date Line*, determines where the calendar date is shifted 1 day earlier going _____ and 1 day later going

Greenwich,
west

east

eastward

_____. For example, if it is 9:00 A.M. in New York then it is _____ in San Francisco, _____ in London, England, and _____ the "night before" in Tokyo, Japan.

westward
6:00 A.M.,
2:00 P.M.
midnight

There are four time zones in the United States. These are named the _____, Central, _____, and Pacific time zones. Within each time zone the clock-time is the same. As we move eastward across the boundary of a time zone the clock-time shifts one hour _____. Moving westward across a time zone boundary we "gain" an hour.

Eastern,
Mountain

forward (or later)

In using numbers we associate them to properties of things and objects. From the earliest historical times certain properties have been recognized as being important for measurement. We have briefly examined the most common of these: lengths, areas, volumes, weights, and time.

Chapter Exercises (8)

Group I.

1. The act of measurement requires three things. Name them.
2. The basic unit of measure in the English system is the _____. The unit probably originated as the length of _____.
3. Using the segment *u* as a unit segment, measure the length of the "polygonal" path shown in Figure 138.

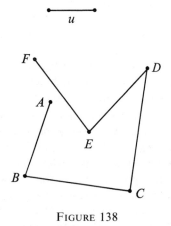

FIGURE 138

4. Find the perimeters (or distances around) of the figures shown in Figure 139.

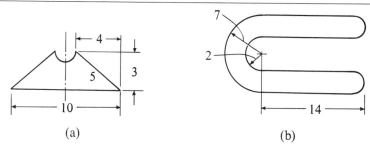

(a)   (b)

FIGURE 139

5. If a segment AB is used as a unit to measure a segment CD, then $\overline{CD} = 4.5$. If CD is used as a unit to measure a segment EF, then $\overline{EF} = \dfrac{8}{15}$. What will be the measure of AB if EF is used as a unit of measure?

6. Find the areas of the figures shown in Figure 139.

7. Find the total surface area of a (right circular) cylindrical container if its diameter is 6 inches and its height is 4 inches.

8. Do as indicated:
   (a) Reduce 5 yd 21 inches to feet
   (b) Convert 12 ft 9 inches to meters
   (c) Reduce 59 sq ft 297 sq inches to simplest form.

9. A rectangular swimming pool is 28 ft 6 inches long and 18 ft 9 inches wide.

   (a) How many times must a person swim the width of the pool to have swum as far as a swimmer going 25 times the length of the pool?

   (b) If 15 swimmers are in the pool, then how many square feet of pool surface area will be available per swimmer?

10. The blocks shown in Figure 140 represent unit cubes. How many unit cubes are in each set of blocks?

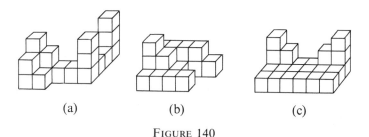

(a)   (b)   (c)

FIGURE 140

11. A spherical ball $10\frac{1}{2}$ inches in diameter fits snugly into a cubical box so that it just touches the sides. What is the volume of the open space between the ball and the box?

12. Find the volumes of the figures shown in Figure 141.

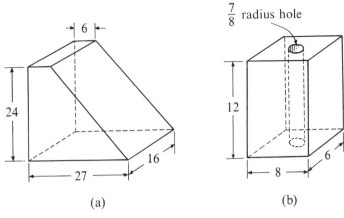

(a)   (b)

FIGURE 141

13. A certain metal is valued at $0.18 per pound. If it weighs 1.8 oz per cubic inch, then what would be the value of a cone-shaped solid of the metal with a base 14 inches in diameter and 16 inches in height?

14. What would be the volume of a cylindrical container with an inverted hemispherical bottom as shown in Figure 142?

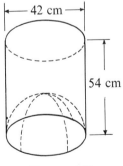

FIGURE 142

15. An athlete lost 18 lb 7 oz during a certain period of training. If he weighed 187 lb 14 oz at the end of the training period, how much did he weigh before beginning the training? What percent of his pretraining weight did he lose?

16. If a block of rubber weighing 0.8 oz per cubic inch is in the shape of a rectangular parallelepiped with edges 4 inches by 6 inches by 8 inches, then what will be its apparent weight when immersed in water?

17. A man wishes to lift a stone weighing 500 lb. If he uses a 7 ft 6 inch lever, as shown in Figure 143, then how much weight must he place on his end of the lever to just balance the stone?

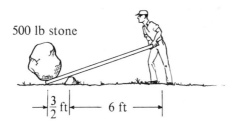

500 lb stone

$\frac{3}{2}$ ft — 6 ft

FIGURE 143

18. Do as indicated:

(a) Find $\frac{5}{8}$ of 2 cu yd 10 cu ft 240 cu inches.

(b) If a cubic foot of a substance weighs 54 lb 6 oz, then how many kilograms will a cubic meter of the substance weigh?

19. The same part of the moon faces the earth continuously. Does the moon rotate about its own axis? If so, how long does it take for one complete rotation on its own axis?

20. What is a calendar?

21. Do as indicated:

(a) What is 2 mo 2 wk 5 days less 5 wk 6 days 18 h?

(b) Find 12% of 1 week.

(c) If we exercise $3\frac{1}{2}$ min per day, how much time will we have spent exercising in one year?

22. At 45 miles per hour a certain auto goes 18 miles per gallon of gasoline. How many gallons of gasoline will it use in 3 h 20 min if it goes at a steady 45 miles per hour?

23. Sand pours from a spout at a constant rate of 14 cubic inches per second forming a conical pile. If it stops when the pile is 3 ft 6 inches in height with a base 3 ft 6 inches in diameter, then how long did the sand pour from the spout?

24. If it is 6:00 A.M. in San Francisco, then what time is it in

(a) New Orleans? (b) Paris, France? (c) Hong Kong?

25. A balloonist goes aloft at 5:45 A.M. in California and drifts eastward for 32 h 25 min landing in eastern Utah. What is the time of his landing?

Group II.

1. Describe five desirable characteristics of a unit of measure.

2. The basic unit of measure in the metric system is the _____. The unit was intended to be _____ of the distance from _____ to _____ along a meridian.

3. Using the segment u as a unit segment, measure the length of the "polygonal" path shown in Figure 144.

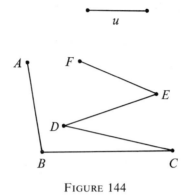

FIGURE 144

4. Find the perimeters (or distances around) of the figures shown in Figure 145.

5. If a segment AB is used as a unit to measure segments CD and EF, then $\overline{CD} = \frac{5}{6}$ and $\overline{EF} = \frac{7}{8}$. What will be the measure of EF if CD is used as a unit of measure?

6. Find the areas of the figures shown in Figure 145.

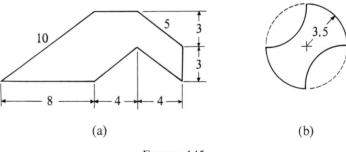

(a)   (b)

FIGURE 145

7. Find the total surface area of a rectangular parallelepiped container if its edges are $22\frac{3}{4}$ inches by 16 inches by $8\frac{1}{2}$ inches.

8. Do as indicated:

(a) Reduce 1 yd $2\frac{1}{3}$ ft to inches.

(b) Convert 2.65 m to feet and inches.

(c) Reduce 32 sq ft 480 sq inches to simplest form.

9. An aquarium in the shape of a rectangular parallelepiped is 26 inches by 9 inches by 14 inches.

(a) If the aquarium is filled with water, how much water must be filtered per minute to have the water completely filtered each hour?

(b) If we can keep at most four fish per gallon in the aquarium, then how many fish should we have at most in the aquarium?

10. The blocks shown in Figure 146 represent unit cubes. How many unit cubes are in each set of blocks?

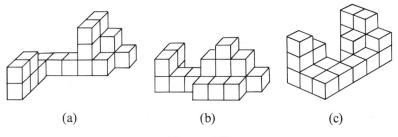

(a)   (b)   (c)

FIGURE 146

11. A (right circular) cone 9 inches in diameter and 14 inches in height fits snugly into a cylindrical box so that it just touches the bottom base and top. What is the volume of the open space between the cone and the box?

12. Find the volumes of the figures shown in Figure 147.

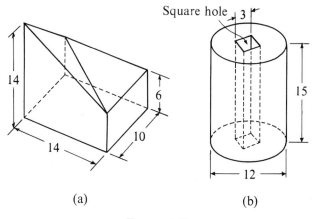

(a)   (b)

FIGURE 147

13. A cylindrical piece of a certain material weighing $1\frac{3}{4}$ oz per

cubic inch is valued at $7.70. If the cylinder is $3\frac{1}{2}$ inches in diameter and 16 inches in height, then what is the value of the material per pound?

14. A dumbbell consists of two 3-inch spheres connected by a 7-inch-long cylindrical handle $1\frac{1}{2}$ inches in diameter. Approximately how many pounds does the dumbbell weigh if it is made of an iron weighing 4.2 oz per cubic inch?

15. The gross weight of a light plane is 4,800 lb at takeoff. If the plane uses 52 gallons of gasoline weighing 6 lb per gallon on a flight, then what will be its approximate weight on landing? What percent of its takeoff weight was the 52 gallons of gasoline?

16. If a solid block in the shape of a rectangular parallelepiped 3 inches by 5 inches by 8 inches has an apparent weight of 27 oz when completely immersed in water, then what would be its actual weight out of the water?

17. A man wishes to just balance an 80 lb weight and a 35 lb weight using a beam as shown in Figure 148. If the 80 lb weight is $2\frac{1}{4}$ ft from the support, then how far from the support should the 35 lb weight be placed?

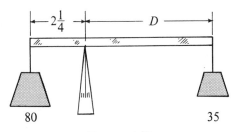

FIGURE 148

18. Do as indicated:

(a) Find $\frac{4}{3}$ of 1 cu yd 13 cu ft 1,450 cu inches.

(b) A cubic meter of a substance weighs 2,700 kg. How many pounds will a cubic foot of the substance weigh?

19. If a satellite circles the earth over the poles once each 110 min, then how far westward at the equator would it appear to move on each revolution? (Consider the earth a sphere of 8,000 miles in diameter.)

20. What is the difference between local clock-time and computing with elapsed times?

21. Do as indicated:

(a) Find the sum of 3 wk 6 days 13 h, 2 wk 5 days 9 h, and 3 wk 2 days 18 h.

(b) If 3 days is 4% of a total of elapsed time, then how long is the total of elapsed time?

(c) If an athlete runs 1 mile in 4 min using a 36-inch wide step, then how many steps must he take each second?

22. An auto uses 12.6 gal of gasoline in 4 h 12 min when going at a steady 60 mph. How many miles does the auto go per gallon of gasoline?

23. If a pump can fill a cylindrical tank with diameter 4 ft 8 inches and height 5 ft 3 inches in 1 h 36 min, then how many gallons per minute can it pump?

24. If it is 9:15 A.M. in Honolulu, then what time is it in

(a) Seattle?   (b) Miami?   (c) Tokyo?

25. A salesman drives 790 miles from St. Louis to his home near Denver at a steady average of 45 miles per hour on the road. If he leaves St. Louis at 2:15 A.M. and takes only two rest stops of 45 min each, then what time is it when he arrives at his home?

Problem Set (8)

1. Carefully sketch and letter perspective figures showing that a tetrahedron is exactly $\frac{1}{6}$ the volume of a parallelepiped.

2. If we are given 9 balls which are identical except for one which weighs slightly less, show how we can determine which of the 9 balls weighs less by using a balancing scale only twice.

3. Given two clocks: if one "gains" time twice as fast as the other "loses" time and they coincide in their indicated time once each 46 h 30 min on the slow clock, then how much actual time does the fast clock "gain" each hour?

4. The act of measurement invariably involves errors, that is, a difference between the measured value and the "true" value or a certain uncertainty in the measured value. Carefully describe the types of errors possible in a measurement and how these errors might be controlled and estimated.

5. The Pythagorean Theorem: The square of the length of the hypotenuse of a right triangle is equal to the sum of the squares of the lengths of the legs. In Figure 149 we have $c \times c = (a \times a) + (b \times b)$. That is, $c^2 = a^2 + b^2$.

The above assertion can be demonstrated with areas. Using Figure

149, can you demonstrate the Theorem? How many other demonstrations can you exhibit?

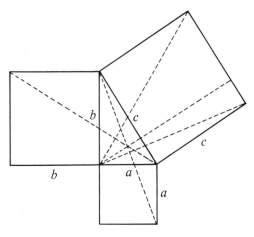

FIGURE 149

CHAPTER 9

Formulas

9.1 Representations

9.1.1   We began our study with the comment that "One of the special advanatages which humans have as a result of their language ability is that they give names to things and ideas." Pursuing this thought we have introduced and discussed many of the aspects of the language of numbers and arithmetic. A few of the more important ideas may be suggested by the following terms:

Numbers and Numerals
Operations and their Properties
Equations and Inequalities
Problems and their Solutions
Notation and Measurement

One might ask "What is the advantage, the purpose and use, in studying the language of numbers and arithmetic?" One important goal lies in the rapid and efficient solution of practical problems and the communicating of these solutions to others. Let us consider a rather simple example.

If an auto covers a distance of 180 miles in 3 hours, then how far does it go per hour?

SOLUTION.

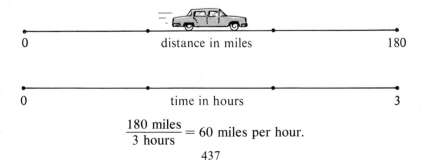

| 0 | distance in miles | 180 |

| 0 | time in hours | 3 |

$$\frac{180 \text{ miles}}{3 \text{ hours}} = 60 \text{ miles per hour.}$$

The above example should seem simple and natural in its solution. However, is there a pattern? Is there a general procedure suggested? Is a general principle involved? Could we solve the problem without the language of numbers and arithmetic?

Now consider the following:

If an auto covers a distance of D miles in T hours, then it must go $\dfrac{D}{T} = R$ miles per hour.

There is a pattern! There is a general procedure! For the type of problem illustrated in the example above we can describe a mathematical relationship which tells us how to obtain answers. $\dfrac{D}{T} = R$, when interpreted correctly, tells us how to find how fast an object is going.

A mathematical relationship with at least one variable which can be used to obtain answers, such as $\dfrac{D}{T} = R$, is called a **formula**. Let us consider this formula $\dfrac{D}{T} = R$ further. First, it is in the form of a ratio. Thus, all that we have said concerning ratios should be applicable to this formula. Second, the formula involves a relationship between units of measure. The ratio of distance to time results in a new unit of "miles per hour" (or distance per unit time). This new unit of "distance per unit time" is called **speed**. Notice that with the formula we can solve not only one but three types of problems involving distance, time, and speed.

Examples.

(a) A missile travels 45 miles in 45 seconds. What is its speed in miles per hour?

SOLUTION. $\dfrac{D}{T} = R$ so that we have $\dfrac{45 \text{ miles}}{\frac{1}{80} \text{ hours}} = 3{,}600$ miles per hour.

(b) A bicyclist rides at 12 miles per hour for 3 h 20 min. How far does he ride?

SOLUTION. $\dfrac{D}{T} = R$ so that $D = R \times T$ and $D = 12 \times 3\frac{1}{3} = 40$ miles.

(c) If a man walks at $2\frac{1}{2}$ miles per hour, then how long will it take him to go 14 miles?

SOLUTION. $\dfrac{D}{T} = R$ so that $\dfrac{D}{R} = T$ and $\dfrac{14}{\frac{5}{2}} = \dfrac{28}{5} = 5\frac{3}{5}$ hours or 5 h 36 min.

Formulas, when used properly, not only lead to rapid and efficient solutions of problems but also represent the relationships between the quantities involved in the problems. For example, the formula for the volume of a cylinder, $V = Bh$, enables us to find the volume quickly and also tells us that the volume is the product of the area of the base and height. Using the formula $B = \pi r^2$ we can obtain the more detailed formula $V = \pi r^2 h$ which tells us that the volume is in cubic units as well as being the product of the indicated quantities.

How are formulas discovered? Formulas are often developed through experimentation, observation, and, on occasion, by sheer insight into the "nature" of a problem. For example, there is the story of the apple which fell on Isaac Newton's head and caused him to study and develop the law of gravitation: $F = ma$. Of course, a thorough understanding of the language of mathematics is of inestimable value in this endeavor. Formulas are also discovered by purely mathematical means. Observing the simple patterns and forms into which formulas "fall" can also be helpful. For example, $D = R \times T$, $V = B \times h$, $F = m \times a$ are all simple product forms. Many other situations suggest this type of formula. Notice that the above formulas can also be written as ratios: $\dfrac{D}{R} = T$, $\dfrac{V}{B} = h$, $\dfrac{F}{m} = a$. Many formulas are in simple ratio forms.

Another type of formula is illustrated by the following example:

A 2 lb weight and a 5 lb weight are balanced on a beam as shown in Figure 150. At what point is the support placed?

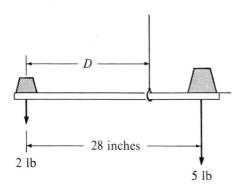

D

28 inches

2 lb

5 lb

FIGURE 150

SOLUTION. A few simple experiments would establish that we must have $2 \times D = 5 \times (28 - D)$. Thus, $D = 20$ inches.

The above relationship is called the **lever principle** and is described by the formula, $W_1 \times D_1 = W_2 \times D_2$, where W_1 and W_2 stand for weights and D_1, D_2 stand for the distances from the support which is called the **fulcrum** of the lever. Using this formula, given any three of the quantities involved we can solve for the fourth and obtain an answer.

Examples.

(a) A man uses a 20-inch long bar as a lever and applies 25 lb to his end of the bar with the fulcrum located 4 inches from the far end. How much force (weight) is exerted at the far end of the bar?

SOLUTION. $W_1 \times D_1 = W_2 \times D_2$ so that we have $25 \times (20 - 4) = W_2 \times 4$ and $W_2 = 100$ lb.

(b) A 7 lb weight is 3 ft from the fulcrum of a lever. How far from the fulcrum on the other end of the lever must a 2 lb weight be placed to balance the lever?

SOLUTION. $W_1 \times D_1 = W_2 \times D_2$ so that we have $7 \times 3 = 2 \times D$ and $D = 10$ ft 6 inches.

The formula describing the lever principle can also be written in the ratio form $\dfrac{W_1}{W_2} = \dfrac{D_2}{D_1}$. Notice that in this form the formula asserts that the ratio of the weights must equal the reciprocal of the ratio of the distances.

Many important formulas used in applications are of this form, that is, assert that two ratios are equal: $\dfrac{A}{B} = \dfrac{C}{D}$. It is said that Thales (c.640 to c.546 B.C.), one of the first men of science, showed how the height of a pyramid could be measured using this equal ratio form. See Figure 151.

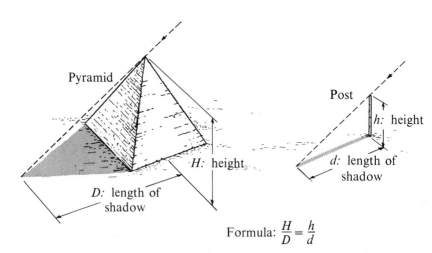

Formula: $\dfrac{H}{D} = \dfrac{h}{d}$

FIGURE 151

Practice 1.

1. The following are measurement formulas from Chapter 8. Describe what each formula asserts and name each literal quantity.

(a) $A = \frac{1}{2}bh$ (b) $C = \pi d$ (c) $P = 2a + 2b$ (d) $V = \frac{1}{3}Bh$.

2. Using the letters indicated, express each of the following statements as a formula:

(a) The perimeter (P) of an equilateral triangle equals three times the length of one side (s).

(b) The selling price (S) of an article equals the cost (c) plus the gross profit (p).

(c) The interest (I) on a sum of money equals the principal (p) times the annual rate (r) in percent times the number of years (t) that the principal has been earning interest.

(d) The lateral area (A) of a cone equals one-half the product of the slant height (s) and the circumference (C) of the base.

3. The measure of hotness or coldness of anything is called **tempera-ture**. Temperature is usually measured in *fahrenheit* degrees or *centigrade* degrees. On the fahrenheit scale of measurement, the temperatures at which water freezes and boils are 32° and 212° respectively. On the centigrade scale, these temperatures are 0° and 100°.

(a) What is the ratio of a change in fahrenheit degrees to the same change in centigrade degrees?

(b) What is the fahrenheit temperature when the centigrade temperature is 0°?

(c) What is the fahrenheit temperature when the centigrade temperature is 1°?

(d) Write a formula to find the fahrenheit (F) temperature given the centigrade (C) temperature.

4. Use the formula obtained in Practice 1, Problem 3 above to find:

(a) the fahrenheit temperature given that it is 15°C.

(b) the fahrenheit temperature given that it is $37\frac{1}{2}$°C.

(c) the centigrade temperature given that it is 50°F.

(d) the centigrade temperature given that it is 72°F.

5. Write a formula to find the centigrade temperature (°C) given the fahrenheit temperature (°F).

6. Use the distance formula $D = R \times T$ to solve the following:

(a) A jet aircraft flies at 875 miles per hour. How far can it go in 1 h 15 min?

(b) Mr. Jones drove 125 miles at a steady 57 miles per hour. How long did he take to drive the 125 miles?

(c) If a man takes 3 h 45 min to walk $8\frac{1}{4}$ miles, then how fast was he walking, at a steady rate?

7. Use the lever formula $W_1 \times D_1 = W_2 \times D_2$ to solve the following:

(a) A 100 lb weight is 6 ft from the fulcrum of a lever. Another weight is 4 ft on the other side of the fulcrum. How heavy is the weight if the lever is balanced?

(b) A 35 lb weight and a 49 lb weight are balanced on the ends of a lever 12 ft long. How far from the 35 lb weight is the fulcrum located?

(c) A 10 lb weight is 2 ft from the fulcrum of a lever. A 6 lb weight is 3 ft from the fulcrum on the other side. At what point on the lever must a 2 lb weight be placed in order to balance the lever?

8. Two autos begin a trip simultaneously. One auto going at 50 miles per hour takes a road 80 miles to a certain crossroad. The other auto takes a road 64 miles to the same crossroad. What must be the steady speed of the second auto to arrive at the crossroad simultaneously with the first auto?

Answers.

1. (a) The area (A) of any triangle is equal to one half of the product of the base (b) and the altitude (h).

(b) The circumference (C) of any circle is equal to the product of the constant π times the diameter (d).

(c) The perimeter (P) of a rectangle is equal to twice the length of one side (a) plus twice the length of an adjacent side (b).

(d) The volume (V) of a pyramid, tetrahedron, or cone is equal to one third the area of the base (B) times the altitude (h).

2. (a) $P = 3 \times s$ (b) $S = c + p$ (c) $I = p \times r \times t$

(d) $A = \frac{1}{2} \times s \times C$.

3. (a) $\frac{9}{5}$ (b) $32°$ (c) $\left(32 + \frac{9}{5}\right) = 33\frac{4°}{5}$ (d) $°F = \frac{9}{5} \times °C + 32$

4. (a) $59°F$ (b) $99\frac{1}{2}°F$ (c) $10°C$ (d) $22\frac{2}{9}°C$

5. $°C = \frac{5}{9} \times (°F - 32)$.

6. (a) $1,093\frac{3}{4}$ miles   (b) 2 h 11.6 min   (c) $2\frac{1}{5}$ mph.

7. (a) 150 lb   (b) 7 ft   (c) 1 ft from the fulcrum on the 6 lb side.
8. 40 mph.

9.1.2 The origin of the idea of a constant ratio is unknown. However, Egyptian and Greek mathematicians used the ratio idea extensively more than 2,000 years ago. The simple ratio and product ideas suggested by $\frac{N}{D} = R$ and $N = D \times R$ are so useful and recur so often in applications that it is convenient to introduce special vocabulary to refer to the relationship between the quantities involved.

For example, in the formula $C = \pi d$ the quantity π is a constant so that C and d are directly related to each other. In repeated use of the formula we might note the following:

If $d =$	0	1	2	5	7	14
then $C =$	0	$3\frac{1}{7}$	$6\frac{2}{7}$	$15\frac{5}{7}$	22	44

When d increases in value, C increases in value. If d is doubled in successive applications, then C doubles as well. If d is decreased, then C decreases as well. Of course, from our original formula $C = \pi d$, we might have observed that we could write $\frac{C}{d} = \pi$ where π is a constant. That is, the ratio of the circumference of a circle to its diameter is a constant. If we know that the relationship between two variables is a constant, then the value of the constant can be determined by a single pair of values of these variables. If $C = 6\frac{2}{7}$ units when $d = 2$ units, then $C = \pi d$ tells us that $\pi = \frac{22}{7}$ (approximately).

In general, the relationship between two variables N and D described by $\frac{N}{D} = K$ or $N = K \times D$, where K is a constant, is indicated by saying that "**N varies directly as D.**" The constant K is called the **constant of variation**. For example, we would say that the perimeter of a square varies directly as the length of a side since $P = 4s$. The constant of variation in $P = 4s$ is 4.

Examples.

(a) A set of ordered pairs of measurements from a succession of experiments led to the following tabulation:

Measurement of D:	2	4	5	10	15
Measurement of N:	5	10	$12\frac{1}{2}$	25	$37\frac{1}{2}$

A careful study of the tabulation reveals that we have $\dfrac{N}{D}=\dfrac{5}{2}=\dfrac{10}{4}=\dfrac{12\frac{1}{2}}{5}$

$=\dfrac{25}{10}=\dfrac{37\frac{1}{2}}{15}$. Thus, we might conclude tentatively that the pairs of measurements from the experiments suggest that N varies directly as D, N $=\dfrac{5}{2}\times D$ or $\dfrac{N}{D}=\dfrac{5}{2}$. The constant of variation being $\dfrac{5}{2}$.

(b) If S varies directly as t and $S=7$ when $t=3$, then find (i) the constant of variation, (ii) the value of S when $t=1$ and when $t=6$.

SOLUTION.

(i) We can write $S=K\times t$ and have $7=K\times 3$ so that $K=\dfrac{7}{3}$.

(ii) Since $S=\dfrac{7}{3}\times t$, we have $S=\dfrac{7}{3}$ when $t=1$ and $S=14$ when $t=6$.

Another form of variation occurs if we consider, for example, the formula for distance traveled $D=R\times t$ where the distance is held constant. Suppose that $D=10$ miles then we have

If $R=$	10 mph	15 mph	50 mph
then $t=$	1 h	$\frac{2}{3}$ h or 40 min	12 min

When R increases in value, t decreases in value. If R is doubled, then t will be halved. If R decreases, t increases. From the relationship 10 $=R\times t$ we also have $t=10\times\dfrac{1}{R}$.

In general, the relationship given by $R\times D=K$ or $R=K\times\dfrac{1}{D}$, where K is a constant, is described by saying that "**R varies inversely as D.**" The constant K is still called the **constant of variation**. For example, we would say that if the area of a triangle is held constant, then the altitude of the triangle varies inversely as the base. That is, if the area A is constant, then we have $K=b\times h$ or $h=K\times\dfrac{1}{b}$, where $K=2A$. The constant of variation in $h=2A\times\dfrac{1}{b}$, where A is constant is $2A$.

Examples.

(a) A set of ordered pairs of measurements from a succession of experiments led to the following tabulation:

D:	1	2	3	6	9
R:	9	$\frac{9}{2}$	3	$\frac{3}{2}$	1

A careful study of the tabulation shows that we have $R \times D = 9 \times 1 = \dfrac{9}{2}$ $\times 2 = 3 \times 3 = \dfrac{3}{2} \times 6 = 1 \times 9$. Thus we might conclude tentatively that the pairs of measurements from the experiments suggest that R varies inversely as D. We might write $R \times D = 9$ or $R = 9 \times \dfrac{1}{D}$. The constant of variation being 9.

(b) If M varies inversely as r and $M = 2$ when $r = \dfrac{1}{4}$, then find (i) the constant of variation, (ii) the value of M when $r = 1$ and when $r = \dfrac{1}{10}$.

SOLUTION.

(i) We can write $M = K \times \dfrac{1}{r}$ so that $2 = K \times \dfrac{1}{\frac{1}{4}}$ and $K = \dfrac{1}{2}$.

(ii) Since $M = \dfrac{1}{2} \times \dfrac{1}{r}$, we have $M = \dfrac{1}{2}$ when $r = 1$ and $M = 5$ when $r = \dfrac{1}{10}$.

In practice we can broaden and combine the above ideas to describe a variety of situations. For example, in describing the formula for distance, $D = R \times t$, we can say that the distance, D, varies directly as the speed, R, and the time, t. The speed varies directly as the distance and inversely as the time. The time varies inversely as the speed and directly as the distance. In $A = \pi r^2$ for the area of a circle, we would say that the area, A, varies directly as the square of the radius, r^2. If the formula $N = \dfrac{3P}{r^2}$ were given, we could say that N varies directly as P and inversely as the square of r.

Practice 2.

1. The following sets of ordered pairs describe direct or inverse variations. State whether the variation is direct or inverse in each case, determine the constant of variation, and write the equation of variation.

(a)

P:	3	5	7	11
Q:	12	20	28	44

(b)

S:	1	$\frac{1}{6}$	$\frac{1}{10}$	$\frac{1}{15}$
r:	$\frac{1}{2}$	3	5	$7\frac{1}{2}$

(c)

I:	8	2	$\frac{1}{2}$	$\frac{2}{9}$
t^2:	$\frac{1}{4}$	1	4	9

(d)

V:	$\frac{1}{10}$	$\frac{2}{5}$	$\frac{8}{5}$	$\frac{5}{2}$
n^2:	$\frac{1}{4}$	1	4	$6\frac{1}{4}$

2. Find the constant of variation:

   (a) $T = K \times s$ and $T = \frac{2}{3}$ when $s = \frac{3}{2}$.

   (b) $A = K \times n^2$ and $A = 18$ when $n = 3$.

   (c) $D = K \times \frac{1}{t}$ and $D = 6$ when $t = \frac{1}{2}$.

   (d) $I = K \times \frac{1}{r^2}$ and $I = \frac{3}{8}$ when $r = 2$.

3. Find the values indicated for the equations of Problem 2:

   (a) T when $s = 3$ and when $s = 2\frac{1}{4}$.

   (b) A when $n = \frac{1}{2}$ and when $n = 4$.

   (c) D when $t = 3$ and when $t = \frac{1}{3}$.

   (d) I when $r = \frac{1}{2}$ and when $r = 1$.

4. If M varies directly as P and the square of R and inversely as Q and is equal to 3 when $P = 2$, $R = 3$, $Q = 4$, then find the equation which describes the relationship between M and P, Q, and R.

Answers.

1. (a) Direct, $Q = 4P$ (b) Inverse, $S = \frac{1}{2r}$

   (c) Inverse, $I = \frac{2}{t^2}$ (d) Direct, $V = \frac{2}{5}n^2$.

2. (a) $\frac{4}{9}$ (b) 2   (c) 3   (d) $\frac{3}{2}$.

3. (a)

If $s =$	3	$2\frac{1}{4}$
then $T =$	$\frac{4}{3}$	1

(b)

If $n =$	$\frac{1}{2}$	4
then $A =$	$\frac{1}{2}$	32

(c)

If $t =$	3	$\frac{1}{3}$
then $D =$	1	9

(d)

If $r =$	$\frac{1}{2}$	1
then $I =$	6	$\frac{3}{2}$

4. $M = \frac{2}{3} \times \frac{P \times R^2}{Q} = \frac{2PR^2}{3Q}$.

9.1.3   We have already noted that another type of useful form is obtained when two ratios are equal to each other: $\frac{A}{B} = \frac{C}{D}$. Due to its usefulness and wide application, we give this form a special name. When two ratios are equal we call the resulting equation a **proportion**. That is,

$\frac{A}{B} = \frac{C}{D}$ is called a **proportion**. At one time proportions were written using colons, $A{:}B{::}C{:}D$. We read the proportion as "A is to B as C is to D." The four quantities involved in a proportion are called the **terms** of the proportion and from the historical form $A{:}B{::}C{:}D$ we call A and D the **extreme** terms and B and C the **means**.

$$\begin{matrix} \textbf{Extreme} \\ \textbf{Mean} \end{matrix} \quad \frac{A}{B} = \frac{C}{D} \quad \begin{matrix} \textbf{Mean} \\ \textbf{Extreme} \end{matrix}$$

$$\text{Ratio} = \text{Ratio}$$

Proportion

Examples.

(a) $\frac{3}{7} = \frac{21}{49}$ is a proportion. The terms are 3, 7, 21, and 49; 3 and 49 are the extremes and 7 and 21 the means of the proportion. The ratios are $\frac{3}{7}$ and $\frac{21}{49}$.

(b) We can use proportions to convert measurements.

Since 1 inch $= 2.54$ cm, to convert say 9 inches to centimeters we write $\frac{9 \text{ inches}}{1 \text{ inch}} = \frac{N \text{ cm}}{2.54 \text{ cm}}$ and obtain $N = 22.86$. The terms of the proportion are 9 inches, 1 inch, N cm, and 2.54 cm. The extremes are 9 inches and 2.54 cm, the means 1 inch and N cm. Notice that we can consider the proportion $\frac{9}{1} = \frac{N}{2.54}$ as expressing the numerical relationship between the terms of the proportion.

Historically the idea of proportions was probably first considered by the Greeks who applied it to geometric figures and extended its development to the ideas of similarity. To begin, we can form the ratio of the lengths of two segments AB and CD: $\frac{\overline{AB}}{\overline{CD}} = \frac{5}{3}$. Now suppose that we are given a third segment EF. Can we find a fourth segment GH such that $\frac{\overline{AB}}{\overline{CD}} = \frac{\overline{EF}}{\overline{GH}}$? In many situations we can!

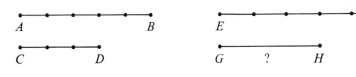

The fundamental geometric idea is illustrated in Figure 152. In comparing figures, they may be of different sizes but have the same shape.

For example, Figures 152(a) and (b) differ in size but not in shape. When two figures are related in this way, that is, have the same shape, we say that they are **similar**. If two figures are similar, then their corresponding sides are in the same ratio, that is, proportional.

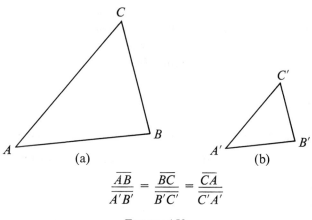

$$\frac{\overline{AB}}{\overline{A'B'}} = \frac{\overline{BC}}{\overline{B'C'}} = \frac{\overline{CA}}{\overline{C'A'}}$$

FIGURE 152

Related similar figures occur in many situations. Figure 153 illustrates three of them. In all cases we can simplify our considerations to the situation illustrated in Figure 154. If a line segment is parallel to one side of a triangle and "cuts" a second side of the triangle in a given ratio, then it "cuts" the third side in the same ratio.

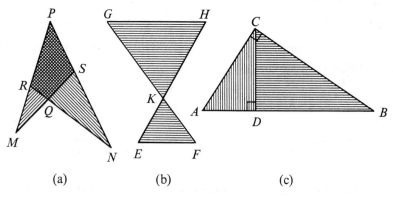

FIGURE 153

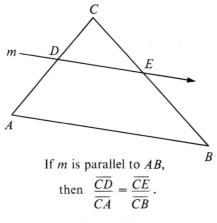

If m is parallel to AB,

then $\dfrac{\overline{CD}}{\overline{CA}} = \dfrac{\overline{CE}}{\overline{CB}}$.

FIGURE 154

An important observation with respect to similar figures is that if we know the ratio of one pair of corresponding sides, then we know that the ratio of any other pair of corresponding sides will be the same. If we know three terms of the proportion, then we can solve for the fourth. For example, if in Figure 154 we are given that $\overline{CA} = 5$ units and $\overline{CB} = 6$ units and if m "cuts" CA so that $\overline{CD} = 2$ units, then we have $\dfrac{2}{5} = \dfrac{\overline{CE}}{6}$ so that $\overline{CE} = 2\dfrac{2}{5}$ units.

Examples.

(a) If in Figure 153(a) we have triangle MPS similar to triangle NPR, then $\dfrac{\overline{MP}}{\overline{NP}} = \dfrac{\overline{PS}}{\overline{PR}} = \dfrac{\overline{SM}}{\overline{RN}}$. Given that $\overline{MP} = 12$, $\overline{NP} = 15$, and $\overline{PR} = 9$, we have $\dfrac{12}{15} = \dfrac{\overline{PS}}{9}$ so that $\overline{PS} = 7\dfrac{1}{5}$. If, in addition, we know that $\overline{SM} = 10$, then $\overline{RN} = 12\dfrac{1}{2}$.

(b) If in Figure 153(b) we have triangle EFK similar to triangle HGK, then $\dfrac{\overline{EF}}{\overline{HG}} = \dfrac{\overline{FK}}{\overline{GK}} = \dfrac{\overline{KE}}{\overline{KH}}$. Given that $\overline{KG} = 8$, $\overline{HK} = 7$, and $\overline{KE} = 4$, we have $\overline{FK} = 4\dfrac{4}{7}$ so that $\overline{FG} = 12\dfrac{4}{7}$.

(c) The three right triangles ABC, ACD, and CBD in Figure 153(c) are similar to each other. Thus, we have

$$\frac{\overline{AB}}{\overline{AC}} = \frac{\overline{BC}}{\overline{CD}} = \frac{\overline{CA}}{\overline{DA}}; \qquad \frac{\overline{AB}}{\overline{CB}} = \frac{\overline{BC}}{\overline{BD}} = \frac{\overline{CA}}{\overline{DC}}; \qquad \frac{\overline{AC}}{\overline{CB}} = \frac{\overline{CD}}{\overline{BD}} = \frac{\overline{DA}}{\overline{DC}}.$$

Notice that for each pair of similar triangles we have three possible proportions. Observe also that the same segments occur more than once. Furthermore, the segment $\overline{AB} = \overline{AD} + \overline{DB}$. The right triangle relationships suggested here are extremely useful so that we will consider them more fully in the next section. Can you write equations which describe two of these most important relationships?

In working with proportions certain relationships between the terms of the proportion are useful to know. For example, if $\dfrac{A}{B} = \dfrac{C}{D}$, then we have $A \times D = B \times C$. That is, given any proportion the product of the extremes is equal to the product of the means. If $A \times D = B \times C$, then we have $\dfrac{D}{B} = \dfrac{C}{A}$ so that the extremes in a proportion may be interchanged to form a new proportion. Of course, we must be careful not to divide by zero, that is, $A \neq 0$.

Practice 3.

1. Name the means, the extremes, and the third term in each of the following proportions:

(a) $\dfrac{3}{N} = \dfrac{8}{15}$ (b) $\dfrac{7}{24} = \dfrac{N}{9}$ (c) $\dfrac{2N}{9} = \dfrac{17}{7}$ (d) $\dfrac{24}{7} = \dfrac{9}{N}$

(e) $\dfrac{2}{6} = \dfrac{3 + N}{9}$.

2. Find the value of N in each of the proportions in Problem 1.

3. Using the idea illustrated in Figure 154, complete the following figures (in Figure 155) so that $\dfrac{\overline{CD}}{\overline{CA}} = \dfrac{\overline{CE}}{\overline{CB}}$.

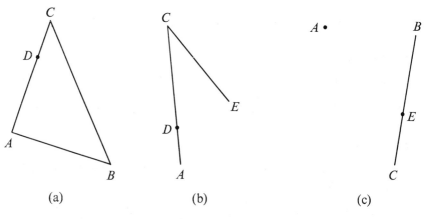

(a)   (b)   (c)

FIGURE 155

4. In Figure 153(a) we have triangles *MPS* and *NPR* similar. Find another pair of similar triangles in the figure.

5. In Figure 153(a) given that $\overline{MP} = 10$, $\overline{RN} = 9\frac{3}{5}$, $\overline{MT} = 4$, and $\overline{RQ} = 2\frac{2}{15}$, find:

    (a) $\overline{NP}$ (b) $\overline{PS}$ (c) $\overline{PR}$ (d) $\overline{SM}$ (e) $\overline{NS}$
    (f) $\overline{SQ}$ (g) $\overline{QM}$ (h) $\overline{QN}$.

6. In Figure 153(b) we have triangles *EFK* and *HGK* similar. If $\overline{EF} = 24$, $\overline{GH} = 42$, and $\overline{FK} = 20$, then what is the measure of:
    (a) $\overline{HK}$?   (b) $\overline{GK}$?

7. Given a proportion $\frac{A}{B} = \frac{C}{D}$, the following relationships are true:

    (a) The means may be interchanged to form a new proportion providing they are not equal to zero.

    (b) The reciprocals of the ratios form a new proportion providing we are not dividing by zero.

    (c) The sum of the first two terms is to the second term as the sum of the third and fourth terms is to the fourth term.

Write the above relationships in equation form.

8. In order to estimate the height of his house Mr. Smith paced off 42 ft from the front of his house and sighted to the top of the house as shown in Figure 156 obtaining the measurements indicated. If Mr. Smith has a shoulder height of 5 ft, then what was his estimate of the height of his house?

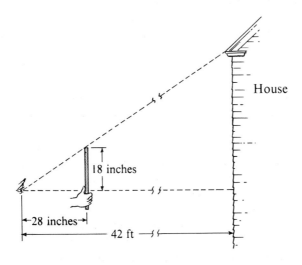

FIGURE 156

Answers.

1. (a) means: N, 8   extremes: 3, 15   third term: 8
   (b) means: 24, N extremes: 7, 9   third term: N
   (c) means: 9, 17   extremes: $2N$, 7   third term: 17
   (d) means: 7, 9   extremes: 24, N third term: 9
   (e) means: 6, $3 + N$ extremes: 2, 9   third term: $3 + N$

2. (a) $5\frac{5}{8}$ (b) $2\frac{5}{8}$ (c) $10\frac{13}{14}$ (d) $2\frac{5}{8}$ (e) 0.

3. $-$.

4. Triangles MRQ and NSQ are also similar.

5. (a) 12   (b) 5   (c) 6   (d) 8   (e) 7   (f) $3\frac{11}{15}$

   (g) $4\frac{4}{15}$ (h) $7\frac{7}{15}$.

6. (a) We cannot determine $\overline{HK}$ (b) $\overline{GK} = 35$.

7. (a) $\frac{A}{C} = \frac{B}{D}$ (b) $\frac{B}{A} = \frac{D}{C}$ (c) $\frac{A + B}{B} = \frac{C + D}{D}$.

8. 32 ft.

Exercises

1. A mathematical relationship with at least one variable which can be used to obtain answers is called a _____. Such a relationship for answering questions concerning distance, speed, and time is expressed by the equation _____. Another relationship called the lever principle is described by _____.

2. Using the letters indicated, express each of the following as a formula:

(a) The percent P of profit on the selling price S of an article is equal to the difference between the selling price and cost C divided by the selling price.

(b) If the unit cost (u) of an article is constant, then the total cost (C) of n articles varies directly as the number of articles purchased.

(c) Charles' law for gases under a constant pressure states that the volume of gas is proportional to the temperature. Use V_1, V_2 for volumes and T_1, T_2 for temperatures.

3. Our daily activities involve work (W) in various forms. We climb stairs, lift objects, and write our lessons. In each of these activities a force (F) is applied and there is motion through some distance (D).

(a) Using the letters suggested above, write a formula for work.

(b) If force (F) is measured in pounds (weight units) and distance (D) in feet, then what will be the resulting unit of measure for work (W)?

(c) If a man weighing 185 lb ascends a flight of 16 steps, each step rising 7 inches, then how much work does he do?

Use one or more of the following formulas to solve the problems of Exercises 4 through 8:

1. $D = R \times T$ 2. $V = B \times h$ 3. $A = \pi r^2$ 4. $P = 2L + 2W$

5. $W_1 D_1 = W_2 D_2$ 6. $°F = \frac{9}{5}°C + 32$.

4. (a) What is the area of a circle whose radius is 21 inches?

(b) What is the volume of a cylindrical can with a circular base of radius $1\frac{3}{4}$ ft and height 2 ft?

5. (a) What is the distance around a rectangular city block if adjacent sides are 265 ft and 385 ft?

(b) How long will it take to go around the block ten times at a steady walking pace of 2 miles per hour?

6. (a) Two pulleys are fixed on a common axle. If a 10 lb weight and a 4 lb weight are hung from the rims of the pulleys, then what must be the ratio of the radii of the pulleys in order for the pulleys to stay in balance? That is, under what circumstances will the pulleys stay motion-less?

(b) If the larger pulley in Part (a) above is 8 inches in radius and a lever is affixed to the axle as shown in Figure 157, then what is the heav-iest weight which can be balanced at the end of the lever? Show the arrangement of weights.

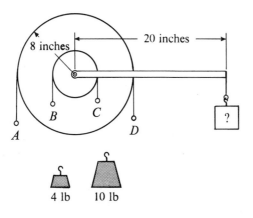

FIGURE 157

7. (a) What is the fahrenheit temperature if it is 23 degrees above the freezing temperature on the centigrade scale?

(b) What is the centigrade temperature if it is 100° F?

8. (a) If an auto going at a fixed speed covers 150 miles in 2 h 5 min, how long will it take to go 500 miles?

(b) If an airplane goes the 500 miles in the same time that the auto in Part (a) covers the 150 miles, then how far will the airplane have gone by the time the auto has gone the 500 miles?

9. The following sets of ordered pairs describe direct or inverse variations. State whether the variation is direct or inverse in each case, determine the constant of variation, and write the equation of variation.

(a)

R:	2	1	4
T:	1	2	$\frac{1}{2}$

(b)

A:	$\frac{3}{2}$	3	9
b:	1	2	6

(c)

P:	$\frac{15}{2}$	30	$\frac{15}{8}$
d^2:	1	$\frac{1}{4}$	4

(d)

S:	0	16	256
t^2:	0	1	16

10. Find the constants of variation and the values indicated:

(a) $V = \dfrac{K}{T}$ and $V = 1$ when $T = \dfrac{2}{5}$, and find V if $T = \dfrac{5}{2}$.

(b) $D = Ks$ and $D = -\dfrac{1}{2}$ when $s = 15$, and find D if $s = -\dfrac{2}{3}$.

(c) $M = Kn^2$ and $M = 8$ when $n = 2$, and find M if $n = \dfrac{1}{2}$.

(d) $I = \dfrac{K}{d^2}$ and $I = 3$ when $d = -2$, and find I if $d = 2$.

11. Observing that rapidly swinging pendulums had short arms and slowly swinging pendulums were long, a student experimented with various pendulums by measuring the time T of one swing of a pendulum in seconds and then by measuring the length L of the pendulum arm in inches. The following data was obtained:

L:	3.51	9.75	19.11	24.96	31.59	39.00 (in inches)
T:	0.3	0.5	0.7	0.8	0.9	1.0 (in seconds)

(a) Write a formula to describe the relationship.

(b) How could the formula be checked or verified?

(c) What should be the length of a pendulum arm, if the time of one swing were 1.5 seconds.

12. Find the value of P in each of the following proportions:

(a) $\dfrac{P}{\frac{2}{3}} = \dfrac{6}{7}$ (b) $\dfrac{5}{2P} = \dfrac{4}{15}$ (c) $\dfrac{3}{5} = \dfrac{7-P}{4}$ (d) $\dfrac{4P}{9} = \dfrac{5-2P}{-2}$.

13. Find a pair of similar triangles in Figure 158.

(a) Write the three proportions resulting from this similarity.

(b) If $\overline{PQ} = 7$, $\overline{OP} = 14$, and $\overline{PR} = 2$, then find $\overline{SQ}$.

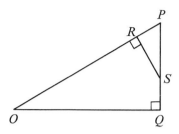

FIGURE 158

14. In an electrical circuit the rate of flow of current (I) measured in amperes varies inversely as the resistance (R) in ohms. The electrical force (E) in volts is equal to the product of the current and resistance. In an ordinary home circuit, the electrical force is a constant 110 volts.

(a) If the resistance in an electrical circuit is doubled, then what would we expect in the flow of current? If the resistance is lowered drastically, then what would we expect in the flow of current?

(b) If there is a 1,000 ohm resistance in a home circuit, then what is the flow of current in the circuit?

(c) If a "short" lowers the resistance in a home circuit to 5 ohms, then what will be the flow of current in the circuit?

15. In using curved mirrors or lenses to obtain images of objects a simple proportional relationship exists between the distances of the object and image from the mirror or lens and the sizes of the object and image.

If a foot-ruler is held vertically 6 ft from a curved mirror, the image appears 3 ft from the mirror. What will be the length of the image of the foot-ruler?

Answers.

1. formula; $D = R \times T$; $W_1 D_1 = W_2 D_2$.

2. (a) $P = \dfrac{S - C}{S}$ (b) $C = Knu$ (c) $\dfrac{V_1}{V_2} = \dfrac{T_1}{T_2}$.

3. (a) $W = F \times D$ (b) ft lb   (c) $1,757\frac{1}{2}$ ft lb.

4. (a) 9 sq ft 90 sq inches   (b) $19\frac{1}{4}$ cu ft.

5. (a) 1,300 ft   (b) 1 h 14 min.

6. (a) 5 to 2; the 4 lb weight on the larger pulley and opposite from the axle from the 10 lb weight on the smaller pulley.

(b) 4.64 lb; the 10 lb weight on the 8-inch pulley and the 4 lb weight on the smaller $3\frac{1}{5}$-inch pulley, both on the side opposite the axle from the end of the lever.

7. (a) 73.4° F   (b) $37\frac{7}{9}$° C.

8. (a) 6 h 56 min 40 sec   (b) $1,666\frac{2}{3}$ miles.

9. (a) inverse; $R = \frac{2}{T}$ (b) direct; $A = \frac{3}{2} \times b$.

(c) inverse; $P = \frac{15}{2d^2}$ (d) direct; $S = 16t^2$.

10. (a) $K = \frac{2}{5}, V = \frac{4}{25}$ (b) $K = -\frac{1}{30}, D = \frac{1}{45}$ (c) $K = 2, M = \frac{1}{2}$

(d) $K = 12, I = 3$.

11. (a) $L = 39T^2$ (b) By using the formula to predict the necessary length of a pendulum arm for a given time and constructing the actual pendulum predicted.   (c) 7 ft $3\frac{3}{4}$ inches.

12. (a) $\frac{4}{7}$ (b) $9\frac{3}{8}$ (c) $4\frac{3}{5}$ (d) $4\frac{1}{2}$.

13. Triangles OPQ and SPR: (a) $\frac{\overline{OP}}{\overline{SP}} = \frac{\overline{PQ}}{\overline{PR}}; \frac{\overline{PQ}}{\overline{PR}} = \frac{\overline{QO}}{\overline{RS}}; \frac{\overline{QO}}{\overline{RS}} = \frac{\overline{OP}}{\overline{SP}}$

(b) $\overline{SQ} = 3$.

14. (a) halved; increased drastically   (b) 0.11 amperes   (c) 22 amperes.

15. $\frac{1}{2}$ ft or 6 inches.

9.2 The Pythagorean Theorem

9.2.1   One of the most important and widely used formulas in mathematics arises from the relationship between the sides of a right triangle. The priests and pyramid builders of ancient Egypt were aware that if three lengths were in the ratio of 3 to 4 to 5, when combined to form a triangle, the triangle would be a right triangle. It is probable that the Egyptians discovered this relationship by trial and error.

For convenience when discussing right triangles, the longest side, the side opposite the right angle, is called the **hypotenuse** of the triangle and the other two sides are called the **legs**. For example, in Figure 159, the side AB is the hypotenuse while the sides BC and AC are called the

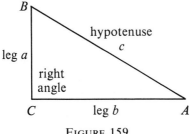

FIGURE 159

legs of the triangle *ABC*. Notice that capital letters are used for the vertex points while small letters are used for the sides.

The Pythagorean Theorem, which is named after the famous Greek mathematician Pythagoras (c.572 to c.501 B.C.), asserts that:
    In any right triangle the square on the
    hypotenuse equals the sum of the squares
    on the legs. That is, $c^2 = a^2 + b^2$.

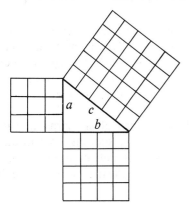

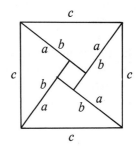

FIGURE 160   FIGURE 161

To examine the right triangle relationship, we can begin by constructing right triangles of various shapes and measuring the lengths of their sides to determine if the relationship holds true. For example, in Figure 162 we have four possible right triangles with estimates of the lengths of the sides. A simple computation will verify that the relationship appears to be true.

Of course we can ask whether "If a triangle has this relationship between the lengths of its sides, then will the triangle be a right triangle?" In order to investigate this question we must first discover numbers *a, b,* and *c* which satisfy the relationship $c^2 = a^2 + b^2$. Triples of integers which

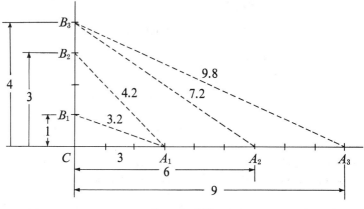

FIGURE 162

satisfy this relationship are called *Pythagorean numbers.* Besides the triple 3, 4, 5 others are 9, 12, 15 and 5, 12, 13. Using segments with these lengths we can construct triangles and determine whether they are right triangles.

The Pythagorean Theorem can be demonstrated in a variety of ways. An interesting demonstration was given by a Hindu mathematician of the twelfth century named Bhaskara (c. 1114 to c. 1185). He presented the arrangement shown in Figure 161 with the single word, *"behold."* Can you rearrange the four triangles and small square to demonstrate the relationship?

The following demonstration applies the idea of similarity and illustrates the unexpected usefulness of a principle such as proportions in conjunction with the careful description of a general situation of interest.

Consider an arbitrary right triangle *ABC* as illustrated in Figure 163.

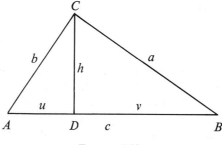

FIGURE 163

Draw a perpendicular to the hypotenuse from the right angle vertex as shown. Let the sides have unknown lengths as indicated by the letters *a*, *b*, *c*, *u*, *v*, and *h*. We assert that the triangles *ABC*, *ACD*, and *CBD* are similar to each other. Thus we have:

$$\frac{c}{b} = \frac{a}{h} = \frac{b}{u}; \qquad \frac{c}{a} = \frac{a}{v} = \frac{b}{h}; \qquad \frac{b}{a} = \frac{h}{v} = \frac{u}{h}; \qquad \text{and } u + v = c.$$

A careful examination of the possible proportions leads us to select: $\frac{c}{b} = \frac{b}{u}$ and $\frac{c}{a} = \frac{a}{v}$. Now we can write that $b^2 = cu$ and $a^2 = cv$ so that $a^2 + b^2 = cv + cu = c(v + u) = c^2$. Thus, in general we have $c^2 = a^2 + b^2$ in any right triangle.

9.2.2 Of course, the practical utility of the Pythagorean Theorem often lies in our ability to find the length of the hypotenuse given the lengths of the legs, or the length of a leg given the lengths of the hypotenuse and the other leg. For example, if the lengths of the legs of a right triangle are 7 units and 9 units, then what will be the length of the hypotenuse of the triangle? We can answer, the length of the hypotenuse c will be $c^2 = (7 \times 7) + (9 \times 9) = 49 + 81 = 130$ square units. However, this does not answer the question completely. If $c^2 = 130$, then what will c equal?

To study this question we can begin with a succession of judicious "guesses." For example, if $c^2 = 130$, then we might consider

If $c =$	10	11	12	11.5	11.4	11.41	11.402
then $c^2 =$	100	121	144	132.25	129.96	130.1881	130.0056

For all practical purposes we might be satisfied with $c = 11.40$ as an approximation of c.

Examples.

(a) If $c^2 = 42$, then approximate c to tenths.

SOLUTION. Since $6 \times 6 = 36$ and $7 \times 7 = 49$ we have $6 < c < 7$ (that is, the value of c must lie between 6 and 7). Thus, we can "guess" if $c = 6.5$, then by computation we have $c^2 = 6.5 \times 6.5 = 42.25$ which is slightly too large. Now if $c = 6.4$, then $c^2 = 40.96$ which is too small. Since for $c = 6.5$ we obtain a closer approximation for $c^2 = 42$, we take $c = 6.5$ as our approximation of c to tenths.

(b) If $c^2 = 789$, then approximate c to hundredths.

SOLUTION. Since $25 \times 25 = 625$ and $30 \times 30 = 900$ we have $25 < c < 30$. Now we can select values of c to obtain "better and better" approximations:

If $c =$	28	29	28.1	28.05	28.08	28.09
then $c^2 =$	784	841	789.61	786.80	788.486	789.048

Thus, we take $c = 28.09$ as our approximation of c to hundredths.

Now "guessing" is better than "shrugging the shoulders," but haphazard and often tedious in obtaining results. Can we develop an algorithm to obtain results? If N is any positive number, how can we find a number c such that $c^2 = N$? How did we "guess"?

To find c if $c^2 = N$ we must first be able to "guess" reasonably. That is, we should know that

$$1^2 = 1,\ 2^2 = 4,\ 3^2 = 9,\ 4^2 = 16,\ 5^2 = 25,\ \ldots,\ 9^2 = 81,$$

and

$$10^2 = 100,\ 20^2 = 400,\ 30^2 = 900,\ \ldots,\ 90^2 = 8100,$$

and

$$100^2 = 10,000,\ 200^2 = 40,000,\ \ldots,\ 900^2 = 810,000.$$

Now suppose that we are to find c given that $c^2 = N$ some known positive number. We can guess a reasonable number g for c and divide N by g to obtain a number, say, q: $q = \dfrac{N}{g}$. If our guess is good, q will almost equal g. If our guess g is small, then q will be larger than g. If our guess g is large, then q will be smaller than g. Since g must equal q to be the value of c, if g and q differ, then we can make a second guess for c between g and q. For example, to find c given that $c^2 = 61,345$ we begin by noting that $200^2 = 40,000 < 61,345 < 90,000 = 300^2$. Let us guess $g = 250$. Then we compute $\dfrac{61345}{250} = 245 + \dfrac{95}{250} = q$. Now we have $245 < c < 250$. That is, $245^2 = 60,025 < 61,345 < 62,500 = 250^2$. With this information we can guess much better. A reasonable guess would be to let $g = \dfrac{250 + 245}{2}$ $= 247.5$ so that we obtain $\dfrac{61345}{247.5} = 247.85$ approximately. To obtain an even better value, we take $g = \dfrac{247.5 + 247.85}{2} = 247.68$ approximately. Now $\dfrac{61345}{247.68} = 247.68$ rounded to hundredths. Thus, $c = 247.68$ to five places. In computational form this would appear as:

Given $c^2 = 61,345$. To find c.
Guess $g = 250$:

```
             245 = q
      250)61345
          500
         1134
         1000
          1345
          1250
            95
```

Second guess $g = \dfrac{250 + 245}{2}$ so that $g = 247.5$

Second guess $g = 247.5$:

$$247.5 \overline{)61345.000} \quad \frac{247.85}{} = q$$

$$\begin{array}{r} 4950 \\ \overline{11845} \\ 9900 \\ \overline{19450} \\ 17325 \\ \overline{21250} \\ 19800 \\ \overline{14500} \\ 12375 \\ \overline{2125} \end{array}$$

Third guess $g = \dfrac{247.5 + 247.85}{2}$

$g = 247.68$

$$247.68 \overline{)61345.0000} \quad 247.68$$

Thus, $c = 247.68$ to five places.

Since the above situation occurs quite commonly, special vocabulary is used to describe the quantities involved. For any number r, if $r^2 = N$, then we have called N the "**square of r**" or "**r-squared**." Now to describe r we say that if $r^2 = N$, then "r is the **square root** of N." The symbol, $\sqrt{\ }$, called a **square root** or **radical** symbol, is used to indicate this latter relationship. If $r^2 = N$, then $r = \sqrt{N}$. Notice that since $r^2 \geq 0$, N must be positive or zero. For example, if $r = 7$, $r^2 = 49 = N$. If $r = 0$, then $r^2 = 0 = N$. If $r = -7$, $r^2 = (-7)(-7) = 49 = N$.

Given $N = r^2$ we can look for $r = \sqrt{N}$. That is, if $N = 121$, we can ask "What is the square root of 121?" Our answer might be "The square root of 121 is $r = 11$." Since $11 \times 11 = 121$, this answer would be correct. However, consider $(-11) \times (-11) = 121$ so that $r = -11$ would also be a solution of $r^2 = 121$. That is, -11 is also a square root of 121. Every positive number N has two square roots, one is the negative of the other. For example, if $N = 121$, then $r_1 = 11$ and $r_2 = -11$ are the two square roots of N. For convenience, unless otherwise stated or implied, it is customary to consider the square root of a number as being positive (or zero). If $r^2 = N$, then $r = \sqrt{N} \geq 0$. The second root, which is negative or zero, can be indicated by $r' = -\sqrt{N} \leq 0$.

Examples.

    (a) If $r^2 = 130$, then $r = \sqrt{130} = 11.40$ approximately.
    (b) If $r^2 = 61,345$, then $r = \sqrt{61,345} = 247.68$ approximately.

If we consider finding r-squared given r as an operation, then finding the square root of r-squared is the inverse operation. That is, square root "undoes" squaring.

By the square N of a number r we mean $N = r \times r$.

By the square root r of a number N we mean $r \times r = N$.

Two useful observations from the above:

$$1.\ r = \sqrt{r^2} \qquad 2.\ \sqrt{N}\,\sqrt{N} = N.$$

The algorithm suggested for approximating the positive square root of a number N can be described briefly as follows:

Given $r^2 = N$. To find r.

Guess r to be equal to g. Compute $q = \dfrac{N}{g}$.

If $q = g$, then $r = g$. If $q \neq g$, then make a second guess $g^* = \dfrac{g + q}{2}$

and compute $q^* = \dfrac{N}{g^*}$. (g^* and q^* are results of g and q.)

If $q^* = g^*$, then $r = g^*$. If $q^* \neq g^*$, then make a third guess and continue until the approximation is sufficiently close to satisfy the problem.

Examples.

(a) If the hypotenuse of a right triangle is 27 units and a leg is 19 units, then find the length of the other leg to within 0.1 units.

SOLUTION. Since $c^2 = a^2 + b^2$ and $c = 27$, $b = 19$, we have $729 = a^2 + 361$. Thus, $a^2 = 729 - 361 = 368$ and $a = \sqrt{368}$.

Let $g = 19$; $q = \dfrac{368}{19} = 19.37$ approximately.

Set $g^* = \dfrac{19 + 19.37}{2} = 19.18$ so that we can say the other leg $a = 19.2$ units to within 0.1 units.

(b) If the area of a square is equal to 9,365 sq units, then find the length of the side of the square to four places.

SOLUTION. Since $A = s^2$ we have $9{,}365 = s^2$ and $s = \sqrt{9{,}365}$.

Let $g = 94$;

$$94\overline{)9365.00} \quad 99.63 = q \qquad \text{Now } g^* = \frac{94 + 99.63}{2} = 96.81$$

$$96.81\overline{)9365.0000} \quad 96.73 = q^* \qquad \text{Now } g^{**} = \frac{96.81 + 96.73}{2} = 96.77$$

$$96.77\overline{)9365.0000} \quad 96.77$$

Thus, $s = 96.77$ units to four places.

Practice 1.

1. Using the segment u as a unit, measure the lengths of the sides

of the right triangles in Figure 164 and verify the Pythagorean Theorem relationship for these triangles.

GIVEN:

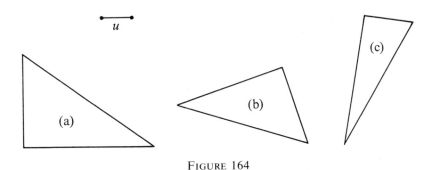

FIGURE 164

2. Find and list all the Pythagorean number triples for integers less than or equal to 20. (Positive integers only.)

3. If a, b, c are the sides of a right triangle, then find the length of the missing side for each of the following:

	(a)	(b)	(c)	(d)	(e)	(f)
$a =$	$1\frac{1}{2}$	5	?	36	2.5	?
$b =$	2	?	$1\frac{1}{4}$	?	6	0.9
$c =$	?	$7\frac{1}{4}$	$3\frac{1}{4}$	39	?	4.1

4. If a, b, c are the lengths of sides, then determine which of the following will form right triangles and which will not form triangles at all:

	(a)	(b)	(c)	(d)	(e)	(f)
$a =$	11	5	0.75	2.75	$3\frac{1}{3}$	$\frac{3}{4}$
$b =$	4	2	1.00	5.25	8	$2\frac{1}{2}$
$c =$	13	8	1.25	6.25	$8\frac{2}{3}$	$3\frac{1}{2}$

5. If a, b, c are the sides of a right triangle with c the hypotenuse, then find the length of the missing side for each of the following to three places:

	(a)	(b)	(c)	(d)	(e)	(f)
$a =$	4	?	20	3.7	?	0.45
$b =$	8	5	7	?	$6\frac{2}{3}$	1.80
$c =$	?	9	?	6.5	$12\frac{1}{2}$	?

6. Find the lengths of the segments indicated in Figure 165 to four place positions.

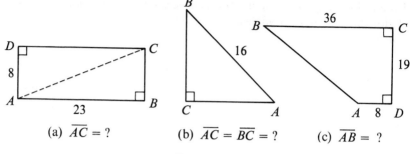

(a) $\overline{AC} = ?$ (b) $\overline{AC} = \overline{BC} = ?$ (c) $\overline{AB} = ?$

FIGURE 165

Answers.

1. (a) $4\frac{5}{16}, 2\frac{7}{8}, 5\frac{3}{16}$ (b) $3\frac{11}{16}, 2\frac{9}{16}, 4\frac{9}{16}$ (c) $1\frac{5}{8}, 4\frac{1}{8}, 4\frac{1}{2}$.

The measured lengths approximate the relationship.

2. (a)   3   6   9   12   15   5.
   (b)   4   8   12   16   8   12.
   (c)   5   10   15   20   17   13.

3. (a) $c = 2\frac{1}{2}$ (b) $b = 5\frac{1}{4}$ (c) $a = 3$ (d) $b = 15$
   (e) $c = 6.5$ (f) $a = 4$.

4. (c) and (e) form right triangles; (b) and (f) do not form triangles.

5. (a) $c = 8.94$ (b) $a = 7.48$ (c) $c = 21.2$
   (d) $b = 5.34$ (e) $a = 10.6$ (f) $c = 1.85$.

6. (a) $\overline{AC} = 23.94$ (b) $\overline{AC} = \overline{BC} = 11.31$ (c) $\overline{AB} = 33.84$.

9.2.3   The following examples illustrate certain recurring right triangle relationships. A key in the solution of many significant problems is the ability to recognize the particular application of a formula. In many problems the Pythagorean Theorem appears as an important formula.

Examples.

(a) To find the altitude to the hypotenuse of a right triangle, given the lengths of its legs.

SOLUTION. Let the triangle be as shown in Figure 166 with the legs measuring as indicated. From the similar triangles we note that $\frac{h}{a} = \frac{b}{c}$ or $h = \frac{ab}{c}$. But by the Pythagorean Theorem, $c^2 = a^2 + b^2$. Thus we have

$$h = \frac{ab}{\sqrt{a^2 + b^2}}.$$

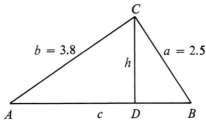

FIGURE 166

Now $ab = 2.5 \times 3.8 = 9.50$ and $a^2 + b^2 = 6.25 + 14.44 = 20.69$ so that $\sqrt{a^2 + b^2} = \sqrt{20.69} = 4.55$. Finally, $h = \dfrac{9.50}{4.55} = 2.09$.

(b) To find the altitude of an equilateral triangle in terms of the length of its side.

SOLUTION. Let the triangle be as shown in Figure 167. By the Pythagorean Theorem we have

$$s^2 = h^2 + \left(\frac{s}{2}\right)^2 \text{ so that } h^2 = s^2 - \left(\frac{s}{2}\right)^2 = s^2 - \frac{s^2}{4} = \frac{3s^2}{4}$$

and $h = \sqrt{\dfrac{3s^2}{4}} = \dfrac{s}{2} \times \sqrt{3}$. But since $\sqrt{3} = 1.732$ approximately, we have $h = 0.866 \times s$.

If $s = 7$, then $h = 0.866 \times 7 = 6.062$ approximately.

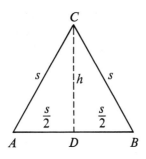

FIGURE 167

Circles and right triangles are related in a variety of interesting ways. Three of the right triangle properties of a circle are illustrated in Figure 168. These relationships are stated as follows:

1. If a triangle is drawn with the diameter of a circle as a side and with the third vertex on the circle, then it will be a right triangle with the right angle subtended by the diameter.

2. If a line has exactly one point in common with a circle (called a **tangent** line), then it will be perpendicular to (form a right angle with) a radial line through the common point.

3. If a point O is the center of a circle with $\overline{OA} = r$ the radius, then the third vertex Q of any right triangle OPQ with P on the line OA and right angle at P with $\overline{OQ} = r$ will lie on the circle.

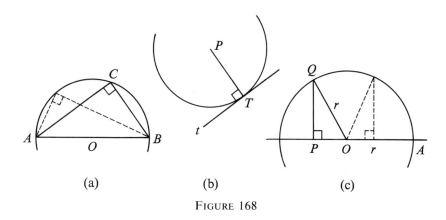

| (a) | (b) | (c) |

FIGURE 168

Examples.

(c) To draw a right triangle with a given hypotenuse c and given leg b.

SOLUTION. Draw a circle with c as a diameter. From one end of the diameter c, draw a circle with radius b. The point of intersection of the two circles (one of the two points) will be the third vertex of the required triangle. See Figure 169.

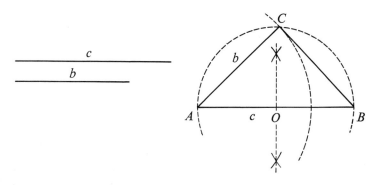

FIGURE 169

1. Find center O.
2. Draw circle with diameter c.
3. Draw circle with radius b.
4. Triangle ABC is the required right triangle.

(d) To find the length of a segment PT which is tangent to a circle with center O and radius $r = 8$, if $\overline{OP} = 30$.

SOLUTION. From the tangent relationship and the Pythagorean Theorem we have $(\overline{OP})^2 = (\overline{PT})^2 + r^2$ so that $\overline{PT} = \sqrt{(\overline{OP})^2 - r^2}$.

Thus, $\overline{PT} = \sqrt{(30 \times 30) - (8 \times 8)} = \sqrt{836} = 28.9$ units approximately. See Figure 170.

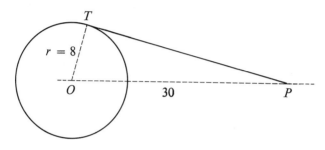

FIGURE 170

(e) To find the radius of a circle if a segment AB joining two points on the circle is 17 units long and 5 units from the center of the circle.

SOLUTION. Drawing a sketch as in Figure 171, we note that if O is the center of the circle with OP perpendicular to AB, then OPA is a right triangle with $\overline{OA} = r$ the radius. Thus, we have $r^2 = (\overline{OP})^2 + (\overline{PA})^2$.

Computing, $r = \sqrt{(5 \times 5) + \left(\frac{17}{2} \times \frac{17}{2}\right)} = \sqrt{\frac{389}{4}} = 9.86$ units.

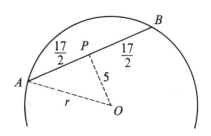

FIGURE 171

Exercises

1. Using a convenient unit carefully construct right triangles as follows (use a straight edge and compass):
   (a) with legs 4 units and 7 units.
   (b) with legs 12 units and 1 unit.
   (c) with hypotenuse 9 units and one leg 6 units.
   (d) with hypotenuse 8 units and altitude to the hypotenuse 3 units.
2. Verify the Pythagorean Theorem for the triangles of Exercise 1.
3. If a, b, c are the sides of a right triangle with c the hypotenuse, then find the length of the missing side for each of the following to four places:

	(a)	(b)	(c)	(d)	(e)	(f)
$a =$	10	?	2.25	3	?	15
$b =$	?	2	3	5	6.5	21
$c =$	26	4.25	?	?	13.5	?

4. Approximate the following to four places:

(a) $\sqrt{3,250}$ (b) $\sqrt{195}$ (c) $\sqrt{5.00}$ (d) $\sqrt{0.75}$

(e) $\sqrt{67.40}$ (f) $\sqrt{\dfrac{5}{8}}$ (g) $\sqrt{12\dfrac{1}{2}}$ (h) $\sqrt{575,000}$.

5. The altitude to the hypotenuse of a right triangle divides the hypotenuse into two segments 6 units and 9 units in length. Find the altitude of the right triangle.

6. If the area of a circle is equal to 47.45 sq units, then find the radius of the circle to four places. (Use $\pi = 3.1416$.)

7. Find the lengths of the segments indicated in Figure 172 to four places.

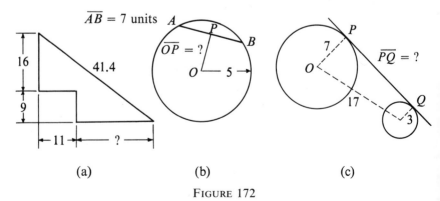

(a)   (b)   (c)

FIGURE 172

8. Find the area of an isosceles triangle if the base is equal to 9 inches and the two equal sides are 24 inches.

9. Find the lengths of the segments indicated in Figure 173 to three places.

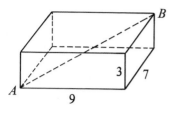

(a) Rectangular parallelepiped; find $\overline{AB}$.

(b) Edges are all equal to 8 units. Equilateral faces; find altitude h.

FIGURE 173

10. Two ships leave the same harbor 1 hour apart. The first ship steams due north at 10 miles per hour and the later ship moves due west at 15 miles per hour. Approximately how far apart will they be 3 hours after the second ship leaves the harbor?

Answers.

1. (a)   (b)   (c)

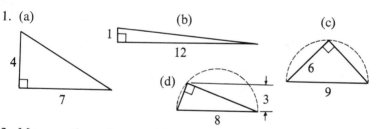

2. Measure the unknown side and check whether $c^2 = a^2 + b^2$ within reason. Use relatively large figures.

3. (a) $b = 24$ (b) $a = 3.75$ (c) $c = 3.75$
    (d) $c = 5.831$ (e) $a = 11.83$ (f) $c = 25.81$.

4. (a) 57.01   (b) 13.96   (c) 2.236   (d) 0.8660
    (e) 8.210   (f) 0.7906   (g) 3.536   (h) 758.3.

5. Notice that $h^2 = uv$, $h = 7.348$ units.

6. $r = 3.886$.

7. (a) 22 units   (b) $\overline{OP} = 3.571$ units   (c) $\overline{PQ} = 16.52$ units.

8. $A = 106.1$ sq inches.

9. (a) $\overline{AB} = 11.8$ units   (b) $h = 6.53$ units.

10. 60.21 miles.

9.3 Averages

9.3.1 We have said that formulas, when used properly, not only lead to rapid and efficient solutions of problems but also represent the relationships between the quantities involved in problems. For example, in our everyday life, objects are often in motion. If an object changes its position with respect to some reference point, we say that it has a certain speed. Recall that we have described speed with the formula $R = \dfrac{D}{T}$. That is, speed is the ratio of a distance covered to the elapsed time in going the distance. However, in using this formula, it would be naive for us to say that the numerical value obtained answers the question of speed completely.

If we drive 12 miles to work and it takes us 40 minutes, then what do we mean when we say that our speed is 18 miles per hour in driving to work? Do we mean that we are going 18 miles per hour during every moment of the trip? If we drive at 18 miles per hour every moment during the trip, then we would cover the 12 miles to work in 40 minutes. The idea of covering equal distances in equal time intervals is called **uniform speed**. However, in actually driving to work we might be going at 35 miles per hour during some moments and be stopped completely during other moments. When unequal distances are covered in equal time intervals we say that the speed is **variable**. Usually, what we mean when we say that we drive at 18 miles per hour is that 18 miles per hour represents the single speed which if uniform throughout the trip would cover the distance in the same given time. In this sense, the speed is called an **average** speed for the trip.

The idea of obtaining a single representative value for a set of values in a given situation is very useful. In general, such a value is called an **average value.**

Examples.

(a) If we wish to find the time it takes for us to get to work each morning, we could time ourselves repeatedly and obtain a set of elapsed times as shown below.

Date:	3/2	3/3	3/4	3/5	3/6	
Time:	24	32	28	24	31	(in minutes)

Date:	3/9	3/10	3/11	3/12	3/13	
Time:	29	28	34	30	25	(in minutes)

QUESTION. What single elapsed time would best represent the time it takes to get to work?

DISCUSSION. To answer 24 minutes or 34 minutes would be misleading. We should determine a single elapsed time such that if each trip takes this time, then the total time will be the same as the actual total time. If we compute the total time and divide this sum by the number of trips involved, we obtain

$$\frac{\text{total time}}{\text{number of trips}} = \frac{285}{10} = 28.5.$$

Now, if each trip took 28.5 minutes, then the total time for the 10 trips would be exactly the same as the actual total of elapsed time. Although no actual trip took 28.5 minutes, we could say that it takes us 28.5 minutes **on the average** to get to work each morning.

(b) If a student receives the following scores on 7 tests, then what single score will best represent his performance on the tests?

Test:	1	2	3	4	5	6	7
Score:	80	72	86	92	78	80	86

SOLUTION. We compute the average $\frac{80 + 72 + 86 + 92 + 78 + 80 + 86}{7}$
$= \frac{574}{7} = 82$. If he had scored 82 on each test, he would have had the same total so that the average score of 82 represents his performance on the tests.

(c) Suppose that we know that a quantity A varies directly as a quantity B and we wish to determine the constant of variation for the relationship. In order to do this, rather than obtain a single ordered pair of values, we might collect a set of ordered pairs as shown below. What single value should we use for the constant of variation?

A:	15.5	18	19.4	21.5	23	24.5
B:	10.5	12	13	14.5	15	16.5

DISCUSSION. Since we know that $A = K \times B$, we can compute K for each of the ordered pairs to obtain a set of values of K.

K: 1.48   1.50   1.49   1.48   1.53   1.48

We might "guess" that the constant of variation must lie between 1.48 and 1.53. If we compute the average of the values of K, we obtain the value $\frac{8.96}{6} = 1.49$. On the basis of the information available to us we might conclude that the best value to use for the constant of variation in this situation would be $K = 1.49$. That is, $A = 1.49 \times B$.

When we wish to obtain a single representative value for a set of values, we often use the **average value**. That is, the value such that when used uniformly for all the values in the set, the total will be exactly the same as in the original set of values. We can describe the average value as:

$$\textbf{Average value} = \frac{\text{Sum of values}}{\text{Number of values}}$$

Examples.

(a) Find the average of 9, 7, 5, 11, 8, 9, and 7.

$$\text{Average} = \frac{9 + 7 + 5 + 11 + 8 + 9 + 7}{7} = 8.$$

(b) Find the average of

10.8	9.6	12.0	10.8	12.0	10.8	14.2
12.0	10.8	9.6	12.0	14.2	12.0	10.8
12.0	9.6	10.8	14.2	12.0	9.6	12.0

We first reorganize the set of values, noting that there are only four different values:

Value	Number	Product
9.6	4	38.4
10.8	6	64.8
12.0	8	96.0
14.2	3	42.6
Totals:	21	241.8

Remembering that we can add the values in any order and that products can be thought of as repeated sums, we first compute "partial sums" as products. The number of values of each kind is often called the **frequency** of the value. Now, we can compute the average easily as the sum of the products divided by the total number (frequency) of values.

$$\text{Average} = \frac{241.8}{21} = 11.5 \text{ to three places.}$$

Practice 1.

1. Find the average of each of the following sets of values:
   (a) 12, 9, 15, 14, 15, 13, 14, 12.
   (b) 16, 37, 28, 17, 29.
   (c) 1.65, 3.04, 8.66, 4.75, 3,80, 5.25, 4.40, 5.95.
   (d) 7, 7, 9, 5, 9, 7, 7, 7, 5, 7, 9, 8, 7, 5.

2. A set of test papers of a class of students resulted in the following scores. What is the average score on the test for the class of students?

Score:	100	90	85	80	75	60
Number:	3	7	6	11	8	5

3. An inspector measured the diameters of a sample of five tubular objects. He recorded the following measurements:

Sample no.:	1	2	3	4	5
Diameter:	1.85	1.87	1.85	1.84	1.86 cm

What is a representative diameter for the sample of five objects?

4. A scientist knows that two quantities vary inversely with respect to each other. Careful experiments have resulted in the following data:

A:	2.057	2.915	3.150	3.605	4.000
B:	0.3040	0.2145	0.1985	0.1730	0.1560

What value should the scientist use as a constant of variation?

5. Describe two specific properties of an average value as related to a set of actual values.

Answers.

1. (a) 13   (b) 25.4   (c) 4.69   (d) 7.07 or 7.1.
2. 80.5.
3. 1.854.
4. 0.6247.
5. (i) An average lies between the smallest and largest value.

(ii) If the average is used for each value, the total will be the same as the total of the set of values it represents. Note: The average value may not occur in the set of actual values.

9.3.2   When an average value is used in a computation, a natural question to ask is "How good is it?" That is, how much does it differ from the actual data or values it represents? The fact that two sets of values can lead to the same average but can be quite different is illustrated by the following simple examples:

Examples.

(a) Consider the set of values 1, 2, 2, 4, 4, 5

The average is $\frac{18}{6} = 3$.

(b) Consider the set of values   2, 3, 3, 3, 3, 4

$$\text{The average is } \frac{18}{6} = 3.$$

Although the averages are the same in the above examples, it should be evident that the average is much "better" in Example (b) than in Example (a). That is, the actual values in (b) differ from the average by at most 1 while in (a) the values can differ by twice as much, 2. The spread between the smallest and largest values in Example (a) is much more than the spread in Example (b). We might indicate this fact by stating that the values in a set have a certain "spread" as well as an average. When using averages, this "spread" is often indicated by computing the difference between the largest and smallest values in the set represented by the average. For example, in Example (a) we would say that the average is 3 and the "spread" is 4. In Example (b) we would say that the average is 3 and the "spread" is 2. The difference between the largest and smallest values in a set of values is often called the **range** of the set of values. That is, the range of the set in Example (a) is 4 and in Example (b) is 2.

Although the range of a set of values will indicate the "spread," it can be misleading if there are only one or two extreme values in the set.

Example.

(c) Consider the set of values: 1, 1, 3, 3, 3, 7. The average is 3 and the range is $7 - 1 = 6$.

The "spread" in Example (c) appears no "worse" than in Example (a), except for the extreme value 7. If we notice that the values in a set may differ individually from the average, we can compute the average of these differences. This may result in an average "spread" which will represent the differences much better than the range. For convenience we first name the difference between an actual value and the average of a set of values a **deviation**. Now if we compute the average of the deviations, we should obtain a measure of "spread."

Examples.

(a)

Set:	1,	2,	2,	4,	4,	5	Average: 3
Deviations:	2,	1,	1,	−1,	−1,	−2	Range: 4

Average of the deviations: 0

If we take the average less each value in the set and average these deviations, the result is 0. But this is as we should have expected for the average represents the set of values. We must consider the positive deviations from the average:

Positive deviations: 2,   1,   1,   1,   1,   2

Average of the positive deviations: $\dfrac{8}{6} = 1\dfrac{1}{3}$

(b) | Set: | 2, | 3, | 3, | 3, | 3, | 4 | Average: 3 |
|---|---|---|---|---|---|---|---|
| Deviations: | 1, | 0, | 0, | 0, | 0, | 1 | Range: 2 |

Average of the positive deviations: $\dfrac{1}{3}$

(c) | Set: | 1, | 1, | 3, | 3, | 3, | 7 | Average: 3 |
|---|---|---|---|---|---|---|---|
| Deviations: | 2, | 2, | 0, | 0, | 0, | 4 | Range: 6 |

Average of the positive deviations: $1\dfrac{1}{3}$

Notice that the representative value, the average, is the same in all three of our examples. But the ranges differ and indicate the extreme "spread" of the sets of values while the average of the positive deviations suggests an "expected" variation of the values from their average. The average of the positive deviations of a set of values from their average is called the **mean deviation** of the set of values. Given a set of values we can represent the values with the average and indicate the "spread" of the values with the mean deviation of the set of values from their average. If an extreme measure of "spread" is sufficient, we can use the range of the set of values.

Examples.

(a)

Date:	3/2	3/3	3/4	3/5	3/6	
Time:	24	32	28	24	31	(in minutes)

Date:	3/9	3/10	3/11	3/12	3/13	
Time:	29	28	34	30	25	(in minutes)

Average: 28.5 min   Range: $34 - 24 = 10$ min
Positive deviations: 4.5   3.5   0.5   4.5   2.5
                       0.5   0.5   5.5   1.5   3.5
Mean deviation: 2.7 min, that is,

$$\frac{4.5 + 3.5 + 0.5 + 4.5 + 2.5 + 0.5 + 0.5 + 5.5 + 1.5 + 3.5}{10}$$

(b)

Test:	1	2	3	4	5	6	7	
Score:	80	72	86	92	78	80	86	Average: 82
Dev.	2	10	4	10	4	2	4	Range: 20

Mean deviation: $\dfrac{36}{7} = 5\dfrac{1}{7}$

(c) Given the following set of values:

12.0	9.6	10.8	12.0	14.2	10.8	9.6
10.8	12.0	14.2	9.6	10.8	10.8	12.0
12.0	10.8	12.0	12.0	14.2	9.6	12.0

Find the average, range, and mean deviation.

Rather than working directly with the set of values, we can organize the values into a table and use a "column" procedure:

Distinct Values V	Number (Frequency) f	Product $V \times f$	Deviations D	Products $D \times f$
9.6	4	38.4	1.9	7.6
10.8	6	64.8	0.7	4.2
12.0	8	96.0	0.5	4.0
14.2	3	42.6	2.7	8.1
Totals:	21	241.8		23.9

Average: $\dfrac{241.8}{21} = 11.5$

Mean deviation: $\dfrac{23.9}{21} = 1.14$

Range: $14.2 - 9.6 = 4.6$

In actual practice, the spreading or variability of a set of values is measured by a more "sophisticated" quantity called the **standard deviation**. The standard deviation measures a "most likely" deviation rather than the average of the deviations. Its mathematical advantages can be described as a "root-mean-square." That is, the standard deviation can be described as the "square root of the mean of the deviations squared." If D stands for a deviation and n the total number of values in a set of values, then we have

$$\textbf{Standard deviation} = \sqrt{\frac{\text{Sum of } D^2}{n}}$$

We can think of an average as somewhat like finding the point of balance along a lever with various weights distributed on the lever. The standard deviation is then like finding the distance from the balance point at which all the weights might be concentrated to obtain the same effect.

Examples.

(a) Set:	1	3	3	4	5	5	5	7	7	10	Sum 50
Deviation:	4	2	2	1	0	0	0	2	2	5	18
Deviation Squared:	16	4	4	1	0	0	0	4	4	25	58

Average: $\frac{50}{10} = 5$

Range: $10 - 1 = 9$

Mean deviation: $\frac{18}{10} = 1.8$

Standard deviation: $\sqrt{\frac{58}{10}} = \sqrt{5.8} = 2.4$

(b) GIVEN:

8.0	9.5	8.5	8.5	8.0	9.0	8.0
7.5	8.0	9.0	8.0	8.0	7.0	9.0
9.0	8.5	8.0	7.5	9.0	7.5	8.0
9.5	8.0	9.5	8.0	7.5	7.5	9.0
8.0	9.0	7.5	7.5	8.5	8.0	7.5

We can organize the values by noting that there are only six different values:

Value V	Fre-quency f	Product $f \times V$	Deviation D	Product $f \times D$	Deviation Squared D^2	Product $f \times D^2$
9.5	3	28.5	1.26	3.78	1.59	4.77
9.0	7	63.0	0.76	5.32	0.58	4.06
8.5	4	34.0	0.26	1.04	0.07	0.28
8.0	12	96.0	0.24	2.88	0.06	0.72
7.5	8	60.0	0.74	5.92	0.55	4.40
7.0	1	7.0	1.24	1.24	1.54	1.54
	35	288.5		20.18		15.77

Now we are ready to compute:

Average: $\frac{288.5}{35} = 8.24$

Mean deviation: $\frac{20.18}{35} = 0.58$

Range: $9.5 - 7.0 = 2.5$

Standard deviation: $\sqrt{\frac{15.77}{35}} = \sqrt{0.45} = 0.67$

Practice 2.

1. Find the range, mean deviation, and standard deviation for each of the sets of values in Exercise 1 of Practice 1.

2. Do as in Exercise 1 above with Exercises 2, 3, and 4 of Practice 1.

3. What is the relationship of size (magnitude) between the range, mean deviation, and standard deviation of a set of values?

4. Complete the following table and compute the average, range, mean deviation, and standard deviation for the 60 values represented.

Value V	Fre- quency f	Product f × V	Deviation D	Product f × D	Deviation Squared D²	Product f × D²
25.0	7	175	6.7	46.9	44.89	314.23
22.5	10					
20.0	8					
17.5	16					
15.0	11					
12.5	6					
10.0	2	20	8.3	16.6	68.89	137.78
	60					

5. Given the following tabulation of values, organize it into a table as in Exercise 4 and compute the average, range, mean deviation, and standard deviation for the set of values:

1.6	1.8	2.0	1.6	1.6	2.0	1.8	1.4
1.2	1.4	1.0	1.4	1.6	1.6	1.6	1.4
1.6	1.4	1.6	1.4	1.0	1.8	1.6	1.6
1.8	1.8	1.6	1.8	1.4	1.6	1.4	1.8
2.0	1.2	1.4	1.2	1.4	1.6	1.0	1.4

Answers.

1. (a) R = 6; M.D. = 1.5; S.D. = 1.9.
   (b) R = 21; M.D. = 7.1; S.D. = 7.9.
   (c) R = 7.01; M.D. = 1.465; S.D. = 1.953.
   (d) R = 4; M.D. = 0.97; S.D. = 1.33.
2. 2. R = 40; M.D. = 7.6; S.D. = 10.25.
   3. R = 0.03; M.D. = 0.009; S.D. = 0.0102.
   4. R = 0.00166; M.D. = 0.0007; S.D. = 0.0016.
3. The standard deviation lies between the range and mean deviation. That is, M.D. ≤ S.D. ≤ R.
4. Average: 18.3;   Range: 15;   M.D.: 3.27;   S.D.: 3.96.
5. Average: 1.54;   Range: 1;   M.D.: 0.204;   S.D.: 0.2546.

When we compute an average for a set of values it is somewhat like finding a "central" position for the fulcrum of a lever, with the values giving us the positions of equal individual "weights" with respect to some fixed position. If all of the values were placed at the position of the average value, the total set would be in balance.

Finding the range is somewhat like finding the total length of a lever, while determining the mean deviation or standard deviation is analogous to finding where the "weights" are concentrated on the lever.

Exercises

1. Is the measurement of length exact? If so, why? If not so, describe how errors might be made small and estimated.

2. What does an average of a set of values tell us about the set of values?

3. What does the mean deviation of a set of values tell us about the set of values?

4. Find the average and range for each of the following sets of values:
   (a) 8, 5, 5, 7, 6, 7, 2, 9, 5.
   (b) 165, 287, 192, 240.

5. Find the mean deviation and standard deviation for each of the sets of values in Exercise 4 above.

6. Three students, conveniently identified as A, B, and C, received the following scores on a series of six tests:

Test:	1	2	3	4	5	6
A:	65	70	70	75	70	75
B:	65	85	65	90	75	60
C:	85	70	60	75	85	80

Compare the three students with respect to their test scores.

7. In Exercise 6 above, which test appears to have been the "easiest"? Which the most "difficult"? Why?

8. Given the following tabulation of values, organize it into a convenient table and compute the average, and standard deviation:

4	3	3	4	3	2	3	5	1	3	5	2	3	3
4	3	2	3	2	1	3	1	2	3	3	1	5	3
4	5	2	3	4	3	2	5	3	3	1	3	4	4
2	3	4	4	1	2	3	2	1	3	5	1	3	2
3	3	4	3	3	3	4	2	4	3	5	2	3	1

9. Measurements of three quantities assumed to be related to a constant according to the equation $K = \dfrac{N \times R}{A}$ resulted in the following

tabulation of data:

N:	0.4	4.2	1.0	2.8	1.8
R:	5.4	1.3	5.2	4.5	6.4
A:	1.2	2.8	3.0	5.8	6.4

Find the average value of K and write a formula for N in terms of A and R. Using this formula, find the value of N if $A = 4$ and $R = 18$.

10. If a 10-inch lever has weights hung from it as shown in Figure 174, then how far from the left "0" end of the lever should the fulcrum be placed in order to balance the lever? What is an "average" distance of the weights from the fulcrum?

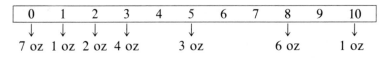

0	1	2	3	4	5	6	7	8	9	10
↓	↓	↓	↓		↓			↓		↓
7 oz	1 oz	2 oz	4 oz		3 oz			6 oz		1 oz

FIGURE 174

Answers.

1. No. Use precise and accurate instruments carefully under controlled conditions and avoid illegitimate errors; take a large number of careful measurements and average them; estimate the error by using the standard deviation.

2. That if the average were used uniformly for all the values in the set, then the total would be the same as in the original set of values.

3. The expected variation of the actual values from the average "on the average."

4. (a) Average: 6; Range: 7   (b) Average: 221; Range: 122.

5. (a) M.D. 1.56; S.D. 1.94   (b) M.D. 42.5; S.D. 46.6.

6. A: Average 71; R = 10; M.D. 3; S.D. 3.5.
   B: Average 73; R = 25; M.D. 10; S.D. 11.
   C: Average 76; R = 25; M.D. 7.5; S.D. 8.9.

Student C appears to do better than A. Although A is consistent, his grades are generally lower than B or C. Student B appears to fluctuate, having both the highest and the lowest grades of all. Student C appears to be a bit more stable and somewhat better in test grades than A or B.

7. Test 4 appears to have been the "easiest" since the average was 80 for the three students and the highest of the set of 6 tests. Test 3 appears to have been the most difficult with an average of 65 the lowest average of the set of 6 tests.

8. Average: 2.9; S.D. 1.13.

9. Average K: 1.89; $N = 1.89 \times \frac{A}{R}$; $N = 0.42$.

10. 3.75 inches; M.D. 2.96 or S.D. 3.33.

Review Summary

What is the advantage, the purpose and use, in studying the language of numbers and arithmetic? One answer lies in the rapid and efficient solution of practical problems and communicating these solutions to others.

In working problems we may note a pattern, a general relationship. We call a mathematical relationship with at least one variable which can be used to obtain answers a formula. For example, $D = R \times T$ is a _____ *formula* which tells us how to obtain answers to questions concerning distance, speed, and time. In studying various formulas, it is helpful to notice that they fall into simple patterns and forms. The formula $D = R \times T$ when written in the form $\frac{D}{T} = R$ is in the form of a _____ so *ratio* that all we have said concerning ratios can be applied with this formula.

Another type of formula is illustrated by $W_1 \times D_1 = W_2 \times D_2$. This is called the _____ principle and *lever* represents the relationship necessary to have a balance when weights W_1 and W_2 are placed on a beam at distances D_1 and D_2 respectively from the point at which the beam is supported. This point of support is called the fulcrum of the lever. When written in the form $\frac{W_1}{W_2} = \frac{D_2}{D_1}$ we notice that the formula asserts that the _____ *ratio* of the weights must equal the reciprocal of the ratio of the distances.

When one of the three quantities in the relationship described by $\frac{N}{D} = R$ is a constant the result leads to the description of many special applications. When $\frac{N}{D} = K$, where K is a constant or $N = K \times D$, we describe the relationship by saying that "N varies _____ as D." *directly* When $R \times D = K$, where K is a constant or $R = K \times \frac{1}{D}$, we say that "R varies _____ as D." The constant K, *inversely* in either case, is called the constant of variation. For example, if $P = 4s$ we would say that "P varies directly as s" while if $h = 5 \times \dfrac{1}{b}$ we would say that "h varies inversely as b." The constant of variation in $P = 4s$ is _____ while in $h = 5 \times \dfrac{1}{b}$ it is _____. If we know that two **4, 5** quantities vary directly or inversely with respect to each other, we can determine the value of the constant of variation given one pair of values of the variables. If $A = K \times B$ and $A = 2$ when $B = 3$, then we have $K =$ _____. $\dfrac{2}{3}$

When two ratios are equal we call the resulting relationship a proportion. That is, when $\dfrac{A}{B} = \dfrac{C}{D}$ we say that we have a _____. The four quantities in the proportion are called _____; A and D are called the extremes while B and C are called means. The idea of a proportion is connected to the geometric notion of similarity. That is, when two figures have the same shape we say that they are _____ and can show that if two figures are similar, then their corresponding sides are _____. If we know the ratio of one pair of corresponding sides in similar figures, then we know the ratio of any other pair of corresponding sides in the similar figures. For example, in Figure 175, if triangles ABC and ACD are similar, then we have $\dfrac{\overline{AB}}{\overline{AC}} = \dfrac{\overline{BC}}{\overline{CD}} = \dfrac{\overline{AC}}{\overline{AD}}$. Given that $\overline{AB} = 16$ units, $\overline{BC} = 8$ units, and $\overline{CD} = 5$ units we can find the lengths of the remaining segments: $\overline{AC} =$ _____, $\overline{AD} =$ _____, and $\overline{BD} = \overline{AB} - \overline{AD} =$ _____.

proportion
terms

similar
proportional

$10, 6\dfrac{1}{4}$

$9\dfrac{3}{4}$

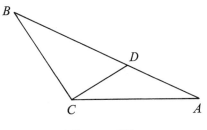

FIGURE 175

In working with proportions, it is often convenient to be able to write the same proportion in a variety of different forms. For example, given the proportion $\dfrac{A}{B} = \dfrac{C}{D}$, we say that the product of the means is equal to the prod-

uct of the extremes and write _____. It is also true that
the reciprocals of the ratios form a proportion _____
(providing, of course, that we do not divide by _____).

$B \times C$
$= A \times D$
$\dfrac{B}{A} = \dfrac{D}{C}$
zero

One of the most widely used formulas arises from the relationship between the sides of a right triangle. In any right triangle the square on the _____ equals the sum of the squares on the legs. That is, _____, where a and b are the lengths of the legs and c is the length of the hypotenuse. The formula, called the _____ Theorem, can be demonstrated using similar triangles and proportions.

hypotenuse
$c^2 = a^2 + b^2$

Pythagorean

We can develop an understanding of the formula by constructing right triangles of various shapes and measuring the lengths of their sides. If a and b are the measured lengths of the legs, then the length of the hypotenuse should be such that its square will equal the _____ of the _____ of a and b. A further experiment would be to find numbers such that the relationship is true and verify that if segments are in this relationship, then the triangle formed by using these segments will form a _____ triangle. Two such triples of positive integers, called Pythagorean numbers, are 3, _____, _____ and _____, 8, 17.

sum
squares

right
4, 5
15

Of course, the practical utility of the Pythagorean Theorem lies in our ability to find the length of one of the sides of a right triangle given the other two sides. For example, given the length of the hypotenuse, say $c = 14$, and the length of a leg, say $a = 6$, we obtain the result $b^2 = (14 \times 14) - (6 \times 6) = 160$. Now we must still find a number b such that $b \times b = $ _____. To describe the relationship of b to 160 we say that "b is the _____ _____ of 160." We write $b = $ _____.

160
square root,
$\sqrt{160}$

An algorithm developed to obtain results can be described briefly as follows:
Given $r^2 = N$. To find r:

Guess r to be equal to g. Compute $q = \dfrac{N}{g}$. If $q = g$, then $r = $ _____. If $q \neq g$, then we make a second guess $g^* = $ _____ and compute $q^* = \dfrac{N}{g^*}$. If $q^* = g^*$, then $r = g^*$. If $q^* \neq g^*$, then we make a third guess $g^{**} = $ _____ and continue until the approximation is sufficiently close to satisfy the problem.

g
$\dfrac{g + q}{2}$

$\dfrac{g^* + q^*}{2}$

For example, to find $b = \sqrt{160}$, we might first guess $b = 13$ and compute $q =$ _____. Since $q \neq g$, we make a second guess $g^* =$ _____. Now we obtain $q^* = 12.6381$

$$\frac{160}{13} = 12.31$$

$$\frac{12.31 + 13}{2}$$

$$= 12.66$$

so that we can approximate the square root of 160 to be $b =$ _____ to four places.

12.65

To obtain successive guesses above, we have used a single representative value for g and q. That is, the idea of an _____. An average value is the value such that when used uniformly for all the values in a set of values, then the total will be unchanged. For example, the average of 3, 5, 2, and 6 is _____.

average

4

When we use an average, a natural question is "How good is it?" That is, how much do the actual values differ from the average? We can roughly indicate this difference by noting the range of values. That is, the difference between the _____ and _____ values in the set of values.

largest,
smallest

For example, the range of 3, 5, 2, and 6 is _____.

4

Although the range will indicate the "spread" of values in a set, it can be misleading. Thus, we considered an average of the differences of values from the average of the set of values. The average of the positive deviations of a set of values from their average was called the _____ _____. For example, the mean deviation of 3, 5, 2, and 6 is _____.

mean
deviation

$1\frac{1}{2}$

In actual practice, the variability of a set of values is indicated by the "square root of the mean of the deviations squared." That is, by the _____ _____. For example, the standard deviation of 3, 5, 2, and 6 is _____.

standard
deviation

1.58

Chapter Exercises (9)

Group I.

1. Describe what each of the following formulas assert and name each literal quantity.

   (a) $A = \pi r^2$ (b) $V = L \times W \times H$ (c) $W = F \times D$.

2. Using the letters indicated, express each of the following statements as a mathematical formula:

(a) The volume (V) of a sphere is equal to four-thirds the product of "pi" and the radius (r) "cubed."

(b) The amount (A) repaid on a loan is equal to the sum of the principal (P) borrowed and the interest (I) on the loan.

(c) The fahrenheit temperature (°F) is equal to 32° more than nine-fifths the centigrade temperature (°C).

3. An Italian philosopher and astronomer, Galileo Galilei (1564–1642), showed experimentally that all bodies fall with the same speed regardless of their weight, providing the resistance of air is neglected. If the distance in feet that a body falls varies directly as the square of the time of falling in seconds, then

(a) what is the formula for the distance (D) in terms of the time (t) if $D = 100$ ft when $t = 2.5$ sec?

(b) how far will a body fall in 7 sec?

(c) how long will it take for a body to fall 500 ft?

4. Rather than lifting a 200 lb package vertically up to a platform 3 ft high, a man pushes the 200 ib package on a dolly up a 5 ft long inclined ramp. How much force (effort) must he use in pushing the package if friction is disregarded? Can you write a formula for this situation?

5. An equilateral triangle is drawn in a unit square with one side of the triangle a side of the square. Find the area inside the square and outside the triangle. See Figure 176.

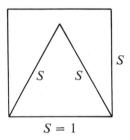

$S = 1$

FIGURE 176

6. If Mr. Jones starts driving from town A to town B at 40 miles per hour and Mr. Smith starts driving from town B to town A, at the same time, at 55 miles per hour and they pass each other 24 minutes after they start, then

(a) what is the distance between the two towns?

(b) how long will it take for Mr. Jones to drive to town B?

7. If a 10 lb force is applied to the end of an 8 inches long nutcracker hinged at one end, then how much force will be applied to a nut 2 inches from the hinged end?

8. Find the value of the constants of variation and the value of the variable indicated:

(a) $F = K \times a$ and $F = 165$ when $a = 30$, and find F if $a = \frac{2}{5}$.

(b) $M = \frac{K}{R}$ and $M = 2$ when $R = \frac{3}{2}$, and find M if $R = 12$.

9. Find the value of B in each of the following proportions:

(a) $\frac{1 + B}{3} = \frac{7}{3}$ (b) $\frac{2}{5} = \frac{-6}{2 - B}$ (c) $\frac{2B}{7} = \frac{9}{B}$.

10. A telephone pole casts a shadow 22 ft 6 inches long. At the same time a 4 ft high fence post casts a shadow 1 ft 8 inches long. Sketch a figure and find the height of the telephone pole.

11. Approximate the following square roots to four places.

(a) $\sqrt{54}$ (b) $\sqrt{360}$ (c) $\sqrt{7.8}$ (d) $\sqrt{6,930}$.

12. Find the lengths of the segments indicated in Figure 177 to three place positions.

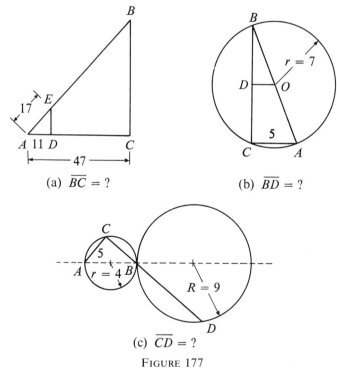

(a) $\overline{BC} = ?$ (b) $\overline{BD} = ?$

(c) $\overline{CD} = ?$

FIGURE 177

13. Find the length of the side of a square to within $\frac{1}{64}$ inches so that its area will closely approximate the area of a circle of radius $3\frac{1}{2}$ inches.

14. Find the average and standard deviation for each of the following sets of values.

    (a) 17, 12, 12, 15, 9   (b) 7.5, 6.0, 8.8, 7.5, 7.5, 9.5.

15. A tabulation of the hours of work as indicated on the time cards of three men for a certain week was as follows:

day \ man	Mon.	Tues.	Wed.	Thur.	Fri.
Smith:	7	$8\frac{1}{2}$	$7\frac{3}{4}$	$8\frac{1}{4}$	7
Jones:	$7\frac{1}{2}$	8	8	$7\frac{3}{4}$	$8\frac{1}{2}$
Pike:	$7\frac{3}{4}$	$7\frac{3}{4}$	8	$7\frac{3}{4}$	$8\frac{3}{4}$

    (a) What was the average length of the working time-card day for these men during this week?

    (b) If they were paid at a uniform rate of $3.37 per hour, then what was the average of the three weekly paychecks?

16. Find the average and standard deviation for the table of organized values below:

Value	Frequency
21.4	17
19.2	34
17.0	23
14.8	48
12.6	37
10.4	11

Group II.

1. Describe what each of the following formulas assert and name each literal quantity.

    (a) $V = \dfrac{Bh}{3}$ (b) $I = prt$ (c) $T = \sqrt{\dfrac{L}{39}}.$

2. Using the letters indicated, express each of the following statements as a formula.

    (a) The area (A) of a trapezoid is equal to one-half the altitude (h) times the sum of the bases (b_1 and b_2).

    (b) The volume (V) of a regular tetrahedron, that is, a solid bounded by equilateral triangles, is equal to the product of the quotient of the square root of two divided by twelve and the square of the length of an edge (e).

(c) The centigrade (°C) temperature is equal to five-ninths of the quantity thirty-two less than the fahrenheit (°F) temperature.

3. Electrical energy is the product of electrical power measured in watts used through a period of time. It is often referred to in terms of kilowatt-hours (1000 watts = 1 kilowatt).

(a) If electricity is priced at 4 cents per kilowatt-hour, then write a formula for the cost (C) of electricity in terms of watts (W) and time (T).

(b) How much would it cost to keep an ordinary 75-watt light bulb lit for 5 days?

(c) If the number of watts is equal to the product of volts (E) and amperes (I), then what will happen to the consumption of electricity in a circuit if the resistance is halved? Can you write a formula which clearly describes the relationship?

4. A boy wishes to lift a 200 lb package up to a platform 3 ft high. If he can only exert a force of 75 lb, then what is the shortest inclined ramp that he can use to push the package on a dolly up to the platform? (Disregard the friction and weight of the dolly.)

5. A circle is drawn in an equilateral triangle just touching the sides of the triangle. If the length of the side of the triangle is 2 units, then find the area outside the circle and inside the triangle. See Figure 178.

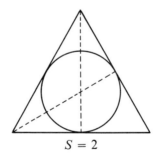

$$S = 2$$

FIGURE 178

6. A 2-mile long convoy of trucks is moving along a highway at 45 miles per hour. If a messenger starts at the rear of the convoy and travels to the front at 60 miles per hour, then

(a) how long will it take for him to reach the front of the convoy?

(b) how far will the front of the convoy have traveled while the messenger was en route from the rear to the front of the convoy?

7. If an old-fashioned wheelbarrow has 160 lb of dirt in its box centered 18 inches from the axle of its wheel and 4 ft long arms measured from the axle, then what force must be exerted upward on the ends of the arms to lift and move the wheelbarrow?

8. Find the value of the constants of variation and the value of the

variable indicated:

(a) $S = K \times t^2$ and $S = 64$ when $t = 2$, and find S if $t = \dfrac{1}{2}$.

(b) $I = \dfrac{K}{d}$ and $I = \dfrac{1}{2}$ when $d = \dfrac{3}{4}$, and find I if $d = 3$.

9. Find the value of B in each of the following proportions.

(a) $\dfrac{5}{1 - 2B} = \dfrac{7}{9}$ (b) $\dfrac{6}{5} = \dfrac{B + 3}{4}$ (c) $\dfrac{27}{B} = \dfrac{B}{3}$.

10. A 30 ft long ladder is placed against a building with its foot 7 ft from the base of the building. If a horizontal brace is nailed to the ladder 25 ft up from the foot, then how long must it be to just touch the building?

11. Approximate the following square roots to four places:

(a) $\sqrt{79}$ (b) $\sqrt{207}$ (c) $\sqrt{4.4}$ (d) $\sqrt{8{,}290}$.

12. Find the lengths of the segments indicated in Figure 179 to three place positions.

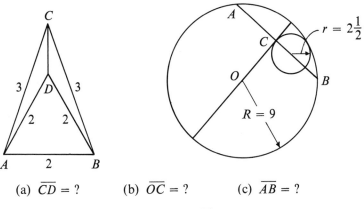

(a) $\overline{CD} = ?$ (b) $\overline{OC} = ?$ (c) $\overline{AB} = ?$

FIGURE 179

13. Find the radius of a circle to within 0.01 inch so that its area will closely approximate the area of a square with sides of 3 inches each.

14. Find the average and standard deviation for each of the following sets of values.

(a) 31, 27, 26, 35, 31   (b) 1.2, 2.1, 1.8, 0.6, 1.5, 1.2.

15. An office supervisor collected the following table of information on typing in an office.

| | Number of errors per sheet | | | |
Typing speed	$0 - 2$	$3 - 5$	$6 - 8$	$9 - 11$
60	4[a]	23	5	3
50	7	18	3	2
40	4	4	2	5

[a] Number of sheets

(a) What was the average number of errors made per sheet of typing?

(b) At which speed of typing is the average number of errors the least?

16. Find the average and standard deviation for the table of organized values below.

Value	Frequency
15.5	13
14.0	17
12.5	9
11.0	14
9.5	32
8.0	15

Problem Set (9)

1. We have noted how formulas describe the relationships between quantities and their units of measure. The fundamental units in the English system are those for length in feet, for mass in pounds, and for time in seconds.

(a) Discuss the relationships and units given by:

(i) speed $V = \dfrac{D}{T}$ (ii) acceleration $a = \dfrac{V}{T}$.

(b) Show how we can obtain the following formulas for free-falling bodies from a consideration of the formulas in Part (a) along with experiments to establish the value of g:

(i) speed $V_f = V_0 + gT$.

(ii) distance $D_f = V_0 T + \dfrac{1}{2}gT^2$.

(iii) $V_f^2 = V_0^2 + 2gD_f$.

(c) Discuss the relationship of units given by force $F = ma$. What is the relationship between force, weight, and mass?

2. We have considered the problem of finding triples of positive integers a, b, c such that $a^2 + b^2 = c^2$ (called Pythagorean triples).

(a) Can you find formulas which will yield all Pythagorean triples of positive integers? If so, exhibit and discuss them.

(b) Pythagorean triples suggest the question as to whether there are positive integers a, b, c such that $a^3 + b^3 = c^3$ or $a^4 + b^4 = c^4$ or, in general, $a^n + b^n = c^n$ for $n > 2$.

Pierre Fermat (1601–1665), a lawyer and mathematician of Toulouse, France, remarked in some marginal notes that ". . . it is impossible to separate a cube into two cubes, a fourth power into two fourth powers, or, generally, any power above the second into two powers of the same degree." This assertion is called *Fermat's Last Theorem.*

Investigate and discuss Fermat's Last Theorem.

3. A formula for the area of a triangle in terms of the lengths of its sides first appeared in the writing of a mathematician, Hero of Alexandria, during the first century A.D. It is known as *Hero's Formula.*

State the formula and show how it can be obtained from the formulas $A = \frac{1}{2}hb$ and $S = \frac{a+b+c}{2}$, where a, b, c are the lengths of the sides of a triangle and h is the altitude to the side b of the triangle.

4. In many problems two quantities, say Y and X, are related by an equation of the form $Y = MX + B$, where M and B are constants. Experiment and consider various values of the constants M and B and describe the roles of these constants in determining the relationship between Y and X.

5. Consider the formula $C = 2\pi r$ for the circumference of a circle. In many situations it is convenient to be able to measure the length of a part of a circle, called an **arc**, in terms of the radius of the circle.

(a) If S is the length of an arc of a circle with radius r, then how is this arc related to r?

(b) If $S = r$, we call the measure of S with respect to the radius of the circle **one radian**. If $S = C$ the circumference, then what is the measure of S in radians? Complete the following table:

S below	Radian measure of S below
$\frac{1}{2}C$	
$\frac{1}{3}C$	
$\frac{1}{4}C$	
$\frac{1}{6}C$	
$\frac{3}{2}C$	
$\frac{5}{4}C$	

(c) If θ stands for the measure of S in radians, then write a formula for the length of S.

CHAPTER 10

The Real Numbers

10.1 Irrational Numbers

10.1.1   Although the rational numbers suffice in any act of measurement, it was discovered long ago that there were quantities which could not be represented by a rational number. It is said that a Pythagorean named Hippasus was drowned by his fellows for revealing that there were quantities which could not be expressed exactly with rational numbers.

As an example, we have noted that the ratio between the circumference of a circle and its diameter is a constant, $\frac{C}{d} = \pi$, which we have approximated with the rational numbers $\frac{22}{7}$ or 3.1416. In 1761, Johann Heinrich Lambert (1728–1777) showed that this quantity was not a rational number. If we conceive of a rational number as a quantity obtained by "breaking" a unit into any number of equal parts, then there will still be quantities which are not represented by these rational numbers.

To better understand the existence of nonrational or **irrational** quantities, let us consider a specific example. Let $ABCD$ be a unit square. By the Pythagorean Theorem we have $\overline{AC}^2 = 2$. That is, the length of the diagonal must equal the square root of 2: $\overline{AC} = \sqrt{2}$. The square root of 2 is not a rational number; for consider:

If $\sqrt{2}$ were a rational number, then we could write that $\sqrt{2} = \frac{P}{Q}$, where $\frac{P}{Q}$ is a reduced rational number. Now we could write that $2 = \left(\frac{P}{Q}\right)^2 = \frac{P^2}{Q^2}$ so that $2Q^2 = P^2$. But if $2Q^2 = P^2$, then P^2 must be even so that P must be even. That is, we must have $P = 2N$. Now we must have $2Q^2 = (2N)^2$ so that $Q^2 = 2N^2$ and Q must also be even. But this leads us to the conclusion that both P and Q must be even which contradicts our initial statement that $\frac{P}{Q}$ is a reduced rational number. Thus, since $\sqrt{2}$ is either rational or irrational, and to say that it is rational leads to a contradiction, we must conclude that $\sqrt{2}$ is not rational. That is, $\sqrt{2}$ is irrational.

Of course, we can approximate $\sqrt{2}$ to any desired number of decimal places through a process of simple repeated divisions.

$$1.4 < \sqrt{2} < 1.5$$
$$1.41 < \sqrt{2} < 1.42$$
$$1.414 < \sqrt{2} < 1.415$$
$$1.4142 < \sqrt{2} < 1.4143$$
$$1.41421 < \sqrt{2} < 1.41422$$
$$1.414214 < \sqrt{2} < 1.414215$$
$$\dots \text{ and so on} \dots$$

Thus, having the irrational number "trapped" we might ask "What further can be desired?" The practical man might be satisfied. To the mathematician, philosopher, and theorist, however, such a situation presents an intriguing challenge.

Observing the decimal approximations for $\sqrt{2}$, we might be led to a more careful study of decimal representations of numbers. We have already noted that decimal representations of all the rational numbers are easily obtained by a simple process of division from the fractional forms. These decimal representations of the rational numbers either terminate in zeroes, that is, the division ends with a zero remainder, or begin to repeat a fixed set of digits in a cyclic manner.

Examples.

(a) $\frac{5}{4} = 1.25000$ (b) $\frac{3}{8} = 0.375000$ (c) $\frac{3}{16} = 0.1875000$

(d) $\frac{4}{7} = 0.571428\ 571428\ 571428 \dots$ (e) $\frac{2}{3} = 0.6666 \dots .$

The reason for the cyclic repetition of digits in the decimal representation of rational numbers is quite evident when we consider that the only possible remainders in a division are those positive integers less than the divisor. For example, in dividing by 7 the only possible remainders are 0, 1, 2, 3, 4, 5, and 6.

Now we can ask "Are there decimal representations other than terminating and repeating decimals?" The answer, of course, is yes. Consider the process exhibited for approximating the square root of 2: $1.414214 < \sqrt{2} < 1.414215$. The process might be continued unending to form a decimal representation of $\sqrt{2}$. In the same way we can conceive of decimal representations for $\sqrt{3}$, $\sqrt{5}$, and so on. As a matter of fact, it should be quite simple to exhibit decimal representations which do not terminate in zeroes or repeat cyclicly. For example, $\pi = 3.1415926536\ldots$ and so on, unending.

Examples.

(a) $0.1101001000100001000001000000100000001\ldots$
(b) $1.61803398\ldots$ (c) $2.7182818285\ldots.$

If we continue the terminating decimal by thinking of zeroes written to the right in unending order, then all decimal representations can be placed in two categories:

1. Those which repeat a set of digits.

These decimal representations name the rational numbers.

2. Those which do not repeat a set of digits.

These decimal representations name the irrational numbers.

A very important idea should be noted here. We have introduced the notion of an unending process. That is, a continuing succession of "well formed" steps which are conceived of as going on indefinitely. For example, as in the algorithmic process for approximating the square root of a positive number. Can we represent all irrational numbers using possibly unending rational processes? For the practical man, this is of special importance, for by systematizing the rational processes and limiting his computations to a certain number of places, he can then obtain rational approximations for any irrational number which may occur in a problem. That we can, in fact, represent any irrational quantity by a rational process is of fundamental importance.

Examples.

(a) An interesting and remarkable irrational number called phi, ϕ, or more commonly the "golden ratio," can be described as the solution to the equation:†

$$\frac{A+1}{A} = \frac{A}{1}.$$

The positive value obtained is $A = \dfrac{1+\sqrt{5}}{2}$ which can be approximated using the square root algorithm. However, ϕ can also be described as follows:

$$\phi = 1 + \cfrac{1}{1 + \cfrac{1}{1 + \cfrac{1}{1 + \cfrac{1}{1 + \cfrac{1}{1 + \cdots}}}}} \text{ and so on.}$$

† See *Scientific American*, August 1959.

(b) The number $\pi = \dfrac{C}{d}$ can be approximated in a variety of ways:

$$\pi = 4 \times \left(1 - \frac{1}{3} + \frac{1}{5} - \frac{1}{7} + \frac{1}{9} - \frac{1}{11} + \frac{1}{13} - \frac{1}{15} + \cdots \right)$$

$$\pi = 2 \times \frac{2^2}{1 \times 3} \times \frac{4^2}{3 \times 5} \times \frac{6^2}{5 \times 7} \times \frac{8^2}{7 \times 9} \times \frac{10^2}{9 \times 11} \times \cdots$$

(c) An irrational number which occurs in the apparently unrelated problems of compound interest and biological growth is named by the letter "e."

$$e = 1 + \frac{1}{1} + \frac{1}{2} + \frac{1}{6} + \frac{1}{24} + \frac{1}{120} + \frac{1}{720} + \frac{1}{5040} + \cdots$$

The irrational number e can be approximated also by considering the quantity $\left(1 + \dfrac{1}{n}\right)^{n}$ as n is made as large as you please.

10.1.2 Decimal representations should immediately suggest the naming of points on a straight line. Recall how we identified a point on a line to each integer, then to each rational number.

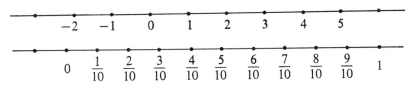

The rational numbers were ordered on the number line; given any two rational numbers, we can tell which is to the right of the other. Furthermore, we noted that between any two distinct rational points we could find further distinct rational points. Thus, the rational points were said to be "dense." To each rational number, however, we assigned a point on the number line.

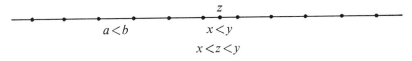

Now, the realization that there are irrational numbers leads us to ask "Are all the points on a line named by the rational numbers?" The answer is, no! There are many, many more points on a line which are unnamed by the rational numbers. These are the points named by the irrational numbers. Now the rational and irrational numbers together name all of the points on a line. Thus we obtain a complete set which names every point on a line. This, the complete set, is called the set of **real numbers**. That is, we conceive of the set of real numbers as corresponding to the set of all points on a line or to the set of all decimal representations of numbers as described above.

We can illustrate certain irrational points with geometric constructions.

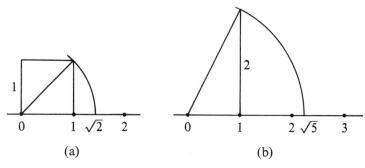

(a)   (b)

FIGURE 180

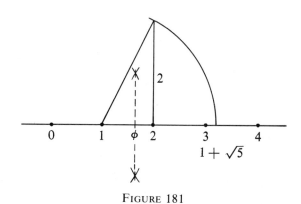

FIGURE 181

Exercises

1. Find decimal representations of the following numbers.

   (a) $\frac{11}{25}$ (b) $\frac{7}{32}$ (c) $\frac{5}{24}$ (d) $\frac{7}{11}$ (e) $\frac{8}{21}$.

2. Find decimal approximations of the following numbers to seven places.

   (a) $\sqrt{7}$ (b) $\sqrt{35}$ (c) $\sqrt{123}$ (d) $\sqrt{653}$ (e) $\sqrt{7090}$.

3. Obtain the decimal approximation of $\phi = \frac{1 + \sqrt{5}}{2}$ to five places and compare the successive values of

   (a) $1 + \dfrac{1}{1 + \dfrac{1}{2}}$ (b) $1 + \dfrac{1}{1 + \dfrac{1}{1 + \dfrac{1}{2}}}$ (c) $1 + \dfrac{1}{1 + \dfrac{1}{1 + \dfrac{1}{1 + \dfrac{1}{2}}}}$ to ϕ.

4. Find decimal representations of the following complex fractions.

(a) $2 + \dfrac{1}{1 + \dfrac{3}{2}}$ (b) $2 + \dfrac{1}{1 + \dfrac{3}{2 + \dfrac{1}{1 + \dfrac{3}{2}}}}$

(c) $2 + \dfrac{1}{1 + \dfrac{3}{2 + \dfrac{1}{1 + \dfrac{3}{2 + \dfrac{1}{1 + \dfrac{3}{2}}}}}}$

(d) Can you continue the fraction? It represents $\sqrt{6}$.

5. Compute the following approximations to π.

(a) $4 \times \left(1 - \dfrac{1}{3} + \dfrac{1}{5} - \dfrac{1}{7} + \dfrac{1}{9} - \dfrac{1}{11} + \dfrac{1}{13} - \dfrac{1}{15} + \dfrac{1}{17} - \dfrac{1}{19}\right).$

(b) $2 \times \dfrac{2^2}{1 \times 3} \times \dfrac{4^2}{3 \times 5} \times \dfrac{6^2}{5 \times 7} \times \dfrac{8^2}{7 \times 9} \times \dfrac{10^2}{9 \times 11} \times \dfrac{12^2}{11 \times 13}.$

6. List the succession (sequence) of numbers obtained by setting $n = 1, 2, 3, \ldots$ in $\left(1 + \dfrac{1}{n}\right)^n$. The numbers approximate e closer and closer.

7. Order the following sets of numbers from smallest to largest.

(a) $\dfrac{11}{180}, \dfrac{1}{18}, \dfrac{5}{72}, \dfrac{7}{120}, \dfrac{1}{15}, \dfrac{1}{20}.$

(b) $\dfrac{5-4}{54}, \dfrac{1}{-60}, \dfrac{0}{75}, \dfrac{1}{4-40}, \dfrac{1+2}{135}, \dfrac{-1}{45}.$

(c) $\sqrt{5} - \sqrt{3}, \sqrt{3} - \sqrt{2}, \sqrt{7} - \sqrt{4}, \sqrt{3} - \sqrt{1}, \sqrt{7} - \sqrt{5}.$

(d) $\dfrac{\pi}{2}, \sqrt{2}, \phi, \dfrac{e}{2}, \sqrt{1 + \sqrt{2}}.$

8. Find three distinct rational numbers in fractional form between each of the following pairs of rational numbers.

(a) $\dfrac{1}{4}$ and $\dfrac{1}{3}$ (b) $\dfrac{19}{54}$ and $\dfrac{13}{36}$ (c) 1.25 and 1.26.

9. Illustrate the following irrational numbers on the number line with geometric constructions.

(a) $\sqrt{3}$ (b) $\sqrt{6}$ (c) $\dfrac{1 + \sqrt{2}}{3}.$

10. (a) Find the sum of the repeating decimals 5.376 376 . . . and 18.21 21 . . . .

(b) Find the sum of the repeating decimals 7.6498 6498 . . . and 2.85 85 . . . .

(c) Find the product of the repeating decimals 2.71 71 . . . and 3.05 05 . . . to six places.

Answers.

1. (a) 0.44   (b) 0.21875   (c) 0.20833 . . .   (d) 0.63 63 . . .
   (e) 0.380952 380952 . . . .
2. (a) 2.645751   (b) 5.916080   (c) 11.09054   (d) 25.55386
   (e) 84.20214.
3. $\phi = 1.6180$;   (a) 1.6 6 . . .   (b) 1.6   (c) 1.625.
4. (a) 2.4   (b) 2.4 4 . . .   (c) $2\frac{66}{147} = 2.449$ approx.
5. (a) $\dfrac{44\ 257\ 352}{14\ 549\ 535} = 3.042$ approx.   (b) $\dfrac{2\ 097\ 152}{693\ 693} = 3.023$ approx.

6.

n	1	2	3	4	5
$\left(1 + \dfrac{1}{n}\right)^n$	2	$\dfrac{9}{4}$	$\dfrac{64}{27}$	$\dfrac{625}{256}$	$\dfrac{7776}{3125}$
		2.25	2.37	2.44	2.488

7. (a) $\dfrac{1}{20}, \dfrac{1}{18}, \dfrac{7}{120}, \dfrac{11}{180}, \dfrac{1}{15}, \dfrac{5}{72}$.

   (b) $\dfrac{1}{4-40}, \dfrac{-1}{45}, \dfrac{1}{-60}, \dfrac{0}{75}, \dfrac{5-4}{54}, \dfrac{1+2}{135}$.

   (c) $\sqrt{3} - \sqrt{2}, \sqrt{7} - \sqrt{5}, \sqrt{5} - \sqrt{3}, \sqrt{7} - \sqrt{4}, \sqrt{3} - \sqrt{1}$.

   (d) $\dfrac{e}{2}, \sqrt{2}, \sqrt{1 + \sqrt{2}}, \dfrac{\pi}{2}, \phi$.

8. (a) $\dfrac{13}{48}, \dfrac{14}{48}, \dfrac{15}{48}$ (b) $\dfrac{153}{432}, \dfrac{154}{432}, \dfrac{155}{432}$ (c) $\dfrac{501}{400}, \dfrac{502}{400}, \dfrac{503}{400}$.

(Note: Other answers possible.)

9.

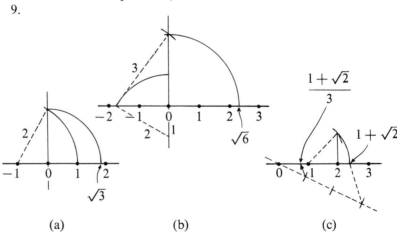

(a)   (b)   (c)

10. (a) 23.588497 588497 . . .   (b) 10.5084 5084 . . .
(c) 8.28874.

10.2 The Real Numbers

10.2.1   With the extension of the rational numbers into a **complete set,**
we have obtained a new set of numbers called the set of **real n**mbers.
Before proceeding to a further examination of the real numbers, let us
review, very briefly, some of the more pertinent aspects in our development and discussion of numbers thus far.

First, we began with the **natural** or **counting numbers**:

$$1, 2, 3, 4, 5, 6, 7, 8, 9, 10, 11, 12, 13, 14, 15, 16, \cdots$$

The idea of the cardinal size of a set led us to a careful naming of these
ideas. As we named the cardinal sizes of sets, there was a natural ordering which slowly led us to the ordinal idea of number. Noting how number
ideas were combined, our attention was drawn to special sets of natural
numbers such as the even and odd numbers, multiples of numbers, square
numbers, etc. Of special importance were the **prime numbers** and the fact
that all other natural numbers, called composites, could be expressed as
a product of prime numbers.

A natural activity was to add natural numbers together to obtain sums.
However, when we asked the question $17 + ? = 11$, we were embarrassed
with no natural number answer. Thus, we were led to the extension of the
natural numbers to the **integers**:

$$\cdots -7, -6, -5, -4, -3, -2, -1, 0, 1, 2, 3, 4, 5, 6, 7, \cdots$$

With the integers we developed subtraction, an operation which "undoes"
addition. The introduction of equations and variables in our developing
language of numbers enabled us to describe some of the specific properties of addition and subtraction. These were:

1. The closure of addition and subtraction with the integers.
2. The commutativity of addition of integers. And the anticommuta-
tivity of subtraction of integers.
3. The associativity of addition of integers.
4. The number zero, called the identity of addition of integers.
5. The negative of a number, called the inverse of the number under
addition.

With growing familiarity in working with integers we introduced a
"short-cut" operation for repeated additions of the same addend: multiplication. With multiplication we studied the important property, called
the **distributive property**, connecting addition and multiplication. As we

began working with larger and larger integers, it became evident that in many practical situations it would be convenient to round and estimate results.

Just as addition led us to subtraction, our concern with multiplication led us to division. Division is an operation which "undoes" multiplication. To help us in obtaining results we introduced the **division algorithm**: $B = (Q \times A) + R$. As we worked with division, it became evident that division was important as a tool for comparing and relating sets of numbers. Thus, we returned to the study of prime and composite numbers to deepen our understanding of the relationship between numbers. Two important comparative numbers for a set of numbers were the greatest common divisor (GCD) and the lowest common multiple (LCM) of the set of numbers.

Second, we began with the **rational numbers or fractions** :

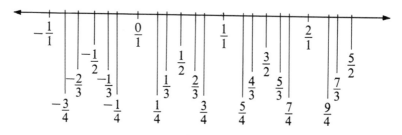

To help our intuitive understanding we introduced the idea of a scale and the rational **number line**. For each rational number we described a procedure to assign a point on the line. In discussing the rational numbers, the **fundamental property** of the rational numbers was a central tool in describing results. Although the rational numbers can be ordered, the ordering was quite distinct from the integers or natural numbers. Between any two rational numbers we can find many more rational numbers. This distinctive property of the rational numbers was named **denseness**.

In developing the four fundamental operations of addition, subtraction, multiplication, and division with the rational numbers we noted that the "standard" procedure was to reduce the situation to a consideration of operations with the integers. In summary, the set of rational numbers with the two basic operations of addition and multiplication form a structure called an **ordered field**. That is, the following properties are true:

Under addition and multiplication the rational numbers are:
1. Closed.
2. Commutative.
3. Associative.
4. There are two numbers, zero and one, called identities, such that
   (a) zero added to any number leaves the number unchanged.

(b) multiplying any number by one leaves the number unchanged.

5. Multiplication is distributive over addition.

6. For each nonzero number there are two numbers, its negative and its reciprocal, called inverses, such that

  (a) if its negative is added to the number the sum will be zero.

  (b) if the number is multiplied by its reciprocal the product will be one.

7. The set of rational numbers can be separated into three distinct subsets:

  (a) negative numbers   (b) zero   (c) positive numbers.

If two numbers are in the positive set, then addition and multiplication of the numbers will result in a sum and a product which are also in the positive set.

In order to develop more sophistication and practical utility in our writing we turned our attention to **decimal notation**. Decimal notation was based on the ideas of place position and the expanded form of a numeral. For example,

$$420.125 = 4(100) + 2(10) + 0(1) + 1\left(\frac{1}{10}\right) + 2\left(\frac{1}{100}\right) + 5\left(\frac{1}{1000}\right).$$

Once we had established the four fundamental operations as written in decimal form we turned our attention to the problems of measurement and applications. A useful tool in understanding many applications and the processes of measurement was to draw **geometric figures**. Studying the properties of simple geometric figures led us to describe various relationships revealed by the figures. In using our language of numbers and arithmetic, we developed **formulas** to obtain answers to special types of problems.

One of the most important and widely used formulas in mathematics is called the **Pythagorean Theorem**: $c^2 = a^2 + b^2$. To make adequate use of this formula, however, we discovered that we must be able to find the **square root** of a positive number. To overcome this difficulty we developed an algorithm enabling us to obtain successive results which approximated the square root as nearly as desirable in any practical situation. For example, we can successively approximate $\sqrt{2}$ with

1, 1.4, 1.41, 1.414, 1.4142, 1.41421, 1.414214, . . .

We might have been satisfied with an approximation but a more careful examination of the situation revealed a familiar problem! A situation which had no exact rational number answer. It became evident that there were many, many **irrational numbers**. That is, nonrational numbers. In examining a line, we could pick many points without rational number names. When the complete set, the rational and irrational numbers, are considered together we call the resulting set of numbers the **real numbers**.

10.2.2 To gain insight into the properties of the real numbers we will proceed with an examination of decimal forms and their corresponding points on a number line. A key tool in our study will be the idea of an unending succession of numbers or points. For example, we can think of the unending decimal 2.537041 . . . as a way of indicating the succession of terminating decimals:

2, 2.5, 2.53, 2.537, 2.5370, 2.53704, 2.537041, . . .

On a number line these decimals would be represented by a succession of unending points.

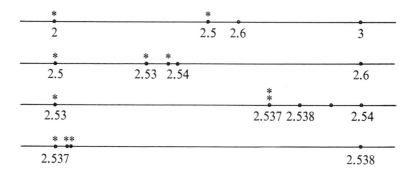

Notice that this succession of decimals or points are ordered, that is, we can count them in succession as first, second, third, and so on. We call such an unending succession an **infinite sequence**. An infinite sequence, in this sense, is an ordered unending set of elements.

Examples.

    (a) 1, 1.8, 1.80, 1.804, 1.8048, 1.80480, 1.804804, . . .
    (b) 2, 2.5, 2.59, 2.599, 2.5999, 2.59999, 2.599999, . . .
    (c) 90, 92, 92.6, 92.62, 92.625, 92.6250, 92.62500, . . .

The idea of infinite sequences has broader and more general interpretations in mathematics. However, it will suffice our needs to restrict ourselves to infinite sequences of terminating decimals and their corresponding points on a number line. The ordered elements of an infinite sequence are called the **terms** of the sequence. Let us examine the relationship of the successive terms in a sequence of terminating decimals and their associated points on a number line.

We can form a simple infinite sequence whose successive terms are obtained by attaching a digit to the right of the preceding term of the sequence. For example, as in the sequences illustrated above. What can we observe concerning the successive terms of such a sequence?

1. Succeeding terms are greater than or equal to preceding terms of the sequence.

2. The successive differences between consecutive terms becomes, in general, smaller and smaller.

3. For every such sequence there is a rational terminating decimal greater than any term of the sequence.

Examples.

(a) 1, 1.8, 1.80, 1.804, 1.8048, 1.80480, 1.804804, . . .

1. The second term 1.8 is 0.8 greater than the first term 1 and the third term 1.80 is equal to the second term.

2. The successive differences form the infinite sequence:

   0.8, 0.0, 0.004, 0.0008, 0.00000, 0.000004, ...

The sixth term of this sequence is only 0.000004 as compared to the third term 0.004.

3. Clearly every term is less than 2. Every term is also less than 1.9 or 1.81, and so on. Can you find the smallest number greater than any term of the sequence?

(b) 2, 2.5, 2.59, 2.599, 2.5999, 2.59999, 2.599999, . . .

1. The second term is 0.5 greater than the first. The third term is 0.09 greater than the second. The fourth term is 0.009 greater than the third and so on.

2. The sequence of differences is:

   0.5, 0.09, 0.009, 0.0009, 0.00009, 0.000009, . . .

We can make the difference as small as we wish by going far enough in the sequence of differences.

3. Clearly every term is less than 2.6. Notice, however, that as we go out in the sequence the difference between 2.6 and the terms of the sequence become smaller and smaller.

(c) 90, 92, 92.6, 92.62, 92.625, 92.6250, 92.62500, . . .

1. Beyond the fifth term the terms are all equal.

2. Beyond the fifth term the differences are all zero:

   2, 0.6, 0.02, 0.005, 0.0, 0.0, 0.0, . . .

3. Every term is less than, say, 100. Better yet, less than 92.7 or 92.63 or 92.626 or 92.6251. Any number larger than 92.625 will do.

Rather than use lengthy and informal language to describe the above properties of sequences, it is convenient to give special descriptive names to refer to them.

1. An infinite sequence is said to be a **monotonic increasing** sequence if succeeding terms either increase or remain the same.

1a. An infinite sequence is said to be a **monotonic decreasing** sequence if succeeding terms either decrease or remain the same.

504 NUMBERS AND ARITHMETIC

2. If the successive differences between terms in an infinite sequence can be made arbitrarily small by going out far enough in the sequence, and if the differences remain arbitrarily small thereafter, then we say that the sequence satisfies **Cauchy's condition** (for convergence) for a sequence.

3. If there is a fixed quantity greater than or equal to every term of a sequence, then we call the quantity an **upper bound** of the sequence.

3a. If there is a fixed quantity less than or equal to every term of a sequence, then we call the quantity a **lower bound** of the sequence.

3b. If an infinite sequence has both an upper bound and a lower bound, then we say that the sequence is **bounded**.

4. The smallest quantity which is an upper bound of a sequence is called the **least upper bound** (l.u.b.) of the sequence.

4a. The largest quantity which is a lower bound of a sequence is called the **greatest lower bound** (g.l.b.) of the sequence.

The three examples we have given are bounded monotonic increasing sequences which satisfy Cauchy's condition. The least upper bound of the sequence suggested by 1.804804 . . . is $\frac{601}{333}$. (Why?) The least upper bound of the sequence suggested by 2.599 . . . is 2.6, and of 92.62500 . . . is 92.625.

Using sequences of terminating decimals we can describe the real numbers as follows.

To begin, let the first term of a sequence be any non-negative integer, say I. For the second term of the sequence attach a single arbitrary digit to the right of the decimal point implied by I. For the third term attach another digit to the right. Continue this process to generate an infinite sequence of terminating decimals. Letting d_i stand for the ith digit attached to the integer, we have

$$I, I.d_1, I.d_1d_2, I.d_1d_2d_3, I.d_1d_2d_3d_4, I.d_1d_2d_3d_4d_5, \ldots .$$

1. All such sequences are monotonic increasing for by the meaning of decimals we have

$$I + \frac{d_1}{10} + \frac{d_2}{100} + \frac{d_3}{1000} + \frac{d_4}{10000} + \frac{d_5}{100000} + \cdots$$

That is, in each succeeding term we are, at worst, adding 0.

2. All such sequences satisfy Cauchy's condition for consider the sequence of differences:

$$0.d_1, 0.0d_2, 0.00d_3, 0.000d_4, 0.0000d_5, \ldots .$$

Each succeeding difference is, at worst, $\frac{9}{10}$ the smallest nonzero preceding difference.

3. All such sequences are bounded for $I + 1$ is greater and $I - 1$ is less than every term of the sequence.

4. Now, since all such sequences have an upper bound, they must

have a least upper bound. Note, the least upper bound may not be a term of the sequence.

Examples.

    (a) 35, 35.1, 35.10, 35.102, 35.1021, 35.10219, ...
    (b) 0, 0.1, 0.10, 0.101, 0.1010, 0.10100, 0.101001, ...
    (c) 3, 3.1, 3.14, 3.141, 3.1415, 3.14159, 3.141592, ...
    (d) 0, 0.0, 0.00, 0.000, 0.0000, 0.00000, 0.000000, ...

The sequence: 0, 0.0, 0.00, 0.000, . . . has the "obvious" least upper bound 0. Let us call it the **zero sequence**. The least upper bound of this sequence is the **real number 0**. Now we can say that the **positive real numbers** are the set of all least upper bounds other than 0 of all sequences of the above kind.

In much the same way, we can begin again with any nonpositive integer $-I$. Note that we could write N for a nonpositive integer, $N = -I$, but our intuition may be served by retaining the negative symbol, " $-$," to emphasize the distinction. We obtain

$$-I, \ -I.d_1, \ -I.d_1d_2, \ -I.d_1d_2d_3, \ -I.d_1d_2d_3d_4, \ \ldots .$$

1. All such sequences are monotonic decreasing for by the meaning of decimals and the negative sign we have

$$-I - \frac{d_1}{10} - \frac{d_2}{100} - \frac{d_3}{1000} - \frac{d_4}{10000} - \frac{d_5}{100000} - \ldots .$$

That is, in each succeeding term we are, at worst, subtracting 0.

2. All such sequences satisfy Cauchy's condition for consider the sequence of differences:

$$0.d_1, \ 0.0d_2, \ 0.00d_3, \ 0.000d_4, \ 0.0000d_5, \ \ldots .$$

Each succeeding difference is, at worst, $\frac{9}{10}$ the smallest nonzero preceding difference.

3. All such sequences are bounded for $-I - 1$ is less than and $-I + 1$ is greater than every term of the sequence.

4. Now, since all such sequences have a lower bound, they must have a greatest lower bound. Note, the greatest lower bound may not be a term of the sequence.

Examples.

    (a) $-15, -15.0, -15.00, -15.009, -15.0090, -15.00901,$ . . . .
    (b) $-1, -1.7, -1.73, -1.732, -1.7320, -1.73205,$ . . . .
    (c) $-0, -0.0, -0.00, -0.001, -0.0010, -0.00100,$ . . . .
    (d) $-0, -0.0, -0.00, -0.000, -0.0000, -0.00000,$ . . . .

As before, the sequence −0, −0.0, −0.00, −0.000, . . . has the "obvious" greatest lower bound 0. It is the zero sequence. The **negative real numbers** are the set of all greatest lower bounds other than 0 of all sequences of the above kind.

The real numbers as described above can be illustrated on a number line:

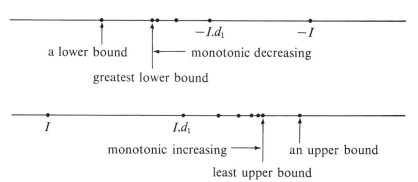

Intuitively, the set of real numbers corresponds to naming the set of all points on a straight line. Notice that the sequences which we have used "pack" toward some fixed point on the line from one side. The least upper bound and the greatest lower bound of these sequences correspond to naming the points on the line. It can be shown that any bounded infinite sequence which satisfies Cauchy's condition will "pack" toward some fixed point on the corresponding number line. We then say that the corresponding value for the point is the **limit point** of the sequence and by our discussion guarantee that it is a real number. That is, any bounded infinite sequence which satisfies Cauchy's condition converges to a limit which is a real number. This latter property of the real numbers leads us to describe the real numbers as **complete**.

10.2.3 Since we cannot compute with unending decimals, all arithmetical operations are actually accomplished with terminating decimals. However, let us consider the infinite sequences of terminating decimals with respect to the arithmetical operations. For definiteness, let us begin with the two sequences

2, 2.5, 2.53, 2.537, 2.5379, 2.53790, 2.537902, . . .
7, 7.4, 7.48, 7.482, 7.4821, 7.48218, 7.482180, . . .

We can add the corresponding first terms, then the second terms, then the third terms in succession to obtain the new sequence

9, 9.9, 10.01, 10.019, 10.0200, 10.02008, 10.020082, . . .

Although this "sum" sequence is somewhat different from the special sequences which we have discussed, notice that it is a bounded infinite sequence which satisfies Cauchy's condition. The digits in the sequence "settle down" and the terms "pack" toward some fixed value as a limit and thus lead us to a real number sum.

When we subtract the terms of one sequence from the corresponding terms of the other, we obtain a new "difference" sequence:

$$5, 4.9, 4.95, 4.945, 4.9442, 4.94428, 4.944278, \ldots$$

This sequence appears to have terms which "oscillate" but again we see that the digits "settle down" and the sequence is a bounded infinite sequence which satisfies Cauchy's condition. That is, the terms **converge** toward some fixed limiting value and thus to a real number.

Multiplying corresponding terms of the sequences leads to a "product" sequence:

$$14, 18.50, 18.9244, 18.981834, 18.98882159, 18.989024522, \ldots$$

Here again the digits in succeeding terms change but the digits "settle down" and the sequence is a bounded infinite sequence which satisfies Cauchy's condition. Thus, the terms converge to some real number.

Finally, dividing the terms of one sequence by the corresponding terms of the other sequence, we obtain a "quotient" sequence:

$$\frac{2}{7}, \frac{25}{74}, \frac{253}{748}, \frac{2537}{7482}, \frac{25379}{74821}, \frac{253790}{748218}, \frac{2537902}{7482180}, \ldots$$

or using rounded decimals

$$0.28, 0.338, 0.3382, 0.33908, 0.339196, 0.3391926, \ldots$$

Notice that, since these computed sequences were obtained from bounded infinite sequences, they are in turn bounded infinite sequences.

Now, what is the significance of what we have said concerning the set of real numbers? It should be clear that our intent has been to associate a real number to every point on a line and a point on the line to every real number. When this has been accomplished we can confidently proceed to use the language of numbers and arithmetic on problems of geometry, and geometric analysis on questions of an arithmetical nature. Of course, we already know that the numbers are well ordered, that is, we can arrange them in order of magnitude. We already know that no matter how large and positive a real number is, there is another still greater; and that no matter how large and negative a real number is, there is another still less than it. By our description it is clear that the real numbers include all the rational numbers and are everywhere dense. But what is distinctive in the real numbers as contrasted to the rational numbers?

The rational numbers are not **closed** with respect to the processes possible with infinite decimals! The existence of the irrational quantities shows this. Now by closing these decimal processes, these processes requiring an infinite sequence, we obtain a **perfect set**, a set which is closed and dense in itself. Furthermore, the set of real numbers forms a **complete ordered field**. That is, retains the ordered field structure of the rational numbers while including as real numbers a least upper bound of all infinite sequences which have upper bounds.

To illustrate the importance in the closing and completing of the processes with respect to infinite sequences, the following three paradoxes posed by an ancient Greek named Zeno of Elea (about 450 B.C.) were not clearly understood until some development of the real numbers was attained in the fifteenth century. As a matter of fact, it was not until Georg Cantor (1845–1918) and Richard Dedekind (1831–1916) developed theories of the infinite that the paradoxes were finally overcome.

The first paradox, referred to as the Dichotomy, asserts that motion is impossible. In order for an object to go from a point A to a point B, the paradox goes, the object must reach the midpoint of the distance between A and B, say M_1. Now in order to traverse the distance AM_1, the object must reach the midpoint, say M_2, of this distance. In order to reach M_2 the object must attain the midpoint of AM_2, say M_3. In order to attain any distinct point, the object must reach an "infinite" number of midpoints. Since an unending number of steps would then be required to reach any distinct point, the object must remain motionless.

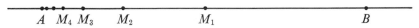

$$A \quad M_4\ M_3 \qquad M_2 \qquad\qquad M_1 \qquad\qquad\qquad\qquad B$$

The second paradox is called Achilles and the tortoise, and asserts that if a tortoise were to start first in a race with Achilles, Achilles, even though he moved faster, could never overtake the tortoise. If the tortoise were at point A when Achilles started, the tortoise would be at a point B further on by the time Achilles reached point A. When Achilles reached point B the tortoise would be at a point C further on, and so on.

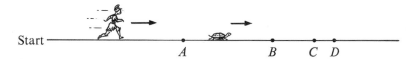

Start —————————————————————————————
$$\qquad\qquad\qquad\qquad A \qquad\qquad B \quad C\ D$$

The third paradox, called the Arrow, concludes that an arrow must always be at rest in flight. Because an arrow on the fly is in some fixed position at any instant, it must be at rest in that instant. Consequently, because the arrow is at rest in every instant, the arrow must always be at rest, that is, motionless!

To overcome the paradoxes we require a sense for the **continuous**, the idea of **continuity**. The real numbers constitute a **continuum**, the arithmetic continuum.

Exercises

1. Describe the single most important and useful property of each of the following sets of numbers:
    (a) The prime numbers   (b) The natural numbers

(c) The rational numbers   (d) The real numbers.

2. State the distributive property in mathematical symbols and give an example of its application.

3. Give three examples of the use of the division algorithm.

4. State the fundamental property of the rational numbers in mathematical symbols and give an example of its application.

5. Using mathematical symbols, show in general how we can illustrate the idea of the denseness of the rational numbers.

6. Give one specific example for each of the properties required in an ordered field which illustrates the property.

7. Name and show that there is at least one irrational number.

8. Express the following unending decimals as infinite sequences of terminating decimals (the first six terms):

    (a) 1.230230230...   (b) 28.019999...
    (c) 0.0001000100010...   (d) 0.4242944810....

9. Set $n = 1, 2, 3, ...$ in succession in each of the following expressions to "generate" an infinite sequence (write the first six terms):

    (a) $\dfrac{1}{n}$ (b) $\dfrac{3n-2}{2n+5}$ (c) $\dfrac{2+3n}{5-2n}$ (d) $\dfrac{n-1}{n^2}$ (e) $\dfrac{n^2}{1+n}$.

10. Find a monotonic increasing and a monotonic decreasing infinite sequence of terminating decimals which have $\sqrt{5}$ as a least upper and a greatest lower bound.

11. Find the least upper bound or greatest lower bound, whichever is applicable, if it exists for each of the infinite sequences "generated" in Exercise 9 above.

12. Add the unending decimals of Exercise 8 (a) and (b) by expressing the sum in a "sum" sequence. Discuss the properties of this "sum" sequence.

13. Find the "product" sequence for the unending decimals of Exercise 8 (a) and (b). Discuss the properties of this "product" sequence.

14. (a) Describe and illustrate what is meant by a perfect set.

    (b) Describe and illustrate what is meant by a complete set.

15. Explain why the real numbers overcome Zeno's paradoxes.

Answers.

1. (a) The natural numbers can be expressed as products of prime numbers, called the fundamental theorem of arithmetic.

    (b) The inductive property of the natural numbers; nonending consecutive counting property of the natural numbers.

    (c) The densely ordered field structure of the rational numbers.

    (d) The completely ordered field structure of the real numbers.

2. $A \times (B + C) = (A \times B) + (A \times C); 3 \times (20 + 4) = (3 \times 20) + (3 \times 4) = 60 + 12.$

3. (i) Checking in division: $\dfrac{16}{3} = 5R1$ since $16 = (3 \times 5) + 1.$

(ii) Divisibility: 16 is divisible by 8 since $R=0$ in $16 = (Q \times 8) + R.$

(iii) In showing the terminating or repeating nature of rational

decimals: $\dfrac{3}{8} = 0.375$ since $3 = 8 \times 0.375$, and note that there are only 7

possible remainders other than 0.

4. $\dfrac{A \times C}{B \times C} = \dfrac{A}{B}; \dfrac{21}{35} = \dfrac{3 \times 7}{5 \times 7} = \dfrac{3}{5}.$

5. If $\dfrac{A}{B}$ and $\dfrac{C}{D}$ are distinct rational numbers, then $\dfrac{(A \times D) + (B \times C)}{2 \times (B \times D)}$

is a distinct rational number between $\dfrac{A}{B}$ and $\dfrac{C}{D}.$

6. (1) $3 + 5 = 8, \ 3 \times 5 = 15$ (2) $3 + 5 = 5 + 3, \ 3 \times 5 = 5 \times 3$
(3) $3 + (5 + 1) = (3 + 5) + 1, \ 3 \times (5 \times 1) = (3 \times 5) \times 1$
(4) (a) $5 + 0 = 5$ (b) $5 \times 1 = 5$
(5) $3 \times (5 + 2) = (3 \times 5) + (3 \times 2)$

(6) (a) $5 + (-5) = 0,$ (b) $5 \times \left(\dfrac{1}{5}\right) = 1$

(7) (a) -5 (b) 0 (c) $5.$
7. $\sqrt{2}$ See text.
8. (a) 1, 1.2, 1.23, 1.230, 1.2302, 1.23023, ...
(b) 28, 28.0, 28.01, 28.019, 28.0199, 28.01999, ...
(c) 0, 0.0, 0.00, 0.000, 0.0001, 0.00010, ...
(d) 0, 0.4, 0.42, 0.424, 0.4242, 0.42429, ...

9. (a) $1, \dfrac{1}{2}, \dfrac{1}{3}, \dfrac{1}{4}, \dfrac{1}{5}, \dfrac{1}{6}, \cdots$

(b) $\dfrac{1}{7}, \dfrac{4}{9}, \dfrac{7}{11}, \dfrac{10}{13}, \dfrac{13}{15}, \dfrac{16}{17}, \cdots$

(c) $\dfrac{5}{3}, 8, \dfrac{11}{-1}, \dfrac{14}{-3}, \dfrac{17}{-5}, \dfrac{20}{-7}, \cdots$

(d) $0, \dfrac{1}{4}, \dfrac{2}{9}, \dfrac{3}{16}, \dfrac{4}{25}, \dfrac{5}{36}, \cdots$

(e) $0, \dfrac{4}{3}, \dfrac{9}{4}, \dfrac{16}{5}, \dfrac{25}{6}, \dfrac{36}{7}, \cdots$

10. 2, 2.2, 2.23, 2.236, 2.2360, 2.23606, 2.236068, . . .
3, 2.3, 2.24, 2.237, 2.2361, 2.23607, 2.236069, . . .

11. (a) greatest lower bound 0   (b) least upper bound $\dfrac{3}{2}$

(c) if first two terms are disregarded, then least upper bound $-\dfrac{3}{2}$

(d) 0 "limit"   (e) no upper bound.
12. 29, 29.2, 29.24, 29.249, 29.2501, 29.25022, . . .

A bounded monotonic increasing sequence, least upper bound $\dfrac{1\ 461\ 049}{49\ 950}$.

13. 28, 33.6, 34.4553, 34.46337, 34.47008098, . . .

A bounded monotonic increasing sequence, least upper bound $\dfrac{573\ 943}{16\ 650}$.

14. See text.

15. Closure and continuity.

10.3 Complex Numbers

10.3.1 As we come to the end of this text and our course of study, we should, to tell the truth, note that the historical development of numbers and arithmetic was not smooth nor logical. The history of mathematics reveals much groping, stumbling, and often erratic and even erring progress. Mathematics began with recognized human needs, it fed on man's intuitions and emotions, and it grew with each succeeding question put to it and faced squarely.

Lest we become complacent in having attained the perfect and complete set of real numbers, let us pose a further question:

What is the square root of a negative number?

The need to answer this question did not arise naturally from the problems of ordinary arithmetic; rather, it grew out of the needs of **algebra**. It is not necessary to consider complicated or intricate equations. Notice that we have already become acquainted with the following simple equations:

(a) $X - 7 = 0$ leads to $X = 7$ a natural number.

(b) $X + 4 = 4$ leads to $X = 0$ a very important number.

(c) $X + 7 = 0$ leads to $X = -7$ a negative integer.

(d) $7X = 3$ leads to $X = \dfrac{3}{7}$ a rational number.

(e) $X^2 - 7 = 0$ leads to $X = \sqrt{7}$ an irrational number.

It is sufficient to consider the following equation to raise the question:

(f) $X^2 + 1 = 0$ leads to $X^2 = -1$ which is impossible to solve in the real numbers.

The twelfth-century Hindu mathematician, Bhaskara (1114 to about 1185), expressed the difficulty with the simple statement:

"The square of a positive number, as also that of a negative number, is positive; and the square root of a positive number is twofold, positive and negative; there is no square root of a negative number, for a negative number is not a square."

If, for $X^2 - 7 = 0$, we write $X = \sqrt{7}$, then a natural impulse might be to write $X = \sqrt{-1}$, if $X^2 + 1 = 0$. But we know by the meaning of $\sqrt{N}$ that $\sqrt{N}\ \sqrt{N} = N$, while the product of two positive numbers is positive and the product of two negative numbers is also positive! Thus, how can N be negative? Yet, we are faced with the question. Having noted the power of notation, however, let us follow our impulse (often called intuition). That is, assert the quantity $\sqrt{-1}$ to be that quantity such that $\sqrt{-1}\ \sqrt{-1} = -1$. Today, the symbol i is commonly used for $\sqrt{-1}$.

What are the consequences of our assertion? Will the structure of numbers which we have built crumble about us? What practical interpretations can we give to this number? Fortunately, we are led to a consistent and enriched set of numbers, called the **complex numbers**, which enables us to solve many problems which might have been thought impossible of solution previously. Practically, the facts of electricity and the presence of television are consequences derived from the use of complex numbers.

10.3.2   Obviously the quantity i and its multiples $2i$, $3i$, . . . cannot be represented on a real number line, the points being taken up by the continuum of real numbers. But, there is little to prevent us from introducing a second number line, the **pure complex line**. This pure complex line will form a continuum of its own. What do the lines have in common? That very important number 0! If our previous rules are to be true, $0 \times \sqrt{-1} = 0$. Now, how can we combine these new quantities with the real numbers? Going again to a simple equation, consider:

$X^2 + 2X + 2 = 0$ leads to $(X^2 + 2X + 1) + 1 = 0$ and
$(X + 1)^2 + 1 = 0$ so that $(X + 1)^2 = -1$ which, in
turn, results in $X + 1 = \sqrt{-1}$ or $X = -1 + \sqrt{-1} = -1 + i$.

Rafael Bombelli (about 1572), in solving a somewhat more complicated equation, wrote solutions in the form $p + \sqrt{-q}$ and $p - \sqrt{-q}$. In his words:

"It was a wild thought, in the judgment of many; and
I, too, was for a long time of the same opinion."

We write $a + bi$, where a and b are real numbers and $i = \sqrt{-1}$. For example, $3 + 2i$ and $-5 + i$ and $4 - 7i$. But can we call these quantities numbers? Do they name points as real numbers do? Can we combine them using the ordinary rules of arithmetic? The fact of the matter is that we can, and they do! The complex numbers supersede the real numbers in much the same way as the latter superseded the rational numbers. The complex numbers lead to a **fundamental theorem of algebra** somewhat analogous to the fundamental theorem of arithmetic.

The complex numbers can be associated with points in the plane as suggested by Figure 182. The number $-4 + 2i$ is located as the point

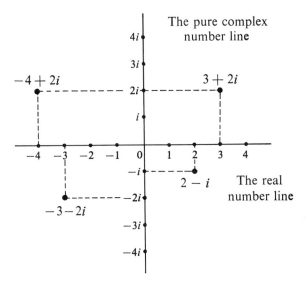

FIGURE 182

above -4 on the real number line and at the horizontal level of $2i$. The number $2 - i$ is located $-i$ below the real number 2. The arrangement suggests a pair of numbers, a real part and a pure complex part, (a, b). We might write $-4 + 2i = (-4, 2)$ and $2 - i = (2, -1)$. The real numbers are all included in the set of complex numbers for we can easily set $b = 0$ in $a + bi$. The pure complex set is a continuum and also included for $a = 0$ and b can be any real number. Now it is evident that every point in a plane can be named by a complex number and every complex number names a point in a plane.

When are two complex numbers equal? If $a + bi$ and $c + di$ name complex numbers, then they will be equal if and only if $a = c$ and $b = d$. Otherwise, they are unequal. If unequal, can we order the complex numbers in the greater than or less than relationship? This is not simple. However, notice that we can "measure" the distance from a complex point to 0 by applying the Pythagorean Theorem. This distance is often called the **modulus** of the complex number.

The sum and difference of two complex numbers can be obtained by separately adding or subtracting the real and pure complex parts. The product and quotient of two complex numbers can be obtained by a careful following of the rules laid down for the manipulation of real numbers. A few notable observations concerning manipulations with complex numbers are useful to remember.

1. The product of factors of i:

$i = \sqrt{-1}$, $i^2 = i \times i = -1$, $i^3 = i \times i \times i = -i$, $i^4 = i \times i \times i \times i = 1$.

2. The modulus of $a + bi$: $\sqrt{a^2 + b^2}$.

3. The **conjugate** of $a + bi$ is $a - bi$ and is distinctive in that:

$$(a + bi)\,(a - bi) = a^2 - b^2 i^2 = a^2 + b^2.$$

Examples.

(a) The sum of two complex numbers:

$$(3 + 5i) + (-2 + i) = (3 - 2) + (5 + 1)i = 1 + 6i$$

or in general:

$$(a + bi) + (c + di) = (a + c) + (b + d)i.$$

(b) The difference between two complex numbers:

$$(3 + 5i) - (-2 + i) = (3 + 2) + (5 - 1)i = 5 + 4i$$

or in general:

$$(a + bi) - (c + di) = (a - c) + (b - d)i.$$

(c) The product of two complex numbers:

$$(3 + 5i) \times (-2 + i) = (3 + 5i) \times (-2) + (3 + 5i) \times (i)$$
$$= (3 \times -2) + (5i \times -2) + (3 \times i) + (5i \times i)$$
$$= -6 - 10i + 3i + 5i^2 = -11 - 7i$$

or in general:

$$(a + bi) \times (c + di) = (a + bi) \times c + (a + bi) \times di$$
$$= (a \times c) + (bi \times c) + (a \times di) + (bi \times di)$$
$$= [(a \times c) - (b \times d)] + [(b \times c) + (a \times d)]i.$$

(d) The quotient between two complex numbers:

$$\frac{3 + 5i}{-2 + i} = \frac{(3 + 5i)\,(-2 - i)}{(-2 + i)\,(-2 - i)} = \frac{-1 - 13i}{5} = -\frac{1}{5} - \frac{13}{5}\,i$$

or in general:

$$\frac{a + bi}{c + di} = \frac{(a + bi)\,(c - di)}{(c + di)\,(c - di)} = \frac{(a \times c + b \times d) + (b \times c - a \times d)i}{c^2 + d^2}$$
$$= \frac{a \times c + b \times d}{c^2 + d^2} + \frac{b \times c - a \times d}{c^2 + d^2}\,i.$$

Not only can we compute with the complex numbers, but we can also represent the computations geometrically as illustrated in Figure 183.

Now we have numbers for every point on a plane. We have gone as far as need be, to the point where any **algebraic equation** has a solution within the system of numbers available to us. Although we end this text, continue the endless questions which may lead to new and satisfying answers.

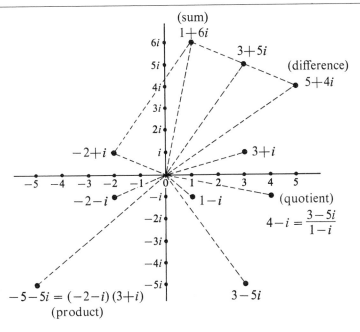

FIGURE 183

Exercises

1. Solve the following equations.
   (a) $2X - 8 = 0$ (b) $7X = 0$ (c) $5X + 5 = 0$ (d) $3X + 5 = 0$.
2. Solve the following equations.
   (a) $4X^2 = 3$ (b) $X^2 + X = 0$ (c) $X^2 + 4 = 0$
   (d) $X^2 + 2X + 1 = 2$.
3. Construct a "complex number plane" similar to Figure 182 and locate the following complex numbers on it.
   (a) $0 + 4i$ (b) $4 + 0i$ (c) $2 + 3i$ (d) $-3 + 4i$
   (e) $-2 - 0i$ (f) $-3 - 3i$ (g) $0 - 4i$ (h) $1 - 3i$
   (i) $2 - 3i$ (j) $-1 + 3i$.
4. Find the modulus for each of the complex numbers of Exercise 3 above.
5. Write the conjugate for each of the complex numbers of Exercise 3 above.
6. Find the sums of each of the following pairs of complex numbers.
   (a) $5 + i$ and $7 + 2i$ (b) $3 - 2i$ and $-5 + i$ (c) $4 + 3i$ and $4 - 3i$.
7. Construct a "complex number plane" and illustrate the sums of Exercise 6 above.

8. Find the products of each of the following pairs of complex numbers.

(a) $2 + 3i$ and $1 + 4i$ (b) $6 - i$ and $1 - 3i$
(c) $-4 - 3i$ and $4 + 3i$.

9. Show by an example that addition and multiplication of complex numbers are both commutative and associative.

10. Find the inverse under multiplication for $4 + 3i$.

Answers.

1. (a) $X = 4$ (b) $X = 0$ (c) $X = -1$ (d) $X = -\dfrac{5}{3}$.

2. (a) $X = \dfrac{\sqrt{3}}{2}$ or $X = -\dfrac{\sqrt{3}}{2}$ (b) $X = 0$ or $X = -1$

(c) $X = 2i$ or $X = -2i$ (d) $X = 1 - \sqrt{2}$ or $X = 1 + \sqrt{2}$.

3.

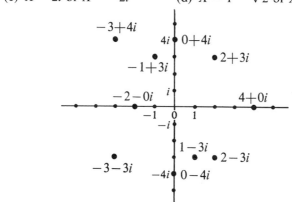

4. (a) 4   (b) 4   (c) $\sqrt{13}$ (d) 5   (e) 2   (f) $3\sqrt{2}$
(g) 4   (h) $\sqrt{10}$ (i) $\sqrt{13}$ (j) $\sqrt{10}$.

5. (a) $0 - 4i$ (b) $4 - 0i$ (c) $2 - 3i$ (d) $-3 - 4i$
(e) $-2 + 0i$ (f) $-3 + 3i$ (g) $0 + 4i$ (h) $1 + 3i$
(i) $2 + 3i$ (j) $-1 - 3i$.

6. (a) $12 + 3i$ (b) $-2 - i$ (c) $8 + 0i$.

7.

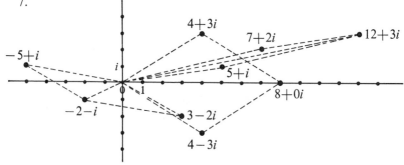

8. (a) $-10 + 11i$ (b) $3 - 19i$ (c) $-7 - 24i$.

9. Addition: $(3 + 4i) + (5 - 2i) = 8 + 2i$ and $(5 - 2i) + (3 + 4i) = 8 + 2i$
so that $(3 + 4i) + (5 - 2i) = (5 - 2i) + (3 + 4i)$.
$(3 + 4i) + [(5 - 2i) + (1 + i)] = (3 + 4i) + (6 - i) = 9 + 3i$
$[(3 + 4i) + (5 - 2i)] + (1 + i) = (8 + 2i) + (1 + i) = 9 + 3i$
so that addition is associative (for this example).

Multiplication: $(3 + 4i)(5 - 2i) = 23 + 14i$ and
$(5 - 2i)(3 + 4i) = 23 + 14i$
so that $(3 + 4i)(5 - 2i) = (5 - 2i)(3 + 4i)$.
$(3 + 4i)[(5 - 2i)(1 + i)] = (3 + 4i)(7 + 3i) = 9 + 37i$
$[(3 + 4i)(5 - 2i)](1 + i) = (23 + 14i)(1 + i) = 9 + 37i$
so that multiplication is associative (for this example).

Note: Other appropriate examples possible.

10. $(4 + 3i)(a + bi) = 1$ so that $a + bi = \dfrac{1}{4 + 3i} = \dfrac{4}{25} - \dfrac{3}{25}i$.

Review Summary

If we conceive of a rational number as a quantity obtained by "breaking" a unit into any number of equal parts, then there will still be quantities which are not represented by these rational numbers. With this realization, we showed that the square root of 2 is not a rational number. Thus, it must be _____.   *irrational*

Noting that decimal approximations of all rational numbers are easily obtained, we observed that they either _____ in zeroes or _____ a fixed set of digits in   *terminated,* a cyclic manner. We asked "Are there decimal repre-   *repeated* sentations other than terminating and repeating decimals?" Yes, it was quite easy to exhibit such decimal representations. In doing this, we introduced the idea of an unending process. We noted that any irrational quantity could be represented by a rational process which might continue indefinitely. For example, $\pi = 4 \times$
$$\left(1 - \frac{1}{3} + \frac{1}{5} - \frac{1}{7} + \frac{1}{9} - \cdots\right).$$

Just as with the rational numbers, we can assign points on a line to the irrational numbers. The rational and irrational numbers together name all of the points on a line. The resulting set of numbers is called the set of _____ _____. That is, we conceive of the set of real   *real num-* numbers as corresponding to the set of all decimal   *bers* representations of numbers and to the set of all points on a line.

Before proceeding to an examination of the real numbers, we reviewed some aspects in the development and discussion of numbers to this point.

First, we began with the _____ or _____ numbers. *natural,*
From successive counting we were led to a study of *counting*
special subsets of natural numbers. Of special importance were the _____ numbers which could be used to *prime*
express all natural numbers. With the consideration of
addition, we were led to an extension of the natural
numbers to the _____ which enabled us to subtract any *integers*
integer from any other integer. The study of operations
with numbers led us to describe some of the important
properties of these operations. The most important
property observed in connection with multiplication was
called the _____ property of multiplication over addi- *distributive*
tion. In division, to help us obtain results, we introduced
the relationship $B = (Q \times A) + R$ called the _____ _____. *division*
algorithm

Second, we introduced the _____ numbers or _____. *rational,*
To help our intuition we used a rational number line *fractions*
and described a procedure to assign a point on the
line to each rational number. The fundamental property
or "Golden Rule" of fractions was the most important
device used in our discussion. Symbolically it can be $\dfrac{A}{B} = \dfrac{A \times C}{B \times C}$
described by _____. The rational numbers formed a
structure called an ordered field.

An ordered field consists of a set with two operations,
usually called addition and multiplication, which satisfy
the following properties: 1. Closure.   2. Commutative.
3. Associative.   4. Identities for both operations.
5. Distributive.   6. Inverses for both operations.
7. A simple ordering.

We next turned our attention to the notation used in

our writing. For example, writing $\dfrac{1}{4} = 0.25$ illustrated the

conversion from fractional form to _____ form. From *decimal*
notation we went on to an examination of a few geometric
ideas and some applications. To solve problems, we often
use _____ to obtain answers. One of the most important *formulas*
formulas, called the Pythagorean Theorem, is described
by the equation _____. This led us to the problem of $c^2 = a^2 + b^2$
finding the square root of a positive number. From the
approximation of square roots we were inevitably drawn

to the consideration of nonrational quantities, that is, _____ numbers. When the irrational and rational numbers are considered together the result is the set of _____ numbers. *irrational*
real

To study the real numbers we introduced the idea of an infinite sequence. That is, the idea of an ordered unending set of elements. Rather than use lengthy and informal language to describe the properties of sequences, we gave special descriptive names to some properties of interest. For example, if succeeding terms of a sequence either increase or remain the same, we call the sequence a _____ _____ sequence. If there is a fixed quantity greater than or equal to every term of a sequence, then we call the quantity an _____ _____ of the sequence. The smallest quantity which is an upper bound of a sequence is called the _____ _____ _____ of the sequence. Using sequences of terminating decimals we described the real numbers as the set of least upper bounds or _____ _____ bounds of special types. Another property which led to the same result was called Cauchy's condition. That is, the idea that an infinite sequence may "pack" toward some fixed value called the _____ _____ of the sequence.
monotonic
increasing
upper bound
least upper
bound
greatest
lower
limit point

The significance of our discussion of real numbers lay in the fact that a real number could be associated to every point on a line and a point on the line could be associated to a real number. This was accomplished by closing our operations with respect to infinite processes. When this is accomplished we say that the set is _____. By closing the infinite processes, we introduced the least upper bounds of all infinite sequences which have upper bounds. When this is done, we say that the set is _____. Thus, the real numbers are a perfect set which form a complete ordered field. That is, we say that the real numbers form a continuum, the arithmetic continuum.
perfect
complete

In our parting section we posed one last question: "What is the square root of a negative number?" We noted that the understanding and development of a subject is neither smooth nor logical. It grows out of questions and feeds on intuition. Our last question grew out of the needs of algebra and led to an enriched set of numbers called the _____ numbers. The complex numbers, in addition to having practical utility, lead to a
complex

fundamental theorem of algebra somewhat analogous to the fundamental theorem of arithmetic.

In closing we suggest the challenge of an infinite sequence of interesting questions which may lead to new and satisfying answers.

Chapter Exercises (10)

Group 1.

1. Find six place decimal representations for the following numbers.

   (a) $\sqrt{8}$ (b) $\sqrt{9}$ (c) $\sqrt{\dfrac{2}{9}}$ (d) $\sqrt{\dfrac{4}{3}}$ (e) $\sqrt{\pi}$.

2. Find a six-place decimal approximation for

$$5 + \cfrac{4}{4 + \cfrac{3}{3 + \cfrac{2}{2 + 1}}}$$

3. Convert the following rational decimals to fractional form.

   (a) 0.09375   (b) 1.06 06 . . .   (c) 2.249 9 . . . .

4. Order the following sets of numbers from smallest to largest.

   (a) $\dfrac{5}{4}, \dfrac{2}{\sqrt{2}}, \dfrac{4}{\pi}, \dfrac{2\sqrt{3}}{3}, \sqrt{3} - \sqrt{2}.$

   (b) 0.590, 0.095, 0.509, 0.905, 0.059, 0.950.

5. Find the radius of a circle whose area is 1.

6. Why is $\dfrac{2}{3} + \sqrt{2}$ an irrational number?

7. Set $n = 1, 2, 3, \ldots$ in succession in each of the following expressions to "generate" an infinite sequence (write the first six terms).

   (a) $5 - \dfrac{2}{n}$ (b) $\dfrac{1}{n} + \dfrac{2}{3}$ (c) $\dfrac{2n+1}{2n-1}$ (d) $\dfrac{n^2 + 3}{2n^2}.$

8. Find the least upper bound or greatest lower bound, whichever is applicable, if it exists, for each of the infinite sequences "generated" in Exercise 7 above.

9. What is the distinction between denseness and completeness of a set?

10. What do the complex numbers enable us to do that is not possible with the real numbers?

11. Given the complex numbers $7 + 2i$ and $3 - 5i$:

   (a) Find their sum   (b) Subtract $7 + 2i$ from $3 - 5i$
   (c) Find their product   (d) Divide $7 + 2i$ by $3 - 5i$.

12. Given the complex number $3 - 5i$:

   (a) Find its modulus   (b) Find its conjugate
   (c) Find its inverse under multiplication.

13. Solve the following equations.

    (a) $X^2 - 5 = 0$ (b) $X^2 + 5 = 0$ (c) $X^2 + 4X = 1$.

14. Write a question of mathematical interest which might have been suggested by this chapter.

Group II.

1. Find six-place decimal representations for the following numbers.

    (a) $\sqrt{12}$ (b) $\sqrt{16}$ (c) $\sqrt{\dfrac{3}{4}}$ (d) $\sqrt{\dfrac{9}{2}}$ (e) $\sqrt{e}$.

2. Find a six-place decimal approximation for

$$5 - \cfrac{4}{4 + \cfrac{3}{3 - \cfrac{2}{2 + 1}}}$$

3. Convert the following rational decimals to fractional form.

    (a) 0.0175 (b) $0.2083\,3\ldots$ (c) $1.049\,9\ldots$

4. Order the following sets of numbers from smallest to largest.

    (a) $\dfrac{2}{3}, \dfrac{1}{\sqrt{3}}, \dfrac{e}{3}, \dfrac{\sqrt{2}}{2}, \sqrt{2 - \sqrt{3}}$.

    (b) $0.270, 0.072, 0.207, 0.702, 0.027, 0.720$.

5. Find the side of a square whose area is 3.

6. Why is $\sqrt{3} - \dfrac{1}{2}$ an irrational number?

7. Set $n = 1, 2, 3, \ldots$ in succession in each of the following expressions to "generate" an infinite sequence (write the first six terms).

    (a) $3 + \dfrac{2}{n}$ (b) $\dfrac{4}{5} - \dfrac{1}{n}$ (c) $\dfrac{2 - n}{2 + n}$ (d) $\dfrac{n^2 - 2}{3n^2}$.

8. Find the least upper bound or greatest lower bound, whichever is applicable, if it exists for each of the infinite sequences "generated" in Exercise 7 above.

9. What is the distinction between a perfect set and a dense set?

10. How many complex numbers are there with a fixed modulus, say 5? Given $3 + 4i$, name three other distinct complex numbers with the same modulus. Describe the set of complex numbers with the fixed modulus, say 5.

11. Given the complex numbers $2 - 7i$ and $5 + 3i$:

    (a) Find their sum   (b) Subtract $2 - 7i$ from $5 + 3i$

    (c) Find their product   (d) Divide $2 - 7i$ by $5 + 3i$.

12. Given the complex number $5 + 3i$:

    (a) Find its modulus   (b) Find its conjugate

    (c) Find its inverse under multiplication.

13. Solve the following equations.

    (a) $X^2 - 7 = 0$ (b) $X^2 + 7 = 0$ (c) $X^2 + 6X = -10$.

14. Write a question of mathematical interest which might have been suggested by this chapter.

Problem Set (10)

1. Which rational numbers $\dfrac{N}{D}$ have terminating decimal representations? That is, how can one tell when the decimal representation of a fraction will terminate?

2. Which of the ordered field properties do the irrational numbers satisfy? Why?

3. (a) Show that a line infinitely long has no more points than a line segment one unit long.

(b) Show that there are as many points inside any circle as there are outside it.

4. A complex number may be represented as an ordered pair of real numbers (a, b). How would we describe the requirements (or conditions) for:

(a) $(a,b) = 0$ (b) $(a,b) = (c,d)$ (c) $(a,b) + (c,d) = (p,q)$
(d) $(a,b) \times (c,d) = (p,q)$.

5. Solve for X in terms of A, B, and C in $AX^2 + BX + C = 0$. Discuss the various possible solutions for X depending on the values of A, B, and C. (HINT. Form a square $(X + K)^2 = D$.)

Vocabulary List, Chapters 6–10

Vocabulary List, Chapters 6–10 — *Continued*

Vocabulary List, Chapters 6–10 — *Continued*

Vocabulary List, Chapters 6–10 — *Continued*

Comprehensive Check-Test, Chapters 6–10.

1. Use a fraction to describe the shaded portion of

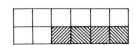

2. Reduce the following fractions: (a) $\dfrac{252}{1224}$ (b) $\dfrac{1386}{4095}$.

3. Order the following set of fractions from smallest to largest.
$$\frac{2}{3}, \frac{5}{6}, \frac{4}{7}, \frac{3}{4}, \frac{5}{9}, \frac{3}{5}.$$

4. Find the value of N in each of the following equations so that the equation will be true.

(a) $\dfrac{3}{7} = \dfrac{N}{91}$ (b) $\dfrac{6}{23} = \dfrac{36}{N}$ (c) $\dfrac{9}{13} \times N = \dfrac{3}{5}$ (d) $\dfrac{2}{3} \div N = 6$.

5. Given $\dfrac{3}{2}, \dfrac{5}{-3}, \dfrac{-8}{12}, \dfrac{2}{3}$:

(a) Which name proper fractions?
(b) Which name positive fractions?
(c) Which name reduced fractions?

6. Find the products in reduced form: (a) $\dfrac{9}{35} \times \dfrac{7}{12}$ (b) $\dfrac{84}{275} \times \dfrac{65}{294}$.

7. The reciprocal of $\dfrac{3}{7}$ is _____, since $\dfrac{3}{7} \times$ _____ = _____.

8. Find the reduced rational quotients: (a) $\dfrac{5}{6} \div \dfrac{3}{4}$ (b) $\dfrac{21}{65} \div \dfrac{15}{26}$.

9. (a) Express $\dfrac{5}{8}$ as a fraction with numerator 25.

   (b) What is the product of $\dfrac{8}{9}$ and $\dfrac{3}{4}$ in reduced form?

   (c) Find the quotient when $\dfrac{7}{11}$ is divided by $\dfrac{49}{66}$.

   (d) How many times larger than $\dfrac{3}{5}$ is $\dfrac{18}{25}$?

10. Find the least common denominator (LCD) for each of the following sets of fractions.

   (a) $\dfrac{5}{6}, \dfrac{9}{14}, \dfrac{16}{21}$ (b) $\dfrac{8}{15}, \dfrac{13}{27}, \dfrac{11}{18}$.

11. Find the following sums and differences.

   (a) $\dfrac{1}{3} + \dfrac{5}{8}$ (b) $\dfrac{7}{12} + \dfrac{25}{42}$ (c) $\dfrac{4}{5} - \dfrac{3}{4}$ (d) $\dfrac{7}{16} - \dfrac{19}{36}$.

12. Do as indicated:

   (a) $\left(\dfrac{2}{3} + \dfrac{5}{6}\right) \times \left(\dfrac{1}{4} - \dfrac{2}{5}\right)$ (b) $\dfrac{\frac{2}{9} + \frac{3}{8}}{\frac{5}{6} - \frac{4}{15}}$.

13. Find the sums in reduced mixed fraction form.

   (a) $6\dfrac{2}{3} + 7\dfrac{5}{6}$ (b) $21\dfrac{15}{16} + 78\dfrac{1}{2}$ (c) $\begin{array}{r} 4\frac{3}{5} \\ 17\frac{5}{6} \\ + 9\frac{3}{4} \\ \hline \end{array}$

14. Find the differences in reduced mixed fraction form.

   (a) $13\dfrac{4}{5} - 5\dfrac{5}{6}$ (b) $2\dfrac{4}{7} - 4\dfrac{2}{3}$ (c) $\begin{array}{r} 35\frac{4}{15} \\ - 8\frac{5}{6} \\ \hline \end{array}$

15. Find the products in reduced mixed fraction form.

   (a) $4\dfrac{5}{7} \times 4\dfrac{2}{3}$ (b) $6\dfrac{3}{4} \times 2\dfrac{1}{6}$ (c) $-5\dfrac{2}{3} \times 9\dfrac{4}{5}$.

16. Find the exact quotients in reduced mixed fraction form.

   (a) $9\dfrac{3}{4} \div 2\dfrac{1}{6}$ (b) $7\dfrac{2}{9} \div 16\dfrac{2}{3}$ (c) $\dfrac{15\frac{5}{7}}{-1\frac{4}{7}}$.

17. Round each of the following to four place positions.

   (a) 31.7243   (b) 1098.694   (c) 5.065509   (d) 409.9507.

18. Convert to decimal forms to the nearest thousandths.

   (a) $\dfrac{31}{28}$ (b) $\dfrac{49}{59}$ (c) $\dfrac{123}{3085}$.

19. Find to five place positions:
    (a)   57.015   (b)   32.017
          14.87 $-$ 7.119
          0.107
          +30.35

    (c) 2.9901 + 0.4095 + 7.0103 + 0.007   (d) 4.60495 $-$ 20.7074.
20. Find to five place positions:
    (a)   82.067   (b) 5.076)$\overline{24.903}$ (c) 1.0749 $\times$ 0.7228
          $\times$73.41

    (d) $\dfrac{16.047}{290.55}$.

21. Solve the following.
    (a) $N = 17.5\% \times 27.64$ (b) $5.39 = P\% \times 1.75$
    (c) $1{,}498.75 = 2\frac{3}{4}\% \times B$.

22. (a) What is 0.05% of 0.05?   (b) $4\frac{3}{8}$ is what percent of $6\frac{9}{16}$?
    (c) If 2.091 is 1025% of a number, then what is the number?
23. Find the perimeters and areas of the figures shown in Figure 184.

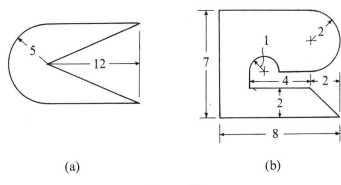

       (a)   (b)

FIGURE 184

24. Do as indicated: (a) Reduce 124 inches to simplest form.
    (b) Convert 6 yd 8.4 inches to meters.
    (c) Reduce 21 sq ft 388 sq inches to simplest form.
25. Find the volumes of the figures shown in Figure 185.
26. Do as indicated:

    (a) Find the sum of $\frac{2}{3}$ of 5 cu yd and $\frac{5}{2}$ of 16 cu ft.

    (b) If a cubic yard of a substance weighs 574 lb, then how many
kilograms will a cubic meter of the substance weigh?

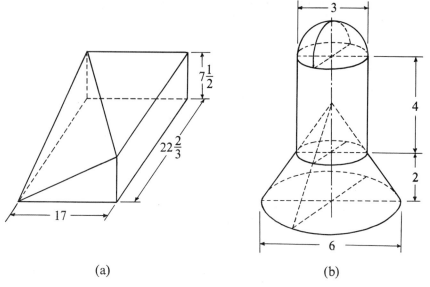

(a)   (b)

FIGURE 185

27. (a) Find 38% of 2 days 9 h 50 min.

(b) If a man is paid $1.78 per hour and works $76\frac{1}{2}$ h, then how much has he earned?

28. If a substance absorbs water which weighs approximately 8.345 lb per gallon at the rate of 1 cu inch per minute, then how many ounces of water will it absorb in 7 min 40 sec?

29. Find the constants of variation and the value of the variable indicated.

(a) $V = K \times A$ and $V = 14$ when $A = 3\frac{1}{2}$, and find V if $A = 8\frac{1}{4}$.

(b) $D = \dfrac{K}{R^2}$ and $D = 3$ when $R = 3$, and find D if $R = \dfrac{1}{3}$.

30. Find the value of P in each of the following proportions.

(a) $\dfrac{2P}{15} = \dfrac{8}{5}$ (b) $\dfrac{2 + 3P}{P} = \dfrac{3}{5}$ (c) $\dfrac{4P - 3}{12 - P} = \dfrac{3}{P}$.

31. Approximate the following to four places.
(a) $\sqrt{178}$ (b) $\sqrt{94.16}$ (c) $\sqrt{40{,}360}$.

32. Find the lengths of the segments indicated in Figure 186 to three places.

33. Find the average value and standard deviation for the following set of values: 96, 83, 88, 74, 92, 89.

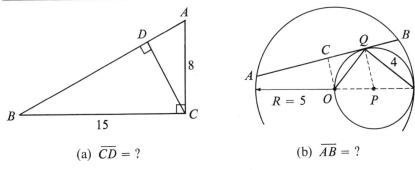

(a) $\overline{CD}$ = ?

(b) $\overline{AB}$ = ?

FIGURE 186

34. Order the following from smallest to largest.
    (a) 10.32, 1.023, 13.20, 0.123, 21.03, 3.021.
    (b) $\dfrac{\sqrt{11}}{3}, \dfrac{15}{14}, \dfrac{7}{2\sqrt{11}}, \dfrac{14}{15}, \dfrac{2}{\sqrt{3+\sqrt{2}}}$.

35. Set $n = 1, 2, 3, \ldots$ in succession in each of the following expressions and write the first six terms of the infinite sequences "generated."
    (a) $\dfrac{1}{2n} - 3$ (b) $\dfrac{3 + 5n}{n}$ (c) $\dfrac{(n + 1)(n - 1)}{2n^2}$.

36. Find the least upper bound or greatest lower bound, whichever is applicable, if it exists for each of the infinite sequences "generated" in Problem 35 above.

37. Given the complex number $-4 + 3i$:
    (a) Find its modulus   (b) Find its conjugate
    (c) Find its inverse under multiplication.

38. Given the complex numbers $5 - 12i$ and $1 + 2i$:
    (a) Find their sum   (b) Subtract $5 - 12i$ from $1 + 2i$
    (c) Find their product   (d) Divide $5 - 12i$ by $1 + 2i$.

39. Solve the following equations:
    (a) $X^2 + \sqrt{3}X = 0$ (b) $6X - X^2 = 17$.

40. If the product of two fractions is $\dfrac{2}{15}$ and one of the fractions is $\dfrac{7}{9}$, then what is the other fraction?

41. Find the smallest natural number N such that N times $\dfrac{3}{4}$ is an integer and N divided by $\dfrac{6}{7}$ is an integer.

42. Two men working together on a job take 3 h 20 min to complete the job. If one of the men does $1\frac{2}{3}$ as much of the work as the other, then how long would it take him to do the job alone?

43. Mr. Smith received 22 checks, each check to the amount of $164.85, during the year. If 16% of his earnings had been withheld from each check, then what were the total earnings represented by the 22 checks?

44. If 32% of the points made by a basketball team came on free-throw attempts and the team made 56% of its free-throw attempts, then how many free-throw attempts did the team have if it had a total game score of 84 points?

45. If a clock gains 2 min 15 sec each 12 hr, then how much will it have gained in one week?

46. If an auto covers 423 miles on a trip taking 9 h 54 min, then what was its average speed on the trip?

47. If a 6-inch diameter ball is dropped in a cone-shaped container with its point down and the cone is 12 inches deep with a diameter of 10 inches, then how far will the bottom of the ball be from the bottom point of the cone?

48. A 6-inch diameter and a 16-inch diameter pulley are fixed on a common center axle. If a 36 lb force is exerted on a nonslipping belt on the larger pulley, then what will be the effective force on a nonslipping belt on the smaller pulley?

49. A one-mile long parade of marchers and floats is moving along a parade route at 100 ft per minute. If a messenger leaves the front of the parade and moves to the rear at 100 ft per minute, then how long will it take him to reach the rear of the parade?

50. A student in a particular course of study is graded on the basis of 8 assignments, 4 regular examinations, and a final examination. If the final examination counts twice as much as a single regular examination, and a regular examination counts twice as much as a single assignment, then what will be the student's course average based on the following record of scores in assignments, examinations, and the final?

Assignment scores:

Assignment #:	1	2	3	4	5	6	7	8
Score:	82	75	94	80	68	72	87	90

Test scores:

Test #:	1	2	3	4
Score:	64	75	70	67

Final examination:
Score: 60.

Answers to Chapter Exercises (1)

Group I.

1. A set with cardinal number eight, the elements are distinguishable and could be easily ordered.
2. (a) A set of seven keys on a key-ring. The set of days in a week.
   (b) A football team. The letters in the word "mathematics."
3.

(i)
    1 2 3 4 5 6 7 8

(ii)

4. (a) ordinal   (b) cardinal   (c) cardinal   (d) ordinal.
5. (a) Missed an element   (b) Counted same element twice.
6. (a)–3, (b)–4, (c)–6, (d)–5, (e)–2, (f)–1.
7. (a) CDXCII, 492   (b) DCCLXX, 770   (c) MMCMXIV, 2914
   (d) MMMMCII, 4102.
8. (a) XVI   (b) CXCIX   (c) MDCLXVI   (d) MMDCCXXIX.
9. (a) 27   (b) 542   (c) 914   (d) 2521.
10. (a) Seventeen thousand, three hundred nine.
    (b) Three hundred fifty thousand, two hundred sixty-eight.
    (c) Ten million, three hundred six thousand, one hundred.
11. (a) 1964   (b) 7,006,304   (c) 11,124,081.
12. million, hundred; 100.
13. 70,020.
14. (a) 4   (b) 3   (c) 5   (d) 6.
15. (a) thousands   (b) hundreds   (c) ten thousands
    (d) hundreds.
16. (a) 100   (b) 10   (c) 10   (d) 1000.
17. six; 1, 2, 3, 4, 5, 6, 10, 11, 12, 13, 14, 15, 16, 20, 21, 22.
18. (a) 4   (b) 10   (c) 13   (d) 16   (e) 20   (f) 21
    (g) 102.
19. (a) 6   (b) 7   (c) 10   (d) 11   (e) 15   (f) 56
    (g) 100.
20. (a) $306 = 300 + 00 + 6$.

(b) $5{,}201 = 5(1000) + 2(100) + 0(10) + 1(1)$.

(c) $348{,}725 = 300{,}000 + 40{,}000 + 8{,}000 + 700 + 20 + 5$.

21. (a) 1002   (b) 740,407   (c) 4,139,310.

22. (a) false   (b) true   (c) true   (d) false.

23. 5, 8, 11, 14, 17, 20, 23, 26, 29, 32, 35.

4, 12, 20, 28, 36, 44, 52, 60, 68, 76, 84.

24. (a) $16 = 1 \times 16 = 2 \times 8 = 4 \times 4$.

(b) $105 = 1 \times 105 = 3 \times 35 = 5 \times 21 = 7 \times 15$.

25. 101, 103, 107, 109, 113, 127, 131, and so on.

26. $105 = 3 \times (5 \times 7)$.

Group II.

1. A set with cardinal number eleven, the elements might be ordered by size.

2. (a) A set of legs on an insect. The set of six senses including "intuition."

(b) A Rugby team. The number of electrons in an ordinary phosphorus atom.

3. (i) From smallest to largest   (ii) Alternating.

4. (a) ordinal   (b) cardinal   (c) cardinal   (d) ordinal.

5. (a) Skipped numeral   (b) Used same numeral twice.

6. (a) 12   (b) 21   (c) 18   (d) 909   (e) 112   (f) 451.

7. (a) CMXIV, 914   (b) MCCXXXVI, 1236   (c) MCDXCIX, 1499

(d) MMDCCCLVII, 2857.

8. (a) XCVI   (b) DXIX   (c) MCLXIV   (d) MMDCLXXI.

9. (a) 54   (b) 442   (c) 1919   (d) 2104.

10. (a) Twenty-three thousand, forty-eight.

(b) Seven hundred eighty thousand, two hundred fifteen.

(c) Seventeen million, six hundred eighty-one thousand, two hundred.

11. (a) 1872   (b) 2,036,127   (c) 20,400,780.

12. ten millions, hundred; 1000.

13. 20,022,000.

14. (a) 3   (b) 5   (c) 2   (d) 7.

15. (a) hundreds   (b) tens   (c) ones   (d) thousands.

16. (a) 100   (b) 1000   (c) 10   (d) 1000.

17. 1, 12, 144.

18. 10, 24, 3L, 50, 101.

19. (a) 14   (b) 32   (c) 58   (d) 132   (e) 275.

20. (a) $630 = 600 + 30 + 0$.

(b) $71{,}009 = 7(10{,}000) + 1(1{,}000) + 0(100) + 0(10) + 9(1)$.

(c) $100{,}371 = 100{,}000 + 00{,}000 + 0{,}000 + 300 + 70 + 1$.

21. (a) 28,594   (b) 105,500   (c) 3,132,291.

22. (a) false   (b) true   (c) true   (d) false.
23. 3, 8, 13, 18, 23, 28, 33, 38, 43, 48, 53.
    2, 8, 14, 20, 26, 32, 38, 44, 50, 56, 62.
24. (a) $36 = 1 \times 36 = 2 \times 18 = 3 \times 12 = 4 \times 9 = 6 \times 6$.
    (b) $70 = 1 \times 70 = 2 \times 35 = 5 \times 14 = 7 \times 10$.
25. 9, 15, 21, 25, 27, 33, 35, 39, 45, 49, 51.
26. $70 = 2 \times (5 \times 7)$.

Answers to Chapter Exercises (2)

Group I.

1. addends, sum; addition.
2. the sum is 230.
3. (a) 1080   (b) 1610   (c) 1790   (d) 2384.
4. (a) 2009   (b) 4201   (c) 12,706   (d) 22,049.
5. (a) 1680   (b) 1315   (c) 18,120   (d) 23,917.
6. (a) 3502   (b) 16,602   (c) 1,304,395   (d) 22,582,878.
7. 1,583,154,276.
8. (a) 20   (b) 9   (c) 9   (d) 21   (e) 133   (f) 259.
9. subtrahend, minuend, difference; subtraction.
10. (a) 96   (b) 192   (c) −96   (d) 0   (e) 96   (f) 96.
11. (a) 141   (b) 204   (c) 516   (d) 216   (e) 55   (f) 708.
12. (a) 531   (b) 32   (c) 9   (d) 47   (e) 868   (f) 1886.
13. (a) 379   (b) 108   (c) 108   (d) 201   (e) 7.
14. (a) 20,419   (b) 7,390   (c) 91   (d) 9,001.
15. (a) 9,895   (b) 78,458   (c) 4,529   (d) 7,855.
16. (a) 159,199   (b) 8,897   (c) 152,606,065.
17. (a) $20 - 2, 9 + 10, 20 + 0, 22 - 1, 22 - 0, 1 + 22$.
    (b) IV, V, VI, VII, VIII, IX, X, XI.
18. (a) 9   (b) −9   (c) −9   (d) 9   (e) 9   (f) 63
    (g) 27   (h) 36   (i) −63.
19. (a) true   (b) false   (c) true   (d) true   (e) false.
20. (a) true   (b) false   (c) true   (d) true   (e) true.
21. (a) 7   (b) 47   (c) 25   (d) 0   (e) −61   (f) −46.
22. (a) −970   (b) 1227   (c) 10   (d) −180.
23. (a) 110   (b) −10   (c) 25   (d) 55   (e) −836   (f) 0.
24. (a) −1809   (b) −827   (c) −989   (d) −1275.

Group II.

1. The sum is 215.
2. The sum is 9503.

3. (a) 1102   (b) 707   (c) 1789   (d) 2318.
4. (a) 2239   (b) 6520   (c) 10,100   (d) 22,272.
5. (a) 2100   (b) 1180   (c) 23,095   (d) 27,303.
6. (a) 2077   (b) 40,172   (c) 157,080   (d) 103,208,525.
7. 4,147,950,972.
8. (a) 9   (b) 12   (c) 14   (d) 361   (e) 89   (f) 89.
9. (a) 19   (b) −15   (c) −19.
10. (a) 35   (b) −35   (c) 0   (d) 70   (e) 35   (f) 35.
11. (a) 178   (b) 119   (c) 637   (d) 99   (e) 97   (f) 89.
12. (a) 111   (b) 84   (c) 448   (d) 396   (e) 1023
    (f) 1088.
13. (a) 97   (b) 366   (c) 38   (d) 449   (e) 46.
14. (a) 56,109   (b) 17,980   (c) 61   (d) 9,997.
15. (a) 16,029   (b) 16,841   (c) 7,519   (d) 1,109.
16. (a) 10,099   (b) 450,090   (c) 198,002,899.
17. (a) 10 − 1, 5 + 5, 10 + 1, 24 − 12, 6 + 7, 17 − 3.
    (b) I, V, X, L, C, D, M.
18. (a) 36   (b) −36   (c) −36   (d) −36   (e) 93   (f) 0
    (g) −36   (h) 39   (i) −75.
19. (a) false   (b) false   (c) false   (d) true   (e) false.
20. (a) true   (b) false   (c) true   (d) true   (e) false.
21. (a) −27   (b) −76   (c) −104   (d) −16   (e) 0   (f) −27.
22. (a) 1890   (b) 130   (c) −263   (d) 566.
23. (a) 8   (b) 16   (c) −32   (d) −20   (e) 55   (f) −882.
24. (a) −5858   (b) −18,963   (c) −45,399   (d) −109,369.

Answers to Chapter Exercises (3)

Group I.

1. (a) $(18 + 7) − 23$ (b) $18 − (8 + 8)$.
2. (a) expression   (b) equation   (c) inequality   (d) equation
   (e) inequality   (f) expression   (g) expression   (h) equation
   (i) inequality.
3. (a) −   (b) false   (c) true   (d) true   (e) false   (f) −
   (g) −   (h) true   (i) true.
4. (a) $5 + 7 > 12 − 5$ (b) $16 = 8 + 8$ (c) $1 + 3 + 5 < 10$
   (d) $−7 < 0$ (e) $10 > −1$ (f) $5 − 9 = 9 − 13$
   (g) $2 + 0 = 2 − 0$ (h) $7 = 3 + 4$ (i) $8 − 1 < 8 + 1$.
5. (a) true   (b) neither   (c) false   (d) false   (e) neither
   (f) true.

6. (a) true   (b) false   (c) false   (d) false   (e) true
   (f) false.
7. (a) true   (b) false   (c) true   (d) true   (e) false
   (f) true.
8. (a) $N + 8$ (b) $N - 3$ (c) $(N - 3) + 8$
   (d) $(N - 3) + 8 = 23 - 11$.
9. (a) –3, (b)–5, (c)–2, (d)–1, (e)–4.
10. (a), (c), (d), and (e).
11. (a) true   (b) false   (c) false   (d) false   (e) true
    (f) false.
12. (a) $-$ (b) equal addition   (c) associative   (d) inverse
    (e) identity   (f) equal subtraction
    (g) closure and associative   (h) inverse   (i) identity
    (j) checking (substitution)   (k) closure   (l) solution.
13. (a) subtract 20   (b) subtract 27   (c) add 38
    (d) subtract 11   (e) add 11   (f) add $N + 7$.
14. (a), (c), (d), (e), and (f) are equivalent.
15. (a) 26   (b) 10   (c) -32 (d) 115   (e) 39   (f) 18.
16. (a) 0   (b) 56   (c) -46 (d) 12.
17. (a) false   (b) true   (c) false   (d) false   (e) true
    (f) true   (g) false   (h) true   (i) false   (j) false.
18. (a) $B - 3 = S + 9$ (b) $S = T + 173$.
    (c) $2{,}261{,}243 = T + 1{,}891{,}243$
19. 22 times, net 179 yards.
20. 48 and 36.
21. 2,088 items.
22. 27 dollars.
23. Shortest route is 42 miles, longest is 70 miles. Yes, in Denine.
24. 21.

Group II.

1. (a) $[5 - (7 - 3)] + 4$ (b) $(5 + 4) - [7 - 3]$.
2. (a) expression   (b) equation   (c) inequality
   (d) equation   (e) inequality   (f) expression
   (g) expression   (h) equation   (i) inequality.
3. (a) $-$ (b) false   (c) true   (d) neither true nor false
   (e) true   (f) $-$ (g) $-$ (h) neither true nor false
   (i) neither true nor false.
4. (a) $16 = 10 + 6$ (b) $N > N - 1$ (c) $N < N + 1$
   (d) $0 + 2 > 0 - 2$ (e) $0 - 2 = -2 + 0$ (f) $3 - 9 < 6$
   (g) $101 < 110$ (h) $12 - 7 = 32 - 27$ (i) $16 + 7 < 32$.

5. (a) true   (b) neither   (c) false   (d) true   (e) false
   (f) true.
6. (a) false   (b) true   (c) false   (d) false   (e) true
   (f) false.
7. (a) false   (b) false   (c) true   (d) true   (e) false
   (f) false.
8. (a) $N - 5$ (b) $N + 12$ (c) $(N + 12) - 5$
   (d) $(N + 12) - 5 = 17 - 10$.
9. (a)–3, (b)–1, (c)–2, (d)–5, (e)–4.
10. (a) and (f).
11. (a) true   (b) false   (c) false   (d) false   (e) false
    (f) false.
12. (a) –   (b) equal addition   (c) associative and inverse
    (d) closure   (e) equal addition   (f) associative and identity
    (g) inverse   (h) identity   (i) check (substitution)
    (j) closure   (k) signs (negative of a negative is positive)
    (l) solution.
13. (a) subtract 37   (b) subtract 9   (c) add 7   (d) subtract 7
    (e) add 9   (f) add $N - 25$.
14. (a) and (f).
15. (a) 8   (b) 6   (c) −11   (d) 109   (e) 117   (f) 66.
16. (a) −27   (b) 0   (c) 94   (d) 98.
17. (a) false   (b) false   (c) false   (d) false   (e) true
    (f) true   (g) true   (h) true   (i) true   (j) true.
18. (a) $D = 180, C - D = P + 90$ or $C - 180 = P + 90$
    (b) $D = (C + C) + 10$ (c) $E = 65,932,000, E = P - 6,277,000$.
19. 72 dollars.
20. 53 students.
21. Arny with 308, round II.
22. 5 hours.
23. Shortest: A-B-E at 35; longest: A-C-F-E at 38.
24. 10 and 14.

Answers to Chapter Exercises (4)

Group I.

1. sum; addend; multiplicand; multiplier; product.
2. 3 and 5.
3. (a) $42 = 2 \times (3 \times 7)$ (b) $91 = 7 \times 13$ (c) $165 = 3 \times (5 \times 11)$.
4. (a) 14,100   (b) 0   (c) 483,000   (d) 1014
   (e) 60,000,000   (f) 1564.

5. (a)

	1	3	7	
	1 /	2 /	/	4
4 /	2	8		
		1 /	/	2
5 2 /	6 /	4		
	7	5	4	

$42 \times 137 = 5754$

(b) $42 = 2 + 8 + 32$

137

$2 \times 137 = 274$ 274

$2 \times 274 = 548$

$2 \times 548 = 1096$ 1096

$2 \times 1096 = 2192$

$2 \times 2192 = 4384$ 4384

$42 \times 137 = \overline{5754}$

6. (a) 110,670   (b) 1,466,199   (c) 78,263,440
   (d) 460,119,000   (e) 914,047,101   (f) 228,394,514.
7. Excesses in products: (a) 6   (b) 0   (c) 7   (d) 3   (e) 0
   (f) 2.
8. (a) 73,080   (b) 436,421   (c) 21,000,000,000   (d) 1944.
9. (a) 111,000   (b) 1,470,000   (c) 78,300,000
   (d) 460,000,000   (e) 914,000,000   (f) 228,000,000.
10. (a) 848,000   (b) 840,000.
11. (a) 2,400,000   (b) 1,200,000   (c) 5,000,000
   (d) 4,000,000.
12. (a) high: 2,780,000   (b) high: 1,300,600
      low: 2,432,500   low: 650,300
   (c) high: 5,871,000   (d) high: 4,391,000
      low: 4,892,500   low: 3,951,900.
13. (a) −89,217   (b) 54,510   (c) −323,578   (d) 10,464
   (e) −153,920   (f) 95,468.
14. Excesses in products: (a) 0   (b) 6   (c) 1   (d) 6
   (e) 2   (f) 5.
15. (a) 4,800   (b) 3,852,000   (c) −32,292   (d) −3,087,000.
16. (a) −140,895   (b) 709   (c) −179   (d) −17,316.
17. (a)−5, (b)−4, (c)−7, (d)−1, (e)−2, (f)−6, (g)−3.
18. (a) 2   (b) 52   (c) 3   (d) −16   (e) 4 or −4   (f) 5.
19. 720 dollars.
20. 4.
21. 2,540,000.
22. 52 years old.

Group II.

1. added; factors; product.
2. 3 and 13.
3. (a) $75 = 3 \times (5 \times 5)$ (b) $119 = 7 \times 17$ (c) $130 = 2 \times (5 \times 13)$.
4. (a) 12,947   (b) 0   (c) 30,000,000   (d) 31,200
   (e) 1,775   (f) 3,800.

5. (a)

	7	4	5	
2	2 / 1	1 / 2	1 / 5	3
7	4 / 9	2 / 8	3 / 5	7
	5	6	5	

$37 \times 745 = 27,565$

(b) $37 = 1 + 4 + 32$

745	745
$2 \times 745 = 1490$	
$2 \times 1490 = 2980$	2980
$2 \times 2980 = 5960$	
$2 \times 5960 = 11920$	
$2 \times 11920 = 23840$	23840
	$37 \times 745 = \overline{27565}$

6. (a) 169,848   (b) 1,133,812   (c) 26,240,090
(d) 378,943,600   (e) 707,871,175   (f) 622,314,980.
7. Excess in products: (a) 0   (b) 1   (c) 5   (d) 4   (e) 7
(f) 8.
8. (a) 4,874,280   (b) 3,000,000,000   (c) 170,286   (d) 918.
9. (a) 170,000   (b) 1,130,000   (c) 26,200,000
(d) 379,000,000   (e) 708,000,000   (f) 622,000,000.
10. (a) 754,000   (b) 760,000.
11. (a) 3,500,000   (b) 3,200,000   (c) 9,000,000
(d) 2,000,000.
12. (a) high: 3,764,000   (b) high: 3,760,500
   low: 3,293,500   low: 3,008,400
(c) high: 9,612,000   (d) high: 2,463,000
   low: 8,650,800   low: 2,216,700
13. (a) −73,840   (b) 100,440   (c) −109,347   (d) 37,240
(e) −173,040   (f) 193,945.
14. Excesses in products: (a) 4   (b) 0   (c) 6   (d) 7   (e) 6
(f) 4.
15. (a) 38,080   (b) 96,233,600   (c) −83,028
(d) −63,125,000.
16. (a) −180,642   (b) −32,742   (c) 484   (d) 64,484.
17. (a)−4,   (b)−3,   (c)−2,   (d)−7,   (e)−5,   (f)−6,
(g)−1.
18. (a) −3   (b) 2   (c) −1   (d) −30   (e) 2 or −2
(f) 0 or 5.
19. 63,360 inches.
20. 17 and 18; 14 and 21; 15 and 20.
21. Checking the addition and subtraction we find no error. Notice that "casting out nines" will not catch transpositions. Since 8,490 is larger than 8,472, the credit must be larger or the debit smaller in the tens and ones columns. The only possible transposition in the credit column is 7,801 to 7,810 which will not correct the error. The possible transpositions which will make the debit smaller are 2,953 to 2,935; 1,060 to 1,006; 397 to 379; and 861 to 816. If 2,953 is changed to 2,935 the balance becomes 8,490 and also if 397 is changed to 379 the balance is

corrected. Thus, there are two possible transposition errors: 2,953 should be 2,935 or 397 should be 379.

22. 65,000 feet.

Answers to Chapter Exercises (5)

Group I.

1. multiplied; dividend; divisor; quotient.
2. remainder; divisor.
3. (a) $7R2$ (b) $13R0$ (c) $9R7$ (d) $6R4$ (e) $12R1$
   (f) $10R5$ (g) $8R1$ (h) $0R5$ (i) $10R2$.
4. (a) $67,513R1$ (b) $174,050R2$ (c) $85,634R0$
   (d) $131,076R3$ (e) $87,500R0$ (f) $86,419R6$.
5. (a) 1   97   (b) $\cancel{8}6$
       2/   194 $\cancel{1}\cancel{2}\cancel{7}3$
       4   388 $\cancel{5}\cancel{7}\cancel{2}\cancel{6}$ $59R3$
       8/   776 $\cancel{9}\cancel{7}\cancel{7}$
      16/   1552 $\cancel{9}$
      32/   3104
      $59R3$
6. (a) $721R22$ (b) $878R0$ (c) $1,080R40$.
7. (a) $12,830R145$ (b) $1,043R43$ (c) $8,342R15$.
8. (a) $4,700$ (b) $6,300$ (c) $11,000$ (d) $5,600$.
9. Primes: 17, 29, 31.
   Composites: $15 = 3 \times 5$, $22 = 2 \times 11$, $25 = 5 \times 5$, $30 = 2 \times 3 \times 5$,
                $32 = 2 \times 2 \times 2 \times 2 \times 2$, $33 = 3 \times 11$, $35 = 5 \times 7$.
10. (a) 74: divisors 1, 2, 37, and 74.
    (b) 196: 1, 2, 4, 7, 14, 28, 98, 196.
    (c) 1925: 1, 5, 7, 11, 25, 35, 55, 77, 175, 275, 385, 1925.
11. (a) 15   (b) 16   (c) 19.
12. (a) 3   (b) 29   (c) 13.
13.

	(a)	(b)	(c)	(d)	(e)	(f)	(g)	(h)
LCM	24	30	143	60	36	42	72	432
GCD	8	3	1	3	3	7	6	1

14.

	(a)	(b)	(c)	(d)
LCM	72	480	390	30,600
GCD	1	4	13	6

15. (a) $-9R5$ (b) $6R19$ (c) $-51R11$ (d) $-10R47$
    (e) $-53R0$ (f) $17R13$.
16. (a) -1 (b) 4   (c) 1   (d) 42   (e) 70   (f) 12.
17. (a) 21   (b) 13   (c) 1   (d) 2   (e) 8   (f) 5.

18. 164 feet.
19. 9 dollars.
20. 16 suits.
21. 75 dollars.
22. 126.
23. 165 and 255.
24. 18 and 3.

Group II.

1. subtract; dividend; divisor; subtraction; quotient.
2. remainder; zero and the divisor.
3. (a) 4R0   (b) 4R7   (c) 31R2   (d) 12R3   (e) 9R5
   (f) 11R3   (g) 7R2   (h) 0R5   (i) 36R0.
4. (a) 81,025R3   (b) 180,267R0   (c) 22,125R2
   (d) 108,201R2   (e) 70,833R5   (f) 142,857R0.
5. (a)   1   73   (b)
        2/   146   4
        4/   292   52
         8   584   643
        16/   1168   6281   86R3
        32   2336   733
        64/   4672   7
        86R3
6. (a) 1,422R4   (b) 402R5   (c) 986R64.
7. (a) 13,341R193   (b) 1,051R1,234   (c) 9,986R5,801.
8. (a) 6,000   (b) 2,300   (c) 1,100   (d) 2,600.
9. Primes: 19, 23, 37, 41, 43.
   Composites: $16 = 2 \times 2 \times 2 \times 2$, $25 = 5 \times 5$, $26 = 2 \times 13$,
            $28 = 2 \times 2 \times 7$, $38 = 2 \times 19$.
10. (a) 125: 1, 5, 25, 125.
    (b) 315: 1, 3, 5, 7, 9, 15, 21, 35, 45, 63, 105, 315.
    (c) 1573: 1, 11, 13, 121, 143, 1573.
11. (a) 18   (b) 19   (c) 19.
12. (a) 2   (b) 23   (c) 11.
13.

	(a)	(b)	(c)	(d)	(e)	(f)	(g)	(h)
LCM	28	25	105	90	77	84	165	182
GCD	2	5	3	6	1	4	3	2

14.

	(a)	(b)	(c)	(d)
LCM	60	90	1512	3465
GCD	2	3	9	35

15. (a) $-16R10$ (b) $7R47$ (c) $-19R24$ (d) $-6R22$
    (e) $-19R11$ (f) $9R26$.
16. (a) 2   (b) 5   (c) 2   (d) 27   (e) 0   (f) 3.
17. (a) 22   (b) -175 (c) 3   (d) 4   (e) 3   (f) 1.
18. 26 inches.
19. 12 dollars.
20. 39 seats in each row except one with 12 seats.
21. 79 dollars each.
22. 420.
23. 196 and 364.
24. 21 and 3.

Answers to Chapter Exercises (6)

Group I.

1. ratio, rational number.
2. numerator, denominator, rational number, fractional.
3. $\dfrac{1}{6}$, $10\dfrac{2}{3}$, $\dfrac{3}{8}$.
4. $-\dfrac{2}{7}$, $\dfrac{5}{7}$, $\dfrac{9}{7}$.
5. (a) 35   (b) 3   (c) 9   (d) 72   (e) 9.
6. (a) $\dfrac{6}{11}$ (b) $\dfrac{14}{15}$ (c) $\dfrac{10}{3}$ (d) $\dfrac{5}{21}$ (e) $\dfrac{31}{32}$.
7. (a) $\dfrac{4}{12}$, $-\dfrac{3}{7}$ (b) $\dfrac{4}{12}$, $\dfrac{-8}{-6}$ (c) $\dfrac{-6}{5}$, $-\dfrac{3}{7}$.
8. $\dfrac{4}{7}$, $\dfrac{3}{5}$, $\dfrac{9}{14}$, $\dfrac{7}{10}$.
9. $\dfrac{25}{72}$ and $\dfrac{13}{36}$.
10. $\dfrac{4}{7}$: one, seven, four $4 \times \dfrac{1}{7}$: four, seven, one.
11. $\dfrac{A}{B} \times \dfrac{C}{D} = \dfrac{A \times C}{B \times D}$.
12. (a) $\dfrac{8}{9}$ (b) $\dfrac{9}{10}$ (c) $\dfrac{3}{5}$ (d) $\dfrac{33}{50}$ (e) $\dfrac{5}{14}$.
13. (a) $\dfrac{1}{7}$ (b) $\dfrac{9}{11}$ (c) $\dfrac{15}{28}$.
14. $\dfrac{9}{7}$, $\dfrac{7}{9} \times \dfrac{9}{7} = 1$.

15. (a) $\dfrac{14}{3} = 4\dfrac{2}{3}$ (b) $\dfrac{3}{14}$ (c) $\dfrac{2}{3}$ (d) $\dfrac{14}{55}$ (e) $\dfrac{63}{50} = 1\dfrac{13}{50}$.

16. (a) $\dfrac{11}{4}$ (b) 0   (c) 1   (d) $\dfrac{25}{9}$ (e) $\dfrac{4}{81}$ (f) $\dfrac{9}{49}$ (g) 0

(h) $\dfrac{8}{11}$.

17. The quotient of two fractions is equal to the product of the dividend times the reciprocal of the divisor.

18. (a) $\dfrac{45}{54}$ (b) $\dfrac{9}{20}$ (c) $\dfrac{3}{5}$ (d) $\dfrac{7}{5} = 1\dfrac{2}{5}$.

19. (a)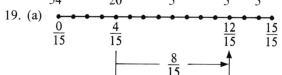

(b)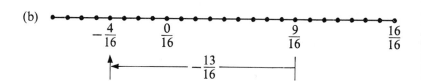

(c)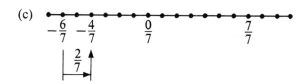

(d)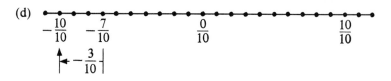

20. (a) 36   (b) 30   (c) 72   (d) 18.

21. (a) $\dfrac{49}{36} = 1\dfrac{13}{36}$ (b) $\dfrac{59}{30} = 1\dfrac{29}{30}$ (c) $\dfrac{115}{72} = 1\dfrac{43}{72}$ (d) $\dfrac{41}{18} = 2\dfrac{5}{18}$.

23. (a) $-\dfrac{5}{504}$ (b) $\dfrac{1}{12}$ (c) $\dfrac{11}{48}$.

24 (a)–6,   (b)–7,   (c)–3,   (d)–2,   (e)–5,   (f)–1,   (g)–8,   (h)–4.

25. $\dfrac{13}{30}$.

26. 2 h 30 min.

27. 7.

28. $R = \dfrac{3}{2}$ or $-\dfrac{3}{2}$.

Group II.

1. scale, rational numbers.

2. denominator, numerator, rational number, $9 = K \times 7$.

3. $\dfrac{1}{6}$, $13\dfrac{1}{2}$, $\dfrac{2}{5}$.

4. $-\dfrac{4}{5}$, $\dfrac{2}{5}$, $\dfrac{7}{5}$.

5. (a) 16   (b) 1   (c) 11   (d) 50   (e) 6.

6. (a) $\dfrac{5}{6}$ (b) $\dfrac{7}{11}$ (c) $\dfrac{12}{7}$ (d) $\dfrac{8}{25}$ (e) $\dfrac{17}{78}$.

7. (a) $\dfrac{4}{-7}$, $-\dfrac{-2}{6}$ (b) $\dfrac{9}{5}$, $-\dfrac{-2}{6}$ (c) $\dfrac{4}{-7}$, $\dfrac{9}{5}$.

8. $\dfrac{1}{5}$, $\dfrac{3}{14}$, $\dfrac{5}{21}$, $\dfrac{1}{4}$, $\dfrac{9}{35}$.

9. $\dfrac{43}{105}$, $\dfrac{44}{105}$.

10. 5, multiplier; 6, divisor.

11. The product of two fractions is equal to the fraction with the product of the numerators as a numerator and the product of the denominators as a denominator.

12. (a) $\dfrac{18}{11} = 1\dfrac{7}{11}$ (b) $\dfrac{32}{3} = 10\dfrac{2}{3}$ (c) $\dfrac{3}{11}$ (d) $\dfrac{32}{75}$ (e) $\dfrac{14}{45}$.

13. (a) $\dfrac{4}{9}$ (b) $\dfrac{3}{11}$ (c) $\dfrac{16}{55}$.

14. reciprocal, $\dfrac{5}{9}$; $K = \dfrac{9}{5}$.

15. (a) 12   (b) $\dfrac{1}{12}$ (c) $\dfrac{2}{3}$ (d) $\dfrac{7}{8}$ (e) $\dfrac{64}{65}$.

16. (a) $\dfrac{2}{3}$ (b) 1   (c) 0   (d) $\dfrac{9}{4}$ (e) 1   (f) $\dfrac{3}{5}$ (g) $\dfrac{49}{8}$

  (h) $\dfrac{16}{25}$.

17. $\dfrac{A}{B} \div \dfrac{C}{D} = \dfrac{A}{B} \times \dfrac{D}{C}$.

18. (a) $\dfrac{27}{72}$ (b) $\dfrac{10}{21}$ (c) $\dfrac{14}{15}$ (d) $\dfrac{17}{7} = 2\dfrac{3}{7}$.

19. (a)
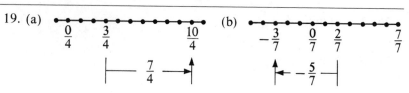
(b)

(c)   (d)

20. (a) 12   (b) 24   (c) 45   (d) 120.

21. (a) $\dfrac{7}{4} = 1\dfrac{3}{4}$ (b) $\dfrac{31}{24} = 1\dfrac{7}{24}$ (c) $\dfrac{68}{45} = 1\dfrac{23}{45}$ (d) $\dfrac{289}{120} = 2\dfrac{49}{120}$.

22. (a) $\dfrac{11}{90}$ (b) $\dfrac{5}{56}$ (c) $\dfrac{25}{84}$ (d) $\dfrac{1}{30}$.

23. (a) $\dfrac{11}{14}$ (b) $\dfrac{1}{2}$ (c) 0.

24. (a)–3,   (b)–8,   (c)–1,   (d)–5,   (e)–4,   (f)–2,
    (g)–7,   (h)–6.

25. $4,736; $\dfrac{16}{25}$.

26. 4 h 24 min.

27. $\dfrac{1}{8}$.

28. $\dfrac{4}{9}$.

Answers to Chapter Exercises (7)

Group I.

1. notation; rational.

2. mixed fraction; sum; 2; $\dfrac{3}{4}$.

3. (a) $\dfrac{26}{3}$ (b) $\dfrac{53}{12}$ (c) $\dfrac{52}{5}$ (d) $\dfrac{11}{10}$ (e) $\dfrac{145}{4}$.

4. (a) $2\dfrac{1}{2}$ (b) $2\dfrac{1}{2}$ (c) $12\dfrac{2}{3}$ (d) $10\dfrac{4}{7}$ (e) $2\dfrac{15}{16}$.

5. (a) $13\frac{19}{24}$ (b) $10\frac{5}{8}$ (c) $114\frac{17}{27}$ (d) $60\frac{19}{35}$ (e) $68\frac{41}{48}$.

6. (a) $2\frac{1}{6}$ (b) $9\frac{5}{6}$ (c) $8\frac{25}{54}$ (d) $-11\frac{11}{35}$.

7. (a) $25\frac{1}{3}$ (b) $12\frac{1}{2}$ (c) $-78\frac{3}{4}$ (d) $199\frac{3}{8}$.

8. (a) $18\frac{1}{12}$ (b) $-63\frac{10}{27}$ (c) $161\frac{4}{7}$ (d) $263\frac{43}{120}$.

9. (a) $1\frac{1}{2}$ (b) $\frac{12}{13}$ (c) -18 (d) $7\frac{1}{5}$.

10. (a) $26\frac{2}{3}$ (b) $458\frac{1}{3}$ (c) $13,437\frac{1}{2}$ (d) $15\frac{5}{8}$.

11. (a) $\frac{389}{1000}$ (b) $\frac{762}{1000}$ (c) $\frac{156}{1000}$ (d) $\frac{109}{1000}$.

12. (a) Four hundred seven and six hundredths.
    (b) Twenty and three hundred five thousandths.
    (c) Seventeen and six hundred fifteen thousandths.
    (d) Five and twenty-nine ten-thousandths.
    (e) Forty-one thousand two hundred seventy-three millionths.
    (f) Three hundred and fifty-three and one-third hundredths.

13. (a) 407.1   (b) 20.30   (c) 17.62   (d) 5.003
    (e) 0.04127   (f) 300.5.

14. (a) 62.051   (b) 101.0011   (c) 0.70505   (d) $7,500.64\frac{2}{3}$.

15. (a) 0.361   (b) 1.417   (c) 0.047   (d) 10.263
    (e) 0.002   (f) 3.608.

16. (a) $\frac{8}{125}$ (b) $1\frac{3}{8}$ (c) $\frac{7}{25}$ (d) $\frac{3}{40}$ (e) $10\frac{5}{7}$ (f) $\frac{7}{1250}$.

17. (a) 55.600   (b) 20.0101   (c) 5.0712   (d) 947.206.

18. (a) 7.6803   (b) 6.98971   (c) 460.998   (d) -0.06826.

19. (a) 78,500   (b) 0.32   (c) 4.036   (d) 0.00575
    (e) 705.9   (f) 0.085306.

20. (a) 72.670   (b) 3.0351   (c) 15,151   (d) 1,745.4
    (e) 36.2   (f) 14,000   (g) 60.9   (h) 0.0000416.

21. (a) 2.616   (b) 5.163   (c) 29.21   (d) 0.3708
    (e) 0.002274   (f) 7.321.

22. (a) 12.0165   (b) -0.06 (c) 2.0655   (d) 4.732.

23. (a) 3.65   (b) 21.4   (c) 2.52   (d) -43.4.

24. (a) 0.35; 35%   (b) $1\frac{23}{40}$; $157\frac{1}{2}\%$ (c) $\frac{3}{16}$; 0.1875

    (d) $0.533\frac{1}{3}$; $53\frac{1}{3}\%$ (e) $\frac{1}{40}$; $2\frac{1}{2}\%$ (f) $\frac{1}{160}$; 0.00625.

25. (a) 26.35   (b) $136\frac{4}{11}\%$ (c) $6\frac{2}{3}$ (d) 17.003   (e) 11%
    (f) 0.94.

26. (a) $83\frac{14}{17}\%$ (b) 0.52155   (c) 7.5.

27. 32.9 square inches.

28. $K = 0.57''$, $R = 3.25''$, $r = 1.50''$.

29. 24.4%.

30. 307.12\frac{1}{2}$.

Group II.

1. forms; notation.

2. mixed fraction; $3\frac{5}{8}$.

3. (a) $\frac{11}{3}$ (b) $\frac{69}{7}$ (c) $\frac{509}{10}$ (d) $\frac{21}{20}$ (e) $\frac{58}{9}$.

4. (a) $3\frac{1}{2}$ (b) $1\frac{1}{5}$ (c) $3\frac{1}{3}$ (d) $7\frac{1}{4}$ (e) $13\frac{3}{8}$.

5. (a) $8\frac{5}{12}$ (b) $20\frac{5}{18}$ (c) $101\frac{1}{6}$ (d) $20\frac{17}{45}$ (e) $100\frac{281}{360}$.

6. (a) $\frac{3}{4}$ (b) $29\frac{5}{6}$ (c) $40\frac{55}{72}$ (d) $-1\frac{1}{28}$.

7. (a) 30   (b) $3\frac{1}{8}$ (c) $-34\frac{2}{3}$ (d) $661\frac{8}{9}$.

8. (a) $62\frac{5}{6}$ (b) $-69\frac{19}{20}$ (c) $168\frac{1}{18}$ (d) $275\frac{4}{9}$.

9. (a) $2\frac{2}{5}$ (b) $\frac{3}{8}$ (c) $-4\frac{5}{7}$ (d) $22\frac{4}{15}$.

10. (a) $31\frac{1}{4}$ (b) $476\frac{4}{21}$ (c) $6,944\frac{4}{9}$ (d) $13\frac{8}{9}$.

11. (a) $\frac{643}{1000}$ (b) $\frac{136}{1000}$ (c) $\frac{305}{1000}$ (d) $\frac{69}{1000}$.

12. (a) Three hundred twenty and seven hundred five thousandths.
    (b) Eighteen and seventy-five thousandths.
    (c) One hundred nine and thirty-two hundredths.
    (d) Seven and seven ten-thousandths.
    (e) Eighty and five and three-seventh hundredths.
    (f) Twelve thousand twenty-five millionths.

13. (a) 320.7   (b) 18.08   (c) 109.3   (d) 7.001
    (e) 80.05   (f) 0.01202.

14. (a) 6.200   (b) 200.11   (c) $5.5\frac{2}{5}$ (d) 9,461.0208.

15. (a) 0.114   (b) 2.077   (c) 0.025   (d) 10.044   (e) 0.003
    (f) 2.428.

16. (a) $\dfrac{3}{125}$ (b) $2\dfrac{3}{20}$ (c) $\dfrac{8}{25}$ (d) $\dfrac{5}{16}$ (e) $30\dfrac{7}{9}$ (f) $\dfrac{1}{2000}$.

17. (a) 50.8000   (b) 425.219   (c) 13.468   (d) 1,026.829.

18. (a) 57.0305   (b) 0.08838   (c) 289.602   (d) -0.02203.

19. (a) 30,700   (b) 0.08   (c) 5.602   (d) 0.00345
    (e) 500.23   (f) 0.205741.

20. (a) 75.370   (b) 0.15305   (c) 52,823   (d) 2,882.2
    (e) 59.1   (f) 7,770   (g) 48.3   (h) 0.0000673.

21. (a) 4.926   (b) 53.40   (c) 23.18   (d) 0.7289
    (e) 0.05382   (f) 5.018.

22. (a) $9.541\dfrac{2}{3}$ (b) $\dfrac{7}{60}$ (c) $6.60\dfrac{3}{11}$ (d) 2.842.

23. (a) -0.591 (b) 245   (c) 0.174   (d) -9.27.

24. (a) $0.583\dfrac{1}{3}$; $58\dfrac{1}{3}\%$ (b) $2\dfrac{16}{125}$; $212\dfrac{4}{5}\%$ (c) $\dfrac{1}{500}$; 0.002

    (d) $0.156\dfrac{1}{4}$; $15\dfrac{5}{8}\%$ (e) $\dfrac{5}{24}$; $20\dfrac{5}{6}\%$ (f) $\dfrac{3}{40}$; 0.075.

25. (a) 2.576   (b) 6.5%   (c) 14.5   (d) 0.1029   (e) 1,056%
    (f) 8.4.

26. (a) $5\dfrac{15}{17}\%$ (b) $12.19\dfrac{9}{16}$ (c) $54\dfrac{1}{6}$.

27. 25.6 square inches.

28. $A = 6.75$ inches, $B = 1.575$ inches.

29. 33%.

30. $629.33.

Answers to Chapter Exercises (8)

Group I.

1. A property of something to be measured; a unit by which to measure; a means to associate the unit to the property to result in a numerical value.

2. yard; an arm.

3. $10\dfrac{1}{4}\,\bar{u}$ approx.

4. (a) $23\dfrac{1}{7}$ units   (b) 90 units.

5. $\dfrac{5}{12}$.

6. (a) $16\dfrac{3}{7}$ sq units   (b) $205\dfrac{5}{14}$ sq units.

7. 132 sq inches.

8. (a) $16\frac{3}{4}$ ft   (b) 3.8862 meters   (c) 2 sq yd 7 sq ft 9 sq inches.

9. (a) 38   (b) $35\frac{5}{8}$ sq ft.

10. (a) 18   (b) 19   (c) 24.

11. $551\frac{1}{4}$ cu inches.

12. (a) 6,336 cu units   (b) $547\frac{1}{8}$ cu units.

13. $16.63.

14. 55,440 cc.

15. 206 lb 5 oz; 9%.

16. 2 lb 10.6 oz.

17. 125 lb.

18. (a) 1 cu yd 13 cu ft 150 cu inches   (b) 864 kg approx.

19. Yes; one month.

20. A system relating the days, months, years.

21. (a) 1 month 5 days 6 hours   (b) 20 h 9 min 36 sec.
    (c) 21 h 17 min 30 sec.

22. $8\frac{1}{3}$ gal.

23. 23 min 6 sec.

24. (a) 8:00 A.M.   (b) 2:00 P.M.   (c) 10:00 P.M.

25. 3:10 P.M. the next day (local).

Group II.

1. Convenience, wide acceptance, uniformity, standardized and reproducible, related to a system of measurement.

2. meter; one ten-millionth; North Pole, equator.

3. $8\frac{1}{2}\,\overline{u}$.

4. (a) 40 units   (b) 22 units.

5. $\frac{21}{20}$.

6. (a) 54 sq units   (b) $24\frac{1}{2}$ sq units.

7. 9 sq ft $90\frac{3}{4}$ sq inches.

8. (a) 64 inches   (b) 8 ft $8\frac{1}{3}$ inches   (c) 3 sq yd 8 sq ft 48 sq inches.

9. (a) $54\frac{3}{5}$ cu inches   (b) 56.

10. (a) 18   (b) 17   (c) 21.

11. 594 cu inches.

12. (a) 1,120 cu units   (b) $1,562\frac{1}{7}$ cu units.

13. $0.23.

14. 20.4 lb.

15. 4,488 lb; $6\frac{1}{2}\%$.

16. 96.4 oz or 6 lb $\frac{4}{10}$ oz.

17. $5\frac{1}{7}$ ft or 5 ft $1\frac{5}{7}$ inches.

18. (a) 2 cu yd $781\frac{1}{3}$ cu inches   (b) 169.9 lb.

19. 1,921 miles approx.

20. Local clock-time refers to a particular moment at a particular location, whereas elapsed time refers only to the passage of time which is independent of location.

21. (a) 2 months 2 weeks 16 hours

   (b) 75 days = 2 months 2 weeks 1 day   (c) $7\frac{1}{3}$.

22. 20 miles per gallon.

23. 7 gallon per minute.

24. (a) 12:45 P.M.   (b) 3:45 P.M.   (c) 4:45 A.M. the "next" day.

25. 8:18 P.M.

Answers to Chapter Exercises (9)

Group I.

1. (a) The area (A) of a circle is equal to "pi" (π) a constant about $\frac{22}{7}$ or 3.1416 times the square of the radius (r).

   (b) The volume (V) of a rectangular parallelepiped is equal to the length (L) times the width (W) times the height (H).

   (c) Work (W) is equal to a force (F) applied through a distance (D).

2. (a) $V = \frac{4}{3}\pi r^3$ (b) $A = P + I$ (c) $°F = \frac{9}{5}°C + 32$.

3. (a) $D = Kt^2$ and $K = 16$ (b) 785 ft   (c) 5.6 sec.

4. $F = 120$ lb; $F_1 D_1 = F_2 D_2$.

5. $A = 0.567$ sq units.

6. (a) 38 miles   (b) 57 min.

7. 40 lb.

8. (a) $K = 5.5$; $F = 2.2$ (b) $K = 3$; $M = \frac{1}{4}$.

9. (a) $B = 6$ (b) $B = 17$ (c) $B = 5.61$ approximately.

10. Height of pole: 54 ft.

11. (a) 7.348   (b) 18.97   (c) 2.793   (d) 83.25.

12. (a) $\overline{BC} = 55.4$ (b) $\overline{BD} = 6.54$ (c) $\overline{CD} = 20.3$.

13. $6\frac{13}{64}$ inches.

14. (a) Average: 13; S.D. 2.76   (b) Average: 7.8; S.D. 1.11.

15. (a) 7 h 53 min   (b) $132.83.

16. Average: 15.9; S.D. 3.7.

Group II.

1. (a) The volume (V) of a cone or pyramid is equal to one-third of the product of the area of the base (B) and the height (h).

   (b) Interest (I) is equal to the principal (p) times the rate (r) times the time (t).

   (c) The time (T) of one swing of a pendulum is equal to the square root of the length (L) of the arm divided by thirty-nine.

2. (a) $A = \frac{h}{2}(b_1 + b_2)$ (b) $V = \frac{\sqrt{2}}{12}e^2$ (c) $^{\circ}C = \frac{5}{9}(^{\circ}F - 32)$.

3. (a) $C = \frac{WT}{250}$ (in cents)   (b) 36 cents   (c) doubles; $W = \frac{E^2}{R}$.

4. 8 ft.

5. $A = 0.68$.

6. (a) 8 min   (b) 6 miles.

7. 60 lb.

8. (a) $K = 16$; $S = 4$ (b) $K = \frac{3}{8}$; $I = \frac{1}{8}$.

9. (a) $B = -2\frac{5}{7}$ (b) $B = 1\frac{4}{5}$ (c) $B = 9$.

10. 1 ft 2 inches.

11. (a) 8.888   (b) 14.39   (c) 2.098   (d) 91.05.

12. (a) $\overline{CD} = 1.10$ (b) $\overline{OC} = 6$ (c) $\overline{AB} = 13.42$.

13. 1.69 inches.

14. (a) Average: 30; S.D. 3.2   (b) Average: 1.4; S.D. 0.48.

15. (a) 4.6   (b) 50.

16. Average: 11.3; S.D. 2.52.

Answers to Chapter Exercises (10)

Group I.

1. (a) 2.82843   (b) 3.0   (c) 0.471405   (d) 2.30940
   (e) 1.77245.

2. 5.83019.

3. (a) $\dfrac{3}{32}$ (b) $\dfrac{35}{33}$ (c) $\dfrac{5}{4}$.

4. (a) $\dfrac{2\sqrt{3}}{3}, \dfrac{5}{4}, \sqrt{3-\sqrt{2}}, \dfrac{4}{\pi}, \dfrac{2}{\sqrt{2}}$.

   (b) 0.059, 0.095, 0.509, 0.590, 0.905, 0.950.

5. $\dfrac{\sqrt{\pi}}{\pi}$.

6. Since $-\dfrac{2}{3}+\dfrac{2}{3}+\sqrt{2}=-\dfrac{2}{3}+\dfrac{2}{3}+\dfrac{P}{Q}$ would require $\sqrt{2}$ to be rational and $\sqrt{2}$ is known to be irrational.

7. (a) $3, 4, \dfrac{13}{3}, \dfrac{9}{2}, \dfrac{23}{5}, \dfrac{14}{3}$ (b) $\dfrac{5}{3}, \dfrac{7}{6}, 1, \dfrac{11}{12}, \dfrac{13}{15}, \dfrac{5}{6}$

   (c) $3, \dfrac{5}{3}, \dfrac{7}{5}, \dfrac{9}{7}, \dfrac{11}{9}, \dfrac{13}{11}$ (d) $2, \dfrac{7}{8}, \dfrac{2}{3}, \dfrac{19}{32}, \dfrac{14}{25}, \dfrac{13}{24}$.

8. (a) l.u.b. 5   (b) g.l.b. $\dfrac{2}{3}$ (c) g.l.b. 1   (d) g.l.b. $\dfrac{1}{2}$.

9. Denseness allows us to have infinite sequences which "pack" to a value, but does not guarantee that the value will be included. Completeness guarantees the least upper bounds (and thus all l.u.b. and g.l.b.) will be included.

10. Solve all algebraic equations.

11. (a) $10-3i$ (b) $-4-7i$ (c) $31-29i$ (d) $\dfrac{11}{34}+\dfrac{41}{34}i$.

12. (a) $\sqrt{34}$ (b) $3+5i$ (c) $\dfrac{3}{34}+\dfrac{5}{34}i$.

13. (a) $X=\sqrt{5}$ or $X=-\sqrt{5}$ (b) $X=\sqrt{5}\,i$ or $X=-\sqrt{5}\,i$
    (c) $X=-2+\sqrt{5}$ or $X=-2-\sqrt{5}$.

14. What is algebra about?

Group II.

1. (a) 3.46410   (b) 4.0   (c) 0.866026   (d) 6.36396
   (e) 1.64872.

2. 4.24324.

3. (a) $\dfrac{7}{400}$ (b) $\dfrac{5}{24}$ (c) $\dfrac{21}{20}$.

4. (a) $\sqrt{2 - \sqrt{3}}$, $\dfrac{1}{\sqrt{3}}$, $\dfrac{2}{3}$, $\dfrac{\sqrt{2}}{2}$, $\dfrac{e}{3}$.

   (b) 0.027, 0.072, 0.207, 0.270, 0.702, 0.720.

5. $\sqrt{3}$.

6. Since $\sqrt{3} - \dfrac{1}{2} + \dfrac{1}{2} = \dfrac{P}{Q} - \dfrac{1}{2} + \dfrac{1}{2}$ would require $\sqrt{3}$ to be rational and $\sqrt{3}$ can be shown to be irrational.

7. (a) $5, 4, \dfrac{11}{3}, \dfrac{7}{2}, \dfrac{17}{5}, \dfrac{10}{3}$ (b) $-\dfrac{1}{5}, \dfrac{3}{10}, \dfrac{7}{15}, \dfrac{11}{20}, \dfrac{3}{5}, \dfrac{19}{30}$

   (c) $\dfrac{1}{3}, 0, -\dfrac{1}{5}, -\dfrac{1}{3}, -\dfrac{3}{7}, -\dfrac{1}{2}$ (d) $-\dfrac{1}{3}, \dfrac{1}{6}, \dfrac{7}{27}, \dfrac{7}{24}, \dfrac{23}{75}, \dfrac{17}{54}$.

8. (a) g.l.b. 3   (b) l.u.b. $\dfrac{4}{5}$ (c) g.l.b. -1 (d) l.u.b. $\dfrac{1}{3}$.

9. If an infinite sequence "packs" then a perfect set enables us to attain the value to which it converges. A dense set allows for "packing" of infinite sequences but does not guarantee that the value to which the sequence "packs" will be included in the set.

10. As many as there are real numbers (except for a modulus of 0). $-3 + 4i$, $3 - 4i$, $-3 - 4i$. The "points" on a circle with its center at 0 and radius equal to 5.

11. (a) $7 - 4i$ (b) $3 + 10i$ (c) $31 - 29i$ (d) $-\dfrac{11}{34} - \dfrac{41}{34}i$.

12. (a) $\sqrt{34}$ (b) $5 - 3i$ (c) $\dfrac{5}{34} - \dfrac{3}{34}i$.

13. (a) $X = \sqrt{7}$ or $X = -\sqrt{7}$ (b) $X = \sqrt{7}\,i$ or $X = -\sqrt{7}\,i$
    (c) $X = -3 + i$ or $X = -3 - i$.

14. Is finding the square root a fifth operation? What about quantities such as n^3, n^4, n^5, and so on?

Index

553

ABCDEFGHIJ 7069876